D1271771

BIRDS OF THE CHUKCHI PENINSULA AND WRANGEL ISLAND

© *1981 Amerind Publishing Co. Pvt. Ltd., New Delhi*

Translated and published for the Smithsonian Institution pursuant to an agreement with the National Science Foundation, Washington, D.C., by Amerind Publishing Co. Pvt. Ltd., 66 Janpath, New Delhi 110001

Translator: P.M. Rao
General Editor: Dr. V.S. Kothekar

Available from the U.S. Department of Commerce
National Technical Information Service
Springfield, Virginia 22161

Printed at Oxonian Press Pvt. Ltd., Faridabad, India

ACADEM

WIT

L.A. Po

BIRDS OF TH
PENINSULA
WRANGEL I

[Ptitsy Chukotskogo poluostrova i os

VOLUME 1

Nauka Publishers
Leningrad Section
Leningrad, 1972

Translated from Russian

Published for the Smithsonian Institution and the National Science Foundation, Washington, D.C., by Amerind Publishing Co. Pvt. Ltd., New Delhi
1981

UDC 598.2(571.651 + 571.651.8)

This monograph describes the avifauna of Far Northeast Asia based on the author's prolonged field studies and a comprehensive survey of the literature. The first part covers the history of research and describes a few orders of birds: Gaviiformes, Procellariiformes, Anseriformes, Falconiformes, Galliformes, Gruiformes, and Charadriiformes. The second part includes the description of species of birds and draws zoogeographic conclusions. The distribution of birds in the area under study, their arrival and migration, nidification, molting and food are discussed in detail. The economic importance of commercial species of birds is outlined. Finally, the subspecific variations are dealt with on the basis of examination of the collection in the museum.

This monograph fills a void in our knowledge of the avifauna of the Far Northeast, taking us to a region whose fauna is in close proximity to American fauna.

Editor-in-Chief

Academician B.E. Bykhovskii
Director, Institute of Zoology
Academy of Sciences of the USSR

Editor

A.A. Strelkov

CAT Feb 15 '82

81-4140

12/3/81

Foreword to the Translation

The late Professor Leonid Aleksandrovich Portenko, former Curator of Birds at the Zoological Institute of the Academy of Sciences in Leningrad, was primarily interested in faunal studies, zoogeography and systematics of birds of the arctic and far east of the USSR. He was an active field explorer whose work was well known to North American ornithologists although he never visited this continent personally. Portenko published extensively, in both German and English as well as Russian, and corresponded with several American colleagues about faunal connections across the Bering Strait and was made a Corresponding Fellow of the American Ornithologists' Union in 1962. He was particularly proud of his *magnum opus*, "*The Birds of the Chukchi Peninsula and Wrangel Island*," but was frustrated by the long delay in having it published in the Soviet Union. He even showed me the manuscript stacked high on his desk when I visited him in Leningrad in 1967 and asked whether the Smithsonian or some other American Institution might be interested in publishing it in English. Had we been able to do so then, Portenko could have translated it himself. At a banquet following a conference of ornithologists, entomologists and arbovirologists in Novosibirsk in 1971, as he stood and raised his glass to begin a toast, the official conference interpreter automatically stood up to help him with translation. But Portenko gestured to her and boomed out in English, "Sit down! Portenko needs no translator!" He was a warm, friendly and generous man and an excellent teacher who was proud and fond of his young students.

The publication of this translation of Portenko's monograph on the birds of extreme eastern Siberia is most timely. In May, 1972, our two countries signed the US-USSR Agreement on Cooperation in the Field of Environmental Protection and in late 1978 both ratified the US-USSR Convention on the Conservation of Migratory Birds and Their Environment. I am only sorry that Professor Portenko, who died May 26, 1972 at the age of 75, did not live to see wider dissemination of his monograph among arctic ornithologists in North America and cooperative US-USSR scientific research in far eastern Siberia and Alaska.

George E. Watson
Curator of Birds
Smithsonian Institution

In respectful memory
of my father
Aleksandr Iustinovich Portenko

Preface

This monograph is a comprehensive survey of available information on the avifauna of Far Northeast Asia, from Chaun Bay, the Anadyr Range and Krest Bay in the west and south to Bering Strait and Wrangel Island in the east and north. The fauna of this area was among the least studied in the USSR when the author began studying the land fauna 40 years ago. What prompted him to undertake this project was not only the scanty information available on Northeast Asia but also a special zoogeographic interest which is only natural on coming into contact with the fauna of an area which brings the continents of the New and the Old Worlds closer. Especially tempting was the possibility of finding American animal species in the extremities of East Siberia. In 1931, when the author was engaged in a study of the birds of Anadyr territory, the search for American affinities was one of his prime tasks. But by August of that year, on completing the field work in Tanyurer and summarizing the results, he came to the conclusion that Anadyr avifauna was essentially Siberian and that closer links with American avifauna would have to be sought more toward the east.

In 1932 the author completed a voyage in small boats along the lower reaches of the Anadyr and reached the sea in July. As early as this he was able to organize a trip by steamboat with halts at different points along the Chukchi coast.

This monograph provides a detailed account of the author's field work in the Chukchi peninsula and on Wrangel Island. In 1933–34 he studied the avifauna in the eastern part of the Chukchi peninsula and spent the winter in Uélen. In 1937–38 his assistant collected birds on the south coast of the Chukchi peninsula and spent the winter at Providence Bay. In 1938–39 he wintered on Wrangel Island and studied the fauna there. It was thought desirable to supplement these around-the-year investigations with a study of the nesting habits of birds in the interior of the Chukchi peninsula. In summer, 1956, he made a special journey on the Amguema River.

The author's own field work formed the basis of the present book. He gathered much original information from various persons who shared their observations enthusiastically or parted with their small collections. Later the author gathered and thoroughly examined the available literature. Though the manuscript was completed in the 40s it was gradually supplemented. Some years ago when an opportunity arose to publish this voluminous work, the entire manuscript was recast afresh. Thus this monograph reflects not only the author's prolonged field work but also his latest concepts concerning the birds of Northeast Asia and his settled convictions as to their taxonomic status.

The present study of the birds of the Chukchi peninsula and Wrangel Island is a natural consequence of his studies in Anadyr (Portenko, 1939b).

This monograph also covers information on the birds of St. Lawrence Island.

Because of its bulk, the monograph has been issued in two parts with the bibliography included in the second part.

In the course of his many years of work on the fauna of Far Northeast Asia the author received the help and cooperation of many individuals, to all of whom he expresses his deep gratitude. On the expeditions the work was carried out with the cooperation of Chukchians and Eskimos, as well as personnel wintering at Polar stations and colleagues at the Arctic Institute and the Institute of Zoology, all of whom contributed much to the success of his research.

Though Far Northeast Asia was one of the least known areas ornithologically 40 years ago, it is no longer so, as the reader will discover for himself.

L.A. PORTENKO

Contents

FOREWORD TO THE TRANSLATION vii

PREFACE ix

GEOGRAPHIC NAMES OCCURRING IN THE TEXT xvii

INTRODUCTION 1

History of Research on the Avifauna of the Chukchi Peninsula and Wrangel and St. Lawrence Islands 1

History of research on the bird fauna of the Chukchi Peninsula from the latter half of the 18th century to 1932 1

Field investigations in the Chukchi Peninsula from 1932 to 1970 12

History of research on bird fauna on Wrangel and Herald islands 28

History of research on bird fauna on St. Lawrence Island (1779 through 1959) 39

DESCRIPTION OF SPECIES 42

Order I. Gaviiformes—Loons 42

1. *Gavia stellata stellata* (Pontopp.)—Red-throated loon 42

2. *Gavia arctica viridigularis* Dwight—East Siberian Arctic loon 47

3. *Gavia arctica pacifica* (Lawrence)—Pacific loon 50

4. *Gavia immer adamsii* (Gray)—White-billed common loon 54

Gavia immer immer (Brünnich)—Polar loon 58

Order Podicipediformes—Grebes 59

Podiceps griseigena holböllii Reinh.—Red-necked grebe 59

Order II. Procellariiformes—Tube-nosed birds 59

5. *Diomedea albatrus* Pall.—Short-tailed albatross 59

6. *Fulmarus glacialis rodgersi* Cassin—Northern fulmar 60

7. *Puffinus tenuirostris* (Temm.)—Slender-billed shearwater 66

8. *Oceanodroma furcata furcata* (Gm.)—Fork-tailed petrel 70

Order III. Pelecaniformes—Paddle feet (Totipalmates) 71

9. *Phalacrocorax pelagicus aeolus* Swinh.—Pelagic cormorant 71

Phalacrocorax urile (Gm.)—Red-faced cormorant 84

Order IV. Anseriformes—Waterfowl 84

10. *Cygnus cygnus* (L.) subspecies?—Whooper swan 84

11. *Chen caerulescens caerulescens* (L.)—Lesser snow goose 90

12. *Anser albifrons albifrons* (Scop.)—White-fronted goose 118

13. *Anser erythropus* (L.)—Lesser white-fronted goose 122

14. *Melanonyx fabalis serrirostris* (Swinh.)—Bean goose 123

15. *Philacte canagica* (Sewast.)—Emperor goose 127

16. *Branta bernicla nigricans* (Lawr.)—Brent goose 137

Branta canadensis minima Ridgw.—Cackling Canada goose 152

17. *Anas platyrhynchos platyrhynchos* L.—Mallard duck 153

18. *Nettion crecca crecca* (L.)—European common teal or Green-winged teal 153

Nettion crecca carolinensis (Gm.)—American green-winged teal 154

19. *Nettion formosa* (Georgi)—Baikal teal 154

20. *Dafila acuta acuta* (L.)—Pintail 155

21. *Mareca penelope penelope* (L.)—Wigeon 158

22. *Spatula clypeata* (L.)—Shoveler 158

23. *Aythya fuligula* (L.)—Tufted duck 159

24. *Aythya marila mariloides* (Vig.)—Greater scaup 159

Bucephala clangula (L.)—Common golden-eye 161

25. *Clangula hyemalis* (L.)—Old squaw 161

26. *Histrionicus histrionicus pacificus* Brooks—Harlequin duck 179

Melanitta nigra americana (Swains.)—Black scoter 182

Melanitta fusca stejnegeri Ridgw.—Hook-nosed scoter 183

27. *Melanitta perspicillata* (L.)—Surf scoter 184

28. *Polysticta stelleri* (Pall.)—Steller's eider 184

29. *Arctonetta fischeri* (Brandt)—Spectacled eider 193

30. *Somateria spectabilis* (L.)—King eider 200
31. *Somateria mollissima* var. *nigrum* Gray—Common eider 219
Mergus merganser L.—Merganser 254
32. *Mergus serrator* L.—Red-breasted merganser 255
Order V. Falconiformes—Diurnal birds of prey 256
33. *Buteo lagopus kamtschatkensis* Dement.—Rough-legged buzzard 256
34. *Aquila chrysaëtos canadensis* (L.)—Golden eagle 263
35. *Haliaeetus albicilla* (L.)—White-tailed sea eagle 263
? *Thallassoaëtus pelagicus* (Pall.)—White-shouldered eagle 264
36. *Hierofalco gyrfalco grebnitzkii* Sev.—Gyrfalcon 264
37. *Falco peregrinus harterti* But.—Peregrine falcon 268
38. *Aesalon columbarius* (L.)—Merlin 276
39. *Cerchneis tinnunculus* (L.)—Kestrel 276
Order VI. Galliformes—Gallinaceous birds 276
40. *Lagopus lagopus lagopus* (L.)—Willow ptarmigan 276
41. *Lagopus mutus pleskei* Serebr.—Rock ptarmigan 286
Order VII. Gruiformes—Cranes 289
42. *Grus canadensis canadensis* (L.)—Sandhill crane 289
43. *Antigone leucogeranus* (Pall.)—Siberian crane 302
Order VIII. Charadriiformes—Shore birds, gulls and allies 303
Family Charadriidae—Plovers, sandpipers, snipes 303
44. *Pluvialis squatarola* (L.)—Gray plover 303
45. *Pluvialis dominica fulva* (Gm.)—Siberian plover 310
46. *Pluvialis dominica dominica* (Müll.)—American plover 316
47. *Eudromias morinellus* (L.)—Dotterel 318
48. *Charadrius hiaticula tundrae* (Lowe)—Ringed plover 321
49. *Charadrius mongolus stegmanni* Port.—Mongolian plover 326
50. *Arenaria interpres oahuensis* (Bloxh.)—Common turnstone 327
Arenaria melanocephala (Vigors)—Black turnstone 334
51. *Totanus erythropus* (Pall.)—Spotted redshank 334
52. *Glottis nebularia* (Gunn.)—Greenshank 335
53. *Rhyacophilus glareola* (L.)—Tiny wood sandpiper 335

54. *Heteroscelus incanus brevipes* (Vieill.)—Siberian tattler 336
55. *Heteroscelus incanus incanus* (Gm.)—American tattler 336
56. *Numenius borealis borealis* (Forst.)—Eskimo curlew 338
57. *Numenius phaeopus variegatus* (Scop.)—Whimbrel 338
Numenius tahitiensis (Gm.)—Bristle-thighed curlew 339
58. *Limosa lapponica menzbieri* Port. 339
59. *Limosa lapponica baueri* Naum.—Bar-tailed godwit 339
Limosa limosa melanuroides Gould—Black-tailed godwit 341
60. *Limnodromus griseus scolopaceus* (Say)—Dowitcher 341
61. *Gallinago gallinago gallinago* (L.)—Common snipe 345
62. *Calidris canutus rogersi* (Mathews)—American knot 348
63. *Calidris tenuirostris* (Horsf.)—Eastern knot 354
64. *Erolia ferruginea* (Pontopp.)—Curlew-sandpiper 354
65. *Pelidna alpina sakhalina* (Vieill.) 355
66. *Pelidna alpina pacifica* (Coues)—Dunlin 355
67. *Pelidna maritima tschuktschorum* Port. 366
68. *Pelidna maritima ptilocnemis* (Coues)—Purple sandpiper 366
69. *Pisobia ruficollis ruficollis* (Pall.)—Eastern little stint 374
70. *Pisobia ruficollis minuta* (Leisl.)—Little stint 385
71. *Pisobia minutilla subminuta* (Midd.)—American stint 386
72. *Pisobia mauri* (Cab.)—Semipalmated sandpiper 386
Pisobia pusilla (L.)—North American semipalmated sandpiper 391
73. *Eurynorhynchus pygmeus* (L.)—Spoonbill sandpiper 393
74. *Limonites temminckii* (Leisl.)—Temminck's stint 401
75. *Actodromas bairdii* Coues—Baird's sandpiper 405
76. *Heteropygia melanotos* (Vieill.)—Pectoral sandpiper 410
77. *Heteropygia acuminata* (Horsf.)—Sharp-tailed sandpiper 423
78. *Philomachus pugnax* (L.)—Ruff 424
79. *Tryngites subruficollis* (Vieill.)—Buff-breasted sandpiper 425
80. *Phalaropus fulicarius* (L.)—Gray phalarope 425
81. *Phalaropus lobatus* (L.)—Northern phalarope 439

SUPPLEMENTARY NOTES TO COLOR PLATES III, VI AND VII 446

COLOR PLATES Between pages

Plate I. White-billed common loon *Gavia immer adamsii* (Gray) 72–73

Plate II. Lesser snow geese *Chen caerulescens* (L.) in Akademii Tundra 96–97

Plate III. Age-wise plumage of male king eiders *Somateria spectabilis* (L.) 176–177

Plate IV. Common eider *Somateria mollissima* var. *nigrum* Gray 192–193

Plate V. Sandhill crane *Grus canadensis* (L.) 280–281

Plate VI. Eggs of sandpipers 296–297

Plate VII. Downy fledgelings of sandpipers 392–393

Plate VIII. Spoonbill sandpiper *Eurynorhynchus pygmeus* (L.) 408–409

Geographic Names Occurring in the Text

The faunal finds presented in this book were made over a period of more than two centuries. During this period the geographic names changed many times or new names were coined. Their correct use in a relatively little known territory like the Chukchi peninsula and Wrangel Island presents considerable difficulty.

The map (facing p. 16) shows only the major place names. Some particular points have been oriented in relation to them. As a rule, preference has been given to the names shown in the latest maps. However, there were many localities not depicted on the maps. In these cases local Chukchian names had to be used, writing them as they are actually pronounced. In the list of place names given below alternate spellings have been included to facilitate identification on older maps and in the reference material. It may be emphasized that in the main the latest maps and the most recent geographic publications have been followed.

In all his works, beginning in the 30s, the author has written "Anadyr" and not "Anadyr' ", the former having long been the local pronunciation. He also writes "Aiok" and not "Aion", which is a Chukchian word meaning "cerebellum of a deer" (the most appropriate name), not denoting exclusively the topography. The same is true of "Kolyuchi", which is the correct Chukchian pronunciation of the name of the island. The similarity with the Russian word of this spelling meaning "prickly" is purely incidental. In Chukchian dialect, "Véem" (river) is pronounced as "Véiem" and to write it as "Veem" would be an incorrect simplification. There is frequent reference in the text to the River "Kol'oam-Véem". It flows out of Lake "Kool'ong", mentioned on the latest maps as "Koolen' ". The names of rivers and lakes have been spelt as actually pronounced by the local people.

The term "Chukchi peninsula" has been used to cover the Asian extremity to the east of a line running from Chaun Bay to Krest Bay. The author could not find any other term that would embrace all of this territory.

Aiok—island at the entrance of Chaun Bay.
Akatylanva—natural boundary on the south coast of Wrangel Island at the point of intersection with the 180th meridian.
Akkani—settlement on the east coast of the Chukchi peninsula between Mechigmensk Gulf and Lawrence Bay.
Ambarchik—village and bay on Kolyma delta.
Amerikanskaya or Khishchnikov—river in the southeastern part of Wrangel Island

which flows into Long Strait between Rodgers and Somnitel'naya bays.

Amguéma (Amguema)—large river in the western part of the Chukchi peninsula flowing into Chukchi Sea between Cape Schmidt and Vankarém village.

Anadyr Range—mountain range extending from Chaun Bay to Krest Bay and separating the Chukchi peninsula from Anadyr territory.

Antoshkina—a rivulet between Cape Bol'shoi Baranov and Malaya Baranikha village.

Anyui Bol'shoi and Malyi—right tributaries of lower Kolyma River.

Anapel'khin—village on the bank of River Apapel'khin, north of Pevek.

Arakamchechen (Kainé)—island at the southeastern tip of the Chukchi peninsula.

Atternon—high mountain in the southeastern part of Wrangel Island, west of Rodgers Bay.

Atuk—the highest peak of the Kukulgit Range in the northern part of central St. Lawrence Island.

Balagan and Balaganchik—settlements to the west of Cape Bol'shoi Baranov.

Balk—islet in Lawrence Bay.

Baranikha Bol'shaya and Malaya—rivers between Chaun Bay and the Kolyma estuary.

Baranov Bol'shoi—cape (Kamen') between Chaun Bay and the Kolyma estuary.

Bennet—islet in Lawrence Bay.

Bering—strait halfway along the south coast of the Chukchi peninsula.

Berri—peak in the central hilly part of Wrangel Island.

Bilibino—settlement on Bol'shoi Keper-Véem, a tributary of the Malyi Anyui.

Blossom—cape at southwestern tip of Wrangel Island.

Bokser (Boxer)—bay in the southwest coast of St. Lawrence Island.

Bol'shevik—cape on east coast of Wrangel Island south of Cape Pillar.

Bruch—spit on the northeast coast of Wrangel Island, northwest of Cape Litke.

Chantal'veergyn—river flowing into the Ekityki River, left tributary of the Amguema.

Chaplin (Indian Point)—cape on the southeastern tip of the Chukchi peninsula.

Chaun—river flowing into Chaun Bay from the south.

—bay on southwest coast of the Chukchi peninsula.

—parish, mostly coastal, from the lower Kolyma to Cape Yakan. The parish church was at the mouth of the Bol'shaya Baranikha River.

Chaunskii Malyi—strait between Aiok Island and the Karchik peninsula.

Chechen—village at the southeastern tip of the Chukchi peninsula.

Chegitun (Shelton)—river and village on the northeast coast of the Chukchi peninsula between Uélen and Cape Serdtse-Kamen' near the Arctic Circle.

Chenlyukvyn—cape closest to Uélen to the east.

Chetyrekhstolb—island in Medvezhii group north of the Kolyma estuary.

Chibukak—cape at the northwestern tip of St. Lawrence Island.

Chicherina—spit on south coast of Wrangel Island.

Chukchi—sea between Wrangel Island, north coast of the Chukchi peninsula, Bering Strait and Alaska.

Chulkhyn—tiny settlement on south coast of Lawrence Bay.

Chutpa—village southeast of Cape Serdtse-Kamen'.

Darovatyi—cape west of the Kolyma estuary.
Davydov—lagoon and bay on south coast of Wrangel Island, east of Somnitel'naya Bay.
Demarkeishen (Demarcation)—cape on the arctic coast of Alaska near the Canadian border.
Dezhnev (erstwhile Mikhailovskaya station)—tiny settlement on south coast of the peninsula, to the south of Uélen.
Dezhnev—cape on the far northeast tip of Asia.
—line of knolls running north-south, east of Uélen.
Diomede Bol'shoi or Ratmanov—island in the middle of Bering Strait east of Cape Dezhnev.
Diomede Malyi or Kruzenshtern—eastern, smaller of two Diomede islands in Bering Strait.
Dzhénrétlen (Dhzenretlen)—rocky cape east of Kolyuchi Bay.
Égvekinot—township (district center) on the northwestern shore of Krest Bay.
Ékiatap—river flowing into a lagoon southeast of Cape Schmidt.
Ékichun—river 20 km to the west of Cape Schmidt.
Ékug-Véem—river flowing into Ukouge lagoon.
Émma—bay, northeast branch of Providence Bay.
Énmen-Véem—rivulet near Bilibino settlement on the southwestern slope of North Anyui Range.
Énmitagin—settlement near Mitkulen, west of Inchoun.
Enraukun—cape between Bolshoi and Malyi Baranov Kamen'.
Énurmino—village near Cape Serdtse-Kamen'.
Érdman—island in Providence Bay.
Erruem—river flowing into a lagoon from Bolshaya Baranikha.
Erulen—bay on eastern shoreline of Krest Bay.
Féruéi—rock in the sea southeast of Malyi Diomede Island.
Florens—cape on west coast of Wrangel Island.
Gambell—village at northwestern tip of St. Lawrence Island.
Gek (Geik)—right tributary of the Malyi Anyui in its upper reaches south of Chaun Bay.
Gek (Zemlya Geka)—cape in Anadyr lagoon.
Hawaii—cape at the southeastern tip of Wrangel Island.
Idlidlya—island off the north coast of the Chukchi peninsula between Kolyuchi Bay and Cape Serdtse-Kamen' opposite of Neskynpil'gyn lagoon.
Ikechurun ("Insurin" according to J. Koren)—cape and village on north coast of the Chukchi peninsula near the Arctic Circle.
Il'khetan—village on Cape Onman east of Vankarém.
Inchoun—cape and village west of Uélen.
Irgunnuk—settlement on north coast of the Chukchi peninsula between Kolyuchi Gulf and Néskynpil'gyn lagoon (second settlement to the east of Pitlekai).
Istiget—village on the south coast of the Chukchi peninsula, close to Providence Bay.
Iul'tin ("Iutl'tyn" in Chukchian)—range west of the lower Amguema.
Ivga—cape on the eastern side of entrance to Providence Bay.

Ivunat—cape on St. Lawrence Island.

Kagupalik (Kaghoopalik)—settlement on northwest coast of St. Lawrence Island, north of Kaval'gak.

Kalashnikovo—village on the Lower Kolyma.

Kamennyi—cape on the west side of the Kolyma estuary.

Kangi—village at the western end of Kuzata lagoon on south coast of St. Lawrence Island.

Karchik (Karchyk, Kyttyk)—peninsula on the northwestern shore of Chaun Bay.

Karpiya ("Karpe" according to J. Koren)—river to the west of Ryrkaipiya village.

Kaval'gak (Kavalghak)—cape on northwest coast of St. Lawrence Island.

Kavuk (Kawook)—village in the central lowlands of St. Lawrence Island.

Keper-Veem—right tributary of the Malaya Anyui in its middle reaches.

Khishchnikov—see Amerikanskaya.

Kiamgak—cape at southernmost tip of St. Lawrence Island.

Kiber—cape east of Chaun Bay, facing Shalaurov Island, and Nol'de Gulf to the west.

King—islet in the southern part of Bering Strait.

Kinipagul'gat (Kinipaghulghat)—mountains at the eastern end of St. Lawrence Island.

Kivak—village on south coast of the Chukchi peninsula between Providence Bay and Cape Chaplin.

Kler (Klark)—river in the southwestern part of Wrangel Island north of Nasha River.

Kol'e—settlement on St. Lawrence Island.

Kol'oam-Véem—river draining Kool'ong (Koolen') Lake and flowing into a lagoon west of Uélen.

Kolyuchi ("Kolyuchin" erroneously)—island north of Kolyuchi Gulf.

Kolyuchin—inlet or a large bay on north coast of the Chukchi peninsula.

Kongkok—settlement on the southwest coast of St. Lawrence Island.

Kon'kovaya—river west of the Lower Kolyma.

Kon'yam—bay in Senyavin Strait in the southeastern part of the Chukchi peninsula.

Kool'ong (Koolen')—lake at the head of Lawrence Bay drained by the River Kol'-oam-Véem.

Korvin—cape at the southeastern tip of Wrangel Island.

Kozhevnikov—cape, one of the cliffs of Cape Schmidt.

Kozmina (Kuz'mina)—river in the western part of the Karchik peninsula.

Krai Lesov—village on the Lower Kolyma.

Krasnaya Glina—natural boundary on the southeastern coast of Wrangel Island east of Rodgers Bay.

Krasnyi Flag—river crossing Tundra Akademii north-south.

Krest—bay in the southwest coast of the Chukchi peninsula.

Kriguigun—cape on east coast of the Chukchi peninsula between Mechigmensk Gulf and Lawrence Bay.

Kuékvun'—river northwest of Cape Schmidt.

Kukulgit (Kookouligit)—central mountain on the north side of St. Lawrence Island. The peak rises 630 m above sea level, the highest point on the island.

Kukuliak (Kukulik)—village and cape halfway along the north coast of St. Lawrence Island.
Kukul'skie—mountains on St. Lawrence Island.
Kurimul' (Kurima)—river east of Krest Bay.
Kurupka—village on south coast of the Chukchi peninsula 40 km northwest of Providence Bay.
Kuvét—tributary of the Pegtymel' River east of Chaun Bay.
Kuzata—large lagoon on south coast of St. Lawrence Island.
Kytrytkan—settlement on east coast of the Chukchi peninsula.
Lavrentia (Lawrence)—bay and settlement on east coast of the Chukchi peninsula.
Lelyu-Véem—river flowing into Chaun Bay from the south.
Litke—cape on east coast of Wrangel Island, northwest of Cape Uéring.
Lyaleran—cape on north coast of the Chukchi peninsula, west of Cape Billings.
Maingatir—settlement west of Cape Dzhénrétlen.
Mainynytum—cape and village on the shore of Anadyr Bay, to the south of Krest Bay.
Mamka—river flowing into the western end of Lawrence Bay.
Mamontovaya—river draining the central part of Wrangel Island, flowing into Predatel'skaya Bay.
Markovo—village on the Anadyr between central and upper reaches.
Mechigmensk—gulf halfway along the east coast of the Chukchi peninsula.
Medvezhii—cape on the eastern side of the Kolyma delta.
Méechkyn (Meechken)—spit east of entrance to Krest Bay.
Merfi (Murphy Bay)—bay on southwest coast of St. Lawrence Island, east of Boxer Bay.
Métégyn—knoll west of the lower reaches of the Amguema River.
Mikhalkino—village on the Kolyma estuary.
Mitkulen—village on north coast of the Chukchi peninsula, northwest of Inchoun.
Mlelo-Véem—river flowing into Chaun Bay from the east.
Mogoveiik (Moghoweyik)—river debouching on west coast of St. Lawrence Island.
Mugum—peak on northwest coast of St. Lawrence Island.
Mushtakova—spit in the extreme north of Wrangel Island.
Nagleinyn—mountain on western shore of Chaun Bay.
Nasha—river in the southeastern part of Wrangel Island, south of Klér River.
Naskak—village on St. Lawrence Island, 15 miles east of Gambell.
Naukan—abandoned village south of Cape Dezhnev.
Navarin—cape southwest of Anadyr Bay.
Néskan (Neshkan)—village on Néskynpil'gyn spit.
Neskynpil'gyn—lagoon and spit east of Kolyuchi Bay.
Néttékenishkhen—village west of Cape Serdtse-Kamen', westward from Énurmino.
Nétté-Véem—river between Néskan and Énurmino.
Nol'de—bay (gulf) to the east of Chaun Bay.
Notapenmen—village on the eastern shore of entrance to Krest Bay.
Novo-mariinsk—old name of Anadyr township.
Nunyamo—cape and village on north side of entrance to St. Lawrence Bay, on east coast of the Chukchi peninsula.

Nutauge (Nut)—lagoon between the Amguema estuary and Vankarém.
Onman—cape east of Vankarém on north coast of the Chukchi peninsula.
"Ozero"—lagoon 8 km west of Rogers Bay.
Padl'onna—village east of Kolyuchi Bay between Néskan and Tepkan.
Pegtymel'—river east of Chaun Bay.
Pereval'naya—meteorological station on the pass between Tadleo and the source of the Amguema River.
Pestsovaya—river in the northern part of Wrangel Island.
Pevek—cape, village and strait to the northeast of Chaun Bay.
Pidlin—village south of entrance to Kolyuchin Bay from the east.
Pil'gyn—river west of Cape Schmidt (general meaning is "strait" or "neck").
Pillar—cape on east coast of Wrangel Island south of Cape Uéring.
Pinkegnei—village north of Cape Chaplin.
Pitlekai—former settlement on north coast of the Chukchi peninsula at the winter anchorage of the "Vega", 67°4′49″ N and 173°23′ W.
Plover—small bay and spit at extreme east of Providence Bay.
Pnoupyl'gyn—village west of Kolyuchin Bay, east of Cape Onman.
Pogynden—right tributary of the Malaya Anyui.
Polyavaam—river flowing into Chaun Bay from southeast.
Poutyn—village on east coast of the Chukchi peninsula, north of Lawrence Bay.
Povuiliyak (Powoojliak)—cape on the southwestern coast of St. Lawrence Island.
Predatel'skaya—bay on south coast of Wrangel Island, west of the 180th meridian.
Preobrazheniya—gulf on south coast of the Chukchi peninsula, southeast of Bering Cape.
Proletarskii—cape at the entrance to Rodgers Bay from west.
Provideniya (Providence)—bay on the southeast tip of the Chukchi peninsula.
Ptichii—island in Bering Sea. Obsolete name of St. Matthew Island.
Punuk—islets at the southeastern end of St. Lawrence Island.
Putgut—plateau west of Kuzata lagoon on south coast of St. Lawrence Island.
Puvukpak (Poovookpuk)—mountains in the southwestern part of St. Lawrence Island.
Rakvazan—river flowing into Chaun Bay from west.
Ratmanova or Bol'shoi Diomede—island, see Diomede Bol'shoi.
Rauchua—lake drained by River Rauchua, west of Chaun Bay.
Rétken (Redken, Redkin vtoroi)—see Vtoroi.
Rodzhers (Rodgers)—bay on the southwestern coast of Wrangel Island.
Routan (Bol'shoi Rautan)—island in the neck of Chaun Bay.
Ryraitinop—village closest to Pitlekai to the east.
Ryrkaipiya (Ir-Kaipiya according to G. Maydell)—Chukchian village near Cape Schmidt.
Ryyanranot—tiny islet off northern shore of Aiok Island.
Savunga—village on north coast of St. Lawrence Island.
Seitun—hamlet west of Mitkulen, on the northeast coast of the Chukchi peninsula.
Seklik—cape on south coast of the Chukchi peninsula, southeast of Bering Cape.
Senyavin—strait separating Arakamchechen Island from the southeastern end of the Chukchi peninsula.

Serdtse-Kamen'—cape on the northeast coast of the Chukchi peninsula.
Seshan (Seishan, Sechan)—village southeast of Cape Serdtse-Kamen'.
Severnyi—cape, former name of Cape Schmidt.
Sevu—cape at northeastern end of St. Lawrence Island.
Shalurova—island on the northwest coast of the Chukchi peninsula, east of Cape Shelagskii.
Shelagskii—cape on the eastern side of entrance to Chaun Bay.
Shelton (Chegitun)—river flowing into Chukchi Sea near the Arctic Circle.
Shmidt—cape (formerly Cape Severnyi) on north coast of the Chukchi peninsula, slightly east of the 180th meridian.
Siknik—cape halfway along south coast of St. Lawrence Island.
Singikpo—cape on hilly north coast of St. Lawrence Island.
Sireniki—village west of Providence Bay.
Sivokak (Sevuokuk)—mountain at the northwestern end of St. Lawrence Island.
Somnitel'naya—bay on south coast of Wrangel Island, west of Rodgers Bay.
St. Lawrence—island in Bering Sea, southeast of the Chukchi peninsula.
Stolbovoi—cape in the Kolyma estuary.
Stoletiya—cape from the west side of entrance to Providence Bay.
Stolovaya (Tafelberg)—mountain on eastern shore of Kolyuchin Bay. Shown on Palmén's map (Palmén 1887, p. 255).
Sukharnoe—village on the Kolyma delta.
Syautokama (Chéutakon?)—river 80 km east of Krest Bay.
Tadleo—tributary of the Kanchalan River, west of Krest Bay.
Tanyurer—large left tributary of the Anadyr.
Tapguk (Taphook)—cape on north coast of St. Lawrence Island near western end.
Tatik—cape on west coast of St. Lawrence Island.
Téeyu-Véem (Téeyun) or Vtoraya—brook originating in Dezhnev knolls, south of Uélen.
Telekai-Véem—river west of the Amguema.
Ténkérgyn—river and village between the Amguema estuary and Cape Schmidt.
Tepkan (Tepka, Tjapka, and Tjupka)—village on the spit separating Néskynpil'gyn lagoon from the sea, on the northeast coast of the Chukchi peninsula.
Tikhaya—river in the western part of the Karchik peninsula.
Trautman—lake near the northwestern tip of St. Lawrence Island.
Tret'ya—brook originating in Dezhnev knolls, south of Uélen.
Troyanov—bay in the Kolyma estuary, south of Cape Medvezhii.
Tundra Akademii—northern lowland part of Wrangel Island.
Uélen—village at the northeastern end of the Chukchi peninsula.
Uél'kal'—village on west side of entrance to Krest Bay.
Uéring—cape on east coast of Wrangel Island.
Ukouge—lagoon 25 km east of the Amguema estuary.
Unikyn (Unin)—cape halfway along the northeastern coast of the Chukchi peninsula between Cape Inchoun and the Arctic Circle.
Unyyn (village Chaplino)—settlement on Cape Chaplin.
Urtykuul'—brook in the Karchik peninsula.
Ushakovskii—settlement in Rodgers Bay.

Utatgyr—brook on Aiok Island.
Utten—village near Seitun village on the northeast coast of the Chukchi peninsula.
Utte-Véem (Utavaam)—river in the eastern part of the Chukchi peninsula flowing into a lagoon west of Inchoun.
Val'karai—village west of Cape Billings.
Val'kumei—cape in Chaun Bay, south of Pevek.
Vankarém (Vankarem)—village, cape and lagoon on north coast of the Chukchi peninsula, west of Kolyuchin Bay.
Vanmaii—tributary of the River Boxer in the southwestern part of St. Lawrence Island.
Vostochnyi (East cape)—cape 15 miles east of Uélen.
Vtoraya or Téeyu(n)—brook originating in Dezhnev knolls, south of Uélen.
Vtoroi Rétkén (Ratkyn or "Red'kin")—village on south coast of the Chukchi peninsula between Krest Bay and Bering Cape.
Yakan—cape on north coast of the Chukchi peninsula.
Yandagai—village on east coast of the Chukchi peninsula, near Cape Kriguigun.
Yanrakynnot—village on Senyavin Strait.
Yarak-Véem—river in the eastern part of northern Anyui Range, left tributary of the Lelyu-Véem River in its upper reaches.
Yararmumny—tributary of the Utte-Véem River in the interior of the eastern half of the Chukchi peninsula.
Yatachan—tributary of Bol'shoi Anyui.
Yulii—cliff on east coast of Wrangel Island, south of Cape Uéring.
Yuni-Véem (Ironi-Véem)—river flowing into Kolyuchin Bay.
Yutkan—village east of Cape Unikyn and west of Seitun.
Zanes—cape on west coast of Wrangel Island, northeast of West Cape.
Zapadnyi (West Cape)—cape on St. Lawrence Island, the westernmost point on the island.

Introduction

HISTORY OF RESEARCH ON THE AVIFAUNA OF THE CHUKCHI PENINSULA AND WRANGEL AND ST. LAWRENCE ISLANDS

History of Research on the Bird Fauna of the Chukchi Peninsula from the Latter Half of the 18th Century to 1932

Though the country adjoining Bering Strait has attracted the attention of scientists from early times it was not until the 18th century that they visited it. The expedition led by Vitus Bering (Miller 1758, Pallas 1781a and b, Berkh 1823, Vakhtin 1890, Dall 1890, Golder 1922, and Berg 1926 and 1946) landed on the Chukchi coast a number of times in 1728 but did not look for fresh water. Nor did it study the fauna of the territory.

The expedition of Capt. James Cook (King 1785) visited Lawrence Bay, Cape Schmidt (Cook first named it Cape Severnyi) and Cape Chaplin in August and September, 1778. However, all the information on birds contained in the travel records related only to Alaska and the Aleutian Islands, none to the Chukchi coast. After Capt. Cook's death in 1779 his expedition, now under the leadership of Charles Clerk, repeated the attempt to find a northern approach to Asia or America. The expedition of July 1 set course for Cape Chaplin and on July 5 sighted Cape Dezhnev and Diomede Island, reaching 70°33′ N on the Chukchi Sea. On July 23 the ships sailed past Cape Serdtse-Kamen' and on July 31 came to Lawrence Bay for the second time.

The account of the second voyage contains some very brief notes on sea birds, incorrectly named (e.g. "sea-parrots" and "small ice-birds"). Prof. Stresemann (1949) pointed out that V.V. Ellis, a participant in Cook's expedition, drew some freehand sketches of birds caught in Bering Strait and to the north in the Arctic Ocean close to the Chukchi coast. The blue-headed wagtail was even given the name Chukchi wagtail (*Motacilla tschuk'tschensis* Gm.). Unfortunately no record of any kind is available about bird finds on the Chukchi peninsula proper because the few specimens collected were not correctly dated, passed through several hands and museums and are no longer preserved.

Joseph Billings, who sailed on Capt. Cook's third voyage was invited to join the Russian service after a few years when he attained the rank of lieutenant. He led sea and land expeditions. Of these, the land expeditions are of interest. After futile attempts to circumnavigate the north coast of the Chukchi peninsula from the west, from the side of the Kolyma, and later from the east, from the side of Bering Strait, Joseph Billings settled for the land route over the arguments and protests of his companions (Billings 1802). He made friends with the reindeer-breeding Chukchians and discharged his responsibilities satisfactorily.

On August 15, 1791, Joseph Billings landed in Lawrence Bay and set off from there to Mechigmensk Gulf in 15 canoes. There he entered into an agreement with an influential Chukchian herdsman, Imlerat, to help him and his 12 companions reach the Russian villages on the Kolyma. On September 6 a reindeer caravan set off with the expedition's baggage piled on 30 sleighs. On October 25 the expedition crossed the head (i.e. the southern part) of Kolyuchin Bay on the ice and continued along the northern slope of the Anadyr Range an average of 50 miles inland from the coast, as shown on the map in the records of this expedition compiled by Sarychev (1811). On November 29 the caravan crossed the Amguema River. On December 25 it crossed Cape Schmidt and on January 29, 1792, reached the River Chaun. On February 28 the expedition arrived safely at Anyui fort.

Carl Henrich Merck, a physician attached to Joseph Billings' expedition as a naturalist, was later referred to with great respect by P.S. Pallas (1811). In the journey through the interior of the Chukchi peninsula Carl Merck was assisted by an English physician, John Mein, in natural history. Unfortunately the scientific results of Merck's Chukchi journey were negligible. The season of field work, from the end of August to the end of February, did not favor making a collection, especially of birds, which mostly migrated southward. Besides, the poor conditions for the movement of reindeer and lack of facilities for the processing and transport of collected material did not meet the minimal technical requirements established by larger expeditions of later years.

As reported by G. Sarychev (1811, p. 11), Merck's records were handed over to Prof. Pallas in the Crimea on completion of the expedition and that was the end. Posterity was unfortunately deprived of many useful discoveries by this hard-working naturalist and the interesting information on natural history collected with great care in the course of the expedition. In the editor's footnote, however, it is mentioned that Pallas described the birds, fish and other animals handed over to the museum and included the information in his major publication on the zoology of the Russian empire. In his *Zoographia Rosso-Asiatica* (1811, vol. I, p. 7), Pallas enumerated Merck's achievements in collecting material from the Arctic and Pacific Oceans, from the islands off Kamchatka and Alaska and in Alaska itself but did not say a word about the Chukchi expedition. However, the text of Pallas' zoogeography contained some Chukchian names of birds, references to the finding of certain species in the Chukchi peninsula and a description of *Emberiza hyperborea* caught there.

Until recently it was assumed that the diaries of Carl Merck were irretrievably lost. In fact, they were preserved in the family archives of his relatives in Darmstadt and were discovered in 1936. The ornithological information they contained was processed by Prof. Stresemann (1950). This concerned Tauisk Gulf, Kamchatka and Alaska. There were no notes whatever on the avifauna of the Chukchi peninsula.

Joseph Billings himself devoted only a few lines to Chukchian fauna (Sarychev 1811, p. 58). According to him the country was barren and hilly; there was a great diversity of animals, invariably in large numbers. During the very brief local summer one could see eagles, falcons, ptarmigans and various species of water birds. But in winter, when the inhabitants migrated, ravens followed the explorers everywhere. Later (p. 61) Billings reported that the birds arrived from warmer areas in the spring and migrated again in the fall. In the winter only ravens, ptarmigans and snow flakes were seen.

The failure of Joseph Billings' Chukchi expedition was emphasized in the literature (Sauer 1802) right from the date its results were published. This was primarily because the season was cold and favored only light trekking on sled routes, which Merck described as arduous. No one followed Billings' route thereafter along the northern slopes of the Anadyr Range. In 1869 Maydell traveled along the southern slopes of the range. Both the routes passed through hilly country and to this day remain almost unknown from the zoological point of view.

In 1816 and 1817 O.E. Kotsebue (1821) sailed the Bering Sea. On July 26, 1816, his expedition visited St. Lawrence Island and on July 30 it was east of the Diomede Islands. On August 19 his vessel approached Cape Dezhnev and, as may be judged from the description of the cliffs and low-lying coast, anchored off Cape Inchoun. From August 21 to 29 the expedition explored Lawrence Bay. Finally on August 10, 1817, it revisited St. Lawrence Island. The naturalist with the expedition, Dr. Adel'berg Shamisso was not interested in mammals or birds, and the artist L. Choris (1822) sketched only a few guillemots. The description of Kotsebue's expedition contains two references to birds.

The voyages of F.P. Wrangel (1841, also anon. 1869[1], and Engelhardt 1839 and 1885) also provided very little information on the fauna of the Chukchi peninsula. His expedition routes in 1821, 1822, and 1823 covered the Anyuev region, the Bol'shaya and Malaya Baranikha rivers and Chaun Bay. In April, 1823, he cruised along the sea coast eastward to Kolyuchi Island. Wrangel did not undertake any special zoological research. Some casual observations on polar bears, foxes and king eiders sprinkle his description of ice treks. Not much information can be had from the diary of his traveling companion Matyushkin. Dr. Kiber worked as a naturalist in the Kolyma party of F.P. Wrangel's expedition (Kiber, 1824a and b). However, the mission was robbed of success by his ill health. The extracts from his diary (Kiber 1824a) refer to the lower Kolyma and include very cursory material on the birds of that region. In another article on Chukchians (Kiber 1824b) there is a reference to ravens.

I.G. Voznesenskii, laboratory assistant of the zoological museum of the Academy of Sciences, who was known for his collections from the erstwhile Russian colonies in America, Kamchatka, the Kuril Islands and Okhotsk Sea coast, only briefly touched the Chukchi peninsula (Gil'zen 1915). In August, 1843, he sailed from Cape Espenberg in Alaska to the Chukchi coast, where he visited Mechigmensk Bay. Bird skins that he collected, preserved in the Institute of Zoology, Academy of Sciences of the USSR, included specimens studied by the present author.

[1]A short history of the voyages of W. Berings, J. Cook and F. Wrangel.

In 1849 Capt. Muir commanded the vessel the *Plover* (Harting 1871), which from October, 1848, to the end of July, 1849, wintered in east Providence Bay in a creek which was later named Plover Bay. In this monograph, the name "Plover" invariably refers only to this small bay. Incidentally, elsewhere in the literature this name was often used to refer to the whole Providence Bay. Beginning from there at the end of June, 1849, the *Plover* made many stops on the Asiatic coast of Bering Strait and on the last occasion in Lawrence Bay. She anchored off the Choris peninsula only from July 14 to 18, i.e. for four days.

The bird collection contained the following species: *Corvus corax*, *Budytes flavus*, *Limosa lapponicus*, *Plectrophenax nivalis*, *Pluvialis fulvus*, *Charadrius mongolus*, *Eurynorhynchus pygmeus*, *Pelidna alpina*, and *Pelidna maritima*. A striking feature is the inclusion of such purely Asiatic forms as *Charadrius mongolus* and *Eurynorhynchus pygmeus*, and the total absence of purely American forms. Harting (1871) in a paper incidentally reported that the birds were taken on the Choris peninsula. Subsequently Dixon (1918, pp. 388 to 391) detected Harting's error. As proof, he cited a communication from the Secretary, London Zoological Society, in 1859 about an exhibition of spoonbills from Muir's collection in which it was reported that the birds were assumed to have been found on the northeastern coast of Asia. Prior to Dixon's correction Muir's specimens were thought for many decades to have come from the Choris peninsula. A century ago, concepts of the Far East regions adjoining Bering Strait were so confused that differentiation of Asiatic and American fauna was not even regarded as important. There was nothing like the accurate labeling which is common practice today. Nevertheless, Muir's was the first ornithological collection, though small, from the Chukchi coast and identified by scientific Latin nomenclature.

In the 40s and 50s of the last century some information on the region was collected by Father A.I. Argentov (1857a and b and 1861a and b). In 1844 he made the first journey from the lower Kolyma to the mouth of the Érruem and to Aiok Island. Being a senior missionary of the Nikolaev parish of Chaun, founded in 1850, Argentov chose as his permanent headquarters the estuary of the Bol'shaya Baranikha River where the church was located. While performing his missionary duties he showed a lively interest in the local setup and geography. In his article on the birds of the Trans-Lena region he provides detailed information on the avifauna. However, from these descriptions, which are generally brief, it is not always easy to determine the species affinity of birds. His definition of the Trans-Lena territory itself is extremely vague. Apparently Argentov included the maritime belt from the lower Kolyma in the east to Cape Yakan and to Anyuev in the south. Some of his findings are not without interest even now.

A small number of birds, mostly sea birds, were collected by the North Pacific Surveying and Exploring Expedition from Senyavin Strait under the leadership of Capt. John Rodgers. His ship the *Vincennes* anchored there in Glazenapp Bay on August 4, 1855 to land a party of scientists and then sailed northward. The party included William Stimpson, who collected hydrobiological samples and birds. On September 6 the ship returned and remained there until September 13, when the camp on the coast was wound up. In her passage north the ship reached Herald Island but Wrangel Island did not come into view. The collection was sent to the museum of the Philadelphia Academy of Natural Sciences and became the subject of a paper by Cassin (1863). In his paper, E.M. Kern made some comments on the species described. Life in the camp and a few of the observations made there were described and extracts published in a collection by W. Heine (1859).

The Russo-American Telegraph Expedition in 1865 and 1866 included scientists who worked on problems for the Smithsonian Institution and the Chicago Academy of Sciences. On the Russian coast they visited Providence Bay, Mechigmensk Gulf and Anadyr lagoon in 1865, and Providence Bay in 1866. W.H. Dall and H.M. Bannister (1869) reported observations on Alaskan birds and incidentally gave some information on Plover Bay. This lacks exact dates and is not of much interest.

G. Maydell (1871, 1893, and 1894; also Semenov 1896) visited Cape Yakan for about a month in 1870. In the spring, he set off from Malyi Anyui, reaching the Arctic Ocean coast near the estuary of the Malaya Baranikha on April 25. From there he proceeded by dog sled along the coast to Cape Yakan. On May 7 he was about 15 versts* from it. He returned by the same route and reached the lower Kolyma on May 25. His descriptions of the journey provide interesting geographic details, for example about Aiok Island and a reference to bird movement toward Wrangel Island.

In the old literature the Anadyr collections of G. Maydell who trekked the southern slopes of the Anadyr Range in 1869 were erroneously referred to as the Chukchi collections. In fact they belonged wholly to the Anadyr region. Before this author's research on the fauna of Northeast Asia no zoogeographic distinctions were made between the Anadyr region and the Chukchi peninsula.

The first real and a fairly thorough investigation of bird fauna in the Chukchi peninsula was conducted by the *Vega* expedition led by Prof. A.E. Nordenskjöld (1879, 1880–81, and 1882). This expedition was organized in Sweden. The *Vega* belonged to the Swedish Navy and the participants were mostly Swedes. But it must be placed on record that one-third of the expenses were paid by a Russian merchant, A. Sibiryakov, the remaining two-thirds being shared equally by a Swedish merchant Dr. Dickson and the Swedish King, Oscar II. O. Nordquist, a 20-year old lieutenant in the Russian guards was one of the 30 participants, including the crew. He was mainly concerned with collecting and observing birds and mammals. Though the *Vega* sailed under the Swedish naval flag the expedition provided the most valuable scientific results on Russian territory. Fauna research of the utmost interest was conducted by an officer in the Russian service and one-third of the expenses were met in Russian currency.

Leaving Norwegian waters on July 25, 1878, the *Vega* proceeded toward Yugorskii Shar and Belyi Island, visited Dixon Island and the Taimir coast, passed the southernmost islands of the Novosibirsk archipelago toward the Medvezhii Islands and finally reached Chaun Bay. The expedition had an opportunity to visit Cape Shelagskii on September 5–6 and Cape Yakan on September 8 and 9. Between September 12 and 18 the *Vega* became ice-bound near Ryrkaipiya village. It was already late for ornithological field work. Only cormorants were found, other birds

*An obsolete Russian land measurement unit equal to 1.067 km—Translator.

having migrated by then. The period up to September 27 was spent in Kolyuchin Bay and on Kolyuchi Island. Later the *Vega* moved toward the coast of the Chukchi peninsula. On September 28 she was stuck in ice opposite Pitlekai settlement (67°4′49″ N and 172°23′ W of Greenwich). The name of this village attained some prominence because the *Vega* wintered there. In fact, there were only a few skin tents, the Chukchians having left for the interior and the reindeer herds, as they always did in the winter, to return to the sea coast in summer for trading. In May, 1934, passing through these places by dog sled, the author did not find a single tent. Pitlekai had long ceased to be inhabited even in the summer. The territory in which the field work was conducted and collections made covered the area along the coast from Kolyuchin Bay in the west to Tjapka village in the east. The expedition could not reach Cape Serdtse-Kamen'. In the course of the winter excursions were made by dog sled into the surrounding country, not farther than 20 miles, but they did not add to the faunal material. Between June 13 and 17 a much deeper journey (30 miles) was made into the hinterland of Kolyuchin Bay. Expeditions were also made to the hilly areas of the peninsula 20 to 25 miles in from the coast to a height of 900 m and later 1200–1500 m. By the time the warm weather set in the environs of Pidlin, Dzhenretlen, Pitlekai, Ryraitinop, Irgunnuk, Najtskaj, Padl'onn and Tjapka villages had been explored. Some bird specimens were supplied by Chukchians of Chutpa village, east of Cape Serdtse-Kamen'. The islet Idlidlya, 14 miles east of the *Vega's* winter anchorage, was also studied.

At midday of July 18, 1879, the *Vega* freed herself from the ice and sailed past Cape Serdtse-Kamen' by night. On July 20 she passed Cape Dezhnev and, entering Bering Strait, dropped anchor at the entrance to Lawrence Bay near Nunyamo village. On July 21 and 22 the *Vega* crossed the strait past the Diomede Islands and moored in Port Clarence on the Alaskan coast. From there she sailed for the southeastern coast of the Chukchi peninsula and on July 28 anchored in Kon'yam Bay in Senyavin Strait. Between July 31 and August 2 the expedition visited the northwestern end of St. Lawrence Island and remained on Bering Island from August 14 through 19.

While the *Vega* was wintering at Pitlekai the collection of vertebrate specimens was entrusted to O. Nordquist, who prepared notes on the specimens collected and on all the birds he observed, together with the required dates. He was assisted by other members of the expedition, particularly the ship's physician E. Almquist, the ship's captain, A.A.L. Palander and the second mate E.C. Brusewitz, besides the industrialist P. Johansen and his naturalist assistant Th.A. Boström. The local Chukchians brought specimens from around their villages and from the interior of the Chukchi peninsula. Observations were made on 80 species of bird and about 300 specimens representing 75 forms collected. In all 130 bird skins were brought. Ninety specimens were preserved in alcohol, 50 tanned, some salted (mostly the specimens preserved in alcohol), 43 skeletons dissected and 47 eggs of 18 species of bird collected. The egg collection was identified by conservator W. Meves in Stockholm, who communicated his findings to J.A. Palmén in Helsingfors. The latter was given the task of writing a book on the birds spotted by the *Vega* expedition. J.A. Palmén, a reader at Helsingfors University, was an outstanding ornithologist of his day and his monograph on Chukchi birds (Palmén 1887) was wholly up to date in terms of the ornithological information available in the 80s of the last century. But his book was in Swedish and was not translated into any of the commoner European languages. His real contribution to the development of ornithology was consequently soon forgotten. It fell to the lot of the present author to include in his work all the data collected by the *Vega* expedition and processed by Palmén. Much of this information was not as accurate and detailed as one would have wished, but there is no underestimating it. Undoubtedly this material is second only to the present author's collection and superior to all the rest.

A month after the departure of the *Vega* from Lawrence Bay, on August 25, 1879, the *Jeannette* expedition arrived there. It included the naturalist R.L. Newcomb and J.J. Collins, the correspondent of the *Herald*, a New York newspaper. On August 29 this ship anchored off Cape Serdtse-Kamen' and on August 31 in Kolyuchin Bay. Newcomb (1888) had very little to add to the bird fauna of the Chukchi coast.

In 1880, Bean (1883 and anon. 1883) studied birds along with ichthyological field work in Alaska. From there he proceeded to Providence Bay, where he collected specimens from August 11 to 14. He visited Cape Chaplin on August 15 and Bol'shoi Diomede Island on August 18. Having studied the northwestern coast of Alaska, Bean returned to Diomede on September 10 and collected specimens from September 12 through 17 in Providence Bay. In the Chukchi peninsula he collected only 25 bird specimens including the spoonbill sandpiper. His observations on the albatross are of interest. The *Actodromas minutilla* that he described turned out to be juvenile eastern little stint. Specimens spotted by Bean were wrongly credited to Dall by Palmén.

In 1881 Edward William Nelson arrived off the coast of the Chukchi peninsula on board the *Corwin*. The *Corwin* had been sent in search of the *Jeannette*, which was lost. Leaving St. Michael on June 21, Nelson arrived at Providence Bay on June 25. His published work contains frequent references to his bird observations made there on June 26. Providence Bay, according to Nelson (1883, p. 56), offered very little of ornithological interest. Some water birds and a few other species were seen there. Next day a brief halt was made in Lawrence Bay and Mechigmensk Gulf and on June 28 at Bol'shoi Diomede Island. On June 29 the *Corwin* visited Tjapka before turning for home. On the 30th Nelson had an opportunity to visit areas close to Dezhnev settlement. In the evening the ship approached Bol'shoi Diomede Island. She made brief stopovers at Cape Chaplin and the northeastern shore of Providence Bay on July 2. Next day the *Corwin* left Chukchi waters. Only on August 4 did she again approach the coast at Cape Schmidt. On August 5 she made a stopover at Vankarem, where Nelson had more time to observe birds than at the previous halts. On August 8 the *Corwin* sailed up to Cape Schmidt but later turned northward. On August 22, on her return trip, the ship passed close to the Diomede Island and on August 24 arrived in Providence Bay, where she took on supplies. On August 27 the *Corwin* again headed for the Diomede Island and on August 28 was at Cape Serdtse-Kamen'. At the end of her journey she sailed past Wrangel Island and the northwest coast of Alaska. The voyage dates Nelson mentions from time to time in his works (Nelson 1883 and 1887) do not always agree with the anchoring dates of the *Corwin* recorded by Capt. C.L. Hooper (1884) in his detailed description of the voyage. Apparently Nelson was unable to collect birds on the Siberian coast and record his observations systematically. To some extent his attention was diverted by ethnographic studies. Since the *Corwin* cruised all the time Nelson could have made only the most cursory observations. He himself notes (Nelson 1883, p. 56a) that the species of bird of the Siberian coast that he mentions represent only a small fraction of the fauna of that region. Nelson's Alaskan observations earned for him fame as an intelligent ornithologist. But the present author was struck by the shallowness of his observations in his published notes on the birds of the Chukchi peninsula and a tendency to apply to the Chukchi coast experience gained in his field work in Alaska. Stejneger, Palmén, and some others including the present author (1937b, pp. 99–100) have had occasion to draw attention to the various inconsistencies, inaccuracies, errors and misprints in Nelson's works which are dealt with in detail in a special section of this monograph. Nelson's work of 1887 was thoroughly edited by H.W. Henshaw. While giving due credit to Nelson for his many interesting observations, one cannot be blind to the deficiencies.

In the summer of 1896 A. Seale (1899) visited Cape Barrow and later went up to the mouth of the Mackenzie to collect material for Stanford University. In his paper on the water birds of Alaska there are two or three references to St. Lawrence Island and Cape Dezhnev.

In 1900 a gold prospecting party led by K.I. Bogdanovich visited the Chukchi coast. I.N. Akif'ev, the physician on this expedition, collected 17 bird skins in Providence Bay, Senyavin Strait, and Mechigmensk and Lawrence bays. These skins subsequently found their way to the zoological museum of the Academy of Sciences. They have been listed by the present author along with the other specimens studied. Akif'ev's book (1904) written in a popular and very lively style gives some idea of the Chukchi peninsula in general in addition to its bird life.

N.P. Sokol'nikov, Chief of Anadyr rural district, traveled the south and east coasts of the Chukchi peninsula by dog sled in April, 1902. The poor travel conditions and the unfavorable time of the year did not permit him to collect bird skins as he did in Anadyr. A few specimens, which included the spectacled eider, were the only ornithological records of his Chukchi expedition. Apparently he obtained a few more specimens in 1903. Sokol'nikov stayed in Unyyn village at Cape Chaplin from April 10 through 30. On May 2, on the return journey, he arrived at Red'kin. He included these meager, scattered observations in his manuscript, referred to in *Fauna of the Anadyr Region* (Portenko 1939b, vol. I, p. 12). While Sokol'nikov did much for the ornithology of the Anadyr basin, the results of his expedition to the Chukchi peninsula were insignificant.

In 1905 S.A. Buturlin (1906a and b, and 1907a) and his associates started from the lower Kolyma and went up to Cape Enraukun between Bol'shoi and Malyi Baranov Kamen', arriving there on May 25. The winter travel conditions on dog sled did not permit collection of any worthwhile material on birds in the northwestern part of the Chukchi peninsula. Wherever the present author considers it necessary he refers to reports of Buturlin's Kolyma expedition.

In 1906 P. Niedieck visited the south coast of the Chukchi peninsula (Niedieck 1907) on a special hunting expedition for bear and walrus. Being a sportsman, hunter and tourist, he has a wonderful narrative style. His itinerary aboard a small vessel extended from the Kamchatka coast past Cape Navarin to the mouth of the Anadyr, where he met N.P. Sokol'nikov and obtained from him 25 bird skins collected in the Anadyr area. In the museum records they were erroneously labeled as belonging to the Chukchi peninsula (for example, *Penthestes montanus anadyrensis*). From Novo-Mariinsk Bay Niedieck sailed to Krest Bay, hunted for walrus at Meechken, visited Providence Bay and halted at Arakamchechen (Kayne). The entire expedition along the Chukchi coast lasted from the last few days of July through August 3, when he set off for Alaska. A dozen of the birds that he collected are enumerated by A. Reichenow in a paper appended to Niedieck's book (Reichenow 1907). The author examined these specimens in 1956 during his visit to the zoological museum of Humboldt University in Berlin.

In 1909 N.F. Kallinikov was the chief of the reorganized Chukchi district. In his popular book (Kallinikov 1912), two pages are devoted to birds. But he was not as familiar with the birds as his predecessor N.P. Sokol'nikov and the book provided no worthwhile material for this compilation.

In the same year, 1909, J. Koren, an energetic and experienced Norwegian collector, started collecting material on the Chukchi peninsula (Koren 1910 and Gribanovskii 1915). Koren had visited Russia many times before. On a small schooner, the *Teddy Bear*, he approached the west coast of Bol'shoi Diomede Island on June 24. He reached Uélen on June 25, crossed the Arctic Circle on June 27 and came to Tepkan village ("Tjupka" in his transcription). Overcast skies hampered field work. A clear day dawned only on June 29 and Koren explored Idlidlya Island. One June 30 the schooner approached Kolyuchi Island and Koren walked across the ice to the shore. Chukchians took him to the entrance of Kolyuchin Bay. Here the collection was scanty because of the local topography, which was more meadow than tundra, with many lakes. The weather was also unfavorable. When clear weather returned on July 24 Koren organized an excursion to the nearest knoll but had to return quickly. He boarded the schooner again and reached Vankarém on July 25. He started his return journey on July 29 after visiting Kolyuchi Island and most of the Chukchi villages in the Far East. Koren was at Cape Serdtse-Kamen' on August 2 and Cape Dezhnev on August 6. From here he set off for Cape Chaplin and returned to Nom on August 11.

In the spring of 1910 Koren once again set off on a collecting trip, financed this time by J.E. Thayer, the owner of an ornithological museum in Lancaster (Thayer and Bangs 1914). He was to winter on Wrangel Island and begin collecting as early as possible in 1911. But the vessel was almost sunk by strong winds and Koren was forced to retreat. Capt. F.E. Kleinschmidt, who sailed aboard another ship a week ahead of Koren, was luckier. He collected eggs and feathered nestlings of spoonbills on Cape Serdtse-Kamen' for Thayer.

In 1911 Koren continued to collect for Thayer, first in Alaska and then in the Chukchi peninsula and the lower Kolyma. In August he crossed Bering Strait and cruised along the north coast of the Chukchi peninsula. On August 22 he was 20 miles northwest of Cape Dezhnev. From September 1 through 6 he was at Cape Schmidt and from September 10 through 12 at Cape Kiber. From September 20 he wintered in the lower Kolyma.

After wintering Koren resumed his journey on June 21, 1912. He stopped in the following places for bird collection: July 5 through 21 at Cape Bol'shoi Baranov Kamen' and eastward; 23 through 26 on Aiok Island; and, from July 30 through August 27, on the east coast of Chaun Bay. He reached Cape Schmidt on September 10 and Kolyuchi Island on September 22. But later the schooner was icebound off Cape Unikin, midway between Capes Serdtse-Kamen' and Dezhnev. Koren was lucky to be able to unload the schooner with comparatively little loss. On November 9 he sailed from Cape Dezhnev to the Diomede Islands, where he spent the better part of the winter. On returning in spring, 1913, to the collection he had left behind he found the specimens all well preserved.

The observations and collections on the north coast of the Chukchi peninsula are of great scientific interest but they were invariably sketchy because Koren was constantly on the move. He was most successful in collecting during July and August. In 1914 we again find him collecting in the lower Kolyma but this time under the banner "Koren's Arctic Expedition", concentrating his whole attention on the fauna of the Kolyma valley. In 1915 he sent Copley Amory to America with everything he had collected up to that time. Of this, more later. Meanwhile Koren continued to collect in Kolyma. He married in lower Kolyma. Leaving his collection in the custody of his wife, Koren tried to leave Russia in the fall of 1917 (M.M. 1918) but was held up at Vladivostok and died of an attack of Spanish 'flu' in the following spring. In the spring of 1922 Roal'd Amundsen (1929, pp. 279 and 282), sailing on ship the *Maud*, acquired Koren's collection. It suffered great damage during transport but ultimately reached the zoological museum in Oslo and was processed by H.T.L. Schaanning (1954). This collection of Koren's contained some bird skins from the Chukchi peninsula.

In the five years from 1910 through 1914 the ship's physician E.E. Arngol'd (1929) and L.M. Starokadomskii (1915, 1916a and b, and 1946) participated in the hydrographical expedition to the Arctic Ocean on freighters the *Vaigach* and the *Taimyr* under the guidance of B.A. Vil'kitskii. At various anchorages they visited many points on the Chukchi coast, mostly in Providence Bay but also at Cape Dezhnev, the Diomede Island, Cape Serdtse-Kamen', Kolyuchin Bay, Capes Vankarem and Schmidt and finally Cape Shelagskii.

Their collection of bird specimens, numbering about 175 skins, reached the zoological museum of the Academy of Sciences (N.V. Nasonov 1916) and was handled by the present author. In Arnogol'd's book (1929) there are some references to observations on birds (pp. 88, 95, 96 and 108).

In 1913 the zoologists Winthrop Sprague Brooks and Joseph Dixon participated in the Harvard University expedition on schooner the *Polar Bear*. In June they collected birds, mostly in Providence Bay, but they traveled north right up to Uelen and Bol'shoi Diomede Island. In July they reached Cape Serdtse-Kamen', which they explored from July 16 through 18. On July 19 they were 80 miles south of Wrangel Island. These naturalists spent the rest of their time, including the 1913–1914 winter, in studying Alaskan birds. On August 29, 1914, on their return journey, they visited Uelen. The Chukchi coast was covered only incidentally, which is reflected in the fragmentary though very interesting data in Brooks' article (1915). No doubt these data would have been more complete had Dixon not lost his diaries.

In 1914 F.S. Hersey was sent by A.C. Bent, the author of the well-known manual *Life Histories of North American Birds* (1919–1953), to collect biological information on the birds of Alaska. On his way he visited four different points on the Chukchi coast: Lawrence Bay on July 26, two points around Cape Serdtse-Kamen' on August 28 and Uélen on August 29. Apparently Hersey also visited Bol'shoi Diomede Island or at least approached it. Hersey gave his paper in such a general and superficial form that it earned the just criticism of reviewers. His notes (Hersey 1916) on birds of the Chukchi coast are extremely casual.

As indicated above, Copley Amory, Jr., took part in Koren's 1914 expedition (Miller 1916). He delivered to the US National Museum 228 (264 according to a different count) bird skins mostly collected on the Kolyma and some on his way to the Chukchi coast. His collections were processed by J.H. Riley (1918). The ornithological and faunal material from the Chukchi peninsula was very fragmentary though not without some scientific importance.

In 1914–15 the ship's physician, A.A. Savich, wintering on board the *Kolyma* made observations and bird collections near Cape Schmidt. The ship was caught in the ice there on September 18, 1914, and freed herself on June 30, 1915. Savich was no specialist collector and the skins he collected were not even labeled. His diary was processed by V.M. Artobolevskii (1929; incidentally, in this paper all the dates were recorded according to the old calendar*). Savich's observations made some contribution to the knowledge of birds of Cape Schmidt which had not been ornithologically studied to the same extent as other parts of the Chukchi peninsula.

In 1921–22 A.M. Bailey, like all of his American predecessors, paid a casual visit to the Chukchi coast (Bailey 1925–26), his main object being to study and collect Alaskan birds. It is unfortunate that this brilliant naturalist and collector along with his assistant R.W. Hendee had very little time for this territory. On June 30, 1921, Bailey arrived in Émma Bay and carried out ornithological field work until July 7. On July 11 and 12 he and Hendee made collections around Uélen. In the spring of 1922, sailing in the Bering Strait with some eskimo hunters, Bailey was caught in a drift at Cape Dezhnev and visited Diomede Island on June 25. Bailey's identifications and descriptions are characterized by extreme precision.

In 1925, under the orders of the "Committee for the North", S.A. Buturlin went to the Chukchi peninsula. The present author heard his report on this expedition at a meeting of the Society on Acclimatization in the large zoological auditorium at Moscow University at the end of 1925. Buturlin left the impression that he had gone inland only briefly under conditions which were far from favorable for systematic ornithological field work. He did not exhibit the bird skins nor did he write an article about the birds of the Chukchi peninsula. But he reported his observations and finds one by one in the different volumes of *A Comprehensive Key to the Birds of the USSR* (Buturlin and Dement'ev 1934–1941).

From M.A. Menzbier's collection, the author became familiar with some bird specimens collected by Sheneberg in the fall of 1926 and summer of 1927 in Uélen. These skins are now preserved in the Institute of Zoology, Academy of Sciences of the USSR, Moscow.

*The new calendar was officially accepted in the Soviet Union soon after the 1917 Revolution. The difference between the old and the new dates is 14 days—Translator.

In the summer of 1928 Francis L. Jaques was a member of the American Natural History Museum's expedition to the Arctic Ocean. The expedition's itinerary is shown on a map appended to Jaques' paper (1930). His observations relate only to sea birds in Bering Strait and slightly northward.

In 1930 the Institute of Zoology, Academy of Sciences of the USSR, obtained some bird skins collected on Ushakov's expedition on the ice-breaker *Litke* in Lawrence Bay.

In March, 1931, L.O. Belopol'skii arrived at Meechken Island, from where he traveled eastward up to Preobrazheniya Bay in March and May. He was studying the trade potential of marine animals and therefore went out to sea. In the summer he devoted part of his time to ornithological field work and returned to Anadyr in August. On Meechken Island Belopol'skii collected fairly comprehensive faunal information which was included in his two articles on the ornithological fauna of the Anadyr region (Belopol'skii 1933 and 1934). Belopol'skii's delineation of the area is more generous than that adopted in this monograph. The bird skins collected by Belopol'skii reached the Institute of Zoology, Academy of Sciences of the USSR, and were studied by the present author along with other specimens.

If we look back now at what had been done before the present author undertook his expeditions in the early 30s we find that ornithological research on the Chukchi peninsula already had a long history. But none of the research was systematic. It was always interrupted or incidental to other tasks or confined to fleeting visits to different points on the Chukchi coast. Though this area contained most interesting and valuable information the casual, fragmentary collections suffered from many drawbacks. These collections are scattered in museums in both hemispheres, which obviously rules out all possibility of bringing them together in one place, examining them and verifying the identifications. The author was very sorry that he could not personally examine the material, at least of the *Vega* expedition. The large number of works published by workers ranging from well-known specialists to persons absolutely ignorant of scientific ornithology meant that the available information had to be sifted with the utmost care. In this the author was guided by his own field experience, which was of immense help, and calls for a detailed discussion.

Field Investigations in the Chukchi Peninsula from 1932 to 1970

Expedition of the author and P.T. Butenko aboard the steamship Itel'men from August 4 through September 2, 1932. I began my field work in the Chukchi peninsula in 1932 as a zoologist on the Chukchi-Anadyr expedition of the All-Union Arctic Institute after completing field work in Anadyr (anon. 1931 and 1933; Portenko 1934a, and 1935a and b). Along with my assistant Butenko, I sailed on the *Itel'men* from Anadyr port on August 4 and visited the major bays on the south and east coasts of the Chukchi peninsula. As soon as the ship anchored we would go ashore and start exploring the area. This method of work yielded excellent results only because of the coincidence of some particularly favorable conditions.

Firstly, in Butenko I had an intelligent assistant trained by myself. Secondly, the ship's command always and without let or hindrance cooperated in the scientific pursuits of the expedition. The ship had a separate cabin for a taxidermy laboratory and offered unrestricted use of launches to go ashore. Thirdly, in those days both of us had abundant physical stamina and endurance.

On August 6 the *Itel'men* approached Krest Bay and the two of us completed an excursion to the neighborhood of Notapenmen village from the east side of the entrance to the bay. By evening a storm had developed that forced us to remain at anchor in the bay for the next few days. On August 10 the ship resumed her course along the rocky coasts of Cape Bering and Preobrazheniya Gulf. There we were confined to deck observations. We had before us an awe-inspiring panorama of fancy rocks against a foreground of stormy waves. A multitude of murres and common puffins and flocks of crested auklets cruised above the waves, pointing to the presence of large colonies of alcids onshore.

On August 11 the *Itel'men* anchored in Émma Bay, a branch of Providence Bay. At that time Émma Bay was an altogether wild fjord and, compared to the open sea, shut-in and gloomy. In spite of the stormy weather we landed on the coast and found marine and ash sandpipers. Cormorants, eiders and alcids flew over the bay.

On August 12 there was intense pitching on the way to Bering Strait. We reached Dezhnev settlement (formerly called Mikhailovskaya Station) on August 13. The route was strewn with large blocks of ice and the launch had to find its way through gaps to reach shore. Traversing the tundra we marched as far as the third rivulet going north (counting the rivulets flowing from Dezhnev knoll to west of Uélen). A pair of yellow-billed loons swam in the lake and there were many sandpipers on the tundra; Baird's sandpipers were collected on the third river. On August 14 we hunted from a canoe at Dezhnev settlement and shot Sabine's gulls.

On August 15 we traveled by dog sled to Uélen. Thanks to the rainy weather the runners of the sled, lined with iron, slid easily over the wet grass. Dog transport justifies itself in that region even under summer conditions. Toward Uélen thick ice was encountered. Eiders flew in the dense fog and the Chukchians took shots at them or cast special nets to catch them (see eiders in the text). The entire atmosphere, biologically as well as ethnographically, was novel and characteristic. After spending the night in Uélen on August 16 we almost ran back to the ship along the sled track for fear of being late. As it turned out, the ship had slipped out to sea without us. To our good fortune the weather changed in the morning and the ship returned to Dezhnev about the time we got back from Uélen. This incident demonstrated the frequent risks encountered in ship travel along the Chukchi coast.

On August 18 the *Itel'men* headed for Lawrence Bay through thin ice. A herd of walrus resting on an ice floe was encountered on the way (Fig. 3). The party skirted the south shore of the bay on the 19th. Many birds were found there on tiny lakes. We shot spoonbills, dowitchers, Sabine's gulls and many other interesting species. Butenko even saw two lesser snow geese in flight.

On August 21 the *Itel'men* made a brief halt in Preobrazheniya Gulf. Fulmars, short-tailed petrels, murres, alcids and puffins swam toward her. Crested auklets flew overhead and whales dived close by. On August 23 we reached Cape Chaplin, where eskimos were hunting walrus. There were many eiders and alcids. From the canoe we were able to shoot a young deer. We explored the coast on August 24.

On August 25 the *Itel'men* made a lengthy halt in Providence Bay, so that we were able to explore the country from Plover to Cape Ivga until the end of August (Fig. 2). From the first day there the weather was mild and warm. Once, we sailed into the bay in a small boat and came across a huge flock of birds feeding on the water; murres, kittiwakes, glaucous gulls and fulmars. But a killer whale suddenly appeared and the party had to hurry back to shore. On the evening of August 26 we found a nesting colony of large crested auklets, which we observed at length, collecting some specimens. The excursion to the eastern shore of Providence Bay was concluded on August 28. The abundant quarry of the last few days compelled the party to spend time preparing the birds. It grew preceptibly cold on August 31.

The *Itel'men* returned to Krest Bay on September 1. The next day the fauna around Uél'kal' village was studied. There were many whales and birds in the sea. This was the last of the 1932 excursions.

Thus a good foundation had been laid for my study of the fauna of the Chukchi peninsula, which demonstrated the need for a very thorough study of the Asian far northeast. The exploration yielded an excellent collection apart from providing many interesting observations (in particular, I discovered the neck sack in crested auklets).

Observations of I.O. Olenev in Émma Bay from the end of the summer 1931 through September 1932. While visiting Émma Bay, I came into contact with Capt. I.O. Olenev, who was wintering there. He was deeply engrossed in bird study and had made a small collection which he kindly gave me for further processing. Thanks to a fortunate coincidence we later traveled together aboard steamship the *Okhotsk* in 1933. In the course of our discussions, Olenev gave me much useful information which is included in the present monograph.

S.G. Pavlov's collection in Providence Bay and Chaun Bay in the summer of 1933. During his travels along the Chukchi coast S.G. Pavlov, a geologist on the Chukchi-Anadyr Expedition of the Arctic Institute, made a small collection of bird skins, mostly in Providence and Chaun bays. The specimens bore dates of the summer months of 1933. They were among specimens examined by the present author.

Station research by the author around Uélen from August 15, 1933 through April 23, 1934. In 1933, together with P.T. Butenko (Portenko 1935a and b), I was deputed by the Arctic Institute to the Polar Station on Cape Dezhnev. We arrived in Uélen on August 15. Since it had been decided to transfer the Station to this place from Dezhnev settlement, we lent a hand in construction of the new installation. For this reason the better part of the fall was not available for field work.

On our way aboard steamship the *Okhotsk* an exceptionally large number of crested auklets were found in the coastal waters when the ship passed Providence Bay and Cape Chaplin. Innumerable sea birds floated on the water in the pleasant weather on August 15 in Bering Strait between Cape Dezhnev and the Diomede Island. In the next few days in Uélen we saw sandhill cranes and emperor geese in flight. On August 22 I climbed the peak of the knoll, from which the Alaskan coast can be seen through binoculars in clear weather. Under the rays of the setting sun even the greenish color on the slopes of the nearest mountains could be seen. Behind could be seen mountains with remnants of snow here and there. Still farther away a backdrop of mountains could be distinguished in the blue haze.

During excursions from August 24 through September 1, I traced the migration of birds. In the fall monotony of the tundra it was interesting to come across a big flock of emperor geese. They were accompanied by black and three lesser snow geese; a peregrin falcon rested close by. This is a characteristic picture of the Chukchi environment which left a lasting impression on me.

On September 6 Butenko took a whaleboat along the coast from Dezhnev to Uélen and traced the bird colonies on cliffs. On September 9 we studied the lagoon coast and ascended the nearby knoll on the 10th and 11th. On September 14, we walked to the foot of the knoll over the fast ice, and climbed it. There was rain and snow on the 15th but on the 16th it was again sunny weather right from morning, so we climbed the Dezhnev knoll once again. A canoe excursion was undertaken on September 18 in Uélen lagoon; among other specimens we got a spectacled eider. An intense cold snap with a snowstorm set in on September 19.

On September 23 the stormy weather finally calmed down and we set out on an excursion to the west along the spit. There was a massive flight of long-tailed ducks. The party went as far as they could on September 25 and 27. Frost and stormy weather were encountered on the peak of the knoll while snow drifted into the valley. We saw gyrfalcons. Black geese were still flying while the hunters in Uélen shot eiders.

In the first half of October, the bird survey was continued farther to the west and east around Uélen. The late bird species migrated. On October 3, many resting walruses could be seen on the ice floes. Their lionlike roaring could be heard from afar. Snowy owls and Ross's gulls were noticed. On October 15, only crows were left in the nearby cliffs. On the knolls the Chukchians killed a bear and on October 19 we found a gyrfalcon and white ptarmigan there. For the next few days, under conditions of a winter desert, there was no question of going far.

In November we set out by dog sled on alternate days to lay traps on the tundra but found only a few birds. In December, there were only seven such outings and none in January.

On February 13, 1934, the steamship *Chelyuskin* sank. The whole staff of the Polar Station took part in the rescue of the passengers aboard the ship. The supplies for biological observations in the field were almost exhausted.

In spite of some unfavorable conditions during fall and winter we traced the entire cycle of seasonal phenomena in the life of birds and made an excellent collection of bird skins of a large number of series.

Winter excursion by P.T. Butenko on Utte-Véem River from January 13 through 19, 1934. It was learned from the local residents that willow grew to more than a man's height on the Utte-Véem (forest) River. The branches they brought confirmed this information. I felt the need to return in the summer because rich and interesting avifauna could be found on the bushy tundra in the interior of the Chukchi peninsula.

Butenko set off to this place by dog sled on a reconoitering trip on January 13. On January 15 he found ptarmigans in abundance on the Yararmumna River. On

January 17 a snowy owl was seen. He returned to Uélen on January 19 fully convinced of the extremely sparse bird life in winter.

Observations of V.S. Stakhanov in April, 1934. Among the passengers aboard the *Chelyuskin* who got down on the ice was V.S. Stakhanov, a zoologist from Moscow (1934). He was brought to Vankarem on April 8 and later undertook a trip to Uélen, where he wrote up his travel observations.

Spring journey by the author from Uélen to Ryrkaipiya and back from April 24 through May 25, 1934. The experience of the earlier exploration in Anadyr prompted me to acquaint myself with the country under the winter conditions of the North, traveling by dog sled. I owed this excursion to the altogether unexpected salvage operation on the *Chelyuskin* in April, 1934. The well-known pilots I.V. Doronin and M.V. Vodop'yanov agreed to fly me and a sufficient stock of dog food up to Vankarem village, where the food was invariably inadequate because of lack of fish and walrus. On April 24 I flew from Uélen in a plane piloted by Doronin, and had the rare opportunity, for that period, of making an aerial survey of the hilly topography of the Chukchi peninsula coast. The mountain range extending from Énmitagin to Cape Serdtse-Kamen' made a deep impression.

On April 25 I went on an excursion to Cape Vankarem. Though the winter was more severe than in Uélen there were already some thawed patches. Ptarmigans, owls and a small number of snow buntings were seen. The excursion was repeated on April 27 and on the 28th I went out from Vankarem on dog sled accompanied by a Yarak team which had served Amundsen earlier.

After the plane flight travel by dog sled was a big comedown: the difference in speed and comfort was dramatic. We spent the night before we reached the mouth of the Amguema River in our tents pitched right on the ice.

On April 29 we set off mostly along a pebbled spit following the fresh tracks of two wolves. A few dozen kilometers to the left of the Amguema rose the Iul'tin Range, running close to the coast near Cape Schmidt. Among the ice chunks we stirred up resting snow ptarmigans. On April 30 we had to rest in a tiny hunting cabin because it had grown too warm for the dogs in the day. There was a slight southeasterly wind and at 1.00 p.m. the thermometer recorded $-17°C$ in the shade. On the thawed turf it was only $-6°C$.

From then on we traveled only by night. At midday on May 1 I reached the Polar Station at Cape Schmidt. Next day I explored the neighborhood of the knolls but found no birds. On the evening of May 3 I started back. I had to hurry, having been informed by radio from Uélen that the flight was leaving. There was no point in waiting for it at Cape Schmidt and one could be cut off by the spring slush.

On May 4 I traveled east from Ryrkaipiya for not more than 30 km. Mist and snowfall made the night ride unbearable. Butenko left Uélen to meet me. On May 7 I was in Vankarém and Butenko reached Cape Serdtse-Kamen'. In the early hours I put up a flock of eiders resting around the snow blocks, and on May 9 reached the neighborhood of Vankarém. Thawing had increased perceptibly over the previous 12 days. The buntings began occupying nesting sites. The local Chukchians set off with dogs to hunt seal 30 km out to sea wherever there were leads. It was impossible to rent out an independent dog team and I had to wait for Butenko who came on May 11. Two days later, we managed to continue the journey with

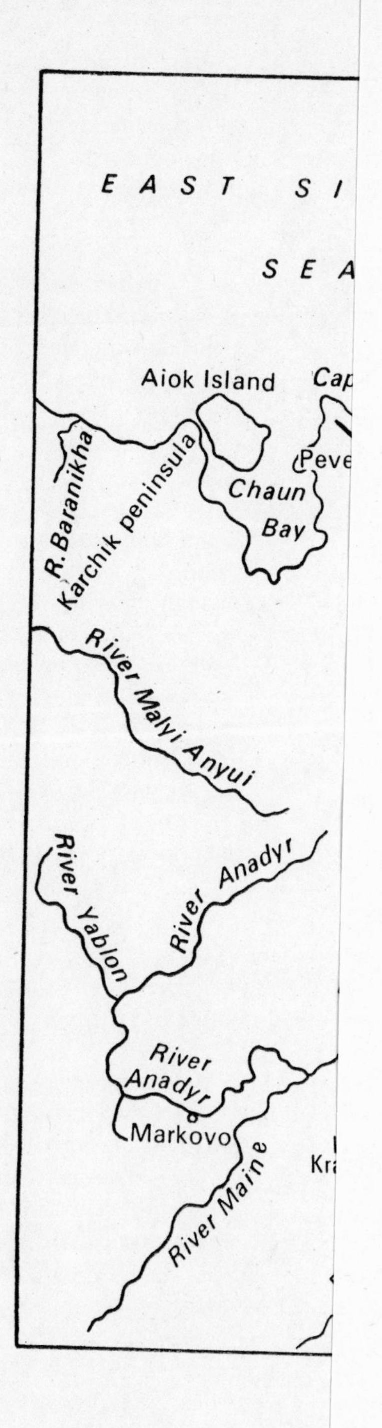
EAST SI
SEA
Aiok Island
Cap
Peve
Chaun Bay
R. Baranikha
Karchik peninsula
River Malyi Anyui
River Anadyr
River Yablon
River Anadyr
Markovo
River Maine
Kra

the team Butenko had hired. At 9.00 p.m. the atmospheric temperature was only −5°C; a huge flock of eiders flew over Vankarém. During the night we reached Cape Onman. On the rocks sat a whole colony of glaucous gulls which had recently flown in. We spent the day of May 14 at Pnoupyl'gyn. At 1.00 p.m. the temperature rose to −1°C while it was +25.5° in the tent. Under my instructions my tent had been made of thick, porous tissue almost black in color. There was a tiny window of white cambric. Light came in through this window and when the sun warmed up it was even hot inside.

Toward evening we took the path to Kolyuchi Island and, crossing it, rested on the ice floes during the day. At dawn on May 16 the journey was resumed on the ice. The monotony of riding was disturbed when we smelt the presence of seals. Their breath excited the dogs, which ran faster. On May 17 we finally reached Cape Serdtse-Kamen', where we were the guests of a former whaler, Voll, a Norwegian. Before setting out on my journey I had made arrangements for provisions, cartridges and walrus meat for the dogs. Voll had preserved all of it carefully. The first crane was sighted there and the mating call of male ptarmigans was heard.

At dawn on May 19 we reached Seishan. Close to the coastal cliffs there were leads which hardly interfered with our passage. Over the water flew fulmars, cormorants, glaucous gulls and other sea birds. From Cape Unin we tried to straighten our course and traveled far out among the ice floes, where there was hardly anything to be picked up. Melt-water flooded large areas and the dogs had to toil through it right up to the belly. There were many streams flowing from the rocks on the coast.

On May 20 we covered the distance from Seitun to Mitkulen (Fig. 5). It was sunny and at times the weather was mild. We traveled across opening leads and pools, sometimes plowing through a thawing mass of snow and ice coming up to the waist. East of Seitun, a small colony of murres was found; cormorants carried grass in their talons for nest building. In Énmitagin the tundra had thawed over very large expanses. For the first time insects, mostly dipterans, were seen in large numbers. A pair of geese flew overhead.

The spring journey concluded happily on May 21. The day was very warm with melt-water streaming from hills and mountains. Over the Inchoun Mountains there was a massive flight of cranes. The first marine sandpipers were noticed. Gophers ran down the slopes. The air carried water mosses.

Though the spring itinerary concluded before the nesting period it greatly enriched my idea of the avifauna of the Chukchi peninsula. In particular, I had successfully tracked the flight of birds on different sections of the north coast.

Spring excursion around Uélen from May 24 through June 18, 1934. During this spring I continued to track the flight of birds and recorded their destination. I also recorded the commencement of nesting. Butenko was engaged almost every day in processing specimens. On May 24 I made a night excursion through Uélen spit and climbed the nearest knoll. Over the sea, there was a massive flight of blue geese. On May 25 Butenko and I rode a sled along the shore ice up to Cape Dezhnev. On the 26th we took aerosleighs to Dezhnev settlement, where we were caught in a snowstorm. On May 31 the weather improved and the daily excursions into the environs of Uélen were resumed.

It got so warm on June 7 that the ice in the lagoon was covered all over with melt-water. I returned from the tundra through the lagoon, the dogs dragging the sled half submerged in water. Sometimes they had to swim. Standing on the flooded sled with all the ammunition, I fought to keep my balance and avoid patches of water among ice floes. Thus ended the season of dog sled rides.

I made a 12-hour excursion on June 10 to one of the highest knolls, looking for Alpine elements in the fauna. On the slopes the first flowers of the season had opened. On June 12 Butenko successfully hunted around Uélen from a canoe. From June 13 through 18, I went daily into the tundra or climbed up the knoll.

Excursion to Bol'shoi Diomede from June 20 through 26, 1934. On June 20 I set off in a whaleboat from Uélen to Naukan. I traveled back down the coast on the 21st and saw bird colonies. Compared to the huge colonies I had encountered before in Novaya Zemlya these looked like miniatures. They were divided into a large number of tiny colonies. However, they were well distinguished by variety in composition of species. Calm prevailed in the evening and it was possible to continue toward Bol'shoi Diomede Island.

We raced toward the island and reached it at 2.00 on the night of June 22. At this time of summer it was very cool, the temperature being −0.5°C. Wet grass and meadows were covered with a thin crust of ice. Clouds blocked out the sky. There was an incredible swarm of crested auklets. During the day I set off to the tip of the island from which Malyi Diomede Island and the Alaskan coast could be clearly seen (Fig. 1). At times the wind was so strong that it was impossible to take aim. On June 23 there was more rain and mist. I preferred to go down to the shore and observe the birds on the surf. Though the windy weather continued I got at many birds on the 24th. The next day was sunny and I used the opportunity for photography. At last, on June 26, sunny, calm weather set in, but by then it was time to hurry back. My colleagues, the eskimos and Chukchians, decided against crossing the Bering Strait in whaleboats in bad weather.

Excursion with P.T. Butenko on the River Utte-Véem from July 2 through 21, 1934. On the evening of July 2 we left Uélen in a whaleboat in a fair southerly wind which, incidentally, soon abated. We had to be towed up to Inchoun cliff and later paddle through thin ice. I disembarked at the foot of the Inchoun bluffs but there was nothing of interest. The bird colonies on the rocks were visible from the whaleboat. We arrived in Mitkulen on July 3 and in the evening I went on an excursion to the nearby hillocks. The entire environment differed sharply from the predominantly marine atmosphere of a week before on the Diomede Island. In the rocky tundra very diverse and beautiful flowers blossomed. Mosquitoes and water moss flew everywhere and gophers came up from their burrows.

There was dense mist on July 4, which caused a restless movement of marine birds. Over the ice along the coast flew emperor geese and mergansers, but eiders predominated. In the evening we returned to the gulf of Inchoun lagoon, the whaleboat being towed by the dogs.

On July 5 we crossed the lagoon under sail, but stopped halfway along the gravel coast where gulls and peregrins nested. Finally we camped on the islet at the mouth of the River Utte-Véem. There we immediately came across some bird nests. Swans rested around the tundra lake and the place appeared to hold much promise.

On July 6 we started the journey up the River Utte-Véem. A small canoe was used to carry provisions. The canoe was made of walrus skin at Uélen to my specifications. It was so light that the two of us could portage it over long distances. Any holes worn in the bottom by dragging were easily patched with moist walrus skin. Such boats readily commend themselves.

Even at the start of the journey low but procumbent willow shrubs were found along the lower banks. The meadows in the flood plains were full of stagnant pools and tiny ponds. Further up the river the shrubs grew quite tall, up to half a meter (Fig. 9). Passing the strong rapids, we reached the dunes with snow cover intact. In the rapids swam white-beaked eiders. Emperor geese were encountered in the wider sections of the river.

Farther up on the right bank of the river we found shrubs rising to a man's height populated with very characteristic avifauna. Here we noticed Siberian pipits, Arctic warblers and American thrushes. The surrounding hillocks were white with cotton grass resembling a field of flowering peas in a temperate clime. The screams of sandhill cranes could be heard from that direction.

On July 7 it was so warm that mosquitoes were noticeably agitated. Along the river the rapids became even more difficult to negotiate and on the 8th we were compelled to rest. Cold weather set in on July 9 and there was rain and intermittent snow, which covered the whole area with a thin white layer. A depressing wind was blowing the whole day, sometimes with snow flurries. There never had been a summer like that. The water began rising in the river and, taking advantage of the strong current, we began a rapid return journey downriver.

Clear, warm weather set in on the morning of July 10 but the evening was cold. The following day was again hot and there were mosquitoes. At 1.00 in the afternoon the atmospheric temperature rose to $+18°$. The tundra banks of the lower reaches of the river dried beyond recognition. The party reached Inchoun lagoon. On July 12 the wind continued; I could see a marine type of tundra 15 km to the southeast of Mitkulen. At the foot of the knolls, along the fringe of a small ravine with dried-up springs and lakelets, there was an islet of shrubbery undergrowth similar to the ones encountered along the river banks.

In the evening we risked our fragile canoe to cross the wide waters of the lagoon and on the other side came face to face with Chukchians who had arrived in a whaleboat the night after we did. There was a sudden northwesterly squall and within a minute it had churned up such waves that we could hardly paddle to shore. The boat rose like a shell on the crest of waves as high as 5 m. This could have ended in catastrophe. Ill luck dogged us. In Mitkulen we were caught in a dense mist. Northerly winds drove the snow right down to the coast and the party was stuck there for eight days.

On July 20 we dragged the loaded boat first along the edge of the ice and then through a network of lakes stretching along the spit. In face of obstacles we had frequently to unload and portage the boat and then load it again. On July 21 two sleds were rented and the entire load and the boat were transported across the watershed between Inchoun and Uélen lagoons. By an irony of fate the party had to travel by dog sled across the sea in the spring and portage the boat overland in the summer.

The journey up the Utte-Véem River yielded exceptionally satisfactory results. I became acquainted with the bird fauna of the hilly interior. I decided to make one more such excursion though the summer was drawing to a close.

Journey on the River Kol'oam-Véem from August 9 through 24, 1934. Up to the mouth of the river the way lay through large lagoons. It was again necessary to seek the help of the Chukchians. It was all the more difficult because the season of walrus hunting had begun and a motor canoe could be had only by depriving the people of walrus hunting. Nevertheless the local people cooperated as a token of friendship.

On the evening of August 9 the Chukchians towed Butenko and myself in the boat to a huge shoal near the mouth of the river as far as the draft of their large canoe would permit. The River Kol'oam entered the lagoon in a very broad, hence shallow, stream not deeper than 20 to 30 cm. Our baggage was transported over tiny islets which remained above water only during the day. Finally we had to spend the night on one of them. Sandpipers were resting two steps away from us, evidently not expecting to meet a couple of sleeping men among the lagoons.

In the morning the boat and the baggage had to be dragged several hundred feet along a silt-sand bottom to a deeper part of the river. Thereafter the way up the river posed no great problems except some strong rapids. The upper pools were deep enough to sail.

On August 11 we reached high cliffs speckled with ocher, brick red and brownish-purple. At that point, visible from the Inchoun bluffs, we were detained hunting peregrins. At places along the banks we encountered willows rising to 0.5 m. In them we found red-throated pipits and blue-headed wagtails. Along the grassy shores flocks of sandpipers and buntings roamed. Butenko shot a white-billed common loon in one pool.

On August 12 the party passed the cap-like knoll distinctly visible from Uélen. The way lay mostly under a high bank with rocky tow-paths. On August 13 we passed rock outcrops on both banks of the river. On August 14 and 15, leaving the rapids, we towed the boat up the river.

Cloudy fall weather set in. Cranes began to flock together, the downy chicks of long-tailed ducks and mergansers (*Mergus* sp.) were caught. On the morning of the 16th the sun warmed up and at midday we reached Lake Kool'ong.

There was rain on August 17. The northerly wind on the 18th was so cold that it was necessary to put on fur coats. I explored the knolls rising not more than 500 to 600 m to the west of the lake. Fauna characteristic of high altitudes was not to be seen but buntings and chats were encountered more often than in the plains. On the lower part of the slope toward the lake osier beds grew to a meter or more. Willow ptarmigans and red-throated pipits, as also blue-headed wagtails and finches, were caught. On August 19 we took the boat 7 km along the west shore of the lake and then climbed a knoll to a height of 345 m. There was a strong northerly wind.

On August 20 we turned back and within four days were at the mouth of the river. Fall set in and the birds began migrating.

On the 24th we crossed the lagoon and arrived at Uélen. The last few days of August were spent in packing for our departure but I missed no opportunity to observe the bird life. On September 3 we left Uélen.

Excursion along Providence Bay on September 7 and 9, 1934. On September 7 I made an excursion along the northwestern shore of Émma Bay. At that time, though it was not blocked, there was not much fauna. On September 9 I went around the eastern shore of the bay but, being late in the year, there was nothing much of interest. On the 10th I left Providence Bay, having completed field work lasting over a year.

Collections and observations by P.T. Butenko on the south coast of the Chukchi Peninsula in 1937 and 1938. An opportunity arose for Butenko in 1937 to continue faunal research on the Chukchi peninsula. He was invited to join the Chukchi hunting expedition led by M.P. Rozanov. He was also given an opportunity to collect birds and mammals and observe them, with the understanding that the material he collected would be processed by myself. The author is obliged to M.P. Rozanov, who fulfilled all of his commitments, and places on record Butenko's services, which were equally helpful to both of us.

The Chukchi hunting expedition left Vladivostok on September 27, 1937. It was late in the year and the ship was caught in a storm, reaching Krest Bay only on September 14. On the west side of the bay, close to Uél'kal' village, Butenko made an excursion on September 16 and succeeded in catching only the emperor goose. On September 24 an excursion was made to the east shore near Notapenmen village. On the 29th the ship arrived in Providence Bay. There Butenko made 14 long trips in November and six in December.

According to my instructions Butenko was to pay special attention to the winter sojourn of birds on the south coast of the Chukchi peninsula. The freezing over of Providence Bay during the winter precluded that study and Butenko undertook a special journey on January 11, 1938, to Cape Chaplin. There he immediately observed the movement of flocks of wintering long-tailed ducks and eiders. On January 14 and 15 he visited Yanrakynnot village via Arakamchechen Island. On January 21 he inspected a rivulet whose bank was overgrown with tall shrubs that were used by the local school for fuel. On returning to Cape Chaplin Butenko energetically collected birds. In less than one and one-half months he gathered 54 specimens. From February 18 through March 15 he stayed at Providence Bay and processed the material he had gathered. On March 15 Butenko again set off to Cape Chaplin but only a few birds remained. The first buntings were sighted on April 10. He again visited Yanrakynnot from April 17 through 21 and from April 22 through May 7 he continued to observe and collect birds at Cape Chaplin; he then returned to Providence Bay. In the course of May he traced the arrival of many birds and caught interesting specimens, mostly around Plover Bay.

On May 18, 27 and 30 Butenko set out on hunting missions to Cape Stoletiya and caught a large number of birds. On the 26th he made an excursion to Sireniki. He also worked at Providence Bay although the game hunting which had started took much of his time, at the cost of ornithological work. On June 11 he went to Istiget village. On July 12 he met me and together we made excursions for two or three days. After my departure Butenko made several brief excursions: July 22 to Kivak, 24 to Chechen, 29 to Sireniki, August 2 and 4 to Sireniki again and 5, 8, and 10 to Cape Stoletiya. He collected specimens at Cape Chaplin from August 17 through 20. In all he gathered 350 specimens of birds and filled two diaries. These and the other material that he and I collected showed that we had covered the avifauna of the south coast of the Chukchi peninsula as completely as that of the northeastern tip of the peninsula. In 1942 Butenko died of a wound he received on the front at Leningrad. This loss is no doubt reflected in my work too. Butenko carried to his grave many of his impressions and observations on the south coast of Chukchi; the diaries recorded far too little.

Ornithological excursion along the Chukchi coast in 1938 and 1939. In 1938 I participated in an expedition of the Academy of Sciences of the USSR, led by R.F. Gekker, to Wrangel Island. On the way I made some excursions to the Chukchi peninsula. On August 12 the party arrived at Providence Bay, where I met Butenko. On the same day, Butenko took me, along with other members of the expedition, to the mouth of the rivulet not far from Cape Stoletiya. As the boat followed the west shore of the bay I kept a careful watch on the high coast rocks. Alcids and cormorants were among the birds seen there.

Having studied the plateau, which is not very hilly at the lower reaches of the river, I climbed up the side of a knoll whose height somewhat exceeded 700 m. The rocky tundra on the slopes was at places intersected by marshy sections inhabited by sandpipers. Along with them were spoonbills. Alpine fauna were not to be seen at the lower levels.

On July 13 I went by motorboat to Plover spit and through the coastal waters to the east as far as Sireniki. Not for the first time, I was attracted by the picturesque coast inhabited by diverse marine avifauna. It was the best time of year when flowers bloom in abundance and the birds are still laying or the chicks have only recently emerged.

On July 15 the vessel passed the Bering Strait (Fig. 4) and on the 18th I and a small group of specialists landed at Cape Schmidt. There I explored a knoll which I had known earlier during my visit of May 2, 1934. It was then winter but now its sides were colored with flowers in bloom and broods of snow buntings flew everywhere. Kozhevnikov cliff had a lively colony of alcids and kittiwakes and innumerable eiders and long-tailed ducks flew over the sea.

The *Okean* had to wait a long time at Kolyuchi Island for favorable ice conditions to approach Wrangel Island. On July 19 the scientists set out on an excursion to the southwestern end. Falling snow forced the ship to sail out for a short while to the north and the party rejoined her only on July 20. For a few days the party rested aboard ship because of stormy weather. On July 24 the *Okean* set off toward Wrangel Island. Ice soon forced the ship to turn back and on July 25, thanks to improved weather conditions, I was again able to explore Kolyuchi Island. Traveling across it, I saw the highest points. On the 26th I circumnavigated it in a Chukchian canoe to study the bird colonies.

The *Okean* was still not in a position to reach Wrangel Island and on August 2 we again set off for Cape Schmidt. There I stayed until August 3 in hopes of an air ride. Because of unfavorable weather it was possible to go up to Cape Kozhevnikov only on the 6th. The party spent August 7 and 8 on the pebbled spit 12 km to the east of Cape Schmidt and then flew to Wrangel Island.

The following year I returned from Wrangel Island on a steamship in the late fall. Passing the Chukchi coast I found very few birds. All the same, on August 30

I noticed the migration of Arctic tern at Cape Schmidt. On the 31st the party stopped on the spit called "Two Pilots" and there I saw a massive movement of short-tailed storm petrels. On September 1 and 2 two crested auklets were shot at the same place. On the 7th the ship anchored at Cape Serdtse-Kamen' and on the 8th at Uélen. Both times I took the opportunity to go ashore. On September 10 the party reached Lawrence Bay. It was in Providence Bay on the 11th, which it left on the 17th. Wonderful fall days had set in; on September 12, 13 and 14 I went to the end of Émma Bay but the gun was not used on the tundra because there were no birds.

Observations by É.V. Schmidt in the northern and eastern parts of the Chukchi peninsula from 1933 through 1939. During my lengthy voyages on shipboard I gathered information about persons returning from the Chukchi peninsula who were in some way or other concerned with hunting or trade. In particular, the zoo technician at the Chaun Cultural Base, E.V. Schmidt reported interesting observations on the distribution and life style of birds that he had made over several years. From 1933 through 1935 he had worked in the eastern part of the Chukchi peninsula roughly to the east of a line between Krest Bay and Vankarém, mainly onshore during winter. In summer he would go to Lawrence Bay and Mechigmensk Bay; from 1936 through 1939 he worked in the Chaun region, all along Bol'shaya Baranikha, Aiok Island, in the basin of the River Chaun, on the Kuvet and Pegtymel' rivers and in the Ryrkaipiya region: on the River Ékiatan and the left tributaries of the Amguema. Being an excellent hunter and an ardent nature lover, Schmidt was an outstanding observer. Unfortunately he was not an ornithologist of such a level as to identify the innumerable species of sandpipers and non-game birds. With this limitation, this author extensively used Schmidt's information in his monograph as very valuable and intelligent data pertaining mostly to the edible species.

Some information on birds was passed on from other friends by K.N. Yakovlev, a hunter employed by the regional business and manufacturing office 'Sevmorputi' in Anadyr. He worked mostly in the Chaun and Eastern Tundra (island) regions from September 1936 through September 1939.

Ornithological collections by E.M. Meller at the Polar Station Pereval'naya in 1939. In the summer of 1939 E.M. Meller, meteorologist, collected birds from the watershed between the sources of the Rivers Amguema and Tadleon. His small collection included only 23 specimens but the skins were prepared very carefully, which greatly enhanced their scientific value. This collection together with Meller's brief observations was given to me for processing.

Some observations on birds on the coast of the Chukchi peninsula were communicated in 1946 by A.P. Andriyashev, who participated in the Eastern High-Altitude Expedition on ice-breaker the *North Pole.*

In 1948 V.N. Lyubin made a small bird collection at Providence Bay, Lawrence Bay and Uélen. A list of his specimens was kindly forwarded to me by K.A. Vorob'ev; I personally examined some of them while living in Vladivostok in 1965. Lyubin's specimens are mentioned at the appropriate place in the species descriptions.

After 1939 there was a prolonged break in my field work on the avifauna of Northeast Asia. Until 1956 my attention was confined to the study of birds of the

Transcarpathians, the Kuril Islands, north Taimir, the Caucasus and other expeditions.

Excursion into the interior of the Chukchi peninsula from June 7 through July 20, 1956. In 1956 the Institute of Zoology, Academy of Sciences of the USSR, provided me with funds for air travel without heavy baggage. Since I had already made a fairly complete collection of material in my earlier explorations I decided to travel without a gun, which would have involved carrying heavy ammunition and other hunting gear. Instead of collecting, I intended to supplement the biological data that I had collected before. So I equipped myself with a good camera. As it turned out, I had little cause to regret the lack of a gun and, thanks to this, observations were longer and more thorough. Where formerly, on encountering nesting birds, I had either collected the nest or, after a vain search, taken the birds themselves, I now had nothing to do but watch for hours and note the behavior of birds in detail, something I had not done before. This time ecological research prevailed over faunal studies. But there was no doubt that this approach justified itself as abundant faunal data had already been collected on earlier expeditions.

On June 7 I flew from Magadan and arrived at Krest Bay before evening. The next day I covered the long way to Égvekinot village by car, driving around the bay because the passage over the ice was blocked (Fig. 7). The ride was long and slow on the thawing tundra. Spring was in full bloom and the sun burned down mercilessly. The mating calls of birds were heard all around.

On June 9 I took the road toward Amguema and soon reached the hills where it was still an altogether winter environment (Fig. 8). Finally, leaving behind the plains adjoining the Amguema valley, I headed for the "91st km", the site of the Polyarnik collective farm.

The place where I set up for prolonged station observations was rather rocky plain tundra adjoining the flood plains of the River Amguema on one side and the chain of knolls rising to a height of 700 to 800 m on the other. In the flood plains willow grew to the waist and sometimes to a man's height. The width of the Amguema varied from 50 to 100 m.

Many rivulets and brooks flowed down from the hills; the brooks flowed down the slopes or fed the marshy areas. Here and there lakes of different sizes were encountered. Four kilometers from the settlement there was a ridge of knolls some with steep, some with gentle slopes. In the valleys rivulets flowed with fairly high willow shrubs on the banks. On the surface of the knolls stony, rocky tundra prevailed; small and large detrital material was also encountered.

It was cloudy and cold on June 10, giving the impression of the end of winter but not the beginning of spring. Before evening a real snowstorm developed. The tundra was freed of snow cover over less than one-third of its area. In the Amguema there were huge patches of thawing ice but the river had not yet opened up. The snow did not thaw uniformly; there were still frosts at night. In contrast to this winter environment, the song of the early blue-throated warbler (*Lucinia svecica*) could be heard.

During six weeks explorations were made almost daily into the surrounding country (Fig. 6). The entire environment and the development of phenological phenomena recalled my sojourn on the River Utte-Véem in 1934 (Fig. 10).

By June 13 almost all of the local species of bird had arrived in the neighborhood of the Amguema. Ice drifting began on the 14th (Fig. 11). On June 15, when the day temperature was +14°, grass began to sprout, insects and spiders appeared and snow-birds and finches began nesting. On June 18 the Amguema started overflowing. The summer had finally set in and most of the birds were laying. The nests encountered were regularly inspected. At the end of the season their number totaled 50.

On June 20 the surrounding highlands were inspected and the composition of hill avifauna studied. Saxifrages and other species of plant characteristic of northern mountains bloomed on the knolls (Fig. 13). On June 24, the tundra looked greenish from the peak of the knoll. On June 26 the level of the Amguema fell to the low-water mark. On June 29 the summer warmth changed to cold and a storm broke by evening. From July 2 hatchlings of sparrows and sandpipers began to emerge. Rain on July 3 hastened the growth of leaves. On the 6th a very powerful storm developed with thunder, which is not to be heard every year. From July 10 the temperature rose to 20° or more. The snow melted so much that the tundra often resembled a flowering meadow somewhere in the temperate climes (Fig. 12). It was high summer. On July 16, I climbed the knoll for the last time, now covered on the slopes with flowering plants. It was totally calm and the thermometer read 25.5°. On July 17 and 18 the warm weather continued.

The observations on nests having concluded, the following season was of minimal interest to an ornithologist. The birds began molting and became inconspicuous. On July 18 I left the Amguema for Égvekinot and flew into Anadyr on the 20th.

The Amguema observations appreciably enriched my storehouse of information on the biology of birds gathered on earlier visits to the Chukchi peninsula. Moreover, they provided more distinct concepts of the composition of the avifauna of the interior of the peninsula. I visited areas forming the flood plains of rivers and where the hills were not high. Study of the fauna of the higher ranges of hills is a task for the future. In writing this I have in view the experience gained in the intense zoological exploration of the higher ranges of the Koryatsz mountains. This showed that the high-altitude fauna of the interior of the Chukchi peninsula was unlikely to prove abundant. Nevertheless, it would be of much interest though calling for disproportionately large resources. The object should be a detailed study of the faunal characteristics of individual mountain ranges. Only after that was completed would it be possible to draw a general picture.

Journey by A.P. Kuzyakin to south and east coasts of the Chukchi peninsula from June 9 through July 18, 1957. Prof. A.P. Kuzyakin visited the Chukchi coast in 1957 at the same nidification time as I had done the year before. The object of his mission was to look for nests mainly of species of bird characteristic of the northeastern extremity of Asia and unknown to westerners.

On June 9 Prof. Kuzyakin flew into Providence Bay, where he mainly toured around the knolls and the surrounding country until June 18. He spent the whole of June 15 searching for Baird's sandpipers and observing them. On the 18th he arrived in Lawrence Bay, from where he made an excursion almost to Yandagai and Akkani. On the 25th he sailed in a whaleboat from Akkani in Nunyamo and

Poutyn and on the 27th set off for Uélen. July 1 was spent searching for the semipalmated sandpiper. On the 3rd Prof. Kuzyakin again took the whaleboat from Uélen to Lawrence Bay with halts at Naukan, Dezhnev and Nunyamo. On the 5th he toured the tundra in the direction of Chulkhyn. The next two days were spent inspecting the island in the bay. The 9th was spent on the coast up to Yandagai. He visited the neighboring tundra on the 12th and collected downy chicks on the 16th. On July 18 he flew out of Lawrence Bay to Providence Bay and thence to Krest Bay, Anadyr and Markovo.

Kuzyakin made several very interesting finds and valuable observations which were incorporated in his manuscript. This he handed over to me for inclusion in the present monograph. For this the author is deeply obliged to Prof. Aleksandr Petrovich Kuzyakin.

Ornithological observations by V.D. Lebedev and V.R. Filin in the vicinity of Chaun Bay and on Aiok Island from May 22 through September 10, 1958. In the summer of 1958 the paleontological expedition of Moscow University and the Moscow Association of Naturalists worked in the northwestern part of the Chukchi peninsula. The participants included V.D. Lebedev and V.R. Filin, who studied the birds on the coast of Aiok Island, except the eastern end, and later in the northeastern part of the Karchyk peninsula, in the west up to the River Kozmina and along the west shore of Chaun Bay to the south as far as the Nagleinyn Range. They sighted 47 species of birds and collected 86 specimens of 36 species. The material collected was published (Lebedev and Filin 1959) and is covered in this monograph. To some extent the results of their observations filled the gaps of information on the birds of Chaun Bay although, as they themselves observed, their finds did not exhaust the local avifauna. In some cases, for example, in relation to the stone-plover, turnstone, dotterel and the curlew sandpiper, they drew conclusions on their nesting with insufficient basis. This was all the more vexing as the concrete information that they furnished on the distribution and biology of the birds was quite substantial and is not to be underestimated.

Finds of Procellariiformes reported by M.M. Sleptsov in the Bering and Chukchi seas. The observations by M.M. Sleptsov (1959) on Procellariiformes in the whaling regions in the northwestern Pacific Ocean contain data on finds of some species in the Bering and Chukchi seas in the period from 1939 through 1954.

Ornithological observations by V.É. Yakobi around Uél'kal' from April 4 through July 5, 1961. In the summer of 1961 V.É. Yakobi worked with the Helminthological Expedition of the Academy of Sciences of the USSR. Between April 4 and July 5 he gathered morphological material on birds around Uél'kal', from the west shore of the entrance to Krest Bay. He collected some hundreds of specimens, some of them of considerable faunal value. In particular the American species *Passerella iliaca* (Mörrem) (fox sparrow) was recorded for the first time in the USSR. Apart from his own observations he included in his manuscript much interesting information supplied by his student O.I. Belogurov on the birds of Uél'kal' in the period from August 17 through September 7. V.É. Yakobi's manuscript was sent to me for my perusal. I decided to use the data of interest in this monograph, for which a grateful acknowledgement is due to Vladimir Éduardovich Yakobi. His records pertain to the extreme southwestern part of the peninsula, for which faunal data are very scanty.

Ornithological observations by F.B. Chernyavskii were made along with his field work on the mammalian fauna. They covered the extreme west of the Chukchi peninsula and adjoining territory. From July 8 through September 22, 1965, Chernyavskii explored the eastern part of the North Anyui Range, mainly at the source of the River Yarak-Véem, a tributary of the River Lelyu-Véem in its upper course. From June 17 through July 15, 1966, he worked around Bilibino settlement on the Bol'shaya Képer-Véem River, the right tributary of the Malyi Anyui in its middle reaches. From July 18 through August 20 he studied the hilly terrain to the southwest of Cape Schmidt; he also studied the basin of the River Kuvét in its upper reaches, the basin of the River Kuékvun' in its middle reaches and around the River Pil'gyn to the west of Cape Schmidt.

Journey by A.A. Kishchinskii to study ornithological problems on the north coast of the Chukchi peninsula from May 30 through July 26, 1970. The members of this expedition led by A.A. Kishchinskii included N.I. Makurin and N.F. Kovriga, students of Moscow University. Field observations were made from May 31 through June 5 while staying at Cape Schmidt. Then, on June 6, the entire group was taken by helicopter to the east shore of Ukouge lagoon 25 km to the east of the Amguema estuary. Here they set up a base. Field work was carried out until July 13 mainly around the coastal tundra. Some excursions were made as much as 25 km inland. From July 2 through 8 the entire group, traveling by boat, visited the lower reaches of the Amguema, and the period from July 13 through 21 was spent along the sea coast from Ukouge lagoon to Vankarém studying the avifauna along the lagoon shore and on the tundra as much as 10 km inland. Some observations were made from July 20 through 25 on the spit at Vankarém before the journey concluded on July 26 at Cape Schmidt.

It is very important that the field work of Kishchinskii and his colleagues covered the nesting period and that biological observations on the nests of some species with eggs and chicks were made. The composition of local avifauna was also determined more accurately. Their collection of 65 bird specimens was given to the Moscow Zoological Museum. Before processing the results of the expedition, A.A. Kishchinskii very kindly gave me the preliminary data on the birds found on the north coast from the Amguema to Vankarem. For this kindness the author offers his sincere thanks to Kishchinskii.

Ornithological observations by V.V. Leonovich in 1970. Beginning his expedition in the Anadyr region, Leonovich studied birds, mostly in the zoological context, in the neighborhood of Lawrence Bay from April 12 through 24. Between April 24 and July 12 he went on expeditions and collected specimens on the north coast of the Chukchi peninsula from Seishan to Énurmino. Leonovich made several interesting finds and observed the nidification of rare and little-known species. Before processing the results in detail, Leonovich briefly gave me the main results of his field work for publication; for this, I express my sincere thanks to Leonovich.

The field research of A.A. Kishchinskii and V.V. Leonovich completed an almost 200-year-long study of the birds of the Chukchi peninsula, beginning in the time of Cook's expedition.

History of Research on Bird Fauna on Wrangel and Herald Islands

Ornithological research before the 1938 expedition of the Academy of Sciences of the USSR. In attempts to explore the island, later named for F.P. Wrangel, the role played by birds was the same as in the discovery of the Bahama Islands by Columbus. It is said that the scientific discovery of Wrangel and Herald islands was made by Capt. R.N. Kellet, who landed on Herald Island on August 17, 1849, and saw a huge elevated land mass roughly 60 miles to the west. A.I. Argentov (1857a) made the first reference to the migration of lesser snow geese from the "northern land" (i.e. from Wrangel Island) to the Chukchi coast. Describing the approach to Chaun, he made remarks (pp. 102 to 106) on the existence of land and people in the Arctic Ocean on the northwestern side of 'Kulyuchi' Island. He reports that lesser snow geese migrate in large numbers from across the sea to Capes Yakan and Lyaleran in the fall. So 1857 can be regarded as the first year birds were recorded as flying from Wrangel Island. In the much later work *Severnaya Zemlya* (Northern Land), Argentov (1861b, p. 7) discusses it in greater detail. He reports that in the area between Yakan and Lyaleran, lesser snow geese migrate daily from the Arctic Ocean at the beginning of the summer. On reaching the coast they halt and rest on the low tundra. Evidently the birds rested there after a strenuous flight, which provided an idea of the distance of the land the lesser snow geese had left to come to the Chukchi coast in their passage from the north to the south. Based on such information, Academician K.M. Bér (1869, p. 259) set the Chukchi expedition of 1868 through 1870 the following problem: To gather all the information they could on migratory birds, swimming reindeer and migrating people originating, according to the Chukchians, from some unknown northern land. The problem was to study, among other things, whether the lesser snow geese came to the Siberian coast from the north. In his reply, G. Maydell (1871, p. 62) refers to the local lore. The Chukchians questioned argued that many migratory birds did not stick to the coast but flew along it in formation. The flight of birds was noticeable 32 versts to the west (from Yakan). All the birds later stopped on the mainland. In the east the flight reached Ir-Kaipiya (Ryrkaipiya). But the birds did not fly due north out to sea. They flew some distance west along the coast and then headed north out to sea. The most beautiful duck species arrived first. Later the lesser snow geese were seen. They also flew on in formation and only in very cold years when the snow on the local mountains did not thaw did they remain on the coast. Later different species of ducks and sandpipers arrived. In the fall these birds returned but not in flocks, so that hunting them was very difficult. In the description of his travels Maydell (1894, pp. 282 and 283) develops the same idea in greater detail. According to him even if Wrangel had not provided any information as to the existence of land to the north, its existence and its large dimensions could have been inferred on the basis of bird movements.

Information on birds provided by the first few visitors to Herald Island was very scanty and general. R.N. Kellet in his report on the discovery of the island wrote (Hooper 1884, p. 54) that innumerable black and white pochards (common at sea) found a safe place for laying eggs and raising the young there. Not one of the tiny land birds so numerous before they landed was found there (see Seemann's translation of 1858, vol. II, p. 127; anon. 1868, p. 4).

In 1879 De Long's expedition sailed for Arctic exploration in the *Jeannette*. The party included the naturalist R.L. Newcomb and the correspondent of a New York newspaper, J.J. Collins. On August 31, after the last halt at Kolyuchin Bay, the ship headed for the southeastern end of Wrangel Island and sighted Herald Island on September 4. The route of the expedition was charted on a map given in Newcomb's book (1888) and also in De Long's records (1883). Having met ice, the *Jeannette* first drifted northwest from September 6, moving very slowly. Toward the beginning of February, 1880, the ship found herself roughly within 50 miles of Wrangel Island and slightly short of the 180th meridian. Wrangel Island was seen to the south from September 21, 1879, but in March, 1880, both Wrangel and Herald islands were lost to view. In 1879 the members of the expedition collected 215 birds; in the spring of 1880 the birds were few but in June and July many phalaropes and alcids were found. This exhausts the ornithological interest of the voyage of the *Jeannette*, which after a second wintering sailed past the island named for her on May 16, 1881. The information on birds gathered there and communicated mainly by Newcomb is of much interest but quantitatively quite modest. Equally scanty is the information on birds recorded in the diaries of De Long. Nevertheless, all of them are included in this monograph though the names of the birds are not always readily indicative of the species. For example, I could not decipher the bird described by De Long on October 13, 1880, to the north of Wrangel Island, as a new bird with reddish and blackish feathers trying to settle on seals which the locals were dragging (De Long 1883, p. 469).

In 1881, the *Corwin* expedition was organized to rescue the missing members of the *Jeannette*. It included E.W. Nelson (1883 and 1887). His information on the birds of Wrangel and Herald islands was gathered in the course of that expedition. Setting off from Cape Lisburn to the southwest, the *Corwin* came within half a mile of Herald Island on July 30 and the members of the expedition landed. Leaving Herald Island on July 31, the *Corwin* cruised around Wrangel for a few days but not closer than 20 miles, and then set off for Vankarém. On August 10, the ship touched the ice on the south coast of Wrangel Island and on the morning of August 12 a party landed on the coast close to the mouth of the River Klér. From there the expedition shaped course for Cape Barrow and thence south. But on August 30 the *Corwin* again approached Wrangel Island; at least, the blue mountain peaks could be seen from the ship. This time, too, her third attempt, the ship could not come closer than 20 miles from the island. She sailed for Herald and returned to Kotsebeu Bay. On September 14 she left the waters of the Arctic Ocean. As an ornithologist who has sailed the same waters and under similar conditions I can fully appreciate why Nelson was unable to make detailed observations and did not encounter any birds on land apart from the inhabited bird colonies. Evidently he did not collect any specimens there.

I.C. Rosse (1883), also a member of the *Corwin* expedition, briefly described the landing on Herald and Wrangel islands. He very generally describes birds found there: the myriad birds found on the cliffs and rocks of Herald Island (p. 166). Equally general are the notes of C.L. Hooper (1884, p. 52), who names all the gulls, murres and alcids nesting on the cliffs as auks, which are Atlantic species. The snow-buntings at the tip of the island, according to his description, gaily hopped from stone to stone (p. 52); in a word, there is no attempt at scientific description.

W.H. Gilder (1883), a correspondent of the New York *Herald*, was a member of another rescue expedition organized in the same year (1881) with the *Rogers*. He completed the excursion to Herald Island on August 23 and to Wrangel Island from August 24 through September 14. His notes contain only two or three references to birds and as many on walruses: that is all there is of interest to us in his very lively book sparkling with wit.

In August, 1911, Capt. F.E. Kleinschmidt succeeded in gathering six specimens of birds on the south coast of Wrangel Island. These specimens found their way to the Carnegie Museum in Pittsburgh. L.L. Snyder (1926) at first presumed that the labels attached to them were erroneous but later corrected himself (Snyder 1935, p. 469). Among the unpublished works of N.P. Sokol'nikov I found a note that in the summer of 1911 L.L. Lane, an American, visited Wrangel Island and was supposed to have seen many spoonbills there. Sokol'nikov was no doubt mistaken. Spoonbills were in fact caught in 1911 but at Cape Serdtse-Kamen'.

The same year (1911), in September, É.E. Arngol'd, physician on board the ship *Vaigach*, landed on the southwestern tip of Wrangel Island. The ship anchored near Cape Foma and then, passing to the north of Wrangel and Herald islands, headed for Kolyuchin Bay. He collected dozens of birds, later preserved in the Institute of Zoology, Academy of Sciences of the USSR, and studied by the present author.

From September 16, 1921, through January 28, 1923, Allan Crawford made a business tour of Wrangel Island. He collected 18 bird skins which he later sent to the zoological museum in Ontario. The skins were peeled off by the commercial method and were poorly identified. They served as the subject of an article by Snyder (1926). It could have been more complete had Crawford's diary not been lost when he died in his attempt to reach the Chukchi peninsula over the ice through Long Strait. However, Snyder's article was the first printed communication devoted to the birds of Wrangel Island.

In the fall of 1922 the ship *Maud* of the Norwegian North Polar Expedition led by Capt. Kh.U. Sverdrup came very close to Wrangel and Herald islands. I have used many of the ornithological observations from Sverdrup's diary and other data contained in an article by Schaanning (1928), who processed the small collection brought home by the expedition.

The well-known Polar explorer G.A. Ushakov wintered on Wrangel Island from 1926 through 1929. During 1927 and 1928 he made a collection of 25 bird skins which in 1939 were donated to the Moscow Zoological Museum. I inspected this collection and later read A.G. Bannkov's article (1941) based on Ushakov's material and some bird skins contributed by A.N. Druzhinin. Some observations of Ushakov's are recounted in this article. The errors in the article rather deprive it of its value.

In the summer of 1928, F.L. Jaques, as already mentioned, took part in an expedition to the Arctic Ocean and made some observations on sea birds. On August 4 the research ship on which he sailed came quite close to Herald Island but ice prevented his landing. After being locked in the ice for some days, on August 9 the ship reached 72°32′ north and 166° west. Jaques' observations were published (1930) as separate articles.

A.I. Mineev worked as the director of the Polar Station on Wrangel Island for five years from August 29, 1929, through September 1, 1934. Together with his wife V.F. Vlasova he studied the folklore of the island and paid much attention to its ornithofauna. Vlasova for her part put in much work in preparing the bird catch with a cleanliness and neatness unusual for most of the collections brought from the Arctic, where because of the dryness and cold a high degree of skill in taxidermy was needed. This ornithological collection comprised roughly 80 bird skins. It was given to me for scientific processing. In addition I also received some nests and eggs. After their return to Leningrad Mineev and Vlasova passed on many of their observations not elsewhere recorded in the course of discussions with me. Mineev also wrote about the brids in his popular books (1936 and 1946). I have used all the information that was of value as factual material (Portenko 1937b and Grote 1938).

M. Zvantsev, a meteorologist, also brought some specimens of birds from Wrangel Island, collected mostly in 1931.

Finally, in October, 1934, N.M. Valkulenko made a collection on Wrangel. Before that he had worked in Novaya Zemlya and, being an experienced Polar observer, could no doubt have gathered valuable material, but he kept his findings to himself. Some bird skins of his reached me, especially of Ross's gull, and also some fragmentary notes. All of these have been included in this work.

Much of the information on the birds of Wrangel Island was based on scattered and random finds, with the exception of the material of Mineev and Vlasova.

Field work on Wrangel Island in 1938–39. In 1938 I had occasion to study the fauna of Wrangel Island when I took part as zoologist on an expedition organized by the Academy of Sciences of the USSR led by R.F. Gekker. We had to check the information on the reported find of the corpse of a mammoth. The news turned out to be false but I was able to make a thorough zoological inspection of the island.

The ship carrying members of the expedition reached Providence Bay on July 11. The excursions made there have already been reported. After two futile attempts to pass through the ice to Long Strait Gekker picked out a group to be flown in. This group included myself who, as a specialist, was interested in reaching the island as quickly as possible. On August 2 this group landed at Cape Schmidt. But because of unfavorable weather we flew to Rodgers Bay only on the 8th. In fact, the ship arrived a day later after breaking through the ice.

On August 10, I attempted to reach the north coast of the island but the plane had to turn back after reaching Cape Pillar because of the cloud cover. Next day I toured the lagoon called 'Ozero' 8 km to the west of Rodgers Bay. There I encountered a brood of Sabine's gulls in which the young ones were already flying well and a family of long-tailed terns with two half-grown nestlings. Covering several kilometers of the raised tundra, I did not find one American knot, one of the most common sandpipers on Wrangel Island; they had already migrated. It was evident that the summer was already over for purposes of ornithological observations and that despite its best efforts the party had flown in rather late.

Journey to Tundra Akademii, August 13 through 27, 1938. I put out from Rodgers Bay in a motor launch on August 13 with a large contingent from this expedition. As we approached Cape Uéring we were shut in by fog. Nevertheless, traveling close to the cliffs I could see the bird colonies. Having seen them on the way, we set off later along the lower northeastern coast of Wrangel Island and, reaching Cape Bruch, entered another lagoon. On August 14 I studied the surrounding country (Fig. 15). Much of the plain was covered by patchy tundra. The patches were so large and numerous that to cross the area meant continually getting stuck in the clay. I preferred the marshy valleys and the river banks, covered at places with low, dense grass. The lakes encountered were very small and there were no birds swimming in them. On August 15 we went up to Bruch spit and then turned northwest to the mouth of the Krasnyi Flag River, where I made a long halt until August 20. My excursions there took me as far afield as 10 km. The general nature of the tundra was the same but birds were present in larger numbers. The broods and flocks of lesser snow geese there were protected from human beings but they suffered noticeably from the attentions of Polar foxes. A characteristic element of the topography was a network of tiny lakelets which could mostly be waded through; around them crowded various birds in large numbers. Many gulls, terns and skuas attracted by an abundance of *Boreogadus saida* were drawn to a small lagoon. On clear days the picture called to mind the Arctic summer, but fall had already set in for the birds; they were found in broods and lived in flocks. On August 17, morning and evening, the entire place was dusted with snow and within a short time presented a winter prospect.

On August 20 we left the camp and moved southeast in the launch among the ice floes on the pebble beach along the northern coast of Wrangel Island. On August 21 the icy air compelled us to hurry back to Bruch spit. On August 22 and 23 violent northerly and northeasterly storms kept us in our tents. Ice seemed to cover everything and though small leads later opened the ice did not leave the north coast again before winter was out. Part of the group set off on foot to Rodgers Bay; I was forced to stay back with my collection and hunting and photographic gear.

On August 24 and 25 calm set in, which I decided to use for an excursion. On the 26th the weather continued calm though somewhat cloudy; I went out on the ice and hunted seal along with the eskimos. Help arrived on August 27 morning and next day we left for Rodgers Bay in a tractor together with the sleds. The passes at lower elevations that we crossed were still dusted with snow. The last few days were spent in packing for the departure of the expedition and in construction work so that I could stay back for the winter. Because of our very late arrival on Wrangel Island my results were very modest compared to the efforts put in and the thought of returning without a rich ornithological harvest was rather painful. There was only one way out: to spend the winter there so as to organize field work from the spring and fully cover the nesting period of birds.

Wintering at Rodgers Bay from September 4, 1938 through May 11, 1939. The winter set in rapidly. There was a heavy fall of wet snow on September 4, and on the 5th the entire neighborhood turned white. About that time most of the birds left. Only from September 12 was I able to begin almost daily excursions, covering 5 to 10 km from the Polar Station. On September 13 it was very warm and thawed patches appeared. The snow buntings which were shot showed bare caterpillars in the gullet though the snow still covered large areas. On September 15 I went out to

Fig. 1. View from Bol'shoi to Malyi Diomede. In background on right can be seen Cape Prince of Wales. June 25, 1934.

Fig. 2. Cape Vega, to east of Providence Bay. August 28, 1932.

Fig. 3. A herd of walrus at the entrance of Lawrence Bay. August 18, 1932.

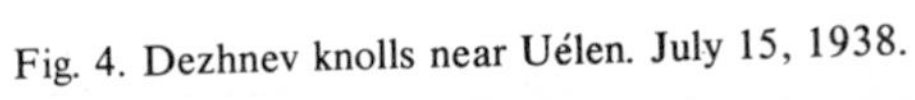

Fig. 4. Dezhnev knolls near Uélen. July 15, 1938.

Fig. 5. Surroundings of Mitkulen. May 20, 1934.

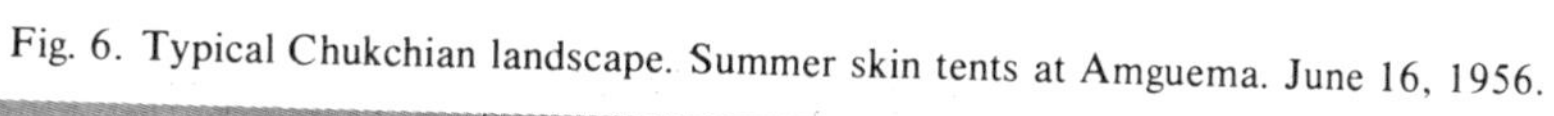

Fig. 6. Typical Chukchian landscape. Summer skin tents at Amguema. June 16, 1956.

Fig. 7. Hills on northwest shore of Krest Bay. June 8, 1956.

Fig. 8. Dividing ridge to northwest of Krest Bay. June 8, 1956.

Fig. 9. Tall willows on River Utte-Véem bank. At left: P.T. Butenko. July 1934.

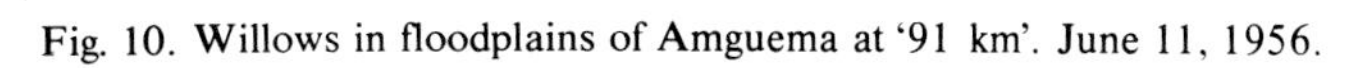

Fig. 10. Willows in floodplains of Amguema at '91 km'. June 11, 1956.

Fig. 11. Amguema River with floating ice. June 15, 1956.

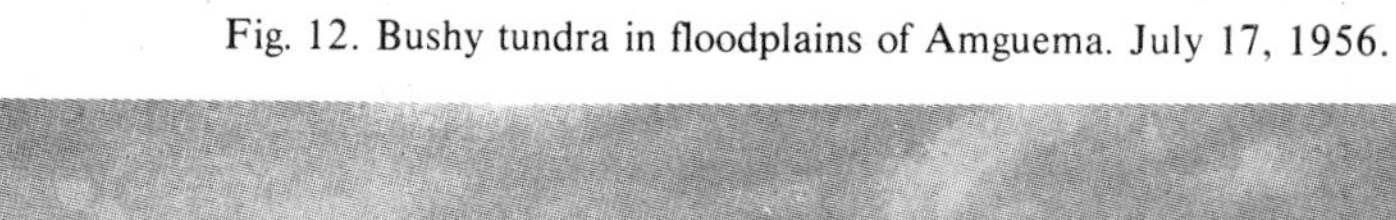

Fig. 12. Bushy tundra in floodplains of Amguema. July 17, 1956.

Fig. 13. Alpine zone in mountain range at Amguema near '91 km'. June 20, 1956.

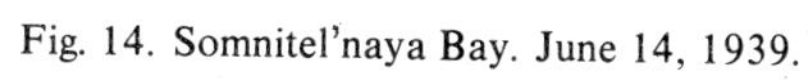

Fig. 14. Somnitel'naya Bay. June 14, 1939.

Fig. 15. Akademii Tundra to east of Bruch spit, Wrangel Island. August 14, 1938.

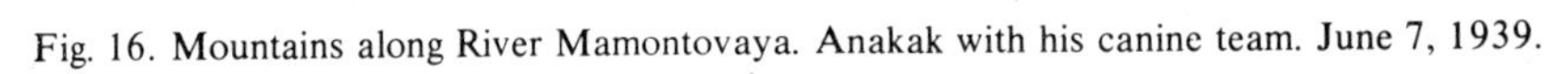

Fig. 16. Mountains along River Mamontovaya. Anakak with his canine team. June 7, 1939.

sea in a motorboat, and landed at Krasnaya Glina to the east of Rodgers Bay. I then suspended these excursions and engaged myself in building my lodge.

From September 26 through October 6 passing Siberian and American species of birds were noticed in the territory of the Polar Station. This phenomenon was no doubt the result of meteorological factors: the eastern part of the Chukchi Sea was ice-free and there was none around Wrangel either. On September 29 I made a prolonged excursion along Rodgers Bay but recorded birds of only four species in a whole day; long-tailed ducks, eiders, glaucous gulls and ravens; snow-buntings had already migrated. In an excursion on October 15 I noticed king eiders, glaucous gulls, murres and ravens. On October 28, setting out on an excursion to the west from the Station, I encountered a huge male polar bear. With only two half-charges of small shot for buntings I was obliged to withdraw in undignified haste.

After a violent and prolonged snowstorm I again set off on an excursion. On October 30 I saw not a single bird. On the 31st I noticed a king eider and ravens and, further, a great flight of alcids. On November 4 I encountered some glaucous gulls, ravens and alcids and also saw a massive flight of ivory gulls. Later, continuous snowstorms for a prolonged period prevented further expeditions. What was evidently to be the last of the king eiders was sighted on November 21 in Somnitel'naya Bay and only the ravens remained to winter on the island.

The chief of the island, the eskimo Tayan, dropped in quite often to pass the polar night with me. He was an efficient and capable person with much hunting experience under the conditions of the south coast of the Chukchi peninsula and Wrangel Island. He passed on much information of interest on birds and mammals, including hunting tips.

On February 18, 1939, thanks to the courtesy of the well-known Arctic flier, M.N. Kaminskii, I was aboard a flight over Herald Island. The day was fine without a cloud at – 20° C, though fog covered the southern horizon. From Rodgers Bay we flew along the coast almost up to Cape Pillar, setting course straight for Herald Island. Circling over it we set off for Tundra Akademii and from Mushtakov spit turned direct south across the mountains. The plane flew over all the knolls of Atternon and, leaving them to the west, landed near the Polar Station. Over Herald Island the plane maintained a height of 2,300 m, descending to 1,700 m over the knolls. Though this flight did not provide any information on the fauna it enabled me to acquaint myself with the natural topography of Herald and Wrangel islands. The flight supplemented what I saw on my flight with I.V. Doronin from Uélen to Vankarém.

On February 25 I set off to study the lair of some polar bears located at the entrance of Lake 'Ozero'. On the 28th I went to the nearest knoll. The weather was clear and excellent with a 30° frost. There was a break in the winter.

On April 13 the first snow-bunting was sighted and on the 18th, the snowy owl. On April 17 the weather was fine, as in early spring: clear and calm at – 20°. The snow evaporated in the sun without being absorbed by the earth. On April 22 I noticed a polar fox and snow-bunting but then there was a snowstorm. On April 27 I went on another excursion in sunny weather but saw only snow-bunting. Their singing could be heard on the 28th and on May 2 I shot a few of them. That set in train the job of skinning. In the course of the winter I had taught taxidermy to S.I.

Korobko, the wife of one of the wintering explorers. She learned to turn out work of excellent quality and engaged herself all the time with the preparation of specimens, leaving me free for field work. It was exceptionally warm on May 3. The thermometer in the soil recorded $+1.3°$ and that in the air $-8°$. The first snow thawed on the soil. On May 7 it was warm enough to move about in fur coats. The snow continued to evaporate and thawing strips of snow appeared. These strips did not touch the absolutely dry soil but rested on the stalks of grass. Male buntings occupied the nesting zones. Spring set in. On May 9 there was violent snowstorm with ground winds but it was not cold. Birds could be seen in the leads formed in the sea and it was time to go to the bird colonies.

Journey to Cape Uéring from May 12 through 16, 1939. The party was ready for departure on May 10 and 11 but the windy weather interfered with our plans. Finally on the 12th we set off: Tayan in one sled and myself with a young eskimo called Anakak in another. But having traveled 0.5 km up to Krasnaya Glina, we turned onto the tundra. By evening we reached the mouth of the River Klér, from where we set off to hunt for alcids in the cliffs close by. On the afternoon of May 13 we went on to Cape Pillar. At one place we crossed the track of a bear and encountered fox tracks quite frequently. In the evening I hunted alcids at Cape Pillar. This was a very picturesque place with a kekur* penetrated by a galleried passage. The next Cape, Bol'shevik, was a gigantic stone block with a triangular apex. On the morning of May 14 we traveled far north and stopped to have tea under Yulii cliff. While I was hunting for alcids Tayan went up to Cape Uéring and returned with the sad news that he had sighted only one pair of murres. Nevertheless, in the evening all of us went there together and were surprised to find the cliffs packed with murres. Evidently they made daily migrations. We shot many of the birds, taking advantage of the good weather. At times the sun even peeped out. Later mist shrouded the peaks of knolls.

North of Cape Uéring, not farther than 0.5 to 1.5 km, leads appeared. For almost 4 km the shore cliffs were populated with murres and other sea birds. Yellowish-red rocks stood out distinctly from the shoreline that we passed. The tops of these rocks looked rather weird against the dark background of the overhanging clouds. Down below beautiful kekurs and caves were humming with the noise of bird colonies. This was one of the most magnificent sights I have ever witnessed in the North. Having loaded the sleds with our abundant kill, we returned to Yulii cliff late in the evening.

On May 15 the weather continually changed, ending finally in a cold snowstorm. I walked toward Pillar and later rode a sled, but the snow covered our faces. Our eyelids stuck together and ice froze on our eyebrows. At the mouth of the River Klér Tayan set up a small tent where somehow we waited until the snowstorm subsided. On the 16th, at dawn, the wind suddenly dropped and we returned safely to Rodgers Bay.

After the prolonged snowstorm of May 13 there was a wonderful sunny spring day and I set out on an excursion along the knolls. On these peaks I observed busy flies and found many caterpillars on the grassy vegetation in the patchy depres-

*Bank of gravel cast ashore with the river ice—Translator.

sions in tundra. On May 26 the first flock of lesser snow geese began flying and the first flowers blossomed. I sent my hired assistant Anakak on ahead with part of the equipment and food for my next expedition. There was a northerly wind on May 28, as a result of which our departure was delayed.

Expedition to Mamontovaya River from May 31 through June 15, 1939. When the windy weather ceased on May 31 I set off on a sled along with Anakak, who had returned, and on June 1 reached Somnitel'naya Bay. Next day we were at the landmark called Akatylanva in Eskimo, which means "bad road". It is almost 180° west and represents a narrow part of the coastal tundra between Somnitel'naya and Predatel'skaya bays. The place had been selected on the advice of Tayan, who regarded it as one of the best areas for hunting lesser snow geese. It was thought that the flight would stick to the low tundra and would more likely come our way in a narrow place than in a wide expanse. The first thawed patches were seen there and the geese gathered on them, waiting for the snow on the much higher tundra to thaw. Had the spring begun early and developed gradually the hunters would have had more time for hunting in this ambush spot on the thawed patches. However, the winter of 1938–39 was less snowy and the tundra was almost totally free of snow very early. This was bad for two reasons: there was not only no place for the geese to settle but there was also no passage for the sled. The expedition was a dismal failure.

It was clear from the morning but there was an easterly wind. The picture of rapidly emerging spring was charming. American knots and plovers arrived in large numbers. Crossing the coastal ridge of knolls, I penetrated the Mamontovaya River valley. But it was impossible to reach the nesting places of geese as the river had opened up and crossing it was out of the question. The geese that were spotted had to be shot from long range using heavy charges.

It got very warm on June 3. Bumble bees were noticed for the first time and caterpillars began to make cocoons. The tundra belt adjoining the mountains was quite free of snow. I went far to the east and found low sections of tundra still covered in snow. Finding lesser snow geese there was beyond my expectations.

On June 4 we shifted camp far to the west. A small pass separated the party from the lower tundra of Mamontovaya River. In the coastal waters the surface of the ice showed huge puddles of melt-water. That was the end of riding dog sleds. From my experience of journeys on the Chukchi coast I was aware that soon the leads in the ice covering the sea would be filled with melt-water, which would rise to the surface. Riding sleds would be impossible after the leads opened up. There was one more unpleasantness: while returning home we had to negotiate full rivers and strong currents of melt-water which mostly discharged from the shore bluffs onto the sea ice, washing it and creating dangerous patches of water in the middle of the ice. These difficult sections along the coast widened as one watched and sometimes a detour of several kilometers was necessary to get past them. Plans were also upset by the need to economize on dog food, which was in rather short supply.

So far we had not shot any birds and there were very many of them in their new camp. Pretty well all the birds had arrived. In the evening the birds stopped singing so that some kind of diurnal regime had set in for them.

On June 5 I hunted for the whole day in close proximity to the camp. As a result of the bad weather flights of birds unusual for Wrangel Island, like the red-throated pipit and the marsh owl, were seen. It rained on June 6. There was a continuous layer of melt-water on the sea ice to a quarter of its thickness.

I went on a major expedition to Mamontovaya River on June 7 (Fig. 16). The dogs could hardly pull even a near-empty sled over the thawed soil. I myself walked. In the day the sling thermometer showed +4.5°. The wind was blowing all the time but it was clear. We descended into Mamontovaya valley and, reaching the cliffs with nests of snowy owl, stopped for a long time.

On June 9 I made a very difficult expedition to Mamontovaya. It took 18 hours. Taking the sleds, we followed a river full to the brim for about 15 to 20 km toward its lower reaches. We visited interesting and picturesque places but we encountered neither willows, where bush birds might be expected, nor the nests of lesser snow geese. On the way back, on the southern slope of the pass, I encountered geese and, though I was exhausted, studied them. I found only goose eggs sucked by gulls. I shot a pair of geese in a ruined nest. The maximum temperature in the day was +2.7°.

On June 10 we rested after our strenuous work. Moreover, it was cold, the wind was blowing and the area was covered with fog. On the 11th I saw the rim of Mamontovaya valley along its upper course. The stony plateau on the high watershed knoll, extending for about 4 km, was thoroughly studied. One might have expected to find the nests of birds representing the fauna of mountain-tundra there but the place was exceptionally lifeless.

I visited the large lagoon and the spit toward Predatel'skaya Bay on June 12. There the tundra bore a marine character; it was intersected by many rivulets and ponds. Along the banks of the rivulets there was porous snow dangerous to walk on. There was still much snow in the depressions. Lesser snow geese were confined to such places but there was no nidification.

At midday on June 13 we struck camp and began moving east. On the 14th the neighborhood of Somnitel'naya Bay was inspected (Fig. 14) and late in the evening we reached the River Amerikanskaya. Next day I shot innumerable eiders in the river mouth and, among other species, bagged a spectacled eider. The ice had to be negotiated on a sled heavily loaded with ornithological trophies. In the June heat the snow thawed rapidly. It was necessary to skirt the thawed patches. To fall in could mean drowning. Sometimes lovely seals stared at us from the leads. I returned to the Polar Station safely and in time. The eskimos traveled on the ice for a few more days. Some of them suffered cold baths but there were no fatalities. In 1934, however, when I was in Uélen, a Chukchian set off with dogs over the sea ice when it was too late for a spring journey, and did not return.

Though I failed to get many nests of lesser snow geese on the River Mamontovaya it was one of my most interesting expeditions to the North. I witnessed the cycle from the arrival of the birds to the end of their sojourn. Finally, I was able to cover the period of initial nidification of birds immediately following their arrival. The westernmost parts of the island remained unexplored. There, according to available information, the avifauna is richer than in the east. To study it is an important task for the future.

Excursion to the southeastern part of Wrangel Island (Somnitel'naya Bay, Atternon Mountain, Nasha River, Rodgers Bay and Cape Hawaii) from June 17 through August 28, 1939. On June 17 I set out to study the neighborhood of Rodgers Bay as far as I could go on foot. Cold fogs constantly obstructed me. Being alone, I could not find the courage to go deep into the hilly interior of the island and risk being cut off by a mountain river or getting lost in dense fog. Even the smallest incident, in the absence of friendly help, could prove fatal and there was no need at all to take a risk. I preferred an intense study of my immediate surroundings.

On June 23 I visited the peak of the knoll in the eastern part of Atternon. On the stony upper terraces, on the dark soil with lichen growing here and there, I found many insects, especially butterflies, for which the dark background represented a warm screen. Everywhere flowers blossomed in bright patches. In the foothills, on the tundra, I found bird nests with incubated eggs. On June 26 I studied the right bank of the lower course of the River Nasha, beginning roughly at the traverse of the Polar Station and going up to the estuary. Later I covered the spit of Rodgers Bay. On the 27th, without resting for fear of losing the opportunity of a sunny day, I repeated the course of June 23. On the 28th I went north toward the River Nasha and on the 29th along it to Atternon Mountain. On these excursions I made interesting observations on the nidification of brent geese, eiders, long-tailed gulls, snowy owls and other species.

On the afternoon of July 2 I set off on an excursion and returned only on the morning of the next day, having reached the western end of 'Ozero' lagoon. I saw many polar foxes and migratory cranes. On July 6 I engaged myself in the study of owl nests: observing, sketching and photographing them.

During the days following, the weather changed sharply for the worse, fog set in and it turned cold. The island was still surrounded by ice packs without cracks or leads. Plant and animal life flourished on it as on a nunatak and steady winds carried away the soil evaporation. Toward midsummer the sea ice cleared and the island came under the direct influence of a marine arctic climate.

On July 11 I went east from the Polar Station. Most of the birds had chicks and after the cold days insects were in short supply.

On July 14 I made a car trip to Somnitel'naya Bay along with Tayan. In the evening we halted at Amerikanskaya rivulet. The whole of the next day we traveled on a tundra plain adjoining Somnitel'naya Bay. Seals and other aquatic animals resting on the sea ice could be seen through binoculars. Lemmings bolted from one hole to another in the path of the automobile. There were very few insects. The birds were with their broods. On the 15th the weather was clear, calm and warm. There had been no such days in June. Gradually the wind intensified and drove fog in from the east. The cloudy weather, cold and rainy, continued until July 22, when I was able to make an excursion to the estuary of the Nasha River. The sun shone for some time and it got quite warm. We even caught some insects. Rodgers Bay was already free of ice. The first walrus appeared.

On July 24 I made an excursion to Atternon knoll in sunny, windy weather. A valley with a rivulet flowing from a knoll caught my attention. Among the succulent, bright greenery it stood out against the yellowish-grey landscape. On July 26

I repeated the excursion but a very cold easterly wind blew and fog settled at the end of the day.

On July 27 I went by car to Cape Hawaii. To the east of the Nasha estuary there was tundra of the type I had noticed in the fall in the northern part of the island. Pebble patches gave way to clay, the grass cover was very thin and lichen and mosses were predominant. Birds were few; even plovers, so common on the south coast of the island, were not to be seen. On July 29, taking advantage of clear weather, I made for the Atternon foothills.

On July 30 news came of the possible arrival of a steamship at Wrangel Island. Packing had to be done quickly. From that day on life was exciting. The ship could arrive any time and if I was not ready I would be left behind for one more winter. On August 2 I took a walk toward Atternon. It was a true summer day but the time of maximum greenery was over. New species of butterflies were not seen but I caught different types of bumble bees.

On August 4 it was again a clear day and I went hunting for walrus in the whaleboat, not farther than 15 km. I got seven of them. The trip and the shoot were repeated on the 5th. We returned late in a very dense fog. Clear weather returned on the 7th and I again set off toward Atternon.

From the evening of August 7 the weather sharply deteriorated and the summer was almost over. Cold northerly winds blew, alternating with fog. It was impossible to go on expeditions and I kept myself busy packing the ornithological collection. This job was far from simple. Foreseeing the inevitably unfavorable transport conditions over long distances, each specimen was packed in a packet of stiff, thick paper and sealed with wax. The birds thus packed were put in strong cases. These cases were then sealed and placed in specially prepared wooden chests. It turned out later that these measures were thoroughly justified. The entire collection reached Leningrad in good condition.

On August 16 the fog dispersed; after midday there was an intense northerly wind. I walked to Atternon. There were flights of lesser snow geese. Most of the birds lived in flocks. The tundra had changed color, becoming more yellow and red. Insects could not be seen at all. The intense northerly wind continued on the 17th but later cloudy, relatively warm days set in. On August 22 I went up to the rim of the Nasha River valley to draw sketches and observe the flight of geese. On the following day I repeated the excursion but returned in such a fog in the evening that nothing could be seen beyond my nose. On August 24 I again went to the Nasha River valley. On the way I shot a juvenile lesser snow goose at a distance beyond the range of a shotgun, about 170 paces. The sun shone almost all day. There were flies on the knoll, and mosquitoes down below. Toward evening it cooled sharply. I returned in fog. On the 25th there was light snow which left a thin layer on the ground. On August 28 I left Wrangel Island.

The conditions for field work on Wrangel Island were much more difficult than on the Chukchi peninsula. With few exceptions I traveled alone and depended more on weather conditions. For an ornithologist the success of an expedition anywhere, and particularly on Wrangel Island, depends on clear weather when the birds are more active and hence are more visible. But the clear days were very few on Wrangel Island. In the fog not only the observation of birds but at times even taking a few steps was chancy. These detailed descriptions of my excursions might be useful to ornithologists who have not yet been in the Arctic but wish to visit places like those described in this monograph.

In 1946 A.P. Andriyashev made some observations on birds from the steamship *Severnyi Polyus* in the waters and on the ice off Wrangel Island. These are also covered in this monograph.

No ornithologist visited Wrangel Island for 20 years after I wintered there. In 1960, in order to check a report that lesser snow geese had been exterminated for food, the Central Board of the Game Industry and Conservators under the Council of Ministers, Russian Soviet Federative Socialist Republic, and the All-Union Society for Natural Conservation sent S.M. Uspenskii and R.L. Bëme to Wrangel Island (Uspenskii, Bëme and Velizhanin, 1963) with the special task of determining the number of lesser snow geese and polar bears. They were on the island for a week from July 17 through 22, studying the main colonies of geese close to the tundra peak. They completed the expedition with the help of a jeep and an airplane. Uspenskii published the results of these studies in the form of articles (Uspenskii 1961 and 1963b, and Uspenskii, Bëme and Velizhanin 1963).

In the same year (1960) A.G. Velizhanin (1965) from Irkutsk Zoological Base worked on Wrangel Island with the object of catching lesser snow geese alive. He stayed on the island from June 17 through October 11 and undertook some journeys to the east end and along the south coast. In order to reckon the geese population and bird colonies he flew along with Uspenskii and Bëme.

In 1964 Uspenskii (1965) continued the work and studied the geese colonies on the tundra peak in greater detail. All of the material that he published has been used in this monograph. His assistant on his last expedition was F.B. Chernyavskii, who very kindly reported his own observations on birds on Wrangel Island to the present author.

History of Research on Bird Fauna on St. Lawrence Island (1779 through 1959)

St. Lawrence Island was discovered and named by Vitus Bering (Golder 1922) in 1725. In his diary he left not even general notes on marine birds. In 1777 Capt. James Cook's ship approached the island, which was renamed Clerk's Island. In 1779, after Cook's death, his expedition again came to the island. In the travel descriptions compiled by J. King (1785) it was reported that the travelers were accompanied for five miles from the island by a strange variety of marine fowl. They noticed some alcids and small crested hawks. This reference opens the chronology of the ornithological study on St. Lawrence Island.

On July 28, 1816, and July 10, 1817, members of an expedition led by O.E. Kotsebue (1821) landed here and acquired freshly shot sea birds from the local residents. Along with his account of this journey L. Choris (1822) gives a colored drawing of the small auklet, which is extremely rare here. If it is correct the first species recorded on the island would be altogether exceptional for this fauna. In 1826 specimens of diminutive auklets were brought from St. Lawrence Island by the leader of an expedition, F. Beechey (Vigors 1839). Eskimos brought large numbers of slain birds to the ship.

In the middle of May, 1843, I.G. Voznesenskii (Gil'zen 1915), an assistant in the Academy of Sciences, visited St. Lawrence Island by traveling from Sitkhi in the northern part of the Bering Sea. I studied the small number of birds he collected and preserved in the Institute of Zoology, Academy of Sciences of the USSR, and have covered them in the present monograph.

From July 31 through August 2, 1879, the *Vega* expedition halted on this island (Palmén 1887) at the northwestern tip.

In the 70s (1874 to 1877 and 1878 to 1881) L.M. Turner (1886) worked in Alaska. His ornithological article contained some notes on the birds of St. Lawrence Island, especially on the albatross.

In 1881 the ornithologist E.W. Nelson (1883 and 1887) visited the island, by which time there was already a record of 40 years of field work in Alaska. The *Corwin* with Nelson on board approached the island on June 23 and next day landed him at the southwestern cape. Although Nelson could not confine himself to ornithological matters he provided information on 20 forms of birds. This was the first attempt at compiling a list of birds on the island.

In 1896 A. Seale (1899) passed St. Lawrence Island on his way to Arctic Alaska and observed there two or three types of birds.

Harriman's Alaskan expedition visited the island on June 13, 1899. The party landed consisted of such eminent biologists as R. Ridgway, C.H. Merriam, L.J. Cole and A.K. Fischer, but unfortunately they had very little to do with bird studies. They collected only 16 specimens of six species and three more species were reported. Fischer gave his notes to H. Friedmann (1932a) for processing.

In the first and the last 10 days of June, 1913, W.S. Brooks and J. Dixon, zoologists on the Harvard University Expedition to Northern Waters, made excursions on the island. They recorded 22 forms of birds and brought specimens of most of them.

The following year, 1914, F.S. Hersey (1916) went there. On July 24 and 25 he landed at two points on the north coast. In his words, St. Lawrence Island represented a very promising place for ornithological studies but, as in other cases, he was able to report only very cursory and superficial observations.

At the end of June and beginning of July, 1921, A.M. Bailey and his assistant R.W. Hendee collected bird specimens there on behalf of the Colorado Museum of Natural History (Bailey 1925 and 1926). In August 1922, Hendee visited the island a second time. In his published work Bailey included some data collected by a local teacher, Dyupertius, and later the finds of a local resident, A. Kulovii (Bailey 1956).

In 1928 F.L. Jaques (1930) came to St. Lawrence Island and noticed three species of birds in the sea.

Later H.B. Collins spent a few months, from June 19 through October 22,

1930, on the island and collected birds whenever he got time off from his main responsibility of studying archaeological and anthropological remains. He brought back 109 bird skins which served as the basic material for H. Friedmann (1932a) in compiling the first report on the avifauna of St. Lawrence Island. The material left by I.G. Voznesenskii and the *Vega* expedition was not known to Friedmann. In the later notes published in the journal "Condor", he reported some new finds made mainly by the eskimo Siluk (Friedmann 1932b, 1933, 1934b, 1934c, 1937 and 1938). Moreover, he processed the bird skeletons found by Collins while excavating eskimo houses, some of which were 2,500 years old or more (Friedmann 1934a).

In the period 1926 through 1935 Otto W. Geist made some archaeological studies on the island. He also gathered at leisure material on the local bird fauna. All this material was processed by O.J. Murie (1936). I have made full use of his article. In the summer of 1937 he visited the island himself and reported additional information on new finds (Murie 1938).

At the beginning of August 1942, I.N. Gabrielson lingered around the island. For three days he made observations without going ashore. He had earlier published the finds made by H. Collins in the summer of 1937 (Gabrielson 1941).

In 1950 T.J. Cade did some field work on the island. Together with J. Shumann he studied the bird population on the west coast. From 1952 through 1957 F.H. Fay conducted protracted research. Combining their efforts, Cade and Fay (1959) published a compilation which, according to them, provided a fairly comprehensive picture of the avifauna of St. Lawrence Island.

Finally, in 1960 E.G.F. Sauer and E.K. Urban (1964) studied the birds, especially the dotterel, on the west coast from Gambell to Kuzata lagoon, mostly around Boxer Bay.

Description of Species

This includes: A systematic review of the species and subspecies of birds found in the Chukchi peninsula and on Wrangel Island, as also on St. Lawrence Island, and to some extent in adjoining regions; bird populations, their habitats; seasonal phenomena in the life of birds: arrival, reproduction, molting and migration; various biological observations, food, weight, etc.; economic importance; systematics of the subspecies; list of specimens found in the Chukchi peninsula and on Wrangel Island.

Order I. GAVIIFORMES—LOONS

1. **Gavia stellata stellata** (Pontopp.)—**Red-throated Loon**

Local name—Chukchian: Iokuàio; jouku in records of the *Vega* expedition. In Eskimo language: yugàyu in Providence Bay and khqãk on St. Lawrence Island.

Distribution and status—Nests but migrates away in winter. Generally common in Chukchi peninsula though relatively small in numbers and not found everywhere. Very rare on Wrangel Island. It is the most common loon on St. Lawrence Island.

L.O. Belopol'skii (1934) observed red-throated loons several times in Krest Bay. P.T. Butenko saw them in the coastal waters off Uél'kal' on October 17, 1937, and encountered three of them on August 6, 1932, in the tiny bay at Notapenmen village. According to V.E. Yakobi's observations in 1961 the red-throated loon was rarer than the Arctic loon at Uél'kal'. Around Providence Bay the former is found in limited numbers. A.M. Bailey (1925) saw two of them on June 30, 1921, in Émma Bay. W.S. Brooks (1915) reported these loons in small numbers in the western part of Providence Bay on June 19 and 20, 1913. I.O. Olenev only heard migrating loons there in 1931/1932. But Butenko got specimens in Plover Bay and near Kivak village. Judging from the season, the one shot on August 22, 1938, was a nesting bird. It should be pointed out that on all my expeditions to different parts of the south coast of the Chukchi peninsula I saw this apparently common bird only once, on August 28, 1932, on the eastern shore of the entrance to Providence Bay.

On St. Lawrence Island R.W. Hendee (Bailey 1925) received information on this species daily from July 1 through 8, 1921. In 1930, H.B. Collins (Friedmann 1932a) shot two summer specimens in Gambell village; these included an old female on October 9 and a young bird in September. In 1935 O.J. Murie (1936) shot nine specimens: a female with a nestling on August 22 around Kukuliak village, a second nestling from the same area on September 3, a female on August 16 around Gambell village, another from the same place on September 6, two females on October 12 and a male on October 24. On June 25, 1950, F.H. Fay (Fay and Cade 1959) found a nest near Gambell and on August 7 and 8 counted almost 10 broods along the west coast of the island between Gambell and Boxer Bay. In 1954 three nests were found in Kuzata lagoon. O.W. Geist (Murie 1936) shot two females on July 26 and 27, 1928, and a young bird on September 19, 1928. According to information obtained from the eskimos the red-throated loon was a common nesting bird on St. Lawrence Island. In June, 1960, E.G.F. Sauer and E.K. Urban (1964) found these birds in twos and threes in the melt-water pools in Boxer Bay. On June 10 a female flying with old squaws was shot. On June 14 a pair was noticed in Kuzata lagoon.

H. Friedmann (1934a) found some bones of red-throated loons of various geological ages in eskimo ruins.

I.O. Olenev found several loons on Arakamchechen Island. In 1957 A.P. Kuzyakin found nests around Lawrence Bay. To one of the specimens, I.G. Voznesenskii attached a label with the remark "Bering Sea" without the exact date.

According to my own observations, the red-throated loon was abundant close to Uélen. But somewhat to the west in the interior of the peninsula it was as numerous in the nesting period as in Anadyr. I often found it along the Rivers Kol'oam and Utte-Véem. A.P. Kuzyakin saw a few pairs on June 29, 1957, in the lowlands from the lakes to the south of Uélen.

W.S. Brooks saw some of them on July 17 and 18, 1913, at Cape Serdtse-Kamen'. V.V. Leonovich noticed one at Énurmino in June-July, 1970.

The *Vega* expedition (Palmén 1887) got bird skins and clutches to the east of Kolyuchin Bay: one specimen was obtained from a Chukchian herdsman not far from Pitlekai; a female bird was brought from Irgunnuk on June 24, 1879, and male from Neshkan on June 28. E.K. Brusevits shot a female at Pitlekai on June 30. Eggs were found in Neshkan and Pitlekai and in the interior of the country.

I did not find nesting loons on Kolyuchi Island for lack of a suitable body of water, but the red-throated loon was undoubtedly common all around Kolyuchin Bay. On July 15, 1909, J. Koren (1910) encountered these loons in freshwater lakes on the northwest shore of Kolyuchin Bay. In the summer of 1956 I did not find one red-throated loon on the Amguema, in the interior of the Chukchi peninsula, though there were arctic loons. According to the observations of A.A. Kishchinskii the red-throated loon was common in the tundra from Vankarem to the mouth of the Amguema River in 1970 and nests were found. V.Ya. Isaev told me that the red-throated loon built nests near Cape Schmidt but that arctic loons were rare. Koren found some broods to the west of Ryrkaipiya village. A.I. Argentov (1857a, p. 85) recalled three species of loons, apparently the red-throated loon, in Chaun parish. In the nesting period S.G. Pavlov shot this species in Chaun Bay. V.D. Lebedev and V.R. Filin caught a female on August 21, 1958, on the west coast of Chaun Bay. According to them the red-throated loon was encountered rarely on Aiok Island, but more frequently in the Karchyk peninsula, from where they got some specimens. Finally, Koren shot a specimen in a nest 30 miles east of Cape Bol'shoi Baranov. In 1917 he found six clutches at the mouth of the Kolyma River

(Schaanning 1954).

On Wrangel Island I encountered the red-throated loon only occasionally. A female from the Nasha River zone was brought to me on June 10, 1939. I heard the call of a bird in Rodgers Bay on June 17 and saw two birds on August 2 which were shot on Ozero lagoon and on the adjoining beach. Finally, around August 10, I saw a red-throated loon flying with an arctic bird high above Rodgers Bay. According to A.I. Mineev, this species of loon was encountered on Wrangel Island in small numbers but nested regularly. He brought a nesting specimen from Rodgers Bay. G.A. Ushakov (Bannikov 1941) caught a male bird on July 7, 1929, and brought two eggs without the dates of collection. According to information furnished by the eskimos, the red-throated loon nests on the island very rarely.

Habitat—During the nesting season this species colonizes lakelets, leaving the large reservoirs to the bigger birds. There are very few suitable lakes on Wrangel Island and hence the loons are very rare there. According to G.A. Ushakov they build nests in tundra lakes, occasionally even on sand spits. In the Chukchi peninsula I encountered red-throated loons more frequently in the valley of the Kol'oam and Utte-Véem rivers. They could be seen on lakes on both sides of the rivers, as also in the river pools. Being a very mobile bird, it often migrates along the rivers, from lake to lake or from a lake to a lagoon. During migration these loons followed the offshore zone between the floes and the lagoons, especially in the tiny inlets joining the lagoons with the sea. I found no loon in the open sea far from the coasts.

Arrival—The red-throated loon arrives relatively late, not before the end of the first 10 days of June. In the nesting areas it is seen even later because the thawing of lakes is delayed compared to the opening of rivers. The spring advancement in the northern parts of the nesting zone is relatively rapid judging from the fact, for example, that N.P. Sokol'nikov reported this species of loon on May 31, 1898, May 27, 1899, May 26, 1900, and May 23, 1901, around Markovo in Anady, region.[1] According to L.O. Belopol'skii, the arrival of this loon in Krest Bay must have been at the beginning of June. P.T. Butenko caught a red-throated loon on June 9, 1939 in Providence Bay. Around Uélen in 1934 the first few arriving birds were noticed only on June 17. They were confined to the coastline, to the leads in the shore ice. At the *Vega's* anchorage in Kolyuchin Bay the first reliable sighting of a red-throated loon in 1879 was only on June 24 though O. Nordquist had shot a species of loon sitting in a lead as early as May 31 and Brusevits shot another on June 22. On Wrangel Island, in the 1939 spring, the first red-throated loon was caught on June 10 in Rodgers Bay. On June 17 I heard the call of this bird there for the first time. It is usually vociferous in midsummer.

Breeding—The testes of the arriving males are much larger than at any other time of the year (Table 1) and the subcutaneous adipose deposit is considerable. After the mating season the testes shrink in size considerably and the adipose layer disappears.

[1]In my *Fauna of Anadyr Region*, vol. II, p. 145, I reported these dates as pertaining to the arctic loon. At that time I had missed V.L. Biank's (*Fauna of Russia*, vol. I, 1911, p. 65) remark that, according to an oral communication from N.P. Sokol'nikov, his data on the arrival of the genus *Colymbus* around Markovo pertained only to *C. stellatus*.

Table 1. Testes sizes in red-throated loon, mm

Date	Left	Right	Point of find
June 9, 1938	15×2	13×2	Providence Bay
June 17, 1934	16×6	12×5	Uélen village
July 9, 1934	8×4	7×3	Utte-Véem River
August 10, 1931	12×6	8×5	Mouth of Tanyurer River
August 16, 1931	6×3	5×3	—do—
September 2, 1931	12×6	10×5	—do—
September 4, 1931	10×4	9×4	—do—

The ovary of a female bird from Uélen that arrived on June 18, 1934 had a fine-grained structure, and the bird herself was emaciated. Evidently, this was a relatively young bird without a nest as the females caught on Wrangel Island on June 10, 1939, had 28 mm long ovaries with developed follicles up to 9 mm in diameter and the subcutaneous adipose tissue covered the body in a continuous layer. The August females in Anadyr, shot in 1931, were devoid of adipose lining and had follicles of 3 to 7 mm in diameter.

The laying occurs much after arrival. On June 25, 1950, F.H. Fay found partly hatched clutches south of Gambell. The nest was located on a low grassy mound in the middle of a tiny lake. A.P. Kuzyakin found two nests on July 12, 1957. One of them was on the flat bank of a tiny lake in Lawrence Bay close to a narrow channel. There were two almost fresh eggs. Another was found 4 km from the bay beside a lake with dry grassy banks. That too contained two eggs but one of them was already pecked through and the chick was squawking loudly inside. On the flat mossy islets of other lakes evidently only one or two more pairs built their nests.

On July 1, 1879, the Chukchians brought an egg to the *Vega* expedition from Neshkan and from Pitlekai the following day. A.A. Palander and F.K. Kjellman found a nest with two unhatched eggs during prolonged excursions in the neighboring country. Externally, they were the same as those of the Pacific loon. On July 15, 1912, east of Cape Bol'shoi Baranov, J. Koren found a clutch of two eggs incubated for roughly a week. The nest was on peat in a lake and was lined with a few sticks. In the Kolyma delta he found a nest at the water's edge on the marshy bank of a lake or on a flat islet in the river. The nest was built of blackened moss and sedge. Two eggs were laid in the second or third week of June. On June 12 the oviduct of a female which was shot down showed an incompletely pigmented egg of bright greenish-yellow color, with very few tiny patches. On July 4 and 6 chicks were about to emerge from two clutches while the rest of the eggs were in different stages of incubation. A.I. Mineev suggested that the red-throated loon built its nest on sandy spits on Wrangel Island. For the conditions obtaining on Wrangel Island, this view appears justified. Near Cape Schmidt, Isaev found two nests with two eggs in each.

Loons continue their courtship ceremonies even after laying. In midsummer of 1934 I observed them deep in the interior of the Chukchi peninsula. On July 6 and 7, in the valley of the Utte-Véem River, red-throated loons incessantly moved from one lake to another, filling the neighborhood with their mating calls. Their call was always heard when they flew from the coast through the tundra to the nesting areas. On July 20, in a tiny bay intersecting the pebbled spit extending from Mitkulen to Inchoun, many loons gathered, mostly in pairs. They were no doubt attracted by food. In this bay there was an adult bird hiding a nestling under the wing. When I moved along the bank the loon quickly swam away and attempted to take off. The bird flew so low that it splashed through the water for fear of dropping the young one. It was remarkable that in this process, the bird did not let the young one fall though it was very inconvenienced in flight.

In August loons were rarely seen on the Kol'oam-Véem River as a result of a perceptible drop in their activity. However, even on August 15 I saw red-throated loons making their mating calls and alighting on the water with wings spread. On the 22nd I heard cries resembling their midsummer call.

On August 22, 1935, a female with a chick was collected on St. Lawrence Island; the chick's outer feathers were still completely hidden by down. On September 3 a second chick of this brood was shot. It sported the winter plumage but the undercoat was seen on the neck and sides. On September 1, 1912, J. Koren observed some broods on the River Karpiya and in one case the chick was not older than eight days.

On the north coast of the Chukchi peninsula, red-throated loons disappear in September. They stay much longer on the south coast. In the fall of 1937, P.T. Butenko noticed this species in coastal waters near Uél'kal' on October 17 and in Providence Bay on November 4 and 6. One of the latter finds was a young bird far inside the bay. On St. Lawrence Island adult birds in winter plumage were shot on October 9, 1930, and October 12 and 24, 1936.

Courtship ceremonies—The mating ceremonies, especially of red-throated loons, are of much interest. Though they are noticed until the end of the summer their sexual activity is very striking. In Anadyr region, I observed (1939b, vol. II, p. 154 and 1941, vol. III, p. 108) lively ceremonies incomparably more intense than in the Chukchi peninsula. This was perhaps due to the more southerly lattitude and the milder summer of the Anadyr region. On Wrangel Island I did not hear the mating calls of these birds at all. It is quite possible that the behavior of loons is a purely local phenomenon. In a very interesting article J.S. Huxley (1923) describes his 1921 summer observations in Spitsbergen. He specially mentions the vertical posture adopted by the birds while swimming and surfacing. I did not see such postures anywhere. On the other hand, in Scotland Huxley observed a red-throated loon diving headlong from a great height producing a noise as from a train. I witnessed this phenomenon in Anadyr in 1932 (1941, vol. III, p. 108). Huxley did not report any such observations in Spitsbergen.

In July and August, on clear warm days, the red-throated loons quite often showed unusual mobility. They flew long distances alone or in pairs, wandered over river pools or from one lake to another, rested and were immediately airborne again. Often before diving into the water they would swing their wings wide or flap them slowly as is done by a sandpiper making a mating call. Their shrieks could be heard almost around the clock. I never heard such calls as in Anadyr.

Weight—The male shot by P.T. Butenko in Plover on June 9, 1938, weighed 1,950 g. It was a plump, well-fed bird.

Economic importance—In the factory at Ryrkaipiya village, I saw some stuffed bird skins, including those of the red-throated loon. These skins had come in incidentally since a special hunt for them is not rewarding. The loon is not hunted for its meat.

Systematics of the subspecies—After processing the material for the Anadyr monograph, I again had occasion to examine several specimens of red-throated loons preserved in the Institute of Zoology, Academy of Sciences of the USSR. I was more than ever convinced of the correctness of my description of the subspecies (Portenko 1939b, vol. II, p. 155). The monotypical species *Gavia stellata* was divided into two subspecies:

1. **Gavia stellata stellata** (Pontopp.)—The color on the upper side is more or less a uniform grayish-brown. The young birds in their nestling plumage are dark, more greenish-gray than bluish, mottled with white. Over 100 specimens were studied from Scandinavia, Novaya Zemlya, northern parts of Europe and Siberia, Novosibirsk islands, Wrangel Island, Commander Islands, Kamchatka and Alaska. Thanks to the courtesy of H. Horring, I received from Copenhagen five specimens from the southwestern part of Greenland. Some of them were indistinguishable from the Russian specimens while the rest were very similar.

2. **Gavia stellata squamata** (Port.)—This is characterized by the very bright grayish color of the back, each feather having a silvery gray border. It produces a soft but distinct scaly pattern. The young bird in its nestling plumage also distinguishes itself by its very gray, pale color on the upper side and very broad white patches. Five specimens were received from Spitsbergen and one from Franz Josef Land.

The two subspecies are indistinguishable from each other in the length of wings and beak.

Specimens— 1) Bering Sea, without date, ○* sen., Voznesenskii; 2) Wrangel Island, July 7, 1929, ♂, G. Ushakov; 3) Rodgers Bay, July 8, 1931, ♀, Mineev; 4) Wrangel Island, without date, Mineev; 5) Chaun Bay, July 2, 1933, ○, Pavlov; 6 and 7) Uélen village, June 17, 1934, ♂ and ○, Portenko; 8) same place, June 18, 1934, ♀, Portenko; 9) middle reaches of Utte-Véem River, July 9, 1934, ♂, Portenko; 10) Plover Bay (Providence Bay), June 9, 1938, ♂, Butenko; 11) Kivak village, July 22, 1938, ○, Butenko; and 12) River Nasha, June 10, 1939, ♀, Portenko.

2. **Gavia arctica viridigularis** Dwight—**East Siberian Arctic Loon**

Local name—Chukchian: Iokuàio. In Eskimo language: thlqō'-puk on St. Lawrence Island.

Distribution and status—Quite frequent in nesting areas in the western parts of the Chukchi peninsula. Seen during nesting period to the east of Krest and Kolyuchin bays and also on Wrangel and St. Lawrence islands though there are no reliable data on their reproduction. Probably nests sporadically since a case of nesting was recorded even in Alaska. In the migratory period in the Chukchi peninsula, not very rare but not numerous either.

On August 6, 1932, I caught an arctic loon around Notapenmen village on the east shore of Krest Bay. I noticed a pair in the vicinity with juvenile and saw a flying loon but was not confident of their subspecies. In October, 1937, P.T. Butenko saw a flying arctic loon near Uél-kal' and Notapenmen and in June, 1937, caught a specimen in Plover Bay during spring flight. W.S. Brooks (1915) found a Pacific loon in Providence Bay but reported the absence of arctic loons.

A.I. Kuzyakin did not find this very important bird even once in his 1957 tour of the Chukchi coast from Providence Bay to Uélen.

Around Uélen, I noticed arctic loons in spring and fall flight but did not find them in the flood plains of the Kol'oam and Utte-Véem rivers in the nesting period. The *Vega* expedition to Kolyuchin Bay found only the Pacific loon. In the interior of the country, in the middle reaches of the Amguema, the loons were rather few because of the hilly terrain. The pairs found by Portenko in 1956 were of the subspecies *G. a. viridigularis*. F.B. Chernyavskii in 1966 found pairs and broods of arctic loons in the middle reaches of the Kuékvun' river to the southwest of Cape Schmidt and in 1965 in the Yarak-Véem river valley in the eastern part of the North Anyui Range. V.D. Lebedev and V.R. Filin regarded this bird as fairly numerous on Aiok Island and in the Karchyk peninsula. A pair of them was caught on June 12, 1958, a female on June 29 on the south coast of Aiok and another female on August 9 on the Kuz'mina River in the western part of Karchyk.

The arctic loon is no doubt rare on Wrangel Island. Unfortunately I was not always able to identify this bird with absolute certainty from a distance. Nevertheless, I saw *G. a. viridigularis* near Somnitel'naya Bay on July 15, 1939. Probably it was a nesting bird. It flew around over the lakes and finally settled down; later, I saw two loons and heard their call. In mid-August, 1939, I saw two loons over Rodgers Bay flying high toward the east. From the perceptible difference in their size they appeared to be one arctic and the other a red-throated loon.

Now our knowledge has been greatly enriched concerning the distribution of arctic loons in northeastern Asia. It is found throughout the Anadyr River basin though very probably it is less well represented than the Pacific loon on the sea coast (Portenko, 1939b, vol. II, pp. 144 and 145). N.P. Sokol'nikov orally reported to V.L. Bianki (*Russian Fauna*, 1911, p. 108) that *G. artcica* built their nests on the lakes of the Anadyr valley but it was nevertheless rarer here than on the lagoons. The arctic loon is quite often found on the Apuka River in Koryatz Zemlya. A.M. Bailey (1925) confidently reported its nesting in Alaska, on the River Mint, in the Seward peninsula. On July 6, 1923, an incubating female with an egg and on July 8, 1924, another female with two eggs were found there. Non-nesting birds were caught before and after, especially on June 18, 1929, at Cape Prince of Wales (Bailey 1930). In 1931 a nesting pair was again found there along with a clutch (Bailey 1932). Finally, he shot a male on June 8, 1953, on St. Lawrence Island. According to Bailey, *G. a. viridigularis* was regularly encountered in small numbers along the entire arctic coast of Alaska. Three finds were reported at Point Barrow, two of them identified as transitional birds between *G. a. viridigularis* and *G. a. pacifica* (Bailey, Brower, and Bishop, 1933, and Bailey 1943).

Habitat—The arctic loon selects for nesting different sizes of tundra lake depending primarily on when they thaw. On the coast of Chaun Bay J. Koren (1910) found a brood on a tiny lakelet though, as a rule, this loon prefers much larger bodies of water. It is found in the summer on lagoons and beaches feeding

Fig. 17. Nest of Pacific loon *Gavia arctica pacifica* (Lawr.). Amguema delta. July 4, 1970. Photo by A. A. Kishchinskii.

Fig. 18. Nest with eggs of white-fronted goose *Anser albifrons* (Scop.). Ukouge lagoon. June 20, 1970. Photo by A. A. Kishchinskii.

Fig. 20. Nest of pelagic cormorant *Phalacrocorax pelagicus* (Pall.) with nestlings, Kolyuchi Island. July 26, 1938.

Fig. 21. Lesser snow geese in nesting site on Tundrovaya River. Wrangel Island. Mid-June 1970. Photo by A. V. Krechmar.

Fig. 22. Pair of lesser snow geese *Chen caerulescens* (L.) in nest. Wrangel Island, Tundrovaya River. Mid-June 1970. Photo by A. V. Krechmar.

Fig. 23. Incubating female lesser snow goose *Chen caerulescens* (L.). Wrangel Island near Tundrovyi Peak. June 15, 1964. Photo by F. B. Chernyavskii.

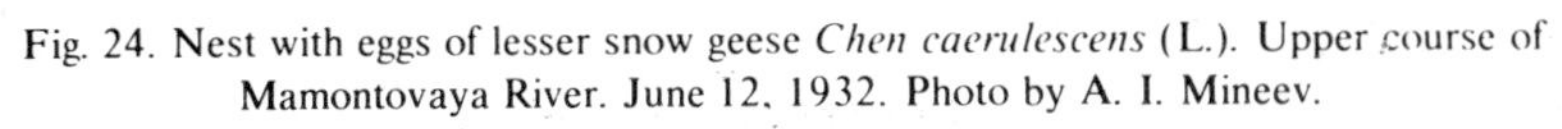

Fig. 24. Nest with eggs of lesser snow geese *Chen caerulescens* (L.). Upper course of Mamontovaya River. June 12, 1932. Photo by A. I. Mineev.

Fig. 25. Lesser snow geese *Chen caerulescens* (L.) chicks in nest. Wrangel Island near Tundrovyi Peak. July 4, 1964. Photo by F. B. Chernyavskii.

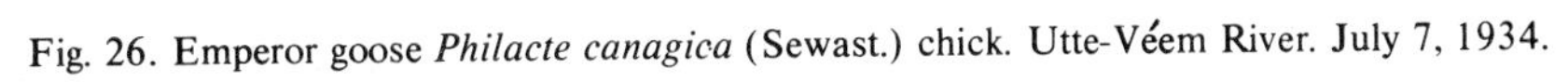

Fig. 26. Emperor goose *Philacte canagica* (Sewast.) chick. Utte-Véem River. July 7, 1934.

Fig. 27. Incubating female emperor goose *Philacte canagica* (Sewast.). Ukouge lagoon. July 11, 1970. Photo by A. A. Kishchinskii.

Fig. 28. Nest with eggs of emperor goose *Philacte canagica* (Sewast.). Ukouge lagoon. June 29, 1970. Photo by A. A. Kishchinskii.

Fig. 29. Pair of Brent geese *Branta bernicla* (L.). Tundrovaya River, Wrangel Island. End of June, 1970. Photo by A. V. Krechmar.

Fig. 30. Nest of Brent goose *Branta bernicla* (L.) with eggs covered by down. Wrangel Island, Nasha River. June 29, 1939.

Fig. 31. Brent goose *Branta bernicla* (L.) chick. Wrangel Island, Somnitel'naya Bay. July 15, 1939.

and resting from flight.

Seasonal phenomena—A.I. Argentov (1861a, p. 485) recorded that the arctic loon arrived together with swallows on May 20 (old calendar) and that the spring runoff waters began overflowing at the same time. In any case, loons do not belong to the class of early arrivals.

In Plover Bay the first arctic loon was caught by P.T. Butenko on June 9, 1938. It was a plump, well-fed male with large testes: 18×8 and 16×7 mm. Around Uélen, I observed shrieking arctic loons flying in pairs on June 14, 1934. Since they did not build nests around the lakes later they were evidently migratory birds. In Amguema I noticed the first loons on June 13, 1956, even before ice drifting, as soon as large channels formed in the river. The loons flew over the river and settled on the water. Toward evening their screams could be heard from the tundra. Consequently they were not the first arrivals but those arriving to occupy the nesting area. On June 18, the Amguema overflowed and the water birds could no longer rest in the swift current. Loons flew high above the river. A pair of them was next seen in the river only on June 26. On the 30th I encountered two of them on a large lake near the hills. One of them was noticeably bigger. Both of the birds were unusually timid and, seeing me, began diving at least half a km away. On July 7, a solitary loon flew toward me, looked around and later settled in a pool in the Amguema River. On the evening of July 8 an arctic loon called across the lake. Evidently the nesting period had just begun. On Aiok Island V.D. Lebedev and V.R. Filin noticed a pair of loons making mating calls at the beginning of June, 1958.

On July 12, 1912, near Cape Bol'shoi Baranov, J. Koren found two nearly hatched eggs on a tiny island in the middle of a lake; there was only one loon around. On July 30 on the shore of Chaun Bay, in a lakelet on the tundra, he found two chicks around five days of age and caught both the parent birds. On August 6, 1932, near Notapenmen, I found a pair of loons with a nestling of the size of a widgeon. The ovary of a female caught on another lake was quite large: 16×7 and 12×5 mm. Sometimes loons arrived from the sea, evidently from their feeding place. I observed similar movements from the beach to the tundra on August 7 and 8, 1938, near Cape Schmidt.

On October 1, 1933, I saw two arctic loons at Uélen flying separately over the lagoon. Undoubtedly the fall migration was over. In 1937 P.T. Butenko observed arctic loons in Krest Bay on October 17 and in Providence Bay on October 24.

Weight—A male that I shot in Notapenmen was of large dimensions. Its length from the tip of the beak to the end of the tail was 76.7 cm. It weighed 4 kg. A male shot in Plover weighed 3.3 kg.

Food—The stomach of a specimen that I shot contained the bones of tiny fish and 26 tiny pebbles of up to 1 cm in diameter.

Economic importance—In view of their relatively small numbers the arctic loons fall into the hands of hunters very rarely.

Systematics of the subspecies—See Pacific loon.

Specimens— 1) Village Notapenmen, August 6, 1932, ♂, Portenko and 2) Plover Bay, June 9, 1938, ♂, Butenko.

3. **Gavia arctica pacifica** (Lawrence)—**Pacific Loon**

Local name—Chukchian: Iokuàio. In Eskimo: thlqō'-puk on St. Lawrence Island.

Distribution and status—Nests in the Chukchi peninsula, is quite common but numerous only at places; no information on finds in the northwestern parts of the peninsula. On Wrangel Island, found in the nesting period, but rare. Common on St. Lawrence Island but nests there in small numbers.

E.M. Meller caught a specimen on June 9, 1939, near Pereval'naya. In Krest Bay, L.O. Belopol'skii (1934) observed the Pacific loon several times during the summer of 1931 and brought a specimen from Meechken Island. W.S. Brooks (1915) caught a specimen in Providence Bay on June 18, 1913. On the southwestern shore of the bay, on a plateau to the north of Cape Stoletiya, I found innumerable nesting Pacific loons on July 12, 1938. Nevertheless, it was not found in Providence Bay either by I.O. Olenev, who wintered there, or by P.T. Butenko. According to Olenev, he had occasion only to hear the call of this bird. V.N. Lyubin brought a specimen he had shot on July 14, 1948, to the Moscow zoological museum. Olenev saw large numbers of this loon on Arakamchechen Island but was not certain about the identification of the subspecies.

H.B. Collins (Friedmann 1932a) caught eight adult and two young Pacific loons in winter plumage on St. Lawrence Island from September 23 through October 16, 1930. O.W. Geist (Murie 1936), based on interviews with the eskimos, thought that it was a common nesting bird. He found a nest with nestlings near Naskak village 15 miles east of Gambell. He found a female bird on July 1, 1930, and males on September 21, 1931, and July 17, 1932. In the fall of 1935 a Pacific loon was found in brackish waters by O.J. Murie: a female in summer plumage in Gambell, September 6; a young male in Kukuliak, September 25; and two more on October 29. According to the observations of F.H. Fay (Fay and Cade 1959), the Pacific loon was as numerous on the south shore of Kuzata lagoon as the great northern diver but it was three times as common on the lakes in the island interior. A pair with two young was sighted on August 6, 1956, in Boxer Bay. H. Friedmann found some bones of the Pacific loon in the kitchen middens of thousand-year-old camping sites.

On August 19, 1932, I saw Pacific loons in Lawrence Bay. The collection of the Institute of Zoology of the Academy of Sciences of the USSR contains two specimens: male and juvenile birds brought by I.G. Voznesenskii with a general label "Bering Sea". There is one more reference by E.W. Nelson (1883, p. 114) to the Bering Sea coast which was usually referred to in the old ornithological literature. He cited two species: *Colymbus arcticus* and *C. pacificus,* but their identification was incorrect, judging from the fact that he regarded the second species as rare compared to the first, and not *vice versa.*

In the neighborhood of Uélen, according to my observations, Pacific loons were not numerous. In the fall of 1933 this species was encountered only in small numbers. On August 28 our plane flying low over the tundra startled and put up the entire feathered fauna. It was an excellent occasion for counting the bird populations. Among them there were only a few shrieking Pacific loons scattered in different directions. In the spring of 1934 I actually counted the pairs.

From August 9 through 24, in my expedition on the Kol'oam-Véem River, I found Pacific loons only twice: some flying above the lagoon on August 9 and a lone bird in the estuary on August 23. On the other hand, on the expedition on the River Utte-Véem from July 2 through 21 these birds were sighted quite often from Inchoun lagoon to the middle reaches of the river. They were recorded in my diary, on July 4, 6, 10, 12, 13 and 20; on the last date many pairs were seen in the channel joining Inchoun lagoon with the sea.

In the summer of 1970 V.V. Leonovich noticed a loon at Enurmino. The *Vega* expedition of 1879 found a few specimens in Kolyuchin Bay. E.K. Brusevits shot two males on July 4 and 6 and a female on July 8 at Pitlekai. O. Nordquist noticed a pair near the estuary of the Ryraitinop River on July 9 and another pair on July 10 south of Pitlekai; he also took a nest. I.A. Palmen's detailed description (1887, p. 408) and the measurements he recorded leave no doubt that they were indeed Pacific loons. In mid-July, 1909, J. Koren (1910) found a nest of Pacific loons on the freshwater lakes on the west shore of the entrance to Kolyuchin Bay.

These were no loons on Kolyuchi Island because of the absence of lakes. According to the observations of A.A. Kishchinskii, along the coast north of Vankarém to the estuary of the Amguema the Pacific loon was the most common of loons. Dozens of pairs and nests were found. All of the arctic loons noticed in the summer of 1970 belonged to the subspecies *G. a. pacifica.* An enumeration was made at the eastern end of Ukouge lagoon over an area of about 48 km^2. In this sample area there were nine pairs and a lone bird. In 1934 I found three skins of Pacific loons among the bird skins in the factory at Ryrkaipiya village. Farther to the west there is no information about this subspecies. In his diary G.U. Sverdrup (Schaanning 1928) recorded sighting a pair of loons with "white necks" on August 24, 1924, west of the Medvezhii Islands at 71°15′ north and 155°18′ east.

A.I. Mineev brought specimens collected on July 27, 1934, in the southeastern part of Wrangel Island. I was not certain of sighting this subspecies. I saw something like a Pacific loon on August 11, 1938, above Rodgers Bay. I heard the calls of loons only a few times in Tundra Akademii from August 19 through 27, 1938, but they were heard incessantly at this time of the year in the Chukchi peninsula. On August 19 I noticed some loons flying from the sea coast to the mouth of the Krasnyi Flag River. A.C. Bent (1919a) reported a couple of specimens found in June on Herald Island. Since this hilly island is devoid of lakes this report could be erroneous.

Habitat—During the spring flight in 1934, Pacific loons were seen flying low over the water. Some pairs rested in the open areas of a big lagoon. As the lakes thawed they made their way from the lagoons and the shoreline to the nearby tundra.

O. Nordquist found a nest on the bank of a fairly large body of water. According to my observations, on the southwestern coast of Providence Bay the Pacific loons often fly from one lake to another, including hilly ones during nesting and courtship. The birds only rested and played on them. Loons hearing the mating call settled on the pools in Utte-Véem River. The lake water was passed through a fine sieve but no fish were found. On the other hand, the Pacific loons, like other loons, performed local migrations to different bodies of water for food. Most often, I found that the birds gathered for feeding in the channel linking the lagoons to the sea, for example near Inchoun. On August 19, 1932, I saw Pacific loons floating on Lawrence Bay. At the same time they were also encountered around the tundra lakes. A.A. Kishchinskii drew attention to the fact that in the neighborhood of Vankarém and Ukouge lagoons pairs of Pacific loons were not confined to the lakes on the flat tundra but were also found on small, sometimes tiny ponds on the uneven ground in the foothills. In the Amguema delta, however, they were found on the lakes on large dry islands. Add to this the fact that loons are encountered even in pools in rivers and it is hard to think of a body of water where loons are never found. Nevertheless, the loon is essentially a lake bird which selects different reservoirs every time for nesting, feeding, rest or play.

Seasonal phenomena—The Pacific loons arrive late, at the end of the first 10-day period or even in the middle of June. E.M. Meller found a specimen around Pereval'naya on June 9, 1939, and L.O. Belopol'skii on Meechken Island on June 10, 1931. In 1934 the first arrivals were recorded in Uélen only on June 12. The following day I saw two or three pairs on the clear water in the lagoon and by the 14th they had already flown to the lakes. Some type of loon was shot on May 31, 1879, in the ice leads at the *Vega's* anchorage.

According to my observations Pacific loons begin calling from their arrival and continue to do so until they migrate again. On July 6 I had occasion to hear a genuine mating call on the lower course of the Utte-Véem River. Like the red-throated loon, they often wandered from one lake to another, made much noise and, before settling on the lake, slowed their wing beat. They could always be easily distinguished from the red-throated loons by the more uniform call, usually without groaning sounds, and slower, less sharp movements. On sighting a man the birds got even more excited. I observed this animation and heard mating calls at Cape Stoletiya on July 12, 1938.

O. Nordquist found a nest on a tiny islet to the south of Pitlekai on July 9, 1879. It was in the form of a turf ring, 24 cm in diameter and 5 to 6 cm deep. It held two eggs 47.9 × 77.3 and 48 × 75.8 mm in size weighing 7.36* and 7.60 g* respectively. They resembled the tiny eggs of Arctic loons.

At the end of June and the beginning of July, 1970, A.A. Kishchinskii and his assistants found some nests with two eggs in each: 1) on June 22 on the bank of a lake close to the Ukouge lagoon, in mossy, low sedge tundra; 2) on July 3, on an island in the Amguema lagoon on tundra of a similar type; 3) on July 4, in the Amguema delta, on an islet among the lakes; and 4) at the same time as before but with only one egg (Fig. 17) on a small lake heavily overgrown with *Arctophila fulva*. Adult birds were seen on the nests or near them.

O.W. Geist found two downy chicks in a nest at the beginning of August on St. Lawrence Island. At the end of September young birds in their first winter plumage were found there. On September 6, 1935, a female in full summer dress was found and on October 14, 1930, a male which had only a few summer feathers on the back, chin and neck. H. Friedmann came to the conclusion that the fall molting in

*An apparent error in the weight of loon eggs. Should read 73.6 and 76.0 g respectively—General Editor.

adults occurred very quickly: they first sported their winter plumage and were then grounded by the loss of their wing feathers.

In the fall of 1933 I found Pacific loons regularly close to Uélen, though in small numbers. At the end of August their shrieks were often heard and birds in flight were seen. On September 9, traversing a good bit of tundra, I encountered only one specimen which, on being pursued, flew from one lake to another. It was evidently the last of the Pacific loons for that year. A distinct migration around Uélen was not observed.

On August 23, 1934, in the Kol'oam-Véem River estuary I encountered a lone Pacific loon which, on being disturbed by my presence, skimmed over the lagoon and the estuary several times uttering loud cries, manifesting an attachment to that place.

Food—The stomach of a male found near Pitlekai revealed blades of grass, straw, eggs of *Cladocera*, etc. The stomach of a specimen found by E.M. Meller on Pereval'naya contained marsh plants and gravel.

Economic importance—In the Chukchi peninsula not many skins of loons were processed. In the factory at Ryrkaipiya, among many bird skins, I found three of the Pacific and one of the red-throated loon. In view of the relatively small number of loons and the difficulty of catching them special curing is hardly practical.

Systematics of the subspecies—The Pacific loon is easily distinguished from the Arctic loon under natural conditions. In the sunlight the upper side of the head and neck appear white from a distance and the entire bird appears more skewbald than the Arctic loon. It is smaller, more agile and mobile and does not rest on the water for long. The voice is less coarse than that of the Arctic loon.

After a review of loons in 1937 (Portenko, 1939b, vol. II, pp. 147 to 151), I studied a small amount of additional material, notably five specimens of Pacific loons from the mouth of the River Yana brought by L.N. Shastin. That find considerably extended the range of *G. a. pacifica* westward. According to the data available then it extended along the Arctic coast of Northeastern Siberia in a narrow strip surrounding, and to some extent overlapping, the range of *G.a. viridigularis.* I did not see even a single specimen with transitional characteristics. In size and color *G. a. pacifica* bears a close resemblance to the Arctic specimens of *G. a. arctica*, but even among them there are no transitional birds. There are three sharply differing forms: *arctica*, *viridigularis* and *pacifica,* which many workers have regarded as species or subspecies at different times. Their ranges are mutually exclusive in general but overlap on the periphery; *G. a. viridigularis* and *G. a. pacifica* are found together from the Yana to Alaska under different ecological environments. It has still to be ascertained whether the Arctic and Pacific loons build their nests alongside one another in small areas, whether they spend the summer together and whether they do not represent the opposite ends of a chain of vicarious geographic forms and not its middle links.

In cases where the subspecies are distinct, a weakly manifest resemblance to the next lower taxon is quite often evident and perhaps enables identification of signs of *natio.** Evidently *suschkini* is one such form of taxonomic importance. Loons

*The author's use of the Latin word *natio* implies incipient subspeciation—General Editor.

from the forest zone in the European USSR are larger than the Arctic loons. A.C. Bent (1919b, p. 238) studied the intraspecific affinities of American Pacific loons and found that long-beaked birds predominated to the east of the Mackenzie River. In the Asiatic population of *G. a. pacifica* there is a predominance of large birds (judging from the length of wings and bills) at the western limit of their range, as can be seen from Table 2.

Table 2. Length of wings and beaks of *G. arctica pacifica*, cm

Locality	Male		Female	
	Wing	Bill	Wing	Bill
Lower reaches of Yana River	33.2	5.30	30.8	5.40
	32.3	5.10	30.8	5.10
	31.1	5.50	—	—
Lower reaches of Indigirka River	31.6	4.80	—	—
	31.0	5.15	—	—
	30.0	5.28	—	—
Kolyma River estuary	—	—	29.1	4.76
Anadyr River basin	32.9	5.04	30.4	4.63
	32.3	4.89	30.0	5.46
	31.3	5.16	30.0	4.80
	31.2	5.50	29.5	4.86
	31.1	4.97	29.2	4.80
	31.0	5.13	—	—
	31.0	4.74	—	—
	29.8	4.58	—	—
Chukchi peninsula	31.8	5.22	29.7	4.97
	30.7	5.70	—	—
	30.0	4.99	—	—
	29.4	—	—	—

Specimens—1 and 2) Bering Sea, without date, ♂ and ○, 1° anno, Voznesenskii; 3) Meechken Island, June 10, 1931, ○, Belopol'skii; 4) southeastern part of Wrangel Island, July 27, 1934, ♂, Mineev; and 5) Pereval'naya, June 9, 1939, ♂, Meller.

4. **Gavia immer adamsii** (Gray)—**White-billed Common Loon**

Local name—Chukchian: Uànkat-iokuàio (literally "walrus-tooth loon") and uvanketsjouku in the records of the *Vega* expedition. In Eskimo: naunkalek in Providence Bay and yū-wă'-yū on St. Lawrence Island.

Distribution and status—Spread sporadically like many other large birds. Nests in the Chukchi peninsula. Common at places, but absent or very rare in the interior of the peninsula, far from the sea. Flies rarely into Wrangel Island. Nests at places on St. Lawrence Island, where it is not rare.

In 1939 E.I. Meller found what was evidently a nesting female near Pereval'-

naya. L.O. Belopol'skii (1934) found the white-billed common loon in Krest Bay throughout the summer of 1931. In 1961, according to V.É. Yakobi, females were collected 18 km south of Uél'kal'. Since this species is common in the marine belt of the Anadyr region it is likely to be common in the nesting areas all along the shores of Anadyr Bay.

This loon is absent from the rocky southern coast of the Chukchi peninsula. Neither I nor P.T. Butenko found it in Providence Bay or at Cape Chaplin. J. Dixon (1916), who went round the Chukchi coast from Providence Bay to Cape Serdtse-Kamen' and visited Cape Chaplin and Cape Dezhnev from June 1 through 22, 1913, did not find this species either.

According to the observations of O.W. Geist (Murie 1936), the white-billed common loon was fairly common on St. Lawrence Island. In October many young birds feed on the northern coasts. According to F.H. Fay and T.J. Cade (1959) this species was rarely encountered on the coasts of the western half of the island but was fairly common on its eastern and southern coasts. Along the Kuzata lagoon at the end of June, 1953 and 1954, an average of only one bird was found every three miles. They are mostly found, however, in pairs. On June 18, 1953, a nest was found in a lagoon, but in the words of the eskimo who found it, it was the first time, whereas this bird nested quite often in the interior of the island. In August, 1956, at least four pairs with chicks were found on the Kuzata River and in the surrounding lakes. Fay and Cade counted the following numbers from Savunga: a ♀, June 11, 1953, two pairs on June 7 and 15, 1932, and a juv., August 19, 1932. A.M. Bailey (1925) sighted a white-billed common loon on June 28, 1921, close to Kukuliak, and two birds were seen in flight in 1930 at Gambell (Friedmann 1932a). On August 22, 1960, E.G.F. Sauer and E.K. Urban (1964) saw a lone bird on the coast about 15 miles south of Gambell. In kitchen middens of 1,000 to 2,000 years ago Friedmann found some bones of this species.

In Lawrence Bay A.P. Kuzyakin was presented with a large bird but he did not find this species in the nesting areas. A young loon found by I.G. Voznesenskii in 1843 bore the general label "Bering Sea". He could have got it near Mechigmensk Gulf or out at sea, or even from the Alaska coast. E.W. Nelson (1883, p. 114) also pointed out in very general terms that this bird built nests on the American and Asiatic coasts of the Bering Sea and Arctic Ocean and that it should not be regarded as either common or rare. All the same, he listed both the forms of large loons: *Colymbus torquatus* Brünn. and *C. adamsi* Gray. Of these, the former, with its dark bill, is no doubt absent from the Chukchi peninsula. At the end of August, 1928, F.L. Jaques (1930) noticed a lone white-billed common loon in the sea to the north of Cape Dezhnev.

I saw it around Uélen not only in the fall flight but, usually, in the nesting areas in the interior of the Chukchi peninsula, in the valleys of the Kol'oam- and Utte-Véem. In the middle reaches of the latter, on July 6, 1934, I found three pairs all at once. From July 6 through 11, I found these loons daily and had no doubt that they nested there. From August 10 through 23, 1934, I encountered them quite often on the Kol'oam River. They were hardly more common than the red-throated loons. Once I collected a family with a chick.

On June 27, 1909, on his way to Cape Serdtse-Kamen', but still south of the

Arctic Circle, J. Koren (1910) sighted the white-billed common loon fairly often among the floes off the north coast of the Chukchi peninsula. On July 3, 1879, a pair was brought to the *Vega* expedition from the deep interior, and on July 10 A. Palander collected a female in a nest on one of the expeditions far south from Pitlekai (Palmén 1887).

Between the Vankarém and the Amguema estuary, in A.A. Kishchinskii's words, this bird was rare and was not found within 5 to 10 km of the coast. Nests were found in the lower reaches of the Amguema.

On June 13, 1956, I sighted a lone loon in open water in a pool in the Amguema, which was just opening up. I thought that this species might be common in that place, below the hilly terrain, but later in the course of the whole summer I did not find another one. V.Ya. Isaev found this loon only two or three times on Cape Schmidt. Three specimens were found there in the spring of 1938 in a lake southeast of the cape; they were later collected by local hunters. A.I. Argentov (1857a and 1861a, p. 492) cited three species of loons including the white-billed common loon for Chaun Bay, as may be judged from the description. According to V.D. Lebedev and V.R. Filin (1959), the white-billed common loon was encountered fairly often on Aiok Island, in the Karchyk peninsula, and especially in Malyi Chaun Bay, where flocks of eight to ten birds were seen. In the Karchyk peninsula they evidently built nests. Loons with fish in their bills were seen flying in the first few days of August on the west coast. A female was seen there on July 26, 1958. On July 27, 1965, F.B. Chernyavskii found a pair on Lake Rauchuagytkhyn, the source of the Rauchua River. J. Koren thought that the white-billed common loon was common all along the arctic coast of the Chukchi peninsula. It was numerous among the floes between Kolyma and Chaun Bays. Copley Amory, Jr. (Riley 1918) found a female on July 19, 1915, at Cape Bol'shoi Baranov and one specimen without date in the Kolyma delta. I was given to understand by persons wintering on the Medvezhii Islands that this loon was quite common there.

On Wrangel Island it is rarely encountered singly; in 1930, one was collected at Cape Hawaii. Based on enquiries, A.G. Velizhanin (1965; Uspenskii, Bëme and Velizhanin, 1963) surmised that although this species was rare it was encountered almost daily on the coast as the sea opened up when the capelin fish began moving. On August 7, 1960, in Somnitel'naya Bay, A.G. Velizhanin supposedly saw a brood of three birds and lone ones on many occasions as late as October 5 and 6. It is striking, however, that Velizhanin does not mention other species of loons while I, on the contrary, found them all in 1938 and 1939 except the white-billed common loon.

Habitat—This loon inhabits areas around large lakes and rivers with mountain streams. In the deep pools below rapids this bird may find adequate amounts of tiny fish. It was precisely under these conditions that I found it on the Kol'oam- and Utte-Véem rivers, quite often along with the red-breasted merganser. I sighted it many times on Lake Kool'ong. It was also encountered in flight along the coastal lagoons. On July 12, 1934, I saw three loons in Inchoun lagoon not far from the mouth of the Utte-Véem River. I saw a bird in flight on August 24 over a lagoon near Uélen. J. Koren, as reported, found this loon off the coast among the ice floes.

Seasonal phenomena—In 1931, L.O. Belopol'skii noticed a flight into Krest Bay on June 3. F.H. Fay and T.J. Cade observed this bird on the coast at Gambell on May 15, 1954, and May 18, 1956. The bird was seen later in the nesting areas on tundra lakes and rivers depending on when the ice cover opened up. In 1956 I noticed it on the Amguema only on June 13. V.D. Lebedev and V.R. Filin noticed the first few birds of this species in Malyi Chaun Bay on June 5 through 10, 1958.

The dimensions of the testes in males found in the nesting period are noticeably larger than of males found later (Table 3).

Table 3. Dimensions of testes in the white-billed common loon, in mm

Date	Left	Right	Locality
July 6, 1934	21×10	9×5	Utte-Véem River
July 10, 1934	24×10	18×4	—do—
August 11, 1934	20×10	22×5	Kol'oam-Véem River
September 28, 1931	9×5	9×5	Middle reaches of Anadyr River

In the ovary of females shot at Pereval'naya on June 9, 1939, the follicles were of the size of a walnut. In two females found on the Kol'oam-Véem River on August 10 and 11, 1934, it was less than 0.5 cm in diameter. On July 10, 1879, to the south of Pitlekai, A. Palander found on the bank of a lake a nest with an egg 94×55.5 mm in size, weighing 15.5 g*. According to the data of F.H. Fay, an incubating bird was frightened from its nest on June 18, 1953, on St. Lawrence Island. The nest was located on a tiny depressed island in the Kuzata lagoon. It contained two eggs with highly developed embryos.

On July 4, 1970, N.I. Makurin found a nest in the Amguema delta on a large island with dry sandy soil. It was located on the lake bank surrounded by a moss-sedge cover. Two adult birds floated on the lake. There was only one egg in the nest.

I found a brood with a chick on August 23, 1934. The chick was of the size of a large duck. From a distance, its color appeared light gray and its bright beak shone in the sun. The adult brids evidently carried the chick down the river toward the lagoon. At least, I and others found a brood in the lower course of the Kol'oam River; it was not, however, seen there when we walked up the course of the river. On our approach the adult birds floating at a distance from the chick flew toward us. Later one of them, uttering shrieks, started circling above the chick, then began to dive repeatedly. It succeeded in hiding in the shallow melt-water. They could not continue their vigil because of a strong wind. The adult birds were very wary and ultimately flew away.

At the feeding time of chicks the birds made a daily flight from the nesting to the feeding area. From July 6 through August 21, 1934, I regularly saw loons flying over the Utte-Véem and Kol'oam rivers, often with loud screeching. They sometimes gathered on the pools and rapids in small numbers. On the evening of July 12 I found a flock of three white-billed common loons on the pebbly shore of the Inchoun lagoon. These flocks were no doubt attracted by the availability of food. I

*An error in the original. Should read 155 g—General Editor.

did not notice such flocking of birds before migration. On September 20, 1921, at Wainwright in north Alaska, A.M. Bailey (1925) disturbed a flock of 30 birds. Such a congregation was perhaps unusual since it is not common for any of the species of loons.

In 1934, I observed for the last time a lone bird in a lagoon near Uélen on August 24, but it was still not time for migration. On St. Lawrence Island Collins found a female in fresh winter plumage on October 14, 1930.

Habits—In places where white billed common loons are common they are encountered quite frequently. For all their bulk they are no less mobile than the Arctic loons. I often saw them flying over a river singly or in pairs at a height of three or four rifle shots. They rise from the water without much effort and dive with the same agility as the much smaller loons. They apparently remain under water much longer. Since they are hardy birds, it is difficult to bring them down with small shot. P.T. Butenko shot some of them with a Winchester.

They are noisy, only slightly less so than the Arctic loons. Their voice is considerably louder and somewhat ominous. It is a vibrant howl which may be represented by the syllables "khu-khu-khu-khu-khu- . . ." five or six times in a row, something like a cackle, but most like the hooting of a *Strix* owl.

Weight—A male collected from the Utte-Véem River on July 6, 1934, weighed 5.3. kg and a female from Uél'kal' 4.993 kg.

Food—On July 6, 1934, the stomach of a bird contained vertebrae of small fish, fibers and grass stalks, and nine round pebbles. The stomach of a male obtained on July 10 was almost empty with three bits of grass stalks and two pebbles of 2 cm each in diameter. The stomach of a bird found by O. Nordquist contained fish bones and small pebbles. E.I. Miller found plant remains and V.E. Yakobi found 300 g of fish 14 to 16 cm in length.

Systematics of the subspecies—The Chukchi specimens, like those from Anadyr, are indistinguishable from the American on the one hand, and from Taimir and Novaya Zemlya specimens on the other. I had occasion to examine in all 33 specimens personally. It is unusually similar to *Gavia immer immer* Brünn. Judging from the nearly identical body proportions and the color pattern of the plumage, both these loons probably formed the links in the same geographic series some time ago. The regions of distribution somewhat overlap. The white-billed common loon is essentially an arctic subspecies while the polar loon is a boreal subspecies. The absence of smooth transitions provides taxonomic grounds for regarding them even as independent species.

Specimens—1) Bering Sea, without date, juv., Voznesenskii; 2) lower course of Utte-Véem River, July 6, 1934, ♂, Portenko; 3) same zone, July 10, 1934, ♂, Portenko; 4) lower course of Kol'oam-Véem River, August 10, 1934, ♀, Portenko; 5 and 6) same zone, August 11, 1934, ♂, ♀, Portenko; and 7) Cape Schmidt, 1933 spring, ○, Portenko.

Gavia immer immer (Brünnich)—Polar Loon

Not found in the Chukchi peninsula or Wrangel Island. Found once on St. Lawrence Island on July 11, 1931, between Savunga and Naskak (Fay and Cade 1959).

Order PODICIPEDIFORMES—GREBES

Podiceps griseigena holböllii Reinh.—**Red-necked Grebe**

The collection of A.A. Savich (Artobolevskii 1927) from Cape Schmidt and the Kolyma delta included a specimen of the eastern subspecies of red-necked grebe without label. It has not been possible to determine the time or place of origin. There is still no reliable information on nesting in the Chukchi peninsula and evidently this bird is not found north of the Anadyr basin.

On St. Lawrence Island, according to A.M. Bailey (1956), on October 3, 1958, a male bird was caught; according to F.H. Fay and T.J. Cade (1959), a female was found near Gambell on June 15, 1954.

Order II. PROCELLARIIFORMES—TUBE-NOSED BIRDS

5. **Diomedea albatrus** Pall.—**Short-tailed Albatross**

Distribution and status—Encountered very rarely in the Bering Sea along the Chukchi coast in summer; found even more rarely in the Chukchi Sea.

On August 10, 1880, a lone albatross was seen by the American expedition to the northern part of the Pacific Ocean led by Capt. J. Rodgers, roughly 40 miles to the west of the entrance to Providence Bay. Since T.H. Bean (1883, p. 170) called it albatross *Diomedea brachyura* Temm., the bird was evidently young. Under the same name E.W. Nelson (1883, p. 111) reported some finds of albatrosses toward the end of the summer of 1881. Older specimens were noticed between St. Lawrence Island and Providence Bay. L.M. Turner (1886) saw an albatross in the sea off St. Lawrence Island. In the words of E.W. Nelson, the ruins of old eskimo villages in this island revealed the mandibles of two albatrosses. H.B. Collins found the upper mandible around Gambell in ruins which were at least 1,000 years old. In the kitchen middens studied by H. Friedmann (1932a and 1934a), he found a large amount of bones of different antiquities, probably older than 2,500 years, right up to recent times. O.J. Murie (1936) witnessed the find of six mandibles among the bones excavated in village Kukuliak. Eskimos narrated that the older of them remembered the fall arrival of both white albatrosses and dark-colored birds, i.e. immature ones. Evidently they were once found in large numbers.

When E.W. Nelson was traveling past the Diomede Islands in July, 1881, a young bird was seen flying back and forth over the stormy sea. On September 4, 1939, M.M Sleptsov (1959) sighted eight albatrosses in the region of Cape Serdtse-Kamen'.

Food—The stomachs of the two specimens obtained by M.M. Sleptsov contained bits of walrus meat and fat as also *Boreogadus saida*.

Economic importance—According to the eskimos albatrosses used to be caught by hand on the shore ice around St. Lawrence Island. Often it was very simple because the birds were very fat and took off with difficulty. Their beaks with the adjoining portion of the skull were used to scoop out water from the tiny leather canoes.

6. **Fulmarus glacialis rodgersi** Cassin—**Northern Fulmar**

Local name—Chukchian: Kaiyakatlu or kaiyakutlu, also kakal'yu. In Eskimo: ăkh-qō'-thluk on St. Lawrence Island.

Distribution and status—In the Chukchi peninsula, evidently nests at different points along the coastline, although a nesting colony authentic beyond doubt was found only in Providence Bay. Occurs sporadically, being common at some places and altogether absent from others. Encountered in the adjoining parts of the Bering and Chukchi seas, outside the nesting zones, also sporadically. On Wrangel and Herald islands nesting not recorded, but was encountered at sea to the south of these islands.

On September 2, 1932, I sighted fulmars in the sea southwest of Krest Bay in large numbers at some places. L.O. Belopol'skii (1934) saw fulmars several times during the summer of 1931 in the open sea off Meechken Island up to 20 km from the coast. On August 21, 1932, I saw these birds swimming in the coastal waters near Preobrazheniya Gulf. Around Providence Bay the fulmar was quite common. It was reported by several workers though it cannot be concluded from this that fulmars could be found at any time. Based on his 1881 observations, E.W. Nelson (1883) reported that this bird was found in great abundance on the west coast of the Bering Sea, in particular around Providence Bay and to the north in the Bering Strait. On some days fulmars were seen in large numbers while on others not a single bird was sighted in the same locale. According to the observations of W.S. Brooks (1915) this species was numerous in June 1913, at the entrance to Providence Bay. On August 25, 26, and 28, 1932, I sighted fulmars in small numbers in a bay to the south of Plover and in the evening found the birds flying over the rocky coast close to Cape Ivga. This provided some grounds for concluding that the birds nested there. On September 10, 1934, at the entrance to Providence Bay, I sighted large flocks of floating Pacific fulmars. During my visit to the bay from July 11 through 14, 1938, I found two males with a large brood patch, which conclusively proved that they were breeding. Finally, in the same year (1938), P.T. Butenko found a nesting colony of fulmar petrels at Cape Stoletiya to the west of the entrance to Providence Bay. There were at least several dozen pairs of birds in the colony. During May, 1938 Butenko quite often encountered fulmars on the coast from Cape Stoletiya to Sireniki village. A resident of St. Lawrence Island told O.J. Murie (1936) that fulmars built nests by the thousands close to Cape Chaplin. Copley Amory, Jr. (Riley 1918) caught two males on August 8, 1914, in the sea around Cape Chaplin, but Butenko did not find them in such large numbers.

In 1879, the members of the *Vega* expedition (Palmén 1887) saw fulmars on their way from St. Lawrence to Bering Island. In the summer of 1881 E.W. Nelson found great numbers of them around St. Lawrence Island. According to O.J. Murie, a dead male bird was found on the shore at Kukuliak village on August 9, 1935, during a northwesterly storm. According to F.H. Fay and T.J. Cade (1959), fulmars were particularly numerous among the ice floes off St. Lawrence Island in early spring. They were found in small numbers in the coastal waters between Gambell and Savunga at the end of June, 1950, and at the end of July, 1953. A lone bird was noticed in Boxer Bay at the end of August, 1957. Moreover, a male was caught at

Gambell on April 28, 1953. On June 6, 1950, E.G.F. Sauer and E.K. Urban counted 15 fulmars during an expedition all along the west coast. Fulmars did not build nests on St. Lawrence Island. H. Friedmann (1934a) found very few bones of northern fulmars in his excavations.

A.M. Sudilovskaya (1950 and 1951) told M.M. Sleptsov that single birds were found on September 11 in Senyavin Strait but that there were generally more birds in the eastern part of Bering Strait than in the western parts.

On July 27, 1879, O. Nordquist (Palmén 1887) sighted this bird in Bering Strait while crossing from Port Clarence to Nunyamo village at the entrance to Lawrence Bay. A.P. Kuzyakin encountered lone birds at sea on the way from Akkani to Uélen from June 25 through 27, 1957, and from Uélen to Lawrence Bay on July 3, 1957.

At the beginning of June, 1922, A.M. Bailey (1925) gathered specimens with brood patches in Bering Strait, evidently not far from the Diomede Islands, but the eskimos told him that fulmars did not build nests there. F.L. Jaques (1930) did not find a single fulmar around these islands from July 27 through 29, 1928. On June 23, 1934, on Bol'shoi Diomede Island, I observed different sea birds at length: cormorants, alcids and gulls wading in the surf. Apart from a single fulmar in flight I saw no more of them although the weather was then by turns calm and stormy. On July 26, 1946, I.N. Gabrielson (Kenyon and Brooks 1960) saw only two birds near Fairway cliff. But in 1953 the eskimos told J.W. Brooks that fulmars did not build nests on Malyi Diomede Island. In 1958, K.W. Kenyon did not encounter them even once around Malyi Diomede cliff. On June 3, 5 and 9 single birds were noticed, on June 10 up to 20 birds and on June 13 innumerable birds. L.G. Swartz (1967) noticed in all only three or four fulmars among a multitude of alcids near Malyi Diomede.

Fulmars were noticed by different observers near Cape Dezhnev. In the summer of 1896 A. Seale (1899) found them quite common and on August 22, 1911, J. Koren (Thayer and Bangs 1914) encountered them about 20 miles to the northwest of Cape Dezhnev but did not see fulmars throughout his expedition along the north Chukchi coast. In the summer of 1914 F.S. Hersey (1916) quite often saw them in large numbers, especially around Cape Dezhnev. In 1925, S.A. Buturlin (1936, vol. III, p. 41) saw fulmars close to Uélen and Naukan. According to the observations of F.L. Jaques, fulmars were seen in large numbers on July 30 and 31, 1928, at Cape Dezhnev. Later, toward the end of August, innumerable birds were seen north of Bering Strait and south of 68°30′ near Cape Dezhnev and in the strait itself. E. Stresemann (1949, p. 252) put a question mark against "fulmars" in the list of birds found by J. Cook's expedition in 1778 or 1779 on ice floes to the north of Bering Strait.

According to the information I have gathered, fulmars evidently built their nests on the cliffs adjacent to Cape Dezhnev but none of the local people were able to show where they were. The number of times I saw them there could easily be counted. On June 12, 1934, P.T. Butenko observed a lone fulmar flying low over the sea off Uélen in calm weather. On June 26, on the way from Diomede to Uélen, I scarcely came across any sea birds in the sunny calm weather in the strait. They began to appear near Cape Dezhnev more abundantly and included fulmars. On

June 4, between Inchoun and Mitkulen, innumerable birds of different species including a large number of fulmars were found floating in a broad undisturbed pool in the river among the ice floes. They no doubt built nests on the cliffs on the elevated north coast of the Chukchi peninsula. I noticed them right from their arrival on May 19, 1934, on a parting near the cliffs close to Seishan village. M.M. Sleptsov encountered fulmars in the first few days of September at Cape Serdtse-Kamen'. It is surprising that the *Vega* expedition observers did not find fulmars at all either around Kolyuchin Bay or in general in the Chukchi Sea. I did not find fulmars on Kolyuchi Island, which I thoroughly surveyed. There is an extremely vague reference by F.S. Hersey to the occurrence of fulmars in the more northerly Chukchi waters. He reported that some fulmars were sighted in the Arctic Ocean some 150 miles north of Cape Serdtse-Kamen'.

On his 1970 expedition A.A. Kishchinskii did not find fulmars at all on the north coast between Vankarém and the Amguema estuary.

The hazy reference by E.W. Nelson (1883, p. 112 and 1887, p. 62) led several authors of excellent repute (Hartet, Schalow, Bent, Bianki, etc.) to write that fulmars built nests on Wrangel and Herald islands. It transpires from Nelson's two works that the *Corwin* expedition in 1881 found numerous fulmars in the Chukchi Sea near the coast of the mainland and northward far from the coasts of Wrangel and Herald islands. Nelson was only inclined to assume that they nested on these islands. So far as Wrangel Island is concerned, neither A.I. Mineev nor any of the eskimo hunters living for more than 10 years on Wrangel and well acquainted with the fulmar in its native Providence Bay found this bird even once on the coast or in the coastal waters of the island. I did not find fulmars on Wrangel either and although I have only flown over Herald Island I am sure that fulmars would have some time or other arrived on Wrangel had they nested on Herald Island. Therefore it is difficult to agree with A.G. Bannikov (1941) who, according to G.A. Ushakov, affirmed that fulmars were encountered regularly in large numbers in the sea along the Wrangel coasts. According to F.L. Jaques an occasional fulmar was encountered in August, 1928, in the Arctic Ocean south of 70° but none was sighted on Herald Island. Until then, no one had found fulmars in the Arctic Ocean from Novosibirsk and the De Long islands to Wrangel.

Habitat—The nesting colony discovered by P.T. Butenko was located on the top of a cliff pointing out to sea at Cape Stoletiya. From the water young birds resting on the ledges could not be seen. In general, the colony of fulmars gave the impression of a colony of kittiwakes but was not as dense.

The nesting areas I have suggested near Cape Dezhnev and at Seishan entirely correspond to the prevailing concepts. It is a high, precipitous, rocky coast, at places rising to tens of meters like a wall overhanging the sea. In such structures were found the nests of other species of sea birds such as murres, kittiwakes, etc.

The sighting of fulmars in the waters along the coasts entirely relates to their foraging. At the end of August, 1932, I noticed them in the southern parts of Providence Bay protected from the sea by a broad spit. Innumerable sea birds, mainly murres and black-legged kittiwakes, were found feeding in a huge undisturbed pool. Sometimes among these flocks of birds the bill, and then the feet of a falcated teal would suddenly appear from the water. I noticed a similar pattern in the coastal waters west of Inchoun on July 4, 1934, where the mixing of a stream of fresh water flowing from a lagoon to the sea with a stream of melt-water was the source of a dense mass of tiny marine organisms which served as food for fulmars, gray phalaropes, black-legged kittiwakes and many auklets.

According to P.T. Butenko, fulmars regularly collected around canoes and whaleboats when the hunters threw overboard carcasses of walrus.

L.O. Belopol'skii sighted fulmars among the ice floes near Meechken and in water free of ice. In my view the fulmars in any case prefer the open expanses of the sea, although they do not avoid the ice. According to the observations of F.L. Jaques, in the Arctic Ocean fulmars were very numerous on the edge of the ice and especially in areas where there were strong currents. On Malyi Diomede Island K.W. Kenyon observed fulmars in the leads among ice floes in the water opening up along the coast.

Arrival—Fulmars evidently arrived on the Chukchi coasts very early, in mid-May. In the spring of 1934, riding a dog sled along the north coast, I found a broad passage under high, rocky, precipitous cliffs near Seishan. At dawn on May 19 many cormorants, glaucous gulls and alcids and some fulmars were seen above the waves. At about the same time of the year P.T. Butenko sighted the first fulmars in the spring of 1938 in Providence Bay: two specimens were collected at Cape Stoletiya on May 18. K.W. Kenyon noticed the first fulmar on May 29, 1958, on Malyi Diomede Island.

Breeding—Nothing is known about the breeding of fulmars in the Chukchi peninsula. The testes of arriving males were only 1.5 times longer than in July birds, i.e. after the mating season (Tables 4 and 5).

The males that I collected in Providence Bay on July 13, 1938, showed big brood patches as in the females shot on May 30, 1938. At the end of May the testes began shrinking. Judging from all the known factors, fulmars begin to breed at the end of May on the south coast of the Chukchi peninsula.

In all the birds listed in the Table the subcutaneous adipose layers were significant but the males with brood patches that I shot in the waters in Providence Bay were very emaciated. One of them was sick and, reached by boat, was easily picked up by hand.

Table 4. Testes sizes (mm) and body weight (g) of fulmars

Date	Testes		Locality	Body weight
	Left	Right		
May 18, 1938	16×8	15×7	Cape Stoletiya	710
May 26, 1938	10×5	9×4	Sireniki village	835
May 26, 1938	11×5	9×5	—do—	795
May 30, 1938	13×6	12×6	Cape Stoletiya	680
May 30, 1938	13×6	12×6	—do—	660
May 30, 1938	10×5	9×5	—do—	780
May 30, 1938	10×5	9×5	—do—	680
July 5, 1934	11×5	8×4	Inchoun village	—
July 5, 1934	9×6	7×5	—do—	—
July 5, 1934	8×5	4×3	—do—	—

Table 5. Size of ovary (mm) and body weight (g) of fulmars

Date	Ovary length	Diameter of largest follicle	Locality	Body weight
May 18, 1938	12	5	Cape Stoletiya	645
May 26, 1938	15	—	Sireniki village	600
May 30, 1938	Granular ovary		Cape Stoletiya	650
May 30, 1938	—	—	—do—	570

According to P.T. Butenko, in the second half of the summer of 1938 he chanced to see a nestling hanging under the rocks of Cape Stoletiya and falling into the water quite accidentally.

Migration—E.W. Nelson (1887, p. 63) observed young dark-colored birds of this species to the northwest of Bering Strait at the end of August, 1881. J. Koren saw many fulmars roughly 20 miles to the northwest of Cape Dezhnev on August 22, 1911. I did not sight these birds at those places so late but I have no doubt that the fulmars deserted the Chukchi Sea at the end of August. I found them much later on the south coast of the Chukchi peninsula. In 1932, I noted a small number of fulmars at the end of August in Providence Bay and on September 2 to the southwest of Krest Bay. On September 10, 1934, as our ship was leaving Providence Bay, a large floating flock was seen. From September 11 through 17, 1939, I did not see any fulmars in Providence Bay. But these birds are not known to occur day after day in the same spot and hence it would be premature to conclude anything as to their migration. In the fall of 1937 P.T. Butenko was recording observations on sea birds from a ship which passed Anadyr Bay on October 14 and anchored in Krest Bay. Here they stayed until October 27, moving on to Providence Bay on the 29th. Neither in Krest Bay nor in Providence Bay, throughout the fall and beginning of winter, did he sight a Pacific fulmar. Nelson (1887, p. 63) unequivocally reported the sighting of fulmars during September 1881, around Bering Strait. Based on these data, I feel that fulmars desert the south coast of the Chukchi peninsula in September.

Flight of fulmars—Their flight over the waves somewhat resembles the leisurely flight of the peregrin falcon. Observing fulmars for the first time, I noticed how different their flight was, though superficially resembling that of gulls. They spread their wings but do not beat them much, often turning the body and the plane of the wings to one side or the other, so that they seem to be sliding parallel to the surface contour of the waves. When the sea is very rough their flight is an endless repetition of the same combination of movements, which appear very stereotyped upon prolonged observation. Sliding along the trough between huge wave crests, they enjoy their own speciality, watching the water "valleys" one after another in the same way as a marsh harrier regularly checks a chain of oxbows in the catchment area of a large river. From a smooth surface fulmars can take off without any perceptible effort. Among the Russian sea birds, fulmars stand out distinctly for their characteristic flight style.

Food—The gullets of birds caught on July 5, 1934, near Inchoun were tightly packed with food. Examination of two of them revealed the following composition: (1) leg of a beetle, heads of insect larvae, bits of insect pupae, about a thousand very small crustaceae, three large sabre-like jaws, three beak-like horny bodies (*Polychaeta*?), a few dozen thread-like worms (parasites) and green shoots of plants, especially of moss, two feet of a large crustacea, about 1,500 very small crustaceae and beak-like horny bodies.

M.M. Sleptsov (1959) found *Boreogadus saida* in the food of fulmars in the northern part of the Bering and southern part of the Chukchi Sea. According to E.W. Nelson, fulmars look for animal food floating on the water, especially fat near rotting cetaceans, which sometimes spreads for miles. P.T. Butenko told me that when walrus were being dressed by hunters fulmars jostled them, splashing in the blood and snatching bits of meat and fat. O.W. Geist (Murie 1936) reported a similar phenomenon. The fulmars lost their reserve and could be caught by hand.

Weight—The body weights given in Tables 4 and 5 show that the females are much smaller than the males.

Economic importance—I am not aware whether anyone has hunted fulmars or collected their eggs in Chukchi. E.W. Nelson reported that the inhabitants of Pribylovye islands relished the eggs for their taste and collected them by lowering themselves down cliffs with ropes. According to O.J. Murie the eskimos on St. Lawrence Island rarely used fulmar for food and regarded it as taboo. This tradition is evidently born of the fact that fulmars gathered in large numbers around seal and walrus processing units in the spring.

Systematics of the subspecies—Lack of fulmar skins gathered in the nesting area precludes an accurate identification of the subspecies in the northern part of the Pacific Ocean. The problem is complicated by the fact that fulmars are found in two different shades: bright and dark. In parts of the sea adjoining the Chukchi coast most of them are of bright color. The dark-colored birds are rare. In 1881, E.W. Nelson recorded two instances of dark-colored fulmars to the north of Bering Strait. F.S. Hersey found fulmars in the Bering and Chukchi Sea with an intense homogeneous gray coloration of the mantle as in the dark-colored subspecies *F. g. glupischa* Stejneger which he recognized. He saw them only from the ship. All the specimens listed below belong to the bright-colored variety. Dark-colored ones were rarely spotted among many bright birds in Providence Bay at the end of August, 1932, and on September 10, 1934. F.H. Fay and T.J. Cade noticed only three birds of dark color among over 1,000 seen at Gambell.

Most observers saw the bright-colored fulmars in the northern part of the Bering Sea. Brooks saw *F. g. glupischa* on May 6, 1913, on Mednyi Island and at the end of May on the way from Kamchatka to St. Lawrence Island around 58° north. At the same time *F. g. rodgersi* was common at 174° east and 58° north and in Providence Bay in June. Moreover, three males were caught on April 3, May 3 and July 27 on Mednyi Island. Two males from Cape Chaplin were identified by J.H. Riley as *F. g. rodgersi* though their backs were very dark, darker than even the bright varieties of *F. g. glupischa*. But they were larger in size. S.A. Buturlin (1936) saw bright-colored Pacific fulmars around Nạukan and Uélen.

I noticed many fulmars in the Bering Sea and Pacific Ocean and on six occasions while crossing the Kuril Range. I had a distinct impression that Kuril fulmars were dark-colored on the whole while the north Bering Sea birds were bright-colored. This difference was noticed even by travelers in the 18th century. Even P.S. Pallas knew that Kamchatka fulmars were dark-colored and differed slightly from the gray northern birds (Pallas 1769b, p. 28). It is necessary to ascertain whether there are two subspecies: *F.g. rodgersi* and *F.g. glupischa*, or only one, *F. g. rodgersi*, with dark and bright variations, on the basis of data on a good number of birds. There could also be a geographic localization factor in this phenomenon.

Specimens— 1 to 3) coastal waters to northwest of Inchoun village, July 5, 1934, ♂♂, Portenko; 4 and 5) Providence Bay, Cape Stoletiya, May 18, 1938, ♂♀, Butenko; 6 to 8) Sireniki village, May 26, 1938, ♂♂♀, Butenko; 9 to 14) Cape Stoletiya, May 30, 1938, ♂♂♂♂ and ♀♀, Butenko; and 15 to 16) coastal waters beyond Providence Bay, July 13, 1938, ♂♂, Portenko.

7. **Puffinus tenuirostris** (Temm.)—**Slender-billed Shearwater**

Local name—In Eskimo: Kapútagak in Providence Bay and on St. Lawrence Island.

Distribution and Status—Arrives from the southern hemisphere for wintering and reaches the coasts of the Chukchi peninsula and Wrangel Island in July and August. It is probably encountered every year but not in the same numbers. It is found sporadically, singly and in small flocks, but also in concentrations of thousands of birds.

On August 21, 1932, I observed the slender-billed shearwater in small numbers in the coastal waters in Preobrazheniya Gulf. A specimen recorded by I.N. Akif'ev on July 10, 1900, in Providence Bay has long been known. On August 26, 1932, I saw stray birds at the entrance to the bay, but on my last visit I did not find even one. American ornithologists did not find any there either. During the latter half of summer, 1938, P.T. Butenko saw the shearwater in Providence Bay but just once or twice. This bird is well known to the eskimos in Providence Bay, where they have their own name for it.

In the words of O.J. Murie (1936), specimens were found on St. Lawrence Island, especially around Kukuliak village: a ♀ on August 29, 1933, and a ♂ found dead in the water on August 13, 1934. According to a report by F.H. Fay and T.J. Cade (1959), O.W. Geist collected nine specimens on August 28 and October 5, 1932. I.N. Gabrielson saw lone birds 10 miles north of Gambell on August 2, 1946, and a dozen on the eastern tip of the island on August 6. At the end of August, 1956 and 1957, thousands of them were observed for two or three days flying along the south and west coasts in a northerly direction. In unusually calm weather on September 1, 1957, most of the resting birds were found scattered on the quiet surface of the sea around Gambell. Five dead shearwaters were found in August, 1957, near the Kuzata lagoon. A.M. Bailey (1956) reported a shearwater seen on June 12, 1951. E.G.F. Sauer and E.K. Urban (1964) saw 10 shearwaters off the south coast at Gambell on August 22, 1960. Among the bones collected from the ancient eskimo colonies near Gambell, H. Friedmann (1934a) found a coracoid of this species.

According to F.L. Jaques' observations (1930), in 1928 shearwaters were abundant in Bering Strait, on the traverse of the Diomede Islands on July 27 and at Cape Dezhnev on July 31. In the second case, Jaques thought he saw *P. griseus* (Gm.), but without specimens to show his assumption remains unsubstantiated. At the end of August, 1881, E.W. Nelson (1887, p. 63) saw numerous dark-colored birds northwest of Bering Strait. These may have included *P. tenuirostris* (Temm.), since in size and external appearance they differed from the dark-colored fulmar petrels which were found along with the shearwaters. L. Stejneger (1884, p. 234) believes that Nelson did not see the shearwater but a dark-colored *Fulmarus glacialis glupischa*. This view was supported by V.L. Bianki (1913, p. 683, etc.). Though Nelson's identification of birds was far from irreproachable I find no reason to doubt it in the case of shearwaters, especially after my own 1939 observations.

On September 7, 1939, I saw a large flock of slender-billed shearwaters in the coastal waters at Cape Serdtse-Kamen'. They often rose from the water and performed a continuous circular movement in the form of a large circle up to 2 km in diameter. Though it was difficult to reckon the exact number of birds there were definitely thousands of them. A week before, at 6.00 a.m. on August 31, I noticed a similar mass of shearwaters even farther to the west of Two Pilots spit. At a distance of not more than 2 km from the coast and parallel to it, the shearwaters flew in a continuous row for over an hour. This was an altogether rare sight. This bird mass numbering very many thousands had the form of a very narrow, very long strip extending from the east to the west, with not more than 15 to 20 birds abreast. Lengthwise, neither the beginning nor the end could be sighted. It is quite clear that such flocks could fly even beyond the far western parts of the Chukchi Sea.

In 1970, A.A. Kishchinskii found old bird skeletons on the sea coast between the Amguema and Vankarém, one of which he took for his collection.

In 1939 slender-billed shearwaters reached Wrangel Island, where I was given two specimens. These were lone birds shot in Rodgers Bay on July 10 and 19. In August, 1928, F.L. Jaques found two shearwaters east of Herald Island around 70 and 71°. These birds were very numerous between 69°30′ and Bering Strait on August 23, 24, 25 and 30 and September 1, 2 and 4.

L.G. Swartz (1967) wrote that shearwaters numbering 500 to 1,000 were once sighted near Cape Tompson but they were never encountered in such large numbers as in the south Bering Sea.

W.H. Dall saw a specimen in Kotsebue Bay (Nelson 1887, p. 63). This was long regarded as the northernmost sighting. Shearwaters were also recorded by J. Cook's expedition (Stresemann 1949, p. 251) on the ice floes between Asia and America, possibly in 1779, to the north of Bering Strait.

Recently slender-billed shearwaters were identified in parts of the Arctic Ocean adjoining Alaska. In the words of A.M. Bailey (1933, p. 18), this bird was encountered there irregularly but at times in numbers. From September through October, 1929, shearwaters were encountered in thousands near Cape Barrow though only a few stray birds that settled on the melting ice were actually caught. R.W. Hendee found a dead bird on the Wainwright coast on September 4, 1921. Two specimens were found dead on September 13 and 19, 1929, at a distance of 30 to 35 miles from the coast. The birds no doubt mistook the flat snow-covered plain of the tundra for the surface of sea ice and crashed. Three very emaciated males were taken from the ice floe on September 9 and December 10, 1929 (Bailey 1931, p. 78).

The specimens that I collected were juveniles. The ovaries of females caught on Wrangel Island were 4 to 5 cm long and as yet revealed no granular structure to the naked eye. The testes of males were very small: left 2 × 3 and right 1 × 2 mm. The birds were not yet completely covered with subcutaneous fat; in fact only traces of thin layers were seen in the females.

The winter penetration of innumerable flocks of young and juvenile shearwaters up to the Arctic coasts of the Chukchi peninsula and Alaska is a very interesting phenomenon.

Habitat—In the Kuril Islands I noticed shearwaters only in stormy weather. They flew along the troughs between the wave crests, in general like fulmars. On the Chukchi coast I saw shearwaters only in calm weather. On the evening of August 21, 1932, on the smooth surface of the coastal waters before the entrance to Preobrazheniya Gulf, they swam in the company of fulmars and alcids. On September 7, 1939, in mild weather with changeable cloud cover, huge flocks of shearwaters swam on the glassy coastal water near Cape Serdtse-Kamen'. Some cetaceans dived among them now and then. On August 31, 1931, on Two Pilots spit, innu-

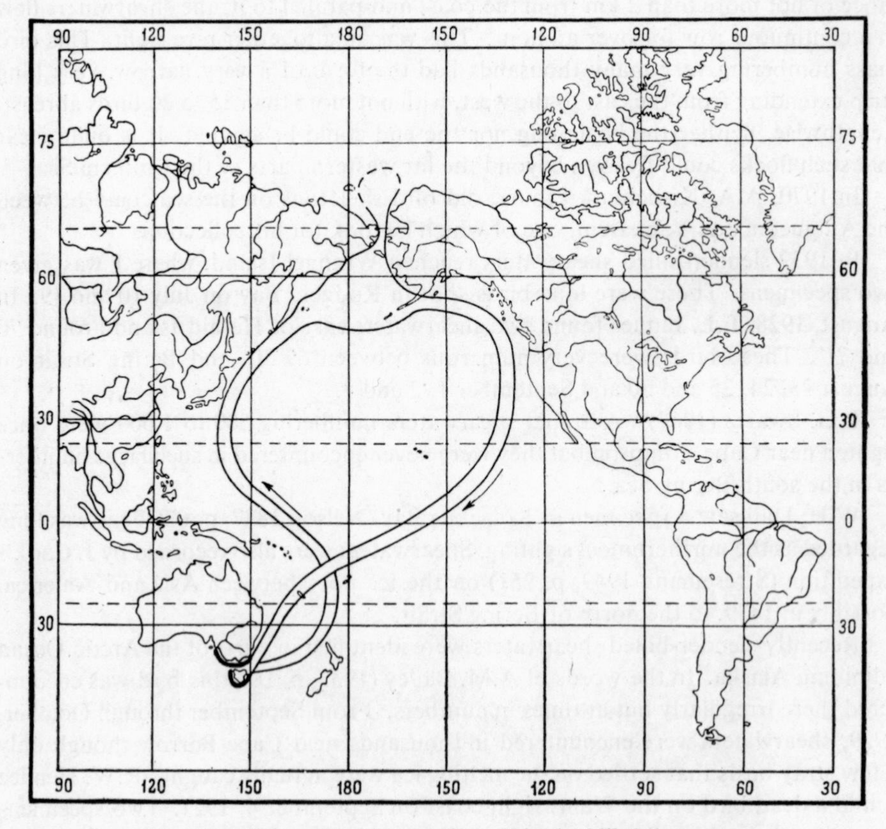

Fig. 19. Flight path and migration of slender-billed shearwater (after Serventy 1953 with changes for Bering and Chukchi seas).

merable shearwaters flew over the coastal waters covered with light ripples at about the height of a ship's deck. At times they were hidden by light banks of mist. But P.T. Butenko reported that he saw shearwaters in Providence Bay only under very turbulent conditions.

The occurrence of the shearwater in an area depends on the availability of food and its accessibility. This in turn is controlled by the weather, the turbulence of the sea and the conditions of the ice floes. So far as its occurrence on the coast is concerned, I made only one observation. On the evening of August 26, 1932, a shearwater flew close to the rocky coast with alluvial formations at the entrance to Providence Bay where auklets and white-bellied birds nested. Even after it got dark the bird did not rest. I have seen shearwaters resting only on the water.

Arrival—In the northernmost sections of the migratory route shearwaters may be seen quite late and generally irregularly. In Anadyr Bay this bird was caught in the middle of June. No information is available for Providence Bay for any dates earlier than July 10, 1900. But here the shearwaters could be seen much earlier. In 1954 the first bird was sighted as early as May 13 on St. Lawrence Island; the next-earliest date is June 12, 1951. In 1939 the shearwater was noticed on Wrangel Island on July 9. Between the first sighting on June 9 on Wrangel Island and the last occasion on September 7 at Cape Serdtse-Kamen' there was a lapse of nearly two months. It may therefore be assumed that on entering the Chukchi Sea the shearwaters remain there for at least two months, which explains the large populations.

Migration—The shearwaters migrate from the Chukchi Sea at the end of August and in early September. E.W. Nelson observed them at the end of August, 1881, and I sighted some on August 31 and September 7, 1939.

Life style—In the last decade the biology of this bird, which is very little known but interesting in many respects, has been elucidated to some extent. Quite a number of articles have been devoted to the subject. The following information from the works of A.J. Marshall and D.L. Serventy (Serventy 1953 and Marshall and Serventy 1956) will serve to supplement our data.

The slender-billed shearwater nests on islands adjoining the southeastern coast of Australia and around Tasmania at places in such large numbers that it is exploited by hunters. This is a pelagic bird not seen on land since it nests in burrows and moves about in the nesting area only at night. The shearwater does not reproduce before the sixth year. As a result, the population of this species consists of a predominant proportion of juveniles, young and single birds.

The female lays a single egg weighing 19 per cent of the weight of the bird and incubation takes more than 50 days. Incubation is initiated by the male, which is very emaciated by the 11th through 14th day, when this duty is taken over by the female, now recovered. Later, on restoring his adipose reserves, the male takes over from the female.

Outside the nesting period the slender-billed shearwater travels a considerable distance, circling the northern half of the Pacific Ocean (Fig. 19) and penetrating the Arctic Ocean up to the latitude of Wrangel Island. In April it was found on the Commander Island and, depending on the floe conditions, it is quite common in July on the Chukchi coast. In September most of them leave to return to Australia.

The innumerable records of dead birds reveal an interesting phenomenon. I found dead birds in large numbers on the Koryat coast. This aspect has been specially discussed in the ornithological literature. To my mind the main reason for mortality, which is sometimes high, is starvation. This is a factor common to large populations of stenophages under conditions of scarcity or inaccessibility of food.

The massive congregation of slender-billed shearwater is not a regular phenomenon. These birds are mostly encountered singly and forage separately, forming large flocks only when there is a superabundance of plankton, which serves as food.

The survival of the slender-billed shearwater in Russian waters is one of the mysteries of the bird world and calls for special research. Suffice it to say that in the fauna of the USSR this is a unique bird which regularly "winters" in the USSR in large numbers in the summer.

Habits—It is very easy to distinguish a shearwater in flight from fulmars, gulls and Jaegers. The shearwater is quick and nimble of movement, agile in turning, effortlessly soars, and has a characteristic mode of flight somewhat resembling that of a bat. This is facilitated by the short tail, the wing design and the head drawn close to the body, as a result of which the neck appears short.

Food—When a ship moored alongside Two Pilots spit on August 31, 1939, many birds gathered around it attracted by the rubbish floating on the water. Glaucous gulls and herring gulls were found among the Jaegers; some stray shearwaters were also seen. Half a kilometer away there was a huge flock of shearwaters which did not notice the ship. Some members of the flock caught something or other on the water now and then before they continued their flight. The last group of birds at the end of the formation rested on the water longer.

Later, near Cape Serdtse-Kamen', I saw a multitude of shearwaters scattered on the smooth surface of a completely quiet sea. Whales sometimes plunged among them. Quite naturally the birds were attracted by the abundance of plankton there.

In the stomach of a shearwater collected on Wrangel Island 22 specimens of amphipods and molluscs (*Astarte* sp.?) were found and, strangely, the stomach of an unknown bird of moderate size containing pebbles and fish bones. Perhaps the shearwater swallowed a meaty bird carcass discarded by my assistant in Rodgers Bay.

Economic importance—In spite of the fact that shearwaters are sometimes encountered in the north in massive numbers they are not eaten by the local people. There is not much meat on this bird and the fat is scanty. In the words of O.J. Murie, the eskimos on St. Lawrence Island rarely ate this bird and regarded it as taboo. So far as the destruction of plankton by shearwaters is concerned, we are not yet in a position to estimate how much is there.

Specimens— 1) Providence Bay, July 10, 1900, ○, Akif'ev; 2) Rodgers Bay, July 10, 1939, ♀, Portenko; and 3) same place, July 19, 1939, ♂, Portenko.

8. **Oceanodroma furcata furcata** (Gm.)—**Fork-tailed Petrel**

Distribution and Status—Flies in small numbers to the Chukchi peninsula coast during fall migrations. Not found in the USSR north of Bering Strait.

In Providence Bay this petrel is not particularly rare. In the fall of 1938, P.T. Butenko saw it there several times. During the *Corwin* expedition in 1881 these birds were noticed several times in Providence Bay, near St. Lawrence Island and in Bering Strait. Moreover, according to E.W. Nelson (1887), they reached the Arctic Circle since some individuals were recorded in Kotsebue Bay.

O.W. Geist (1939) collected a petrel on September 2, 1932, northwest of the cape on St. Lawrence Island during a violent snowstorm. A large flock flew into the rigging of the ship anchored off the coast and one bird was killed. This was the only petrel Geist managed to collect in nine seasons. They were quite rare on the coasts.

T. Pennant (1785, p. 535) recorded collecting a petrel on an ice floe between Asia and America. According to Stresemann (1949, p. 251) this could have been on July 13, 1779, when Cook's expedition saw some petrels, shearwaters and arctic gulls. This petrel is unknown on the east and north coasts of the Chukchi peninsula or on Wrangel Island.

Habitat—The petrel is confined to areas of the open sea adjacent to the coast but flies into closed bays like Providence Bay. It has been collected in the Anadyr lagoon. E.W. Nelson gave instances of its flying as far as the lower course of the Yukon and Tanan Rivers in Alaska, 75 miles from the estuary. According to P.T. Butenko, petrels were seen in Providence Bay only in stormy weather, probably sheltering from the rough water in the open sea.

Seasonal phenomena—Petrels do not nest on the Chukchi coast and are seen only in the post-nesting period in the northern part of the Bering Sea. E.W. Nelson regarded them as frequent fall visitors all over the Bering Sea; for example, in St. Michael he usually collected a few specimens in October. September 10, 1906, is the date of occurrence around Novomariinsk, which should be regarded as a rare instance of fall wandering of birds and not as an uncommon flight.

Order III. PELECANIFORMES—PADDLE FEET (Totipalmates)

9. **Phalacrocorax pelagicus aeolus** Swinh.—**Pelagic Cormorant**

Local name—Chukchian: Yurgvyn, more rarely yurvýn and iúrkhvyn; ijurgui in tne records of the *Vega* expedition. In Eskimo: nytl'kak in Providence Bay and nĭthl'-qŏk on St. Lawrence Island.

Distribution and Status—Numerous on the coast of the Chukchi peninsula, nesting mostly in colonies. Encountered only occasionally to the west of Cape Schmidt. Nests also on Wrangel and Herald islands but in much smaller numbers. Migrates in the winter.

L.O. Belopol'skii (1934) found innumerable colonies on the hanging cliffs on the coast between the Anadyr lagoon and Krest Bay on August 21 and 22, 1931. Flocks and single birds were noticed several times around Meechken Island in June and July. On the island itself, which is in the form of a depressed spit, cormorants cannot build nests. Later, in the fall, on October 14 and 24, 1937, P.T. Butenko saw cormorants at the entrance to Krest Bay.

Beginning there, cormorants built nests almost everywhere on the coast wherever suitable sites are available. On May 18, 1931, L.O. Belopol'skii found a large colony in Vtoroi Red'kin Bay. In Providence Bay several workers saw this species. According to E.W. Nelson (1883 and 1887), in June and July, 1881, pelagic cormorants [*Phalacrocorax violaceus* (Gm.)] were numerous there as on other section of the coast. In June, 1913, W.S. Brooks (1915) found them very common while entering the bay, and Copley Amory Jr. (Riley 1918) reported them very common in Émma Bay in 1914. In the same years (1913 and 1914), L.M. Starokadomskii and É.E. Arngol'd collected cormorants there. In 1921, A.M. Bailey (1925) during his stay in Providence Bay saw cormorants daily and in large numbers. On September 19, 1929, P.V. Ushakov collected a young bird there. According to I.O. Olenev, who wintered in the bay in 1930 and 1931, cormorants nested at places in very large colonies of several hundred birds. Sometimes the colonies did not include other sea birds. I found cormorants on each visit to Providence Bay. The colony I saw (August 25 through 28, 1932) to the east of the entrance to the bay was in the form of scattered groups and stray nests. On these rocks various alcids and gulls also built their nests. On July 13, 1938, I again visited this section of the coast and remained on the lookout it for almost up to Sireniki village. Cormorants built nests there at some places, especially among massive rocks jutting out from the sea. In 1932, on the east coast of Providence Bay near the entrance to Émma Bay, i.e. Slavyanka, I saw a lone nest of the cormorant and noticed such isolated nests at several places in 1938 between Émma and Plover. On July 12, 1938, I took a motorboat along the southwest shore of Providence Bay and encountered several relatively small colonies. In Émma Bay cormorants did not build nests but often came there for feeding. I observed them there in large numbers on August 11, 1932, and September 7, 1934, and some lone birds in July, 1938, and on September 11, 1939. According to P.T. Butenko, cormorants nested in very large numbers on the northeast shore of Providence Bay to the west of the entrance to Émma Bay. He also found a colony at Cape Stoletiya. On July 16, 1957, A.P. Kuzyakin skinned two birds at Providence Bay.

On the lowlands of Cape Chaplin cormorants did not build nests but came down to the shore for food, especially on arrival. In the spring of 1938 Butenko found them there in large numbers.

The pelagic cormorant is very common and abundant on St. Lawrence Island. E.W. Nelson mistook this species for the red-faced cormorant. He named it the most common representative of this genus inhabiting the islands in the Bering Sea. At the same time, Nelson (1887, p. 66) wrote that *P. urile* (Gmel.) was fairly common in the summer on Mathew and St. Lawrence islands and also on the cliffs on both shores of Bering Strait and on the islands in the strait. On the whole the red-faced cormorant does not penetrate the northern parts of the Bering Sea.

W.S. Brooks received information on the nesting of pelagic cormorants on St. Lawrence Island in June, 1913. A.M. Bailey found the cormorants nesting in large numbers on the rocks below Savunga village in July, 1921. H.B. Collins (Friedmann 1932a) collected four birds near Gambell in 1930. O.J. Murie (1936) had six specimens in his collection. On July 9, 1950, T.J. Cade (Fay and Cade 1959) found five nests near Boxer Bay and listed some birds collected on the southwestern tip of the island. According to the eskimos, small numbers of cormorants even wintered on

PLATE I

White-billed common loon *Gavia immer adamsii* (Gray).
Pic. by V.S. Rozhdestvenskaya.

the south coast of the island. Finally, O.W. Geist (Murie 1936) reported that most of the colonies were located on Punuk islets where the eskimos shot 300 to 400 young birds every year. Also, according to E.G.F. Sauer (Sauer and Urban 1964) these cormorants nested in large numbers on the cliffs between West Cape and Povuiliyak.

H. Friedmann (1934a) found the bones of pelagic cormorants in 17 excavations on St. Lawrence Island, in such unusual numbers that the extent of their exploitation in days gone by caused astonishment.

On the east coast of the Chukchi peninsula, too, cormorants occur in large numbers. In mid-August, 1855, W. Stimpson encountered them in large numbers in Senyavin Strait. A specimen obtained there on July 24, 1900, was brought by I.N. Akif'ev to the Zoological Museum of the Academy of Sciences. The collections of the Institute of Zoology, Academy of Sciences of the USSR, also contain five specimens from Mechigmensk Gulf collected on August 6, 1843, by I.G. Voznesenskii. In the words of É.V. Schmidt, cormorants are few in Mechigmensk Gulf but there are many of them in Lawrence Bay, which is explained by the local conditions. O.E. Kotsebue (1821, p. 149), who discovered two lofty, craggy islets in Lawrence Bay on August 22, 1816, wrote that they were inhabited only by marine birds. They were probably cormorants. They were so common there that in my 1939 diary I wrote that Lawrence Bay could not be imagined without the cormorants flying over it. I found cormorants there on August 19, 1932, August 13 and 14, 1933, and September 10, 1939. In 1957, A.P. Kuzyakin studied the neighboring colonies in detail. He found cormorants nesting on the rocky south shore of the bay, 8 km to the west of the village, and later close to Yandagai, to the north of Nunyamo, and around Poutyn. The colonies consisted for the most part of several dozen pairs and sometimes more. In the colony at Yandagai he counted up to 50 nests. In other places there were up to 150 or 200 nests. All along the coast from Lawrence Bay to Naukan the cormorant was a common species. In the sea nearby they were seen singly, in pairs and in flocks.

On August 18, 1932, I saw cormorants in the sea on my way from Dezhnev settlement to Lawrence Bay and on August 13 in the immediate vicinity of the settlement. They did not build nests around the settlement but were very numerous toward Cape Dezhnev and Uélen on the cliffs. In August, 1855, the expedition led by J. Rodgers (Cassin 1863, p. 325) obtained a specimen in Bering Strait. In J. Cassin's catalog it is listed under the name *Graculus violaceus* (Gmelin).

On June 24, 1909, J. Koren (1910) noticed a small number of cormorants on the west coast of Bol'shoi Diomede Island. On June 3, 1922, A.M. Bailey found numerous birds on both the Diomede islands; however, according to the observations of F.L. Jaques (1930), in 1928 they nested there in small numbers and were seen in large numbers only in the fall, on September 3 and 4. In 1934, I found no colonies on the cliffs of Bol'shoi Diomede Island but saw the birds when I drove around the island on June 22 and again on June 23 along the coast, floating and feeding with other sea birds. According to the observations of K.W. Kenyon (Kenyon and Brooks 1960), cormorants nested in large numbers at the southern and northern ends of Malyi Diomede Island in 1958. According to L.G. Swartz (1967) a lone cormorant was noticed 20 miles to the south of Malyi Diomede Island. This was the farthest a cormorant has been found from the coast.

On July 20, 1879, O. Nordquist (Palmén 1887) saw cormorants at Cape Dezhnev. A flock resting on an ice floe had been noticed the day before from the *Vega*. F.S. Hersey (1916) collected a specimen at Cape Dezhnev at the end of August, 1914.

On September 22, 1912, a specimen was collected in Uélen. It was given by L.M. Starokadomskii to the Zoological Museum of the Academy of Sciences. During his stay in Uélen A.M. Bailey was given a small number of cormorants. On May 20, 1927, Sheneberg shot a specimen which later entered M.A. Menzbier's collection. During the journey from Uélen to Naukan on June 20 and 21, 1934, I noticed a large number of cormorants flying along the coast. On the cliffs examined to the north of Naukan these birds nested in separate pairs and were numerically fewer than even the alcids. This was probably because of the proximity of the village. To the east of Uélen I often visited large nesting colonies which began less than a kilometer from the village, where the cliffs were high enough, and continued up to Cape Chenlyukvyn. I traveled farther along the coast only in the spring on May 25, 1934, when colonies of cormorants were encountered at different places right up to Cape Dezhnev. On August 15, 1948, V.K. Lyubin shot a cormorant near Uélen.

In the rocky sections of the north coast of the Chukchi peninsula cormorants nested in large numbers. On July 3, 1934, I found a small colony on the cliffs rising sheer from the sea east of Inchoun. Many times I saw cormorants feeding in the lagoons near Uélen and to the west of Inchoun. On May 20, 1934, riding a dog sled from Seitun village to Mitkulen, I often came across cormorants resting on high cliffs. Roughly in this area, in any case south of the Arctic Circle, J. Koren noticed a small number of cormorants on June 27, 1909.

I saw many of them at Seishan on May 19, 1934, and a colony around Néttékenishkhen village, right at Cape Serdtse-Kamen'. On September 7, 1939, I saw a flying pair there. E.W. Nelson noticed single birds in the sea there on June 29, 1881. Chukchians told the members of the *Vega* expedition that cormorants and gulls nested on the cliffs of Cape Dzhenretlen, but no specimens were collected from that place. Only on October 25, 1878, were four birds noticed resembling cormorants flying to the east of the ship. On May 31, 1879, O. Nordquist found the head of a cormorant on an ice floe near the wintering station at Pitlekai and two birds were shot there on June 1.

Early in July, 1909, J. Koren found a nesting colony on the north coast of Kolyuchi Island and gathered a small number of clutches. On September 22, 1912, he again noticed many birds there. When I was riding a dog sled on that island in 1934, Chukchians told me that cormorants nested there. During a second visit to Kolyuchi Island on July 26, 1938, I had occasion to go around studying the nesting areas of sea birds. Colonies of cormorants were situated mostly on the north coast of the island and I even came across stray nesting pairs at some places on the south coast. Numerically, among the birds inhabiting the colonies cormorants occupied third place. On the island as a whole their number totaled perhaps two to three thousand.

Farther to the west along the north coast of the Chukchi peninsula cormorants probably inhabited the rocky capes interrupted at places by the depressed coastal topography. On September 26, 1878, they were noticed by the *Vega* expedition at Cape Onman but it was not known whether they nested there. According to the information I collected during my stay in Vankarém, cormorants were very rare there. The *Vega* expedition found abundant cormorants from September 12 through 18, 1878, at Cape Schmidt. On the voyage of A.E. Nordenskjöld it was recorded that these birds inhabited the hanging precipice on the north side of Irkaipiya in such numbers that the cliff could be called a real bird colony. On September 5, 1911, J. Koren found a large number of young cormorants at Cape Schmidt among a few adults. According to the data of A.A. Savich (Artobolevskii 1927) cormorants nested at Cape Schmidt in abundance. V.Ya. Isaev told me that only about 20 pairs nested there in 1934/1935, most of them at Cape Veber and only a few at Cape Kozhevnikov. However, É.V. Schmidt told me that he did not see cormorants anywhere there. I myself did not find them during my visit to Cape Kozhevnikov on August 6, 1938. In Ryrkaipiya village I saw cormorant skins processed in the factory. It is possible that the population of this species there, i.e. at its western boundary, underwent annual fluctuations, but it no doubt also depended on the activities of hunters.

O. Bangs (Thayer and Bangs 1914) argued that cormorants did not occur west of Cape Schmidt on the arctic coast of the Chukchi peninsula but J. Koren found about a dozen of them on August 30, 1912, at the northern limit of Cape Kiber (Shalaurova Island). É.V. Schmidt told me that he did not see cormorants anywhere at Cape Shelagskii. Nevertheless, birds in flight were to be seen there, judging from the fact that H.U. Sverdrup (Schaanning 1928) saw a lone cormorant on May 28, 1923, in the sea at 165° east and 74°42′ north and some were noticed on August 24, 1924, around 155°18′ east and 71°15′ north. H.T. Schaanning related this observation to the species *Phalacrocorax carbo*, but this is totally incorrect.

In 1881, E.W. Nelson noticed one or two cormorants near Wrangel Island off the east coast and E.E. Arngol'd found one on September 17, 1911, near the southwestern tip of the island at 73°53′ north and 179°15′ east. In 1929, G.A. Ushakov collected two but did not place identification labels on them. A.I. Mineev (1936) was aware of the nesting areas only on the east coast at Cape Uéring and elsewhere up to Cape Hawaii, where cormorants did not nest owing to the absence of sufficiently high cliffs. According to my observations, on the east coast of the island pelagic cormorants were very few in their nesting areas. On August 13, 1938, I saw some at Cape Uéring at the northern end of the bird colonies. In one case there was a flock of five birds in flight. On May 14, 1939, I came across three birds there one after another. According to Tayan, cormorants built nests on the cliffs and on the west coast of Wrangel Island. On the south coast they came only to feed in the nonbreeding season. In Rodgers Bay two cormorants were noticed by N.M. Vakulenko on October 9, 1934, and I, too, roused some stray birds on August 4 and 5, 1939. On September 15, 1938, I saw one on Krasnaya Glina beyond Rodgers Bay.

In 1960 S.M. Uspenskii and R.L. Bëme (1963), based on enquiries and observations from the air, determined the approximate population of cormorants on the island at not more than 50 to 100 pairs. On the east coast they nested at Bol'shevik and Corwin capes and Ptichii colony.

E.W. Nelson is the first and so far the only naturalist to report cormorants on Herald Island.

Habitat—The nesting sites of pelagic cormorants are invariably on hanging cliffs forming the coast line. Such cliffs are sometimes washed by the surf and rise far above the beach. Quite often there is a narrow strip of pebble beach between the rock wall and the surf where people can walk. In such cases the cormorants built their nest much higher up. Finally, cormorants nest even on cliffs not washed by the surf, even on the walls of gorges perpendicular to the coastline but far from it. In a word, this is a marine bird invariably overlooking the sea from its nest. With minor exceptions the nests are built high up, often tens of meters above sea level. In mixed nesting colonies of sea birds the nests of cormorants jut out in small groups at different levels. But I often found them, for example, near Uélen and on Kolyuchi Island, above the nests of other species of birds. The site selection for the nest no doubt depends invariably on the inclination and surface characteristics of the cliff. Cormorants are not satisfied with the narrow cornices that meet the needs of murres and even black-legged gulls. The cormorant's relatively spacious nest requires a larger area and hence is built on broad cornices many centimeters wide. Nests are built in several pairs next to each other as densely as possible in the area. In Providence Bay cormorants built their nests high up on the cliffs extending from Plover spit to the cape called Ivga by the eskimos, because people frequented the pebble beach under the cliffs. There, I did not find any nests less than 15 to 20 m above sea level; frequently they were as high as 100 m or so. In such cases the birds enjoyed complete security. Sticking out their necks curiously they eyed me when I passed below under the cliffs. At the same time cormorants perched at lower levels took precautionary measures and flew off in time. In the so-called kekurs, i.e. large stone blocks interrupting the rocky coastline or in the form of tiny islets, individual pairs of cormorants built nests at a very low level from 3 to 5 m above the water; surrounded by stones, they were protected from landward enemies. In Providence Bay, for example, at Slavyanka as also on Kolyuchi Island, I noticed that some pairs had their nests very low but they had selected an inaccessible part of the cliff projecting in such a way that it would be difficult to reach it, or overhanging the sea. A.P. Kuzyakin examined nesting areas in two canyons between the coastal cliffs near Yangdagai with smooth, rounded walls. He got at the eggs by lowering himself on a rope to the lofty nests. Near Naukan, according to my observations, cormorants nest in isolated pairs near the top of the cliffs. To the east of Uélen the nests were not less than 25 m above sea level, and mostly on the upper cornices at a height of 40 to 50 m. Near Cape Serdtse-Kamen', I saw a colony on very high cliffs. On Kolyuchi Island the nests were also located very high and J. Koren got at the eggs by descending on a rope. On Wrangel Island cormorants nested at a height beyond the range of a rifle shot.

The size of the colonies, as also whether the nests are of one species or more, evidently depends on the nature of the cliffs occupied and on the history of formation of the colonies. I examined this aspect in detail in Uélen, where there were completely independent, isolated colonies of cormorants. In some only two or three pairs of puffins lived among them while in others the cormorants built nests among those of puffins and auklets. In some cases the cormorants nested in very small groups and even in individual pairs, becoming aliens in a colony.

I never once saw pelagic cormorants on Chukchian rivers, for example, on the Utte-Véem or Kol'oam-Véem, even in their lower reaches, but they were quite often sighted in the lagoons. Nor did I ever see cormorants flying over the tundra. They followed a path parallel to the coastline even when it would have been quicker to cross a tiny cape. Even when flying low up to 200 m or so, they avoided the land.

I was always astonished that cormorants visiting Rodgers Bay first flew out to sea and then turned east along the coast although it would have been quicker to cross the spit simply. This characteristic behavior is due to their helplessness on a flat land surface. On one occasion, sailing in a boat in the Uélen lagoon, I came within 100 feet of a cormorant sitting on a flat sand bar which had appeared above water due to the low tide. The bird looked uneasily at the approaching boat and finally began stepping awkwardly and swimming in the shallow water. That bird could have taken off only after reaching the required depth of water. In Émma Bay I also saw cormorants resting on flat land but right next to the water, which was quite deep.

Cormorants do not usually go far from the coast but they may be compelled to do so by the ice fields along the shore. Cormorants are particularly fond of leads and polynyas in the ice. I saw them even in a thawed opening in flat ice in a lagoon at Uélen. These birds love to sit on the ice floes on isolated stones and kekurs. Only, they must be able to take off easily.

Arrival—The pelagic cormorants arrive on the Chukchi coast in small numbers and begin to appear even in the middle of April. By mid-May the arrival is evidently complete. In the spring of 1931, around Meechken Island in Krest Bay, L.O. Belopol'skii registered the first sighting of cormorants on May 1 in large openings in the drift ice. On May 18, somewhat to the east in Vtoroi Red'kin Bay, he observed a large flock of them on the cliffs and hence the arrival could be regarded as complete. According to the observations of I.O. Olenev, in 1932 cormorants arrived in Providence Bay in the first few days of May. In the spring of 1938 P.T. Butenko particularly noticed the flight of these birds at Cape Chaplin. The first two cormorants were sighted on April 22; later they were noticed on April 23 and May 2. On Malyi Diomede Island J.W. Brooks found them on April 25, 1953. K.W. Kenyon (Kenyon and Brooks 1960), arriving on the island on May 11, 1958, found cormorants but up to May 18 they were still very few on the cliffs. Only on May 20 was their cawlike mating call often to be heard. In the words of the eskimos, the cormorants might feed throughout winter in the leads in the surface ice, especially around the northern tip of the island.

In the spring of 1934, at Uélen, Butenko came across the first cormorant on April 30 on a lead which opened up that day. On my way from Cape Serdtse-Kamen' to the east up to Énmitagin, May 18 through 20, I found many cormorants already resting on the cliffs; the arrival was evidently complete. According to A.A. Savich's diary there were hundreds of cormorants in pairs at Cape Schmidt even on May 7, 1915, and they raised an intolerable din. Their appearance on Wrangel Island is possibly delayed by a fortnight. On a trip to Cape Uéring on May 14, 1939, I saw three cormorants individually. Even if it were not the first day of the arrival they certainly were not there for long.

Breeding—The first arrivals are usually seen along the coast and only later do they occupy the cliffs. At that time, they lead a very noisy and animated life, more than in late summer. Normally the call of the cormorant can be heard only rarely but it is quite frequent around their nests. On May 14, 1939, a male in magnificent spring plumage flew over me with a dull "caw".

I more often heard the voice of cormorants when they had nestlings with them. A bird flying in from the sea utters a "caw" which is answered from the nest by the other member of the pair. In the spring cormorants do a lot of flying, usually in pairs. They return frequently to the cliffs, probably for fear that their nest sites may be occupied by rivals.

In the spring of 1934 as early as May 20, I noticed that the cormorants carried bits of grass to the nest in their bills. Often they did not fly straight to the nest but flitted here and there with a fairly large load before settling. The grass comes from the top of the cliffs where the vegetation is different from that of the tundra plain. Sometimes, they would bring material from far off. This airlift continued for almost a month. I observed it even on June 17, 1934, which showed how different pairs built their nests at different times. On that day I saw empty nests and eggs

Table 6. Size of testes in pelagic cormorants, mm

Date	Left	Right	Locality
May 18, 1938	33 × 7	26 × 6	Cape Stoletiya
May 18, 1938	31 × 12	27 × 12	—do—
May 18, 1938	31 × 7	21 × 7	—do—
May 25, 1934	13 × 7	10 × 6	Cape Dezhnev
May 29, 1939	26 × 12	20 × 6	Cape Uéring
June 3, 1934	12 × 6	10 × 5	Uélen
June 12, 1934	33 × 10	20 × 8	—do—
June 12, 1934	14 × 4	12 × 3	—do—
June 20, 1934	21 × 10	18 × 9	Naukan
July 13, 1938	25 × 8	24 × 7	Providence Bay
August 1, 1932	25 × 11	21 × 9	Alyumka Island, Anadyr Gulf
August 5, 1938	12 × 4	10 × 3	Cape Stoletiya
August 21, 1939	20 × 7	17 × 3	Cape Pillar
August 26, 1932	20 × 5	16 × 4	Providence Bay
August 28, 1932	20 × 7	17 × 5	—do—
September 14, 1933	17 × 3	15 × 2	Cape Dezhnev
September 14, 1933	15 × 4	13 × 3	—do—

Table 7. Condition of ovaries in pelagic cormorants

Date	Ovary changes	Locality
May 25, 1934	Biggest follicle, 16 mm	Cape Dezhnev
August 1, 1932	—do— 5 mm	Alyumka island
August 1, 1932	—do— 4 mm	—do—
August 21, 1939	—do— 3 mm	Cape Pillar
September 14, 1933	Ovary length 30 mm. Granular structure	Cape Dezhnev
December 4, 1937	Filmy ovary	Plover Bay

on which the males were brooding. In one nest there were still three eggs. Other observers, too, noticed this variation in the time factor. However, in 1938, on Kolyuchi Island, I was struck by the fact that almost all the pairs had nestlings of the same age.

The seasonal variation in the size of testes also reveals a time variation, if we compare for example the size in males caught at Uélen on June 12, 1934 (Tables 6 and 7).

The males as well as the females possessed a fairly significant subcutaneous adipose layer at the time of arrival but lost it very soon. The formation of new layers was evident only in some post-fall birds. A female caught on December 4, 1937, was emaciated.

The nest is built of grass and waste plant material mixed with tiny pebbles. Sometimes, but not always, the nest is small. According to A.P. Kuzyakin the nests he examined had a characteristic shape. The height of the outer edge ranged from 26 to 73 cm. The structure gradually tapered off to the rear edge resting against the cliff. Much of the nest was compacted and surrounded by a smooth bolster whitened by excreta. The trough was lined with fresh, very dry, even powdery, grass unsoiled by the white excreta.

Nest sizes, in cm

Size of structure	47 × 50	42 × 50	42 × 60
Area of grass cover	35 × 36	30 × 35	33 × 36
Length and width of trough	24 × 24	22 × 25	23 × 23
Depth of trough	6	6	6
Height of nest	73–0	26–0	70–0

The oviduct of a female collected around Uélen on May 31, 1934, contained an egg with a soft shell of size 38 × 61 mm. On June 17 I saw a nest with three eggs. In Providence Bay, in 1932, I.O. Olenev noticed the first clutch on June 1. Usually he found four eggs to a nest. According to W.S. Brooks, in 1913 on St. Lawrence Island cormorants began laying on June 2 and incubated eggs were found on June 28. In 1932, A.M. Bailey did not see eggs in the nests even on June 25 on the Diomede Islands. In 1909, on Kolyuchi Island, J. Koren found freshly laid eggs in the beginning of July; there would be only two or three eggs. According to A.A. Savich's observations cormorant eggs usually hatched around June 21 at Cape Schmidt.

On June 24, 1957, A.P. Kuzyakin inspected a colony near Yandagai consisting of roughly 50 pairs of cormorants. Most of them had just built their nests and some had settled in. In some nests there would be both birds at the same time. In three clutches there were four eggs each, in two three each and in one two. On July 9, A.P. Kuzyakin again visited the colony. Of the eight nests examined closely, seven contained three eggs each and one had four. In four of the five clutches taken, the eggs were slightly incubated and in one the embryos developed so well that the eggs had to be macerated for preservation. The weight of the slightly incubated eggs was 35.1 to 47.4 g, the average of 13 of them being 42.6 g. Their sizes were: 33.6–38.9 × 56.3–62.8 mm, the average of 16 being 36.7 × 59.6 mm.

On June 20, 1970, V.V. Leonovich visited the same colony. The number of cormorants nesting there had somewhat increased. Leonovich counted up to 60 pairs. This was explained by the fact that the nearest settlement, Akkani, was unpopulated. In two of the clutches taken there were five eggs each, in five of them four each, and in one three. All of the eggs were incubated.

On July 12, 1938, when I was touring Providence Bay under the cliffs where the cormorants had built their nests, the birds did not leave their nests in spite of the noise of the motorboat and continued to sit even after some gun shots. The behavior of the cormorants at the end of summer is altogether different. I am therefore inclined to believe that the birds at that time were either about to complete incubation of the eggs or had tiny nestlings.

On the north coast of the Chukchi peninsula V.V. Leonovich examined the coastal cliffs for a distance of 40 km to the east of Énurmino and encountered three colonies of cormorants containing a few dozen pairs each. Nestlings were already seen in these colonies by July 9, 1970.

During my visit to Kolyuchi Island on July 19 through 26, 1938, each cormorant nest usually contained three downy nestlings (Fig. 20). Some of them were of the size of teals while others were as big as widgeons. They were dressed in ash-gray down, the wing feathers had just begun growing, and their shafts had not yet come up. On seeing people, the nestlings pressed close to the bottom of the nest and held their breath. If they were taken in the hand they sprayed excrement. The adult birds flew away well in time. At Cape Schmidt, according to A.A. Savich's observations in 1914, nestlings were seen in the nests of cormorants at the end of July (old calendar).

As the young ones grew the cormorants became increasingly indifferent to them but did not lose their attachment until their offspring attained total independence. If a hunter approached the nesting area they would become terribly agitated, would fly around and, if the cliffs were high enough, would sit on the upper ledges. Sometimes, when the birds returned from the sea straight to the cliffs, some of them would sit a few meters away if there were no human beings around. Usually cormorants are wary and those acquainted with rifle shots become inaccessible to the hunter, as they can recognize danger at some distance.

In the spring, during courtship ceremonies, cormorants flew in pairs for a long time but in July, with the onset of the breeding season and the emergence of nestlings, their flights out to sea were restricted to the search for food. Quite often, I saw cormorants returning from the sea to Providence Bay in the company of other birds. They would fly in single file in a long chain formation with cormorants interspersed among murres and eiders. Around Uélen the cormorants flew in a chain formation by themselves without mixing with other birds. Once I noticed a flock in an angular formation resembling that of cranes. The distance cormorants will fly from the nest in search of food may be judged from the fact that they were seen in Rodgers Bay though nesting on Cape Uéring.

The young cormorants remain in the nests a long time, some until very late in the fall, especially in the more northern zones. According to L.O. Belopol'skii's observations, on the coast between Anadyr and Krest Bay on August 21 and 22, 1931, most of the broods consisting of two, three or four nestlings to a nest still could not fly. On an expedition to the coast from Plover spit to Cape Ivga from

August 25 through 28, 1932, I noticed much activity among the broods on the cliffs. On the 28th I saw a nestling in the nest still unable to fly. Adults were noticed in the nests throughout the day. Most of them fed in Providence Bay together with murres, gulls and other species of birds. Toward evening the cormorants would fly to their nests in large numbers. I noticed a similar pattern in the colonies to the east of Uélen in the latter half of August 1933. In the nests sat nestlings, the older birds moving from the nest to the sea and back time and again. They sometimes flew out to the lagoon singly, rarely in pairs. When the ice floes approached the cliffs the cormorants swam to the same place between the floes or in the openings without flying far. On September 11 I saw very many young birds sitting in the nests but observed only flying birds on the 14th. Many cormorants sat on the cliffs and our appearance and the sound of rifle shots created much commotion. From the high ledges of the cliffs a general buzzing could be heard. The call of the adult birds was either a muffled cackle or a coarse, bass groan. The earnest calls of the young birds were very high-pitched. On September 16 in that colony I did not find anything that might presage a migration but I found only a few pairs there by September 25. The adult birds still flew to their young. One of them flapping its wings revealed very slight growth of wing feathers. Because of the ice closing in the cormorants again had to fly far out to sea, at least 2 km, and were absent for a long time. Utilizing this opportunity, ravens began to invade the colony with impunity, flying from nest to nest, almost brushing their wings against the nestlings which could hardly defend themselves. The consequences could be guessed from the torn remains of a nestling found once under a cliff. On September 27 some cormorants were confined to the cliffs and a young bird was noticed in a nest on October 5. Nearby there was an adult bird that had not deserted its young even so late in the fall. On September 22, 1912, J. Koren noticed many cormorants on Kolyuchi Island still around their nesting areas and in 1946 A.P. Andriyashev encountered a young cormorant even on October 7 on this island. At Cape Schmidt, on September 5, 1911, J. Koren saw near the colonies a large number of fully feathered young birds along with a very small number of adults.

Migration—On October 4, 1914, A.A. Savich observed there many cormorants on the water and on the ice floes. By October 9 they were reduced to a small number and soon the last of them had left.

I had occasion to study the migration in greater detail in Uélen in the fall of 1933. On the evening of September 18 the weather worsened with a sharp northwesterly wind. On the 19th a snowstorm broke, followed by intense cooling. It appeared as though winter had set in. The cold storms, continuing for some days, compelled most of the cormorants to migrate. On September 27, I noticed some on the cliffs and six of them flying above the lagoon. There were only stray birds on October 1 and 3 on the cliffs. In the first half of October winter set in rapidly and the cormorants disappeared. P.T. Butenko noticed the last of the single birds on October 22 over the sea, which was something of an exception.

In October cormorants were encountered even on Wrangel Island. N.M. Vakulenko's diary contains a record of two lone cormorants taking shelter in Rodgers Bay from the southeasterly wind on October 9, 1934. In 1960 A.G. Velizhanin (1965) noticed a migration from the bird colonies to the west coast of the island on

October 5 and 6. Cormorants flew eastward along the coast, bypassing Somnitel'naya Bay.

In Providence Bay the cormorants stayed on for a considerably longer period. In the fall of 1937 P.T. Butenko found them on November 4, 6, 11, 12, 15, 17 and 25. The latest date he saw one was December 22.

The period of migration of cormorants depends very much on the ice conditions and the weather, and hence can vary very widely from year to year. Nevertheless, the massive migration from the Chukchi coast may be regarded as occurring at the end of September and the last by the end of October. On the south coast of the Chukchi peninsula cormorants are a normal feature even in November but they do not remain beyond December.

Habits—The pelagic cormorant is one of the most characteristic and typical birds of the Bering Sea and especially the coasts of the Chukchi peninsula. In its body build, posture and body movements it differs markedly from the common cormorant and is much closer to the red-faced cormorant. The sitting posture is highly characteristic. Sitting on a narrow ledge and pressing its chest to the surface of a hanging cliff, the pelagic cormorant can flex its neck far back, keeping its balance with the aid of the protruding tail. Sometimes it hangs there as stable as a woodpecker on a tree. Flying off from the cliff, the frightened cormorant usually looks around and in this process stretches its neck sideways as a heron does in such cases. The pelagic cormorant is very inquisitive and if, for example, there is a ship offshore it invariably flies to have a look at it. After circling several times, but at a considerable distance, it departs. It is not afraid of the proximity of villages and builds its nest not far from Uélen and Naukan.

Weight—The weight of three well-fed May males caught at Cape Stoletiya was 2,295, 2,290, and 2,040 g. The weight of winter-emaciated birds from Providence Bay shot on December 4 and 11, 1937, was much less: a young female weighed 1,520 g and a young bird of unidentified sex 1,170 g. Of a pair of cormorants caught at Cape Pillar on August 21, 1939, the male weighed 2,200 and the female 1, 930 g.

Food—The stomach of a bird collected by the *Vega* expedition was filled with fragments of *Hyas araneus* L. The stomachs of birds that I collected contained the following: 1) Providence Bay, August 26, 1932: headbones of a tiny fish and 30 shrimps; 2) Providence Bay, August 28, 1932: bones and flesh of nearly 10 tiny fish and 17 calcified plates of cephalopods; 3) Providence Bay, August 28, 1932: bones of one or two tiny fish, antennae and legs of some (not more than five) crustaceae and calcified plate of a mollusc; 4) Uélen, May 31, 1934: bones and flesh of roughly 10 tiny fish, two shrimps and two calcified plates of cephalopods; 5) Wrangel Island, May 29, 1939: 32 specimens of Amphipods, six tiny crawfish *Spirontocaris* sp., one *Stegocephalus inflatus* Kr., and four *Boreogadus saida* (Lep.); 6) Wrangel Island, August 21, 1939: *Boreogadus saida* and two shanny fish, *Myocephalus* sp., juv. and seven crawfish *Weyprechtia pinguis* Kr.; 7) Wrangel Island, August 21, 1939: *Boreogadus saida* and two shanny fish, *Myoxocephalus* sp., a much-digested unknown fish, two crawfish *Spirontocaris* sp., two crawfish *Atylus carinatus* (O. Fabr.) and three crawfish *Gammarus wilkitzkii* (Bir.).

Fish remains were also found in the other specimens.

Economic importance—N.F. Kallinikov (1912), who wrongly referred to cormorants as pelicans, thought that they comprised a definite item in the food of Chukchians. In my time, however, the Chukchians at Uélen rarely shot cormorants; even the visiting Russian hunters rarely shot this bird and generally disliked its meat. Chukchians sometimes consumed cormorant eggs. I happened to taste a hard-boiled egg and it was very unpalatable for one fastidious about eggs. The albumen was very dense and from the yoke emanated the marine or fishy smell and flavor that spoils much seafood. In the words of O.W. Geist, in August the eskimos on St. Lawrence Island made a vast collection of non-flying young birds, from 300 to 400 nestlings, for food. Judging from the fact that H. Friedmann discovered a large number of bones of the pelagic cormorant in excavated kitchen middens, this bird in bygone times was eaten by people in large quantities. Only four pelvic bones and a breastbone and none of the skull or jaw were found. Evidently the skull was torn open or cracked with strong teeth to eat the brain.

In olden times the tough cormorant skin with its firm, beautiful plumage was made use of. In the factory at Ryrkaipiya village in 1932/1933 I had occasion to see some processed cormorant skins. It is well known that the Aleutians made clothes out of bird skins. These garments have their advantages under the conditions of a humid coastal climate. Now in face of mass production of modern clothes, including mackintoshes and cloaks which protect the wearer from rain and spray, there is hardly any reason to revert to primitive types of animal wear.

Systematics of the subspecies—The differentiation of the subspecies of pelagic cormorants has already been dealt with in sufficient detail (Portenko 1939b, vol. II, pp. 141 and 143, Table 12). On the Russian coasts of the Pacific Ocean there are two subspecies: the small bird on the Commander Islands and the large one on the mainland coast. The former should be regarded as a typical form and the latter given the old name *Phalacrocorax pelagicus aeolus*, which has so far remained in oblivion.

1. **Phalacrocorax pelagicus pelagicus** Pall. differs noticeably in its smaller size, which is noticeable even when comparing bird skins. It nests on Commander and Aleutian islands. I am aware of summer specimens from Kad'yak Island, but they were probably non-breeding birds.

2. **Phalacrocorax pelagicus aeolus** Swinhoe is much bigger. In Russian territory it nests on the mainland coast and offshore islands from Vladivostok to Kamchatka, the Chukchi peninsula and Wrangel Island. The large form certainly inhabits Alaska too, since I have a specimen from Norton Sound. Non-breeding birds were collected on Bering Island and Atka.

Specimens— 1 to 5) Mechigmensk gulf, August 6, 1843, ♂♂ ♀♀ ○, Vozhnesenskii; 6) Senyavin Strait, July 24, 1900, ○, Akif'ev; 7) Arctic Ocean off southwestern Wrangel Island 70°53′ north and 179°15′ east, September 17, 1911, ♂, 1° anno, Arngol'd; 8) Uélen village, September 22, 1912, ♂, Starokadomskii; 9) Émma Bay, August 5, 1913, ♂, Starokadomskii; 10) same place, July 30, 1914, ♂, Starokadomskii; 11) Providence Bay, August 15, 1914, ♀, Arngol'd; 12) Uélen village, May 20, 1927, ○, Sheneberg; 13 and 14) Wrangel Island, June 7 and 8, 1929, ♂♀, G.A. Ushakov; 15) Providence Bay, September 19, 1929, ○, 1° anno, P.V. Ushakov; 16 and 17) Cape Uéring, June 8, 1932, ♂♀, Mineev; 18) Wrangel Island, without date, ♂, Mineev; 19 to 21) Providence Bay, August 26 and 28, 1932, ♂♂, Portenko; 22 to 24)

Uélen village, September 14, 1933, ♂♀ and ♂, 1° anno, Portenko; 25 to 27) Providence Bay, end of summer 1933, ○○, Pavlov; 28 to 30) Cape Dezhnev, May 25, 1934, ♂ ♀○ Portenko; 31) Uélen village, May 31, 1934, ♀, Portenko; 32 to 35) same place, June 3 and 12, 1934, ♂♂, Portenko; 36) Naukan village, June 20, 1934, ♂, Portenko; 37) Providence Bay, Plover Bay, December 4, 1937, ♀, Butenko; 38) same place, December 11, 1937, ○, Butenko; 39 to 41) Providence Bay, Cape Stoletiya, May 18, 1938, ♂♂♂, Butenko; 42) Providence Bay, July 13, 1938, ♂, Portenko; 43) same place, July 21, 1938, ○, Butenko; 44 to 47) Kolyuchi Island, July 26, 1938, ○○ and pull., Portenko; 48) Providence Bay, end of July, 1938, ○, Butenko; 49 and 50) Cape Stoletiya, August 3 and 5, 1938, ♂, Butenko; 51) Cape Uéring, May 29, 1939, ♂, Portenko; and 52 and 53) Cape Pillar, August 21, 1939, ♂♀, Portenko.

Phalacrocorax urile (Gm.)—**Red-faced Cormorant**

I did not come across this species either on the shores of Anadyr Bay or on the Chukchi coast, or even on Wrangel Island, but saw it at very close range from the ship when I was traveling to Pyatyi Strait in the Kuril Range. This bird immediately caught my attention by its more massive body build and a red patch on the cheeks and throat as a result of the spread of warty, bare skin. I cannot exclude for certain the red-faced cormorant in the far northern areas. E.W. Nelson (1887, p. 66) erred by including this species in the fauna of St. Lawrence Island and extending its boundary to the coasts of Bering Strait. It is interesting that H. Friedmann (1934a) found the bones of red-faced cormorants in at least eight excavations of kitchen middens, the oldest of them being in the northwestern and southwestern parts of St. Lawrence Island. The species was evidently more widespread and common than now.

In 1953 J.W. Brooks (Kenyon and Brooks 1960) reported the occurrence of two species of cormorants on Malyi Diomede Island: a very large bird and some small birds. I am more inclined to believe that it was the smaller subspecies *Ph. p. pelagicus* rather than the red-faced cormorant on this island.

Order IV. ANSERIFORMES—WATERFOWL

10. **Cygnus cygnus** (L.) subspecies?—**Whooper Swan**

Local name—Chukchian; Nérkuk, also l'ópett in Uélen; nérku in the records of the *Vega* expedition. The inappropriate "swan" is not only used extensively but is additionally applied to the lesser snow goose. In Eskimo: kuk in Providence Bay (pronounced nearly like kkhuk; evidently phonetic) and qōwq on St. Lawrence Island.

Distribution and Status—Nidification of swans on Chukchi peninsula is not established but its possibility cannot be excluded, especially in the western parts of the peninsula. Apparently it comes only to molt. Found very rarely in the eastern parts of the peninsula in the summer, more frequently in the west, where at places they are even numerous. Seen very rarely on Wrangel Island.

The swan is altogether unknown on the southern coast of the Chukchi peninsula and in most of its eastern part. It was not shown in Krest Bay by L.O. Belopol'-

skii in spite of the fact that he made prolonged observations there and swans were regularly, though occasionally, encountered not far away, near the Anadyr estuary. I.O. Olenev and P.T. Butenko, who wintered on Providence Bay, did not see swans either.

On St. Lawrence Island swans nested regularly but in very small numbers. Harriman's expedition (Friedmann 1932a) on July 13, 1899, first noticed a pair, later a pair with downy chicks of which one was collected. W.S. Brooks (1915) noticed two pairs on June 28, 1913, on the southeastern tip of the island. A.M. Bailey (1925) saw a photograph of four downy chicks in a nest taken on the island in the summer of 1922. According to him, swans nested there regularly. H.B. Collins (Friedmann 1932a) established the presence of swans on St. Lawrence Island in 1930 but did not collect a specimen. According to a report by O.W. Geist (Murie 1936) swans nested on the southern side of the island. Over many years he knew of only one occasion when a swan was shot by an eskimo.

According to the information gathered by F.H. Fay (Fay and Cade 1959), a pair of swans was noticed on May 24, 1956, on the River Mogoveiik on the west coast of St. Lawrence Island. On August 23, 1957, a pair with five young ones was noticed close to Mugum Peak on the northwest coast. In the center of the island, south of the Kukul'skie Mountains, lone swans and pairs were encountered almost every day in summer. On August 22, 1956, adult swans with three young ones were noticed on the River Kuzata. A brood of four birds was sighted on August 25, 1957. In another work, F.H. Fay (Fay 1961) records that in the western part of the island less than 10 pairs nested and there were roughly as many young birds.

According to the observations of E.G.F. Sauer (Sauer and Urban 1964), in the southwestern part of the island lone swans and groups of up to nine birds were noticed quite often in June, 1960, on the lake and in the valley of the River Boxer. On July 2 a lone bird was seen sitting on the nest in an inaccessible marsh in the lake to the northwest of the Puvukpak Mountains. Two swans were sighted on June 14 at Kangi on the north coast.

H. Friedmann (1934a) found a couple of collar bones and pieces of other bones of swans in 1,000 to 2,000-year-old excavations and O.J. Murie (1936) cites the discovery of two excavated humeral bones.

On the Siberian coast of Bering Strait swans were rare even in the 70's of the last century. At least, E.W. Nelson (1883, p. 92 and 1887, p. 93) could not gather positive information about them. In the words of E.V. Schmidt swans were very rare in the eastern part of the Chukchi peninsula. He noticed one pair deep in Mechigmensk Gulf in spring 1938; a pair was noticed in the same area by hunters in spring, 1938. V.V. Leonovich saw a pair of swans in Lawrence Bay on June 23, 1970.

K.W. Kenyon (Kenyon and Brooks 1960) reported that two swans flew over Malyi Diomede Island toward Siberia on May 20, 1958.

The Chukchians said swans were very rare in Uélen. I myself saw one only once: on July 6, 1934, at the mouth of the River Utte-Véem. Since I saw the swan in the morning and evening of the same day (it flew off and later returned) and the Chukchians accompanying me saw two swans, their nesting is probable. But I did not find swans there on my return journey, nor did I find them anywhere on the

Utte-Véem and Kol'oam-Véem rivers. In an unpublished manuscript by N.P. Sokol'nikov, I found a reference, as reported by the residents of the Chukchian village Énmitagin, to swans molting in small numbers around lakes. V.V. Leonovich sighted a young swan near Énurmino on June 26, 1970.

In the spring of 1879 the members of the *Vega* expedition (Palmén 1887) saw swans many times. In particular, on May 27 during an excursion to Cape Dzhenretlen the call of a swan was heard, and two small swans were noticed flying noisily in a northwesterly direction. On June 18 two small swans flew around F.R. Chel'man and A.A.L. Palander. On June 27, too, O. Nordquist saw two swans in the lagoon near Dzhenretlen; they flew in a southeasterly direction. Another member of the party noticed two swans at Pitlekai. On July 3, there was an unsuccessful attempt to shoot a bird on the Pitlekai River and, on July 8, during a journey deep inland, E.K. Brusevits saw 13 swans. Finally, on July 9, T.A. Bostrém shot eight of them.

In the hilly interior of the country to the west of Kolyuchin Bay swans are absent or very rare. In 1956, on the Amguema, I did not sight any nor did I hear anything about them. G. Maydell (1894, p. 207) reported that the absence of swans on the southern slopes of the Anadyr Range was very striking. Once they killed a much molted specimen of *Cygnus olor* (erroneous name) but did not see any more of them.

In the words of É.V. Schmidt quite a number of them were seen on the lower course of the Amguema. At the beginning of June, 1935, V.Ya. Isaev saw four of them in the valley of the Ékiatap River east of Cape Schmidt 40 km from the coast. A.A. Savich noticed two swans on May 7, 1915, not far from Cape Schmidt. At the end of June, 1935, Isaev saw two in the lagoon there; in general, according to him, swans were rare in that region.

A.I. Argentov (1857a, pp. 85 and 101) also referred to swans in Chaun Bay. According to him the Chukchians caught molted birds there. In 1958, on the west coast of Chaun Bay and on the south coast of Aiok Island, V.D. Lebedev and V.R. Filin noticed two or three swans many times. Argentov's data for the Trans-Lena region were mainly related to the lower reaches of the Kolyma River. In his travel records Argentov (1857b, p. 49) referred to the red breasted swans he saw on a lake somewhere near Cape Bol'shoi Baranov at the end of August, 1844. Evidently these birds had rich russet plumage.

According to the data for the 30s of this century communicated to me by É.V. Schmidt and K.N. Yakovlev, swans were innumerable in Chaun Bay. Moreover, they were quite common on Aiok Island, in the Karchyk peninsula, and farther west in the so-called East (in relation to Kolyma) tundra. F.P. Wrangel's travel notes (1841, vol. II, pp. 71, 206 and 249) covering the latter area are much older than Argentov's. In the summer of 1821 a member of his expedition, Reshetnikov, noticed a flock of molted swans 30 versts east of the mouth of the River Bol'shaya Baranikha. Another member of the expedition, Matyushkin, bagged a well-fed swan on July 31, 1822, in the Berezova River valley known as Malaya Baranikha. On August 13, 1822, a group of participants shot 18 swans some versts from the Baranikha estuary. These old reports tally with the present concept of relative abundance of swans in the tundras adjoining the lower reaches of the Kolyma.

Only lone specimens are seen arriving on Wrangel Island, and then very rarely. According to G.A. Ushakov (Bannikov 1941), six swans were seen flying along the north coast from east to west in June, 1929. In the early spring of 1931 the industrialist, I.M. Pavlov, noticed swans in Rodgers Bay. In summer, 1935, the eskimo Nanauk collected a swan in Somnitel'naya Bay and this find was reported even in the national press. In spite of my telegraphic requests, I could not get hold of that specimen because there was no one among the residents wintering there that could process a bird, so the skin rotted on the shelf of the factory. I personally have not come across swans on Wrangel Island but on June 22, 1939, hunters who went to the mouth of the Nasha River saw a lone bird which took fright and flew away inland.

Habitat—A.I. Argentov records (1861a, p. 586) that Bewick's swans usually nest in broad zones around lakes and on special islands in shallow sea bays. In the mouth of the Utte-Véem River I noticed a swan on a low, flat islet faintly formed by the delta. This river joined a lagoon system. On Wrangel Island a swan was seen in the lowlands of the Nasha River estuary. Evidently river mouths and lagoon banks as also the neighborhood of lakes served as summer habitations of swans.

Arrival—A.I. Argentov reports (1861a, p. 485) that swans were sighted for the first time on April 30. A.A. Savich noticed swans on Cape Schmidt on May 20, 1915. V.D. Lebedev and V.R. Filin noticed the first two birds on the southeastern coast of Aiok Island on June 7, 1958. For the eastern parts of the Chukchi peninsula the earliest arrival data was May 27 (1879), on Cape Dzhenretlen. F.H. Fay gave May 24 as the earliest date of the arrival of swans on St. Lawrence Island.

Breeding—The absence of a distinct spring migration on the south and east coasts of the Chukchi peninsula and the relatively last appearance on the north coast are explained by the fact that non-nesting swans advanced northward leisurely. Like other large northern birds, swans do not nest every year. This phenomenon was noticed long ago by Argentov whose arguments, at once correct and naive, are no doubt of interest. He reports (Argentov 1861a, pp. 486 and 487) an interesting phenomenon in bird life with respect to fertility. It is well known that many birds entering the far north do not reproduce at all, as though condemned by nature to infertility. This is especially applicable to Bewick's swans, not of course to each and every bird; the same can be seen among the species of northern geese. The local residents there know well that most of the swans and geese arriving on the coasts of the Arctic Ocean are altogether incapable of laying. According to the research of knowledgeable experts on northern birds this importance is the result of underdevelopment or perhaps improper development of the gonads. Infertility has been noticed in males as well as females. In the birds of this category sexual attraction is slight. In the spring they do not form pairs and do not engage themselves in nest building activities but usually fly and swim together in large droves.

The information on the nidification of swans given by A.I. Argentov pertained to the whole of the Trans-Lena region. May 21 through 31 (Argentov 1881a, p. 485, old calendar) was the best time to look for the eggs of swans and geese; they were freshly laid and hence unincubated.

On St. Lawrence Island, according to F.H. Fay (1961), courting and protection of the nesting areas were noticed on May 24 and 25. Broods with two to five downy chicks were encountered from August 13 through 25. A flock of seven nonflying juvenile swans was sighted on July 29 but such birds continued to be seen until the end of September.

Molting—In F.P. Wrangel's work (1841) there is a reference to molting. Reshetnikov, who camped at the mouth of the Baranikha, noticed that swans molted in large numbers in that neighborhood (chap. II, p. 71). At another place (p. 206) it is mentioned that around August 1 (old calendar), 30 versts to the east, flocks of swans arrived and molted. Another observer of the same group reports (p. 246) that swans molted not in flocks like geese but in pairs and rarely in groups of four on the same lake. Some 10 years later, Argentov (1857 a, p. 101) recorded that the Chukchians caught molting swans in August (old calendar). In his words (Argentov 1861a, p. 489), ducks, geese and swans usually molted in large groups. In Kolyuchin Bay, on July 3, 1879, E. Brusevits encountered 13 completely white swans, i.e. undoubtedly adult birds, which gathered there in a flock to molt. On July 9 eight swans were sighted. It therefore follows that they continued to live in a flock. My understanding is that molting in flocks is characteristic of non-paired swans and the number of birds present there represents the total population, but nesting birds probably molt while brooding. G. Maydell found a lone bird which was molting.

In the Chukchi peninsula the swans are rather conspicuous by their absence in the fall. There is not a single reference to young birds in that season.

Economic importance—To the east of Chaun Bay swans are collected very rarely and hence are not of interest to the hunter. In the Chaun depression and farther to the west hunting for this bird, at least in the first half of the last century, reached commercial proportions. As pointed out above, one of the parties of Wrangel's expedition bagged 18 molting swans on August 13, 1822; now it is hardly possible to obtain that many birds in a day.

Hunting flourished even in the 50s. In "*Opisanii Chaunskogo Prikhoda*" (Description of Chaun Parish), A.I. Argentov reports (1857a, p. 101) that the sedentary Chukchians went out in August (old calendar) for "swanning", i.e. to catch molting swans. Apart from that, there was collecting of eggs. Argentov himself in another article on the birds of the Trans-Lena region writes (1861a, pp. 485 and 486) that the best time to collect swan and goose eggs is from May 21 through 31 (old calendar). Egg collecting was very interesting. The natives knew all the local places where the birds laid eggs. An experienced guide could lead one to a genuine quarry and within a verst one could collect a large load of eggs. Make a small fire right there and make yourself a soft-boiled egg. Only you cannot eat many swan's eggs; one is enough for one person.

The information given by N.E. Kallinikov (1912) is very superficial and apart from the Chukchi peninsula pertains partly to the Anadyr and Kolyma basins. Nevertheless, he provides some idea of "swan hunting" in the first decade of this century. He writes (p. 151) that even in those regions there were not so many swans as to make a pile of them although at places a relatively good flight was noticed. From the birds killed only the contour feathers are plucked and then the entire skin is removed. The skin covered with soft white down commands a good price in distant markets.

Systematics—Recently, and not for the first time, some systematists have deemed the four species of northern black-beaked swans conspecific and grouped them sometimes into two species and at other times one. I am inclined to regard the four subspecies *C. c. cygnus*, *C. c. bewickii*, *C. c. columbianus*, and *C. c. buccinator* as belonging to the same species *Cygnus cygnus* (L.). The differences between them are mainly in the size of the birds and in the size of the yellow patch on the beak. In fact, there are no gradual transitions between them, although hybrids are known, if rare. Ecologically they are classified into forest and tundra birds; geographically, too, they are distinct.

The relationships between the subspecies of swans call to mind the relationship between the redpolls. The ranges of the latter have a similar zonal distribution: there are forest and tundra and forest-tundra redpolls. There are no gentle transitions, and hybrids are rare. According to ornithologists their taxonomic importance has not been firmly established.

Apart from the taxonomic evaluation of swans, it is not yet clear which of the subspecies build nests, which of them come to molt and which of the records are purely accidental in the territory in question. The reason for this is that there are no birds among the collections of an age at which the subspecies can be identified. The three subspecies *C. c. cygnus*, *C. c. bewickii* and *C. c. columbianus* can be found in this territory with equal significance.

1. **Cygnus cygnus cygnus** (L.). Undoubtedly nests in the Anadyr basin. From there I obtained 12 well-studied specimens and there is no doubt as to the accuracy of identification of subspecies. The rarity of swans in the central and eastern parts of the Chukchi peninsula makes it more likely that whooper swans came there to molt. A bird I noticed at the mouth of Uttez-Véem River was not a small swan but I could not positively decide at a distance whether it was *C. c. cygnus* or *C. c. columbianus*.

In the absence of any specimens I.A. Palmén was compelled to designate the swans by the generic name *Cygnus*. But American ornithologists, also without any specimens in hand, classified the swans found to the west of Bering Strait as whistling swans, from their inertia.

2. **Cygnus cygnus bewickii** Yarr. is perhaps rarely encountered in the Chukchi peninsula but the small or Bewick's swan nests in the western part. There are, however, no entirely reliable references to this in the literature. In an article on the birds of the Trans-Lena region A.I. Argentov himself distinguishes four species of swans (1861a, p. 493): white Bewick's swan, Bewick's swan with a red neck, white forest swan and forest swan with a red neck. If the swans with red necks are excluded as birds with a rusty bloom on the neck plumage it becomes apparent that Argentov in fact distinguished between the whooper and Bewick's swans. But the exact area covered by his "Trans-Lena" region—whether it extended to the west coast of the Chukchi peninsula—is not clear.

V.D. Lebedev and V.R. Filin recorded their observations of Bewick's swan on Aiok Island and in Chaun Bay but did not secure any specimens.

At the wintering site of the *Vega* observers on two occasions noticed that the swans overflying them were of small size. I.A. Palmén did not assign any importance to this observation but they could have been *C. c. bewickii*. According to available information, Bewick's swan was quite common in the nesting areas in the lower reaches of the Kolyma. J. Koren (Schaanning 1954) in 1916–1917 collected a female with chicks in the Kolyma delta. The measurements of three specimens supplied by G.T. Schaanning quite clearly establish that the subspecies *C. c. bewickii* nested in that delta. Its migration farther east is highly probable, however rare it may be.

3. **Cygnus cygnus columbianus** Ord. is a subspecies well known as a migrating bird in the coastal Anadyr region. I have the skins of three of them. Its occasional nesting in the eastern part of the Chukchi peninsula is very likely. It is also very possible that the swans noticed on Wrangel Island belonged to this subspecies, since whistling swans quite often came to the island.

Based on the information provided by the hunters of the *Vega* expedition on the black beaks and black band across the eyes, I.A. Palmén thought that the whistling swan might possibly be found in the Chukchi peninsula.

K.W. Kenyon remarks that the swans noticed around Malyi Diomede Island and flying low over the leads in the frozen sea had all-black beaks. These observations cannot be regarded as absolutely reliable. At a distance the beak of even the whooper swan appears completely black.

American ornithologists classify the birds observed on St. Lawrence Island under *C. columbianus* Ord. but there is not a single adult bird to support this conclusion. They have only used a name common for them.

11. **Chen caerulescens caerulescens (L.)—Lesser Snow Goose**

Local name—Chukchian: Lepet in Chaun region according to Argentov; l'ippa in the records of the *Vega* expedition (widely used name originating from the Russian word "lebed", meaning swan). In Eskimo: kannu (cangu) in Providence Bay and qăăng-ū on St. Lawrence Island.

Distribution and Status—In the Chukchi peninsula it nests only on the western part of the north coast, sporadically and in very small numbers. Very rarely seen in flight on the south coast and more commonly seen in the east, becoming sometimes even numerous in the north. Nests in large numbers on the northwestern and central parts of Wrangel Island. Seen in flight all over the island.

Distribution in Chukchi peninsula—On the south coast of Chukchi peninsula it is almost as rare as on the Anadyr. L.O. Belopol'skii (1934) did not find it at Krest Bay and P.T. Butenko did not notice it in Providence Bay in 1937/1938, though each of them spent a whole season in the respective areas. I.O. Olenev, who wintered in Providence Bay in 1931/1932, only once noticed a small flock in the fall, flying over the tundra halfway between Istiget village and Providence Bay.

On St. Lawrence Island, according to the information gathered by O.J. Murie and O.W. Geist (Murie 1936), lesser snow geese were regularly found in fall flight. An adult female was collected east of Kukuliak on September 3, 1934, and a young bird at Savunga village on September 23, 1935. In the fall they were usually observed flying high over Kukuliak village. F.H. Fay and T.J. Cade (1959) wrote that lesser snow geese flew in small flocks every year near Gambell; such flocks were few in the spring and many in the fall.

S.A. Buturlin wrote to V.E. Ushakov (1925) that he managed to collect two specimens of lesser snow geese on a Chukchi headland in 1925.

É.V. Schmidt himself noticed lesser snow geese in flight in Mechigmensk Gulf and near the cultural base in Lawrence Bay. P.T. Butenko saw two flying lesser white geese over this bay on August 19, 1932. According to the information gathered by A.P. Kuzyakin (1965, p. 116), every spring lesser snow geese flew in very large flocks along the east coast of the Chukchi peninsula northward from Lawrence Bay; they could also be collected in large numbers. On June 18, 1970, V.V. Leonovich saw three lesser snow geese in Lawrence Bay.

On Malyi Diomede Island J.W. Brooks noticed the spring flight in 1953 and K.W. Kenyon (Kenyon and Brooks 1960) in 1958. The geese walked over the floes to the south of the island in a westerly direction. According to A.M. Bailey (1925), in the first few days of June, 1922, hundreds of lesser snow geese were seen from his ship; they were crossing the Bering Strait roughly 30 miles south of Cape Dezhnev and turning toward the Chukchi coast.

Around Uélen, I noticed a distinct, massive flight in the spring of 1934 and only a few in the fall of 1933. In the immediate vicinity, as also in the valleys of the Utte-Véem and Kol'oam-Véem rivers, lesser snow geese did not nest, as confirmed by trustworthy Chukchian hunters from the eastern part of the peninsula.

On June 12, 1952, near Uélen, a young bird of more than one year was collected while it was feeding in a thawed patch; it had been ringed in California on April 15, 1952.

V.P. Teplov and T.P. Shevareva (1965, p. 30) write that on the eastern tip of the Chukchi peninsula 10 lesser snow geese in all were collected up to 1954: in Lawrence Bay, around Cape Dezhnev, at Uélen and in Inchoun.

I was given a specimen collected at Cape Serdtse-Kamen' at the beginning of June, 1934.

In 1879 some geese were noticed around the wintering *Vega* (Palmén 1887). Evidently they were late birds or had been left behind by the main body of migrating flocks. On June 10 a one-year male was caught at Pitlekai; on July 14, six birds were seen from the ship and on July 15, two.

The Chukchians told É.V. Schmidt that lesser snow geese nested on the Yuni-Véem River, which flows into Kolyuchin Bay. In the fall they were fairly numerous in the southern part of the bay. According to the local teachers, some pairs nested in the lagoon stretching past Énmelin, Neshkan and Tjapka villages. According to the information obtained by A.P. Kuzyakin, a massive flight of lesser snow geese was noticed at Toigunen village near Kolyuchin Bay. T.P. Shevareva (1959) cites a male ringed in California on October 27, 1954, and collected on June 8, 1956, 15 km west of Kolyuchin Bay, also a female ringed in California on April 8, 1952, and shot on June 5, 1954, at Cape Onman. According to the information I have been able to gather, the lesser snow goose is one of the most common of geese found on the Vankarém tundra but it does not nest there or on the Amguema River, where even their flight is rarely observed. A.A. Kishchinskii noticed wandering flocks around the Ukouge lagoon between June 6 and 21, 1970.

In some years a massive flight has been noticed from Cape Schmidt. On May 14, 1915, A.A. Savich counted up to 500 birds. In the course of three weeks he got some specimens of which two are preserved in the ornithological collection of the Institute of Zoology, Academy of Sciences, USSR. V.M. Artobolevskii's assumption (1927, p. 34, note 4) as to probable nidification there was based only on the sighting of some pairs by Savich at the end of the flight. It is more probable that they were the birds left behind, or single birds. In mid-June, 1935, V.Ya. Isaev observed flights of 60 to 70 birds each near Cape Schmidt. On June 17 and 18 there were up to 800 birds; however, none was seen anywhere around the nesting areas. During my stay at Cape Schmidt in 1938, I met Podkuargyn, a local Chukchian who in 1933–1934 wintered with me in Uélen, and gave wholly reliable information on birds. We have his word that the lesser snow geese did not nest on the tundra adjoining Cape Schmidt and were seen only in flight.

Recounting the recoveries of ringed lesser snow geese up to the end of the 1957 hunting season, V.P. Teplov and T.P. Shevareva referred to one recovery in Vankarém and three in the Amguema estuary, as also at Cape Schmidt. In the three years 1961 through 1963 six reports were received by the "Ringing Center": lesser snow geese were found at the beginning of June near Vankarém, in Iul'tin region in Amguema and on May 29 at Cape Schmidt.[1]

Evidently the section of the Chukchi coast where the migrating lesser snow geese are encountered in their largest numbers begins around Cape Schmidt. This is because Long Strait, separating Wrangel Island from the mainland, is very narrow at that point and hence the aerial distance to Wrangel is the shortest. A.I. Argentov (1861b, p. 7) wrote a century ago that in the region between Yakan and Lyaleran east of Cape Shelagskii (200 and 60 versts respectively), lesser snow geese would take off from the Arctic Ocean every day at the start of summer and, on reaching the coast at these points, would halt and settle on the low tundra. Evidently the birds rested there after a strenuous flight, which indicates the distance from the Chukchi coast of the land they came from on their way from north to south. G. Maydell (1894, p. 282) to a large extent reproduces the route given by Argentov and points out roughly the same section of coast from 50 versts west of Yakan up to Ryrkaipiya. In this section, there is a break in the abundance of birds that is characteristic of the Arctic Ocean coast. This is explained by their migration, including most lesser snow geese, to Wrangel Island.

Quite recently their regular spring and fall flights were confirmed in the vicinity of Cape Yakan (Shevareva 1959 and 1960). In particular, at the end of August, 1953, a female collected there had been ringed on September 2, 1952, in California.

S.A. Buturlin (1906b) writes that lesser snow geese nested on the north coast of the Chukchi peninsula in very large numbers only from Chaun Bay to the east and not as far west as Bol'shaya Baranikha. In another article (Buturlin 1908a) the Latin name of the lesser snow goose appears in italics to denote birds not found in the nesting areas. Finally, in his last compilation, he writes (Buturlin 1935) that they nested in very large numbers along the north coast of Chukchi land up to Cape Shelagskii in the west and formed the predominant species (25 years ago) of goose in Chaun Bay; it was very rare to the west. Unfortunately, these reports cannot be

[1]Evidently the last find was reported in another article by T.P. Shevareva (1961a) in which the find of a ringed male was dated March 29 (obvious error for May), 1957.

regarded as accurate; they were not based on any bird sightings and Buturlin himself did not see lesser snow geese. Strangely, É.V. Schmidt reported to me that lesser snow geese were common in the nesting areas in the lower reaches of the Kuvét River near the foothills. On the Apapel'khin River, 10 km from its mouth and 15 km east of Pevek, he found a nest of the lesser snow goose. The geobotanist K.F. Yakovlev found two nests. On the River Rautan, opposite Pevek, a flock of lesser snow geese was once observed, probably coming from Apapel'khin. In the extensive lowlands, as in Chaun, where many other geese nested, lesser snow geese were not to be found.

According to information I have obtained from Pevek, at the beginning of the 60s the lesser snow goose was sometimes seen on the eastern shore of Chaun Bay during the spring flight, for example in 1961 and 1963. In those years the spring was late and snow did not thaw for a long time. One goose was shot. In 1962 a lone bird was noticed near Cape Shelagskii along with four brent geese.

On Aiok Island in 1928 lesser snow geese were noticed by Schmidt throughout the year. He was told by the Chukchians that this species nested there. In the fall a late flock in passage was noticed from the island.

In the summer of 1944 Buchin, an observer at the Polar Station, found a small nesting colony on Aiok Island. Evidently it was an exceptional year since lesser snow geese were formerly seen there only in flight. In the same year (1944) a few pairs of lesser snow geese nested at Cape Billings. V.D. Lebedev and V.R. Filin (1959) noticed a small flock at the end of May and the beginning of June, 1958, i.e. in spring flight, on the west coast of Aiok Island. On June 10 a pair was collected. The female had no feathers on the abdomen. Local residents said the lesser snow goose nested rarely on that island. According to F.B. Chernyavskii a lone young bird was found in the eastern part of the north Anyui Range on September 15, 1965, during a massive flight of bean geese.

V.P. Teplov and T.P. Shevareva cite the records of lesser snow geese ringed in the USA and recovered west of Cape Schmidt. One bird was shot 160 km west, another at Val'karai village and a third at Pevek. At Pevek a goose ringed on Wrangel Island was recovered.

A.I. Argentov (1861b, p. 6) writes that before the fall the geese took off from the sea toward Bol'shoi Baranov Kamen'. According to É.V. Schmidt the local hunters confirmed categorically that lesser snow geese did not nest on the Baranikha and Kuz'micheva. On the Kolyma, lone birds in flight were very rarely seen. Farther west the occurrence of lesser snow geese nowadays should be regarded as a rarity.

Distribution on Wrangel Island—The old assumptions as to the nidification of lesser snow geese on Wrangel Island were based on conjectures about the very existence of this island. They are as outdated as the description of the lesser snow goose itself. The first reliable specimen there was collected by Capt. F.K. Kleinschmidt (Snyder 1935) in August, 1911. But only after the publication of the material collected by V.F. Vlasova and A.I. Mineev did the massive nesting there become precisely known. In 1938 and 1939 I gathered additional details there.

Nesting of lesser snow geese on Wrangel Island is an interesting phenomenon. During my visit they nested in colonies of different strengths and in individual pairs both in the interior and in the southwestern part of the island. Their nests were not found on the northern periphery or on the eastern side. I was acquainted with the migration conditions from the eastern half of the island but in summer, 1939, I could not find a single nest. I spotted nesting pairs east of Predatel'skaya Bay. In Rodgers Bay the geese nested right in front of the settlement of wintering personnel. From 1927 through 1929 commercial parties did not have to go very far to gather eggs. Despite the activities of hunters the population of nesting birds varies considerably from year to year.

In 1932 A.I. Mineev gathered around 800 goose eggs in a nesting colony, which reflects the population of the birds, but in 1933 the eggs were not to be seen there. Mineev attributed their abandoning the nesting area to the destruction of owls' nests (the owls protected the goose nests from being attacked by polar foxes). But perhaps there is some other reason for moving out. The location of colonies is not dependent on such specific conditions as, for example, the availability of a precipitous coast with terraces for sea birds.

In the first half of June, 1939, I inspected the lower course of the River Mamontovaya but did not find nests; evidently they were nearer the upper reaches. In June and July I traveled from Somnitel'naya Bay to Cape Hawaii and also visited the Nasha River valley. I nowhere found lesser snow geese except for a wounded bird. The eskimo Anakak, who accompanied me on the spring expeditions later the same year (1939), collected geese in nests close to his home on the southwesterd tip of the island. At the beginning of July, Tayan traveled by car from Rodgers Bay in the north to Bruch spit but did not find nesting geese. All the enquiries of hunting parties were directed at finding out whether these birds nested in the southwestern and central parts of the island.

In the spring flight the lesser snow geese are encountered almost everywhere on Wrangel Island but mostly along the south coast and only rarely on the northern side of the island, where they were numerous only at the time of molting and fall migration.

After my departure from Wrangel Island additional fragmentary information reached me. In summer, 1940, a geological party traveling by car along a valley in the western part of the island encountered a large, dense nesting colony through which the driver had to steer his way. Later I got information from I.S. Sei, who had occasion to visit a large colony in the southwestern foothills of Tundra Peak in the northwestern part of the island at the beginning of June, 1954. In 1954, in Égvekinot, I came to know that an animal nursery had been set up at Wrangel and that lesser snow geese, among others, served as the food source.

With the development of an air route to Wrangel Island it has ceased to be the inaccessible corner which it was 30 years ago. In spring, 1939, using only a dog team, I was stopped by the thawing Mamontovaya River and could not reach the colony of lesser snow geese. Now it is visited time and again by planes and even automobiles.

In 1958, P. Bocharov, a hunter from Somnitel'naya Bay, wrote that only one large colony remained around Tundra Peak hill while two others in the western and eastern parts of the island were gradually disappearing. In 1960, V. Lavrent'ev, Chief Game Inspector of Magadansk region, visited Wrangel Island (1960, p. 26). He stated in his report that the nesting areas of lesser snow geese were situated in the upper reaches of the Tundrovaya and Gusinaya rivers, in the valley of the Mamontovaya River and at the source of the Pestsovaya River. The main nesting zone covered a large area at Tundra Peak hill, the rest being relatively small.

In 1960, S.M. Uspenskii and R.L. Bëme made a special study of the colonies of lesser snow geese at the behest of the Central Board of Wild Life, the conservators at the Council of Ministers of the Russian Soviet Federative Socialist Republic and the All-Union Society for Natural Conservation. Further, A.G. Velizhanin from Irkutsk Zoological Station studied the nests in order to collect lesser snow geese for the zoos. In their combined report (Uspenskii, Bëme, and Velizhanin 1963), it was stated that there had been three or four isolated though large nesting areas on the island at the beginning of the 40s. They were in the west (in the Gusinaya River valley), in the center (in the valleys of the Mamontovaya and Tundrovaya rivers) and in the east (in the valley of the Klér River). By 1960 only one large nesting area in the upper reaches of the Tundrovaya River remained. It still covered a large area but was only one-half its size in 1958. However, in an independent article, A.G. Velizhanin (1965) stated that there were several nests in the western hilly part of the island. The residents of the island said there were also nesting areas in the eastern part of the island. On July 3 Velizhanin saw a flying flock over the middle reaches of the Klér River. They were probably geese which had nested nearby but this, of course, is speculative. In 1964, S.M. Uspenskii (1965) continued and advanced the study of goose colonies on Wrangel, mainly of the biggest area around Tundrovaya Peak. According to F.B. Chernyavskii (1967), who took part in his expedition, two small colonies each consisting of a few dozen pairs were found during special trips by jeep in the middle reaches of the Gusinaya River and in the upper reaches of the Mamontovaya River.

Though the distribution of lesser snow geese on Wrangel Island has now been fairly thoroughly studied the information is still not complete. An exact mapping of the boundaries of the largest colony and of the smaller ones is necessary. There is no doubt that the location of nesting areas may vary even without human interference. Nesting areas are selected not only by individual pairs but by a large flock. On the Siberian coast the lesser snow geese were hardly affected by hunters. The greater danger was the absence of safe nesting places with abundant food to sustain a large colony. Until the end of the first quarter of the present century Wrangel Island fulfilled all of these requirements. The one serious enemy, the polar fox, can be withstood by colonies of lesser snow geese with minor losses but on the mainland, apart from man, the bird has to face such enemies as wolves, wolverenes, brown bears, and other predators.

Observers noticed that the grass and moss in nesting areas was thoroughly cropped by the geese and the restoration of this pasture in the brief growing season is slow. The nesting area could easily be deprived of fodder. It would therefore appear that if the conservation measures adopted are to lead to an increased population of lesser snow geese on Wrangel Island they should be colonized in small groups in new sites.

None of the naturalists visiting Herald Island saw lesser snow geese there. The members of the *Krasina* expedition did not find them there in 1935 (personal communication).

Population on Wrangel Island—According to V.F. Vlasova, the sportsman S.A. Skurikhin who went to the island in 1926 collected 1,600 to 1,700 eggs at a time in fair weather. In 1932 he gathered 500 eggs in the upper reaches of the Mamontovaya River; a day later in the same places A.I. Mineev collected 600 eggs and later Tayan collected 200 eggs. In all, in an area of 3 × 1.5 km, about 1,500 eggs were collected. In short the eggs of lesser snow geese were collected in thousands on Wrangel Istand. According to Vlasova's data 15 to 20 nests could be counted in small colonies and in large ones, thousands. A.I. Mineev, who found one such place on June 5, 1932, was amazed at the tundra being dotted with geese over several square kilometers.

On the lower reaches of the Mamontovaya River, I encountered flocks of over one thousand birds. In August, 1938, in Tundra Akademii, I noticed an abundance of lesser snow geese gathered there before migration. On August 13 I rounded Cape Uéring in a launch and came across a plain where white patches and lines of geese were to be seen everywhere. Near the mouth of the Krasnyi Flag River the geese were even more numerous. There is no doubt that Tundra Akademii contained many thousands of these birds. In the fall of 1939 I saw thousands of flying lesser snow geese near Rodgers Bay. On August 16, I counted through binoculars roughly one thousand birds in a single flock. There were several halts in the day. In one flock I counted exactly 103 birds, in another 72 and in a third 43. Since hunters had noticed thousands of birds somewhat to the west the day before and the flight had already been going on for about two weeks I came to the conclusion that tens of thousands of lesser snow geese migrated from Wrangel Island in 1939.

Twenty years after this visit to Wrangel Island, in 1958, P. Bocharov wrote that in the last 10 to 15 years the population of lesser snow geese had sharply decreased. This was to be explained by the indiscriminate hunting and collecting of eggs. From 1950 through 1952 members of the mining and geological expedition comprising about 100 persons with their base near one of the disappearing nesting areas daily gathered 40 to 50 thousand eggs and shot a huge number of geese in flight and during molting. From 1954 through 1957 the staff of the Polar Station and airport continued the rapacious destruction of eggs and geese. Hunting was done from tractors, motor cars and even helicopters. The main nesting colony at Tundrovyi Peak hill covered an area of 250 to 300 sq km and was densely populated.

V. Lavrent'ev (1960 and 1964), who visited this colony in 1960, determined its area at 120 sq km and the number of geese at roughly 400,000 to 500,000. Not more than 40,000 to 80,000 birds lived in each of the smaller colonies. He put the total population of lesser snow geese on Wrangel Island at 700,000 to 800,000. When overflying Tundra Akademii, 972 flocks were counted, each containing 200 to 1,000 birds. Before the arrival of V. Lavrent'ev, poachers around the nesting areas shot about 750 geese and gathered about 10,000 eggs.

As a result of a special count made together with R.L. Bëme (Uspenskii, Bëme, and Velizhanin 1963) on July 18 and 19, 1960, S.M. Uspenskii (1961) arrived at somewhat lower figures. The total area of the main colony was 10,000 to 12,000 hectares. A sample count of nests left behind after hatching showed that around 130 (110 to 160) thousand pairs nested there. The population of geese colonizing the

PLATE II

Lesser snow geese *Chen caerulescens* (L.) in Akademii Tundra.
Pic. by V.S. Rozhdestvenskaya from the sketches of L.A. Portenko.

other, smaller zones did not exceed 20,000 to 30,000 pairs, based on local enquiries. S.M. Uspenskii and R.L. Bëme put the total number of lesser snow geese nesting in 1960 on Wrangel Island at roughly 200,000 pairs. In 1964, S.M. Uspenskii with his assistants made a repeat count of lesser snow geese. According to his report (Uspenskii 1965, pp. 127 and 128) there were 114,200 nests in the main colony. Based on visual observations of nesting geese, their number was determined at 300,000, somewhat less than in 1960, which was explained as due to the particularly unfavorable spring.

However approximate the calculations may be, they nevertheless show that many tens of thousands of lesser snow geese still nest on Wrangel Island.

Distribution of lesser snow geese in northeastern Siberia, formerly and now—In discussing the role of Wrangel Island in the distribution and future of lesser snow geese, the following review of the available information should not be without interest:

In the first description of lesser snow geese, by P.S. Pallas (1769b, pp. 25 to 32), we find detailed data on their distribution along the mainland in the first half of the 18th century, as collected mainly by Steller. Pallas called this species, which was very rare even at that time (rarissimam speciem), the most common in some arctic regions.

He writes (pp. 25 and 26) that *Anser hyperboreus* is encountered only in the northern country from the east up to 130°, i.e. up to the Lena and Yana....It comes in very small flocks to more western countries and was even seen in flight at places in Europe....Only in the north of Eastern Siberia is it regularly encountered in flight as the bird follows the same route year after year. With the onset of spring and before the arrival of the other water birds in the far southern parts of Siberia from the east, innumerable flocks of lesser snow geese invade the far north through the Arctic Ocean and are first noticed near the Kolyma River. Somewhat later, they arrive at the estuaries of the Yana and Lena rivers even before the formation and drifting of ice.

In the absence of pastures the birds compelled to follow the Lena turn south in search of lakes, marshes and springs on the land, which by then abounds in insects and plants. Every year they are seen flying into Yakutiya in dense flocks. They hardly penetrate deeper; only occasionally are they seen separately or in small numbers on the Olekma River and, rarely at the mouth of the Vitima on the Lena.

However, they do not stay in that country like other types of geese such as *Anseres feri vulgares* and *erythropodes*, which came from the opposite direction. The lesser snow geese cannot withstand the heat, so they return to the coast of the Arctic Ocean as the spring advances in order to raise the offspring there. It should be pointed out that they did not return by the same route as they came but changed course on reaching Yakutiya. Going east, they turned to the lake at the Yana and Indigirka and returned to the icy country of the Arctic Ocean, in whose atmosphere they could survive with minimum deprivation.

Where they went with the onset of winter and from where they came in the spring would not be an enigma if it was remembered that they followed the same course, almost at the same time of year, as the *Anser bernicla*.

Pallas further states (p. 29) that *Anser hyperboreus* arrives in a considerably larger number of flocks than all the other species of goose. Quite often there were up to 400 in a flock, this being characteristic of birds nesting in colonies.

Flights into Yakutiya as described by Pallas are not seen today. Perhaps he was victim of some confusion between flights of lesser snow and Brent geese. Nevertheless, the information he gives about the distribution and migration of lesser snow geese does not much contradict the information now available and would appear to be very reliable. More than two centuries ago, lesser snow geese came from the east and stopped on the arctic coast of Siberia roughly as far west as the Lena. Before the onset of summer in the Arctic they wandered to the south for better foraging but flew back to nest in arctic country which was then unknown. In his Zoogeography, P.S. Pallas also wrote (1811, vol. II, pp. 227 and 228) that lesser snow geese were very numerous on the Yana. According to legend they were less common at Kolyma and Indigirka and rare in Kamchatka (here Pallas follows Krasheninnikov 1755). But they also inhabited the promontories of the mainland into the Arctic Ocean: Taimir and farther to the west up to Ob Bay. However, they hardly ventured beyond the lower Ob at any time. In Yana, men and dogs earned their living by hunting goose throughout the winter. But to my knowledge although molting flocks gathered there nesting birds were absent.

G. Gedenshtrom (1823, p. 9) reports that the rivulet Iryungastakh flowing into Abelyakhsk Bay derived its name from the numerous lesser snow geese (*Anser niveus*) formerly molting at that rivulet. Even in the first quarter of the last century the number of these geese in Yana decreased considerably. In any case, in the 18th century they were far more numerous than at present. Though they nested mainly in unknown arctic lands, that they bred on the arctic coast of Siberia is certainly possible. A.I. Argentov (1861b, p. 10) gives information on the gradual disappearance of this goose from this coast. He reported that from time immemorial the lesser snow geese had been confined to maritime zones between the Yana and the Kolyma. There the hunters killed them in thousands every summer; later, their numbers steadily decreased. From 1830 to 1849 the members of this species were still very abundant but they were confined to the Alazeisk tundra. From 1850 through 1855 they came there in small numbers but did not come at all in 1856. The residents of Tungusk and Yukagir of Alazeisk region thought that it was not due to a complete annihilation of these birds in Alazeisk tundra but because of a change of summering place. According to them on leaving Alazeisk tundra the lesser snow geese summered somewhere in the unknown islands of the Arctic Ocean.

According to the hunter, A.A. Birulya (1907, pp. 182 to 184), there was an instance in the 60s of the last century of the lesser snow goose nesting on Kovrishk Island (Bol'shoi Lyakhovsk Island). After A. Bunge's expedition in 1886 there was no information about lesser snow geese on the Novosibirsk islands right up to very recent times when V.D. Lebedev and V.R. Filin (1959) cited a male bird collected from a pair on June 5, 1956, on the south coast of Bol'shoi Lyakhovsk Island. According to hunters, lesser snow geese in flight were seen almost every year. G.L. Rutilevskii (1958) also reported a goose shot in 1956. According to the information gathered by Birulya in the 90s, these geese were encountered throughout Priyansk tundra from the Lena estuary, but very sporadically, two or three birds being seen in flocks of bean and brent geese. S.A. Buturlin (1935, p. 85) reports that, according to the local residents, this goose nests in small numbers in the Yana estuary. There is, however, no documentary evidence to support this. According to V.M. Zenzinov (Zhitkov and Zenzinov 1915, p. 16), the lesser snow goose was found very rarely near the Russkii estuary in 1912. On August 6, I collected a lone molting bird from a flock of bean and brent geese. In 1929 and 1930 N.M. Mikhel' (1935) did not find lesser snow geese in Indigirka.

S.M. Uspenskii, R.L. Bëme, S.G. Priklonskii and V.N. Vekhov reported in an article (1962) that records of lesser snow geese from the end of the 40s became more frequent on the lower reaches of the Indigirka. From May 23 through 25, 1951, several flocks flew into the Chokurdakh region. These geese were regularly found in the delta. On August 6, 1960, S.M. Uspenskii and his associates happened to see from a plane a flock of 20 to 30 adults and 40 to 50 nonflying young geese on the lower reaches of the Keremesit River.

In the lower Kolyma, even in F.P. Wrangel's time, (1841, vol. II, p. 199), local residents regarded the lesser snow goose as a vanishing species. In 1905, S.A. Buturlin's expedition saw in the whole of the summer only one flock, of four geese, in the Kolyma delta. In 1912, J. Koren did not find a single lesser snow goose though, according to lower Kolyma residents, it was still found regularly in the early spring. In 1925 the *Maud* expedition (Schaanning 1928) saw a large flock of these geese on June 6 on Chetirekhstolb Island. According to a report of V.D. Lebedev and V.R. Filin, four young birds from Chetirekhstolb Island were preserved in the ornithological collection of the geography faculty of Moscow University.

In 1959 E.P. Spangenberg visited the Kolyma estuary, where he gathered information on the lesser snow goose and actually saw it. He was informed in Kolyma Krests that this goose was found at the estuary in the spring and lived in stray pairs in the summer. Nesting pairs were encountered repeatedly by the fishermen in the far western part of the estuary on small islands washed by the sea. On June 30 and July 5 Spangenberg himself visited these places and found some abandoned nests and egg shells. He also saw a lone goose in worn-out plumage.

There is an old reference by C.H. Merck (Stresemann 1950, p. 116) to the Okhotsk coast. In 1789, in a letter to P.S. Pallas, he wrote that lesser snow geese were always seen singly in the spring but were numerous in the fall and extended to the north along the Tatkeijam River 70 versts from Yama.

The hunter's report by N.M. Antipin (1939) would supplement my information (1939b, vol. II, pp. 103 and 104). Some years before, near the Varkhadam River (entering Gizhiginsk Bay), Antipin saw lesser snow geese living along with bean geese. According to Yakutians, these geese flew into the Upper Kolyma region only rarely. Antipin himself noticed 10 to 12 birds flying north-south over the Taskan River (western tributary of the Upper Kolyma) at the end of May, 1938.

According to information on lesser snow geese gathered by Prof. S. Krasheninnikov, in the 30s and the 40s of the 18th century there were many of them along the North sea around the Kolyma and other rivers and the local hunters killed them in large numbers. The best down was exported to Yakutiya. In Kamchatka, however, they were very rare. There and on the Commander Islands the lesser snow goose was rarely encountered in flight. I came to know from Academician

M.A. Menzbier that there was a specimen of a lesser snow goose from Commander Islands in N.P. Sokol'nikov's collection. Several instances of migrations into Siberia, Tuvinsk Autonomous Soviet Socialist Republic and northern Mongolia, as also into different parts of the European USSR, are found in the ornithological literature.

Analyzing the steady disappearance of this species on the arctic coast of Siberia, H. Grote (1939) came to the conclusion that the time was not far off when the lesser snow goose would altogether vanish from the Soviet Arctic and that the main reason for this tragedy would be the excessive destruction of the molting birds. One could not agree more. The reduction in the population was undoubtedly influenced by the rapid development of human activity in the American wintering places of this species. To the north, because of destruction, the nesting area also shrank. Its western limit in Alaska now runs from Cape Barrow. One hundred twenty years ago the lesser snow goose nested in Norton Sound, judging from the fact that I.G. Voznesenskii caught two downy chicks on the Unalakhlit River on July 13, 1843. These birds are kept in the display and main collections of the Institute of Zoology, Academy of Sciences of the USSR.

The absence of planned ornithological field work in the Arctic in the 18th and 19th centuries prevents our knowing the varying population dynamics of lesser snow geese with any accuracy but it is altogether evident that (i) the population of the species fell sharply and (ii) the area of its distribution greatly shrank. In my opinion Wrangel Island was invariably the refuge for a large colony and constituted the main place of habitation in USSR territory, while flocks of wandering nonbreeding birds found the Siberian coast a convenient place for summer residence and molting. In the past many of these molting birds must have been destroyed. The lesser snow geese first flew away in an easterly direction into America and thus gave rise to the American form. It is altogether natural, therefore, that as its population decreased its range shrank from the far western flange eastward.

In spite of a general population reduction, the lesser snow goose in its present strength is far from being reckoned as a dying species.

Habitat—In the hilly interior of Wrangel Island this goose nested in colonies in tundra sections locked in the mountain ranges. A.I. Mineev (1936, p. 200) gives a highly picturesque description of one of the large colonies: the place selected by the geese and owls for nesting was interesting. Enclosed on all sides by high mountains, the broad valley of the Mamontovaya River is almost inaccessible to the winds. The sky is clear around the clock and the sun shines very brightly. It rises over the hills and lavishes light and warmth on this isolated land. The slope from the foothills to the river bed is green with grass and provided with abundant moisture. Innumerable brooks and miniature lakes shine under the rays of the sun like splinters of a mirror. The faintest murmuring of streams fills the area and mingles with the cackle and the rustling of wings of birds ceaselessly in flight.

With no less admiration P. Bocharov describes his visit to the colony at Tundrovaya Peak. The entire panorama of the nesting area presents a memorable sight. In the bright polar sun hundreds of thousands of the white birds run from end to end of the territory. The loud cackle is heard day and night (though the sun does not set) throughout the mating period.

However, the sunny days often give way to unpleasant weather conditions. F.B. Chernyavskii (1965, p. 136) writes that when summer is at its height the sun floods the tundra with its rays, turning it green. The blooms of polar poppies and saxifrages in their multicolored beds beautify the rugged slopes. But the arctic weather is unsteady. Suddenly it turns cold; there is incessant rain all day, giving place to snow; the wind gathers strength and soon a real snowstorm develops.

The following morning the nesting area presents an altogether strange picture: only the heads and necks of the geese project from the snow in a completely white field. The birds do not desert their nests. The snow thaws only a day later but most of the clutches remain intact.

According to a description by S.M. Uspenskii (1963, p. 59), the bulk of the geese nest in the center of the island in a dry enclosed trough intersected by the upper reaches of the Tundrovaya River and some rivulets which are its tributaries. In any weather it is relatively calm and much warmer than on the coast. The unusual abundance of greenery is striking, considering the northern latitude of the island. Everywhere there are flower beds and grass (though mostly cropped by the geese); willow shrubs, unlike in other parts of the island, rise to 20 to 30 cm; the ptarmigans find even the grass beds there more tender and succulent. However, all of this is due not only to the protection from the winds but also to the much thicker snow cover in the winter and the constant fertilization of the soil by the birds. Geobotanically, according to F.B. Chernyavskii, much of the nesting area is covered by the dryad-willow tundra with a considerable admixture of herbage.

As far as I could ascertain, the lesser snow geese select for their colony grassy sections of the tundra by the side of rivulets, sometimes very small ones like those trickling from the slopes after snow thaws. They also like extensive grassy depressions or grass banks of lakes and rivulets with a gentle current. I found a nesting pair to the east of Predatel'skaya Bay on an uneven, gentle slope with grassy tundra, low hummocky marshes and innumerable rivulets flowing to the sea.

In their spring flight the geese are confined to congenial places. After a winter with heavy snow the hunters on Wrangel Island chose the thawed patches for hunting the first geese. However, in the spring of 1939, when the snow was scanty, these geese were driven away by the strong wind. The arriving geese, according to my observations, rested in low-lying areas covered with snow where the yellow grass of the previous year showed at places. Their white color merged with the background of the snowfield. I also noticed that, as the snow thawed, the geese gradually moved over to places where snow remained. On June 12, I noticed a huge flock, probably of nonpaired birds, which lived on the marine tundra for some days. There were many lakelets and rivulets in the estuaries from which strong currents of thawed water flowed, and snow banks formed on the banks. According to Argentov (1861, p. 7) in the spring the lesser snow geese rest in the depressed tundras on the north coast of the Chukchi peninsula.

In August, 1938, I noticed molting geese along the banks of Krasnyi Flag River. Traces of their residence—a large accumulation of excrement and feathers—were seen everywhere: on the mossy hummocky marshes, slimy muds and other sections of the bank. Here and there along the water line there were long ridges of discarded feathers. In certain areas the geese were in such huge concentrations that they could be compared with the lagoons soiled by domestic birds as seen along the rivulets in the densely populated central regions of the USSR. Broods and flocks gathered in Tundra Akademii for migration stayed mainly on the flat sandy river banks, which were sometimes rust-colored, sometimes covered with short grass on which they fed. As a result of constant cropping by the geese the grass was very short, forming a dense green cover. It was on precisely such dense grass, in the spring of 1933, that I encountered the lesser snow geese along with emperor geese at the mouth of a rivulet to the southwest of Uélen. In Tundra Akademii, lesser snow geese also lived on lakes, which for the most part were so shallow that groundsel *Senecio congestus* DC. (R.P. Br.) shrubs showed even in the middle. The yellow flowers and succulent green leaves of this plant presented a striking contrast to the generally colorless background and the entire picture, enlivened by these flowers and the lesser snow geese, presented a rare sight. In the fall of 1939, near the Nasha River and Rodgers Bay, I saw flying flocks resting in the marshy upper reaches of mountain streams and also on the tundra plains but invariably near rivulets with grass banks. In the latter case the birds were attracted by food resources. But young and molting birds found additional protection from the attacks of polar foxes in the open water in lakes and rivers in Tundra Akademii.

Spring flight—On St. Lawrence Island the lesser snow goose is seen in the spring, according to F.H. Fay (Fay 1961), usually between May 20 and 29, and on the north Chukchi coast, as we will see later, in the last few days of May. Its flight is subject to sharp variations in different years with respect both to the period of appearance and to its numbers. Sometimes the geese alight on ice floes far from the coast. Sometimes they stay on the coast. It so happens that after the flight of nesting birds the single birds, mostly of the previous year's broods, along with their parents, branch out in secondary directions and wander. The course of the spring greatly influences the flight path. On the south coast there is nothing like a regular flight at all.

In the spring of 1934, around Uélen and near Cape Dezhnev, I noticed a massive flight of lesser snow geese over the sea on May 24. Birds in bunches flew toward the west one after another, sometimes separating and sometimes joining to form larger flocks. On May 25, I noticed a very big flock flying from the south past Bol'shoi Diomede Island. On crossing Bering Strait, the birds turned northwest.

On Malyi Diomede Island, according to the observations of J.W. Brooks in 1953, the first few flocks were seen on May 22 and the flights ceased on the evening of May 24. In 1958, according to the observations of K.W. Kenyon, four geese along with three cranes flew in single file over the ice floes to the south of the settlement, heading dead west. On May 23 a flock of six geese rested on the ice drifting past the southern tip of the island. On May 29 and 30 some flocks were seen flying west and on June 1 the call of geese flying west was heard.

In 1879 the members of the *Vega* expedition saw only the late geese in June near Kolyuchin Bay. As far as can be ascertained from A.A. Savicn's diary, in 1915 near Cape Schmidt, many geese were seen in flight by May 26. Up to 500 birds were seen on the 27th; two flocks were sighted on the 28th, considerable numbers on the 29th, one flock of five birds and five individuals on the 30th, two flocks including a large one, and two geese on the 31st, and one more flock on June 1. On June 2, these geese flew in several flocks, many of them resting at the cape. This species was seen flying high on the 3rd; many birds including a pair were seen over the tundra on the 4th. On June 6, many birds were seen and two were bagged on the 8th, but not a single goose was noticed on the 11th. On June 19th two more geese were shot and this evidently marked the end of the flight of geese.

In 1935, near Cape Schmidt, V.Ya. Isaev saw some flocks in mid-June. On two occasions they flew east toward Vankarém, and one flock came from the north. On the morning of the 17th or the 18th of June the coastline of the lagoon contained up to 800 geese. A correspondent of the Bureau of "Ringing" who observed the flight 160 km to the west from Cape Schmidt reported that the geese reached that area from the end of May through early June and flew away north out to sea in mid-June. This late season, evidently, could be of the nonbreeding lone members of the population.

In 1958, on Aiok Island V.D. Lebedev and V.R. Filin noticed a flock of nine birds on May 31. Another flock was seen on June 2 on a lake to the northeast of the settlement. On June 3 they saw nine birds in the morning and six in the evening. The flocks flew from southwest to northeast. On June 6 a pair, perhaps settled down for breeding, was seen on the marshy plain along the sea coast.

On May 13, 1840, G. Gedenshtrom, who was then on the ice floes in the East Siberian Sea roughly 250 km from Bol'shoi Baranov Kamen', saw a flock flying northwest. On May 6, 1851, A.I. Argentov (1861b, p. 8) noticed a small flock flying from the mouth of Bol'shaya Baranikha (about 100 km east of Baranov Kamen') northwest out to sea. Sometimes lesser snow geese were seen quite early even in the west. According to a report by Dr. Kiber (1824b, p. 122) the first geese, including *Anser hyperborens*, flew into the Lower Kolyma at the end of April (old calendar), 1821. April that year was particularly warm, the temperature sometimes crossing zero.

On Wrangel Island, according to hunters, the lesser snow geese arrived after May 20, sometimes even in the first few days of June. For example, in the bad spring of 1931 the arrival of these geese was delayed. According to my observations, in the spring of 1939 the first flock was sighted near Rodgers Bay on May 26 on a clear though somewhat cold day. Heading west, the birds flew low along a chain of knolls at a leisurely pace. They were seen to arrive at a place and were evidently not migratory. On the morning of May 28 one flock moved in the opposite direction and another, also coming from the west, was resting around the knoll. The hunters saw a few more flocks. On May 29 one flock came close to the Polar Station. Later observations showed that arrival that year was uncoordinated and corresponded fully to the bad weather pattern. The preceding snowstorms disrupted the massive movement and delayed the arrival.

Even on June 1, on my way by dog sled along the coast from Rodgers Bay to the west, I noticed several flocks between the estuary of the Khishchnikov River and Somnitel'naya Bay. The geese arrived almost straight from the south over the sea. At Akatylanva, on June 2, I found the arriving geese which were moving in different directions in small flocks. Along the coast they flew mostly low to the east. Along the knoll they flew to the west, higher. For the most part, however, they crossed the mountains at a considerable height toward the Mamontovaya River. Passing through the coastal chain of knolls I found a huge flock of more than one thousand birds in the upper reaches of the hill rivulets entering the Mamontovaya River. The birds appeared fatigued, as could be seen from their attempts initially to flee on foot on my approach. They would go 100 to 120 paces and, after the first few shots, 200 to 300. They withdrew a few km away only after persistent chasing. The same day I saw two or three newly arrived flocks, flying low in a broad cackling row. I noticed some flocks coming from the sea on June 5; the flight of geese next day was very small. They were the last of the arrivals. Only local movement of the flocks was observed thereafter; these movements, too, gradually tapered off with the onset of the nesting season. On arrival the geese would choose places where grass was available. The rapid thawing of snow in early June opened up new feeding zones which were also responsible for local movements. The geese would not immediately settle in the nesting sites, which were still under snow. On my way back from the River Mamontovaya to Rodgers Bay on June 13 and 14 I found very few geese performing local migrations. On June 15 a flock passed over the estuary of the Khishchnikov River and another opposite Atternon.

The information that has appeared on the flight of lesser snow geese on Wrangel Island during the past decade has in general been very uncoordinated. S.M. Uspenskii (1965) gave the dates of the advance and massive flights in 1957 as May 22 and 25, respectively, in 1963 as May 21 and 25 and in 1964 as May 21 and June 4. According to P. Bocharov (1958) the first few flocks arrived around May 20 when the island was still covered with snow. The massive flight was seen on May 25 to 28. In 1964 F.B. Chernyavskii saw the first flock at the nesting site on May 26 though the spring was very late. The bulk of the birds came only on June 3 and 4.

Direct observation convinced me that a large number of lone birds come to Wrangel Island. Quite often the flocks included two large, adult geese and some immature ones, the latter undoubtedly of the previous year's brood. Evidently the adult birds were still emaciated after raising the late brood while the immature ones were not yet strong; some of them were not able to breed in the ensuing summer. Some flocks consisted exclusively of one-year-old birds which were still not paired, while at the same time adult birds flying in pairs were seen. The latter could always be identified from their very large size, much clearer white color without any admixture of gray and their bright red feet and beaks.

At least under the conditions prevailing on Wrangel Island, I believe the lesser snow geese nested from the third year and later every other year. It should be remembered that the single birds would invariably wander about without nesting sites in the latter part of the season. As can be seen from the above excerpts from the work of P.S. Pallas, these geese in Yakutiya formerly followed a complicated spring flight course with several detours, moving to the south along the Lena and then returning north to the more easterly regions.

For this reason they were noticed at different places that did not fall on the conventional flight paths of breeding populations. In the spring of 1915, on May 27, A.A. Savich noticed a large flock to the west of Cape Schmidt. Later the geese were seen in large numbers behind the hills to the south, while the next flock flew in from the east. On June 2 flock after flock of geese migrated in different directions. According to É.V. Schmidt, although geese in flight were seen in small numbers over Mechigmensk Gulf they follow definite routes. In the spring they flew in the direction of the Yuni-Véem River, entering Kolyuchin Bay. They returned thence in the fall but emerged from deep inside Mechigmensk Gulf, later heading north for Uélen. In Lawrence Bay the flight is less in evidence: usually three or four flocks are seen. In the spring they invariably fly west-east from deep in the bay. On Wrangel Island the lesser snow geese are mainly sighted in the southwest. But in the southeastern part of the island some flocks are sighted coming from the east and the south. According to A.I. Mineev's observations high-flying geese were usually seen coming from the south or south-southeast.

Breeding—In all of the specimens I have obtained subcutaneous adipose tissues were found in the form of a dense layer. The specimens obtained at the end of summer, adult molting birds and young birds, had only traces of their tissues if any. The older males of not less than three years arrive with enlarged gonads. From the size of the testes alone they could easily be distinguished from the two-year-olds, as can be seen in Tables 8 and 9.

Table 8. Seasonal changes in testis size of lesser snow geese, mm

Date	Age	Left	Right
June 4, 1939	Adult	36×26	27×18
June 4, 1939		35×20	29×15
June 4, 1939		30×22	23×16
June 6, 1939		27×19	24×13
June 7, 1939	Two-year-old	11×6	10×4
June 9, 1939		15×8	10×6
June 9, 1939		11×5	10×6
August 17, 1938	Yearling	7×1	6×1
August 17, 1938		Long strip-like testes	

Table 9. Sizes of ovaries of lesser snow geese, mm

Date	Age	Ovary length	Biggest follicle
August 8, 1938	Adult	20	3
June 2, 1939	Two-year-old	19	1
June 3, 1939		16	1
June 5, 1939		20	1
June 5, 1939		15	3
June 7, 1939		20	1
June 12, 1939		15	2
June 13, 1939		18	2
June 13, 1939		10	5
August 24, 1939	Yearling	14	2

On dissecting recently arrived females V.F. Vlasova saw highly developed follicles. Once in the spring two goose eggs were found right on the coast. In some specimens mating and laying set in almost immediately on arrival, this being highly characteristic of arctic birds in general.

On Wrangel Island the lesser snow geese nested in colonies of different sizes and also in individual pairs (Figs. 21 and 22). Such pairs were seen on the tundra to the west of Akatylanva. Even as early as June 1, 1939, I noticed migrating pairs. On June 4, on the gentle southern foothills of the knolls 4 or 5 km from the sea I saw some of them. When approached they set off unhurriedly. One pair came very close. I thoroughly searched the area but found no nest. When I shot one the other bird soared slightly but did not fly off even after the shot. I shot this one too at a distance of 60 to 70 paces. This, then, is the usual behavior of geese around the nests. On June 11 I noticed for the first time lone birds in flight, which showed that their mates were already in the nest. On June 12 I found a goose egg pecked by a jaeger on the tundra. The clutches had begun to appear but immediately after the arrival of the geese the weather warmed up so much that the snow disappeared in two or three days. This made the nesting colony on the upper reaches of the Mamontovaya River inaccessible by dog sled.

Discussions with hunters about the nesting of geese along with the snowy owl generally confirmed what I have already cited (1937b) from V.F. Vlasova and A.I. Mineev. I myself witnessed the cohabitation of the snowy owl and brent goose. According to Mineev's counts the small colonies of lesser snow geese contained only a few nests. Others had anywhere from 15 or 20 to a few thousand. The individual nests were located only 10 paces or so from each other and 50 paces away from an owl's nest. The colonies lay sometimes only 1 or 2 km apart. While the females sat in the nests (Fig. 23), according to Mineev, the males either stood in a row with their feet overlapping or browsed close by. On being approached the geese did not take off from the nest; in their own time they quietly left without demonstrating any special behavior, though they cackled all the same and nibbled at the grass. They also returned leisurely to the nests on sighting a man. If the female was killed the male would fly around cackling and sometimes settle down. This pair bond, however, was not as strong as in brent geese.

According to V.F. Vlasova's description the nest was invariably a pit in moss lined with dry grass and a very small quantity of down, much less than in the nest of the brent goose (Fig. 24). When flying off to a pasture the geese would thoroughly cover the clutch with moss and grass, so that locating it called for a good bit of skill. The number of eggs in a nest does not exceed five or six. They are of a dirty cream color and the sizes of four of them were: 78.7 × 52.3, 76.8 × 53.0, 86.7 × 48.8, and 76.7 × 49.8 mm. The eggs lie on their sides in the nest in disorderly fashion. Incubation begins even before the clutch is completed. According to V.F. Vlasova, in a fairly warm summer incubated eggs could be found up to June 10. If the entire clutch is taken away the gander deserts the nest but the goose lays one more egg and raises the young.

The observations by S.M. Uspenskii and R.L. Bëme in many ways supplement the descriptions by A.I. Mineev and V.F. Vlasova. In 1960 some goose eggs laid at the time of arrival were found around Somnitel'naya Bay. The normal clutches quite often contained four or five eggs but some had as many as 10 or 12, evidently laid by two geese. The sizes of the eggs were: length 73 to 87 (average 73.9) mm, width 39.5 to 56 (average 48.1) mm, and weight 96 to 142 (average 119) g.

Exhaustive field work in 1964 showed that most of the geese occupied old nests, although 12.9 per cent (96 of 741) of them were not occupied at all. In terms of the density of occupied nests, a density of up to 20 nests to a hectare is termed sparse, 20 to 50 nests to a hectare, moderate, and from 50 to 100 nests, dense. The density of colonization of the nesting area depended on the abundance of vegetation, which in turn was related to the topography of the area and its exposure. During nesting the lesser snow geese fed mainly in the nesting area, where the goslings, too, would feed.

The non-breeding birds stayed where the nests were few and where the snow thawed later. The number of eggs in a clutch averaged 3.27 for 645 nests. In a year with a normal spring season it reached an average of five or six. The maximum number of eggs in a clutch was five to seven. According to the information collected laying began on May 26, 1957, June 10, 1958, May 31, 1960, June 2, 1962, May 30, 1963, and June 5, 1964, but for most pairs laying began in the first few days of June. In the late spring of 1958, after a very snowy winter, it was observed as late as June 13.

F.B. Chernyavskii, who accompanied S.M. Uspenskii in 1964, told me that the nests of lesser snow geese were built in a natural depression or on a heap with moss, last year's stalks of dryads and willow shoots. Nest density varied from 4 to 40, average 12, to a hectare along the periphery of the area, to 40 to 80, average 64, in the center. The number of eggs in a clutch varied from two to eight, more often three to five. Measured sizes of eggs in a clutch taken by F.B. Chernyavskii were: 85.5 × 52.7, 81.1 × 54.3, 80.9 × 53.2, 79.1 × 54.2 and 77.2 × 52.9 mm. The color of the eggs was dirty cream. At the same time, among the eggs collected by A.I. Mineev, there was one of very small dimensions: 50.5 × 38.6 mm. The nest bed was in the form of a flat thick lump of grayish white down, tiny bits of leaves and stalks of herbage and bits of lichen. The birds evidently plucked these bits with the beak. It is difficult to say which predominated, down or the plant matter. To this was added a small amount of discarded white feathers from the belly of the female. This bed may be just a handful but represents a loose mixture and easily disintegrates into shapeless lumps.

While the goose settles down to brood the gander is around the nest almost all of the time. Some of them go after another female or quarrel with the neighbors. When leaving for a while to feed the goose covers the eggs with down, sometimes mixed with moss. The emerging chicks dry off within a few hours (Fig. 25), after which the brood gradually wanders to the north. Most of the broods travel down along the valley of the Tundrovaya River. Others cross through a low mountain pass.

According to S.M. Uspenskii, in 1960, the mass emergence of chicks occurred from July 5 through 10. The families averaged three chicks each. In 1964 the first chicks were noticed on July 1 and 2. Even by July 3 and 4 the colony began thinning and there was a mass migration between July 6 and 8. Around July 10 the colony was nearly deserted though some stray late broods were found even on July 14 and 15. The number of chicks in the families varied from one to five. According to a count made on July 7 and 8, 33 broods averaged 2.7 chicks apiece.

During my stay on Wrangel Island in 1938 hunters on Bruch spit shot nonflying young birds with remnants of down in early August.

On August 14, to the south of Bruch spit, I found broods which, though quite far off, took to the air. On August 15, I went to the estuary of the Krasnyi Flag River. A nonflying gosling was shot from the first flock I spotted. The broods lent a whitish color to the scene literally everywhere. Some of the broods formed flocks to which a medley of older birds was joined; these older birds were evidently molted single ones. The families usually contained four young birds and more rarely three or five. Only a few still could not fly. They became agitated on being approached even to within half a kilometer. Then they gradually withdrew or took off, not letting me come closer than 300 to 400 paces. The older lone birds were the first to move off. The remaining nonflying young birds walked away without any attempt to fly.

At one place there was a brood around some large lakelets. The adult goose had four young ones. Stealthily I approached closer (200 paces) than the other broods. The adult goose suddenly cackled and flew off with a squawk while the young ones swam away to the center of the pool. When I moved to a distance, the adult returned to the brood. This brood flew off in a day or two. Not far from these lakes I noticed a second family of two adult and five young birds. On my approaching the young ones tried to leave the flock but could not do so and walked away very quickly. Chased on another day, the brood flew off. These goslings learned to fly before my eyes.

On August 17, on one of the tributaries, I saw a lone young bird standing beside the remains of an older goose eaten by a polar fox. In the morning the same lost gosling came to the camp. My friends drove it toward me so I could photograph it. But the sudden barking of the dog frightened it and it flapped into the air, perhaps for the first time. It settled not far off on the lagoon, swam to the bank again and was shot without difficulty.

In 1960, S.M. Uspenskii and R.L. Bëme found lesser snow geese along with their broods in flocks of 50 to 100 birds in Tundra Akademii. The lone birds gathered in large numbers of up to 1,000 or more.

The life of lesser snow geese living in small colonies or individual pairs runs somewhat differently. In the words of A.I. Mineev and S.M. Uspenskii, these geese colonize around the nest of a snowy owl, which drives polar foxes away from its territory. Two small colonies found by F.B. Chernyavskii in 1964 were thus formed around the nest of a snowy owl. Sometimes, they settle down along with eiders or brent geese. The protective role of such cohabitation is evident. Cohabitation with owls is known even in the case of other species of geese. Nevertheless, geese also nest away from owls. The latter, too, in most cases are found without neighbors. However, goose nests built right under the surveillance of predators are not totally free from the attacks of enemies, as my own observations in north Taimir showed. Though cohabitation with the snowy owl is common and represents an interesting phenomenon in the life of these birds such behavior is far from being invariable.

Molting—According to A.I. Mineev, even in mid-July the lesser snow geese lose their flight feathers and become flightless. Most of the flocks of molting geese gather on rivulets in different parts of Wrangel Island, especially near the estuaries and in the bays. Thousands of birds could be counted in such flocks. Toward the end of August the molted geese can fly quite well again.

In early August, 1938, hunters in a boat chased a flock of molting geese in a lagoon off Bruch spit and I examined 40 of the birds bagged. In all of them most of the flight feathers had already grown, in some to 20 cm. On August 14 I visited the same place and saw many geese but not a single molting bird. On August 17, near the mouth of the Krasnyi Flag River, on a tributary, I nevertheless came across a small flock of molting birds. Noticing me, they first swam away up the rivulet, and then, reaching the bank, began running so fast that I could not find the strength to compete with them. The late molting in this case confirmed that, as in bean and white-fronted geese, the lone birds were the first to molt, followed by the young broods.

In 1960, A.G. Velizhanin (1965) noticed the commencement of molting at the end of June. On July 3, in the eastern part of Tundra Akademii, freshly dropped feathers of lesser snow geese were found all over. In four of the flights seen that day two birds were found flying with difficulty. On July 26, some of the geese had already migrated. Molting was complete in early August. Broods gradually attached themselves to flocks of molting geese numbering 200 to 400 birds each. Since the young birds did not go far to the east the flocks in the eastern part of the island were fewer than on the west coast. According to S.M. Uspenskii and R.L. Bëme, on July 18 and 19, 1960, 11 male (seven young and four single) and 10 female (eight young and two single) flightless molting geese were found in Tundra Akademii. In most of them the primary flight feathers had begun emerging from the stubs or were even half-grown, while the quill feathers remained as before except in one female. According to observations made in 1964 (Uspenskii 1965, p. 128), nonbreeding geese completed their molting and began the migration in the first 10 days of August. Nesting birds and yearlings began in the next 10 days. The difference is not much and S.M. Uspenskii explains it as due to the short summer in the high latitudes. But I do not agree that the lesser snow geese differ in this respect from other species of geese inhabiting the same latitudes.

Fall flight—According to A.I. Mineev and V.F. Vlasova, the migration from Wrangel Island began in the last few days of August and early September, depending largely on the weather conditions. The birds fly off early if the fall sets in rapidly. In 1929, with a good, prolonged summer, the migration took a long time. In 1931, cold persisted until the latter half of June, there were frequent snowstorms and the snow did not drift for long. The geese nested in small numbers. They almost left without the young, beginning the migration in the first half of August. By mid-August the nonbreeding birds had left and the rest went in September.

In the fall of 1938 I made observations in Tundra Akademii. As early as August 17 the number of geese decreased sharply. From the 18th I did not find many of them in the estuary of the Krasnyi Flag River or near Bruch spit. Lesser snow geese were seen in Rodgers Bay on the night of August 26/27. The following night, on my way back from Bruch spit to the Polar station, I did not find a single goose; snow was falling in Tundra Akademii.

In 1939, I made observations in the southeastern part of Wrangel Island. From August 8 the weather changed sharply for the worse. Cold northerly winds alternated with fog. On August 15 thousands of flocks of flying geese were seen. On the morning of August 16 I saw huge flocks flying side by side at a very great height in a southwesterly direction. Though the geese were 5 to 6 km away their calls could be distinctly heard. In one big flock up to 1,000 birds at a height of more than 1 km were counted. The flights went on all day, diminishing in the afternoon; some flocks were set directly southward and I followed their course over the sea with the binoculars. Most of the flocks were, however, set in a south-southwesterly direction as though on a course to Cape Billings. In the evening a small flock swept low over the tundra in a westerly direction, turning later to Ozero lagoon. Three small flocks flew very high over the knolls in a northeasterly direction, uttering loud calls. I noted that the geese that flew that day were all the same size, evidently single birds that had recently molted. In two or three small flocks of five birds each broods of that year were recognizable. The migration of small flocks continued from August 18 through 20, mostly very high in the westerly or southwesterly direction. Their aerial course usually traced an irregular line. The birds mainly followed the coastline. On August 22 the presence of broods with young birds of small size in the flights was striking. Cackling was heard all the time. All of the young birds were in flocks flying close to the ground. On being fired at, the flock moved eastward. The flocks also flew along the Nasha River. On August 24 small flocks passed high over the knoll and the sea. In the upper reaches of a mountain stream, I crept up on a brood and shot a young goose with downy remains among the feathers of the upper part of the neck. The remaining five geese surrounded me squawking and later flew away. They returned after some time, still shrieking, then flew off to a neighborhood above the valley of the Nasha River, two hours after I came. Later the flight ceased. On August 28, on the day of my departure from Wrangel Island, I saw for the last time a flock of geese showing up white through fog over the tundra beyond Rodgers Bay.

In the fall lesser snow geese flew past the Polar Station, with some exceptions, from east to west, as in spring, though they should have been flying in the opposite direction. This strange phenomenon was also noticed by A.I. Mineev and other observers on Wrangel Island. It is explained by the fact that toward the end of the summer the geese gathered in the north and northeast of the island and later did not set off immediately by the shortest route to the wintering zones. They would wander about for some time, deviating from the straight course depending on the availability of food and other factors. Before migration the geese on Wrangel Island followed a loop-like course resembling the one they sometimes made in Yakutiya in the spring, according to P.S. Pallas. From the historical point of view this itinerary may be explained by the hypothesis that the geese used to fly over the isthmus connecting Wrangel Island with Cape Billings but now prefer to cross the much narrower Long Strait zone. It should also be remembered that, having reached the south shore of Rodgers Bay from the northeastern tip of Wrangel Island, the geese changed direction very little, roughly following the coastline as though reluctant to tear themselves away from the land.

According to the observations of A.G. Velizhanin, in mid-August, 1960, the lesser snow geese remained for some time on the south coast of Wrangel Island before migrating. The last few geese deserted the islands from Cape Blossom. The migration there was from August 14 through 29. In 1958 P. Bocharov recorded that the migration was from August 20 through 25 on Wrangel Island. According to S.M. Uspenskii (1965) it usually ended between August 20 and 30.

A.I. Argentov wrote about the flight course between Wrangel Island and the Chukchi coast (1857a, p. 82) before Wrangel Island got its name. From Yakan a coast could be seen at times to the north across the sea, and the geese would head for it and return from it in large numbers. Later, Argentov pointed out (p. 104) that the lesser snow geese flew in from the sea in large numbers at Yakan and the sandbank at Cape Lyaleran. In 1850, while at sea somewhere between Kolyma and Chaun Bay, even on August 27, Argentov (1861b, p. 6) saw a flock of geese appear over the horizon flying north-south. The geese from the coasts of the Arctic Ocean did not migrate before early September (around August 20, according to the old calendar). G. Maydell (1871, p. 63) also wrote about the flight course of lesser snow geese northeast from Yakan in the direction where land had been sighted, i.e. toward Wrangel Island.

In 1928, according to É.V. Schmidt, a flock of 50 lesser snow geese was observed on Aiok Island in the first few days of September; after remaining there for 10 to 12 days the flock flew away when frost covered the marsh, before other species of geese left.

According to a report by V.P. Teplov and T.P. Shevareva, in the last few days of August and in mid-September, lesser snow geese were encountered at Cape Schmidt (two birds) and at the Polar Station at Val'karai to the west. In 1956 the fall flight was noticed in the region of Kolyuchin Bay (Shevareva 1959). It continued until September 16 and moved southeast. Around Uélen, in the fall, I saw only once three lesser snow geese in flight on August 30, 1933. They were found around a flock of emperor geese. The latter remained there for some days but the lesser snow geese flew away. I.O. Olenev saw a flock in flight at the end of August and early September 1931, over Providence Bay. On St. Lawrence Island a good flight was noticed in the latter half of August and during September.

In 1959 T.P. Shevareva[1] reported 14 instances of the return of identification rings from lesser snow geese ringed in the wintering areas in California and recovered later on Wrangel Island. By 1965, 452 reports of the recovery of geese ringed on Wrangel Island had been received at the Bird Ringing Center. The Russian lesser snow goose wintered along the west coast of the USA from Washington State to California. S.A. Buturlin's (1935) reference to wintering in the Bering Sea zone is unreliable.

Not all of the lesser snow geese raised on Wrangel Island return every year. Lone specimens are found in summer at different places on the east Siberian coast. Moreover, an instance is known (Teplov and Shevareva 1965) when a goose nesting and marked on Banks Island on July 6, 1955, was found in May, 1963, in a nesting colony on Wrangel Island.

Habits—During flight, flocks of lesser snow geese fly in broken echelons, breaking away and rejoining, and also in angular formations with sides that are some-

[1]Referring to the lesser snow goose, T.P. Shevareva cited, among others, an article by M. Morov on "Wrangel Island" incorporated in the collection *Preobrazhennyi krai* (1956, Magadan, pp. 318 to 341). This collection has references to birds but the information is from nonspecialists, not first-hand, and cannot in any case serve as material for scientific ornithological research.

times quite straight lines. Goslings also form small flocks. The lesser snow goose soars very easily; in this respect it surpasses all other northern geese. In the spring of 1939 I noticed lesser snow geese playing in the air.

Geese performed aerial maneuvers in which the entire flock participated. Flying at a great height above the knolls, they sometimes dived and scattered as plovers do. Some somersaulted in the air, turned from side to side, the experts among them turning on their back for an instant. Among all of the birds I have studied, I have seen such aerobatics only among Chukchi ravens and the booted eagle in Ukraine. One may say that a flock of lesser snow geese playing in the summer against a clear blue sunny sky is a sight of surpassing beauty.

As far as is known, not all the species of goose play in the air in spring and there is no doubt that the mating ceremonies of individual species proceed differently. It is interesting that the Indian goose *Eulabeia indica* (Lath.), as reported by N.M. Przheval'skii (1876, p. 151), sometimes somersaults like the Russian raven when chasing a female in flight in the spring. This characteristic could be of importance in judging the genetic associations between the lesser snow and Indian geese if the behavior of other geese was accurately known.

In a windy atmosphere the lesser snow geese prefer to move at a great height. They fly low over the ground in a fog within the range of a good rifle shot.

I quite often saw geese flying silently but nevertheless heard their calls so often as to refute P.S. Pallas' statement (1811, vol. II, p. 227) that lesser snow geese fly without calling. The call of this goose is reminiscent of the cackling of the graylag goose but in very high tones, sometimes sounding squeaky but generally pleasing to the ear. Particularly when playing in the air these geese cry excitedly and squeakily.

The lesser snow goose is a very wary bird and my observations in this respect do not agree at all with Steller's (Pallas 1769b, p. 30). He regarded them as stupid. In wariness it surpasses the emperor and brent geese, among which I had occasion to observe the lesser snow geese. At the nest these geese allowed one to approach within the range of a light shot. A flock that had yet to experience hunting allowed me to come that close. Being persistently hunted, the birds became very alert and ultimately deserted the place.

According to a description by F.B. Chernyavskii (1965) lesser snow geese in the nest did not show much fear on being approached by a man, leaving the nest at the last minute. In this process they would unwittingly enter foreign territory where the neighbors would greet them with fierce hissing. A brawl would then begin with the flapping of wings and deafening shrieks. When a polar fox approaches an incubating female the adult male goes for it, stretching his neck and raising his wings. The fox quite often avoids an open conflict and disappears with his tail between his legs. It does not venture into a colony. If it wants to steal the eggs, the fox emerges stealthily from behind a little hummock and throws itself on the geese with a great howl. The geese take to their wings in surprise and the predator snatches the eggs. When there are chicks adult geese will even go for a man.

According to A.G. Velizhanin, on domestication the older geese, unaccustomed to man, remained hostile but the young birds quickly became tame. It is for this reason that they are raised every year on Wrangel Island.

Food—I found in the stomachs of dissected geese only the remains of grass or sand. Stomachs preserved in alcohol had the following items:

1) Estuary of Krasnyi Flag River, August 17, 1938. Sand and two tiny pebbles. 2) Akatylanva, June 4, 1939. Very finely ground plant remains and 20 tiny pebbles 3 to 5 mm in diameter. 3) Akatylanva, June 5, 1939. Finely ground shoots of grass *Dupontia fischeri* R. Br. and more than 200 tiny pebbles. 4) Akatylanva, June 9, 1939. About 70 rootlets of grasses, ground shoots occupying one-third of the stomach volume and sand filling the remaining two-thirds. 5) Akatylanva, June 13, 1939. Ground remnants of plant matter and fine sand filling one-fifth of the stomach volume. 6) Rodgers Bay, July 24, 1939. Fifteen grass shoots and sedges and two panicles of grasses.

The stomach of a specimen found at Pitlekai also showed sand and grass which, as identified by F.R. Chel'man (Palmén 1887), was probably the tender shoots of *Elymus*. Direct observation of pasturing geese showed that grass plucking was the main means of sustenance.

According to S.M. Uspenskii (1963b) lesser snow geese are very simple in their choice of food and are capable of feeding on very modest pastures. They eat grasses, horse-tail and willow shoots but there is not much even of these in the arctic desert. At the end of summer, 1960, the vegetative cover in Tundra Akademii along the river valleys, lakes and pools had been completely cropped by the geese. The grasses particularly affected were *Dupontia fischeri* and *Pleuropogon sabini*. The birds shot did not appear well fed. The thickness of subcutaneous fat did not exceed 0.5 mm and the inner layer 1 mm (Uspenskii, Bëme, and Velizhanin 1963). A.G. Velizhanin writes that before the emergence of greenery the geese fed on "the roots of last year's grasses" (perhaps the stubble of stalks) and "the shoots of green mosses". At the beginning of July the moss in large areas of peatland was literally pecked all over. Under captivity lesser snow geese avidly eat alpine foxtail, micro-leaved arctogrostis, Arctic bromegrass, and also wheat, pearl barley and grains. According to the observations of F.B. Chernyavskii, around their nests the geese feed mainly on grasses, especially bromegrasses and horse-tails, and some species of herbage.

Weight—The two-year-old males caught from June 7 through 13, 1939, weighed 2,390, 2,350, and 2,265 g, the females 2,705, 2,242, 2,218, and 1,990 g. These variations in weight and in the dimensions of the gonads showed that some young geese, due to differences in the date of hatching, had not caught up in growth even by the spring. P.S. Pallas (1811, vol. II, p. 228) reported that the weight varied but did not exceed five pounds. According to T.P. Shevareva (1960), the June birds from Vankarém weighed 2,800 g. The weight of 11 adult males shot by S.M. Uspenskii's expedition varied from 1,900 to 2,500 (average 2,123) g and of 10 females from 1,700 to 2,150 (average 1,925) g.

Economic importance—When lesser snow geese were abundant on the arctic coast of Siberia in olden days they were important as game. From G.V. Steller's diary, without discounting S.P. Krasheninnikov's legends about geese (1755), P.S. Pallas (1769b) reported that since this species is the most stupid among the representatives of the genus, was caught in large numbers every year by Yakutians and Russians and the residents of Yana and Indigirka. The technique of capture was very amusing and once again demonstrated the stupidity of the birds.... The best time to catch them was between the end of April and June (old calendar). The geese collected on arrival were very lean. In June, when they began to molt and suffer, they again lost accumulated fat. Two to four men would join up to catch the geese. They would spread a huge net in the form of a wall or raise a hut by stitching together bird skins near a flock of geese settled by a river bank. After this one of the catchers, dressed in a white reindeer skin, went over to the flock while the others surrounded it from behind. They would hiss and drive the flock steadily toward the ambush.

The geese would follow the hunter in white walking ahead of them without hesitation or fear, mistaking him, because of their stupidity, for their leader. When they walked into the net it was drawn tight with ropes and quite often the entire flock was entangled. If the hut was used in place of the net, the hunter walking in front would enter the open door of the hut and stop at the door on the opposite side until the hut was filled by the entire flock and the other hunters closed the door. With the birds locked up their fate was easily decided with hands and sticks. It was very interesting that the lesser snow geese were so fearless of man that they would let him approach to within a stone's throw. Any other flock that happened to fly by while the round-up was going on would also land and join the one trailing the hunter.

The catching of geese in that country was of great benefit to the people there. Since the permafrost did not thaw deeper than one foot, thousands of geese caught by a family in the summer could be plucked and cleaned and placed in deep, spacious pits. They were not covered but filled with soil. It has been established that if these food reserves were covered with hay or leaves before sealing, for cleanliness, they would rot in the winter. But when they were covered with soil, the covering was found to be clean and frozen in the form of a dome when the geese were taken out of the pit for consumption.

This information pertains to the mid-18th century. A.I. Argentov (1861a, p. 489) gives an eyewitness account of such a hunt, but it was only of molting birds.

On the Chukchi coast lesser snow geese are now shot only rarely. On Wrangel Island this bird was an essential food item for men and dogs for the original settlers in the 20s and the early 30s. Initially the hunting was reckless and without restraint, as in many places in the Far North from time immemorial. When the wintering people were few and access to Wrangel Island was difficult, this approach did not pose any special threat to the survival of lesser snow geese. Nevertheless, even in A.I. Mineev's time, i.e. in the early 30s, the geese stopped nesting in the southeastern part of the island adjoining the Polar Station in Rodgers Bay. When I was on the island the number of geese shot was small. There was no particular shortage of fresh meat since there was a good supply of a few head of live cattle. Moreover, the wintering people shot some bear and walrus. I did not participate in the general hunt but shot about 30 geese, mainly for ornithological collections. In the Institute of Zoology of the Academy of Sciences of the USSR there were only a few specimens of this species before my time and there was an urgent need to enlarge the collection.

My experience of hunting lesser snow geese was limited but I will record it. I shot them only in flight. I selected Akatylanva, roughly where the 180th parallel crosses the south coast of Wrangel Island, as the area of spring hunting. The geese usually flew along the tundra lowland stretching east-west parallel to the coastline. At Akatylanva, the strip of tundra lowland was very narrow. If one sat in the middle of it the geese would generally have to fly within close range.

When there was much snow it was useful to wear a loose white overall to make oneself inconspicuous. With the onset of thawing, a time comes when it is advantageous to wear dark clothes. When the flight of geese is noticed the hunter must remain still in his position; it is better if he is pressed close to the ground. For the most part the geese could be shot at a range of 80 to 150 paces. Hunters advised me to use a larger shot and more powder so that the shot was more powerful and scattered. I was satisfied with No. 00 shot but because of my poor gun I had to use more powder.

The geese cannot stand injury. Those I wounded in the head, neck, chest or wing quite often fell dead or were killed by the impact of the fall. However, firing at a longer range left many wounded birds. Often it was very difficult to reach ones lying far off across melting snow. Ultimately the wounded birds would recover enough to rise and fly for over half a km. After extended shooting I would scan the locality with binoculars from some elevation and locate the dying birds. Shooting a flying gosling from the side was best. If one's aim was not good the slug might hit the next one, the one in front or the one behind. My friend, Anakan the eskimo, could lure the birds by imitating their honk. On hearing the call the birds would turn and surround the hunter even after shots were fired. He would also place dead birds close by, propping their necks and heads. I saw how the geese would settle around them.

It would happen that when I roused a large sitting flock the small ones in front would fly to me. On other occasions, knowing that the geese loved to sit along rivulets, I approached them stealthily from behind. But mostly I had to sit and wait for hours in places frequented by the geese. It might happen that the geese did not notice me and would come within 40 or 50 paces. It was even possible to approach undisturbed sitting birds openly and shoot them as they took off, but the birds beyond the range of a shot could not be scared. In the spring of 1939 none of the hunters on Wrangel Island could secure more than 20 or 30 lesser snow geese. The birds caught on arrival were good game and their meat was very tasty without any undesirable aftertaste. I liked it better than that of brent geese, not to speak of eiders.

The molting birds are caught in incomparably large numbers. In the summer of 1930 Tayan processed over 600 molting geese at Cape Blossom. According to A.I. Mineev, hunting for molting birds is done mostly from canoes by forcing them ashore where other hunters wait for them with dogs. Men attack the geese by hand and the dogs finish them. Once it so happened that an entire flock was driven into Rodgers Bay. The geese were caught in such numbers that they were thrown to the dogs and the people got sick of goose. Mineev ultimately prohibited the killing of molted geese but this ban was not enforced by the other leaders of the island. In 1938 the hunters at the Polar Station chased the geese in a motor boat and shot 40 of them in a lagoon at Bruch spit. In 1939 not a single molting bird was caught because they did not molt near the Polar Station and deeper expeditions were not possible because of ice conditions.

The original settlers on Wrangel Island made a practice of collecting thousands of eggs of lesser snow geese. A whole chapter of A.I. Mineev's book (1936) is devoted to describing this. This did not pose any particular difficulty. In 1932, for three and one-half days, Mineev went around the nests on the upper reaches of Mamontovaya River with the hunters and gathered about 1,500 eggs. Since local conditions did not always favor finding fresh eggs, and it was difficult to ascertain when the geese began laying, a hunt for eggs might turn out to be futile. In 1939, for example, in spite of my best efforts, I could not approach the nesting areas on the upper reaches of the Mamontovaya River because of the poor condition of the sledways. The collection of eggs is also rendered difficult when mountain rivers flood and block the way. The eggs of lesser snow geese are very tasty, boil well and hard and constitute useful fresh produce for the wintering people.

In the 40s the number of people arriving on Wrangel Island rose steadily. The expeditions brought automobiles and people began visiting the interior of the island. With the improvement in air communications regular contact with the Chukchi coast was established.

Human activity increasingly influenced the population of wild fauna on the island. The hunting of lesser snow geese was often an outrageous, rapacious affair, which P. Bocharov (1958) and V. Lavrent'ev (1960) described in their articles. From 1957, hunting of lesser snow geese and the gathering of their eggs were prohibited by the Magadansk Regional Executive Committee, but the ban was relaxed in 1960 in favor of local hunters and a norm of 30 geese per hunter was laid down. Poachers were severely fined. However, in actual practice it has not been possible so far to rationalize the hunting of geese in the area. The question of effective conservation of lesser snow geese on Wrangel Island calls for timely and radical resolution; it will become more acute if not dealt with now.

Enemies—The polar fox, from among the animal kingdom, is the most serious enemy of these geese. They suffer from attacks from the time of arrival right up to the last days of migration.

Hunters often told A.I. Mineev (1936, p. 97) of the onslaught of foxes on flocks of geese. Some would sit in ambush while others gave chase. There is nothing improbable in this though I personally did not have the opportunity to observe it. A joint attack by several fox families is possible: while the adult animal hides the young ones roam around the geese, and ultimately the birds are ambushed. Mineev saw huge flocks of geese shifting along the tundra when surrounded by polar foxes.

On June 7, 1939, I noticed a polar fox openly running close to a flock on the right bank of the Mamontovaya River. The birds did not show much anxiety and went near the rivulet leisurely. In the first half of June I saw many polar foxes running across the tundra but did not notice them hunting geese even once. I found an altogether different picture in mid-August, 1938, in Tundra Akademii. Innumerable foxes were found there with the remains of geese scattered all around. In most cases the remains were the feathers and down of young birds with shreds or bits of skin and parts of wings. Once I found the remains of an adult goose. The topography of the area showed that the foxes used convenient high points in the area to fall on the geese pasturing in a clearing. It was striking that the remains of brent geese were never found, though they were more numerous than the lesser snow geese on Tundra Akademii. Evidently the exceptionally tasty young lesser snow goose was the food of polar foxes. It was interesting that the dogs, too, showed a preference for these geese whenever they had a choice. In one case the dogs even made a tunnel under a building with stored birds I had shot in it. They stole only geese and did not touch other birds, nor did they attempt to make a tunnel when there were other birds available in the store earlier.

Apart from the polar fox the lesser snow geese suffer from feathered enemies also. Ravens, glaucous gulls and especially jaegers pose much danger to the eggs and chicks. I once saw an attack by a jaeger (*Stercorarius pomarinus*) on an adult goose standing quietly by the side of a rivulet. The jaeger leisurely flew in, stalled its flight above the goose or came down near it. The goose kept rising on its toes, slightly sticking out its wings and pointing its beak at the intruder.

Systematics—The geese inhabiting Wrangel Island and the Chukchi peninsula belong to the subspecies *Chen caerulescens caerulescens* (L.). It is clearly distinguished from *Ch. c. atlanticus* (Kennard) by its much smaller size and, first of all, by its much shorter wing; the difference becomes apparent even on a simple comparison of the bird skins. The large form *Ch. c. atlanticus* is found from Elesmirova and Baffin Island to north Greenland, and its distribution is not continuous.[1] The discontinuous distribution and the remarkably large size might even place it in a special species, which of course is difficult to concede.

In the ornithological literature the taxonomic affinity of the so-called blue goose has not so far been conclusively established. For many decades now it has been observed in the natural nesting areas and in captivity. For example, T.H. Manning (1942), who observed the neighborly habitation of blue and lesser snow geese on Southampton Island and also mixed pairs of them, nevertheless called the former *Ch. caerulescens* (L.) and the later *Ch. hyperborea hyperborea* (Pall.). At the same time he adduced many grounds in favor of the view that these geese were merely different color phases of the same species. These grounds were as follows: identical body proportions and shapes, same color of the unfeathered body parts, identical behavior and call, eggs and nests, inhabiting and nesting together, joining to form mixed flocks, and forming hybrids. The duration of incubation and many other phenomena in their life cycles were also identical although the number of eggs in the clutch of the blue goose is smaller. At the same time, the feather color of the blue goose differs sharply and forms a complex pattern, and is surprisingly constant even in the hybrids. It does not go on varying as happens usually in dichromatic species. Mixed pairs are relatively few. There is a well-known geographic localization of the blue goose, which nests only in the northwestern part of Hudson Bay, on Southampton Island and in Baffin Island, but winters in Louisiana. Further, there is no region where only the blue goose is found but, on the contrary, in much of the range of the lesser snow goose the blue goose is not found at all. Within the USSR the blue goose has not been found at all; it is also absent from the mass win-

[1]Attention is particularly drawn to L.L. Snyder's map (1957, p. 62) depicting the distribution of these two species of goose in arctic Canada.

tering places in California.

My special studies on such dichromatic species as the falcon, grouse, hawk, booted eagle, jaeger, Atlantic murre, *Strix* owl, paradise flycatcher, etc. convinced me that dichromatism in diverse birds manifests differently and the taxonomic assessment must vary, but in no case does it reach the species level. Hence, I am inclined to acknowledge the blue goose as only a color phase of the lesser snow geese.

J. Delacour (1954, p. 92) regarded the lesser snow goose as nearer to the graylag goose. Without disputing this well-known affinity, I want to draw attention to the characters that place it closer to the Indian goose. As already pointed out, aerial somersaults during mating ceremonies are characteristic of these two species and apparently have not been seen in other geese. There is one more, quite interesting observation in captivity. E.P. Gee (1961) reported that at Slimbridge where the birds lived under nearly natural conditions, the lesser snow goose mated with the Indian goose, the mixed pair always living along with the latter. Finally, there is no doubt about some similarity in the external features and plumage color of the blue and the Indian geese.

Specimens— 1 and 2) Cape Schmidt, June 8 or 19, 1915, ○○, Savich; 3) central part of Wrangel Island, June 13, 1932, ♂, Mineev; 4) Rodgers Bay, August 20, 1932, ♂, Mineev; 5) same place, August 22, 1932, ♀, Mineev; 6) Cape Serdtse-Kamen', first few days, of June, 1934, ○, Portenko; 7) western part of Wrangel Island, August 7, 1938, ○, Druzhinin; 8 to 26) Bruch spit, August 8, 1938, ♂♀, and 17 birds (10 sen. and 7 juv.), Portenko; 27 and 28) Krasnyi Flag River mouth, August 17, 1938, ♂♂, and subad., Portenko; 29) Akatylanva to the west of Somnitel'naya Bay, June 2, 1938, ♀, Portenko; 30) same place, June 3, 1939, ♀, Portenko; 31 to 33) same place, June 4, 1939, ♂♂, Portenko; 34 to 36) same place, June 5, 1939, ♀♀, Portenko; 37) same place, June 6, 1939, ♂, Portenko; 38 and 39) same place, June 7, 1939, ♂♀, Portenko; 40 to 43) same place, June 9, 1939, ♂♂♂♀, Portenko; 44) same place, June 12, 1939, ♀, Portenko; 45 and 46) same place, June 13, 1939, ♀♀, Portenko; and 47) Rodgers Bay, August 24, 1939, ♀, 1°anno, Portenko.

Biological collection— 1 to 5) Five eggs from different clutches on the upper reaches of Mamontovaya River, June 11 and 12, 1922, Mineev; and 6 to 10) clutch of five eggs in the nesting area on Tundrovyi Peak hill, June 10, 1964, Chernyavskii.

12. **Anser albifrons albifrons** (Scop.)—**White-fronted Goose**

Local name—Chukchian: Eitóchkhyn.[1]

Distribution and status—Species nesting and migrating in the winter, common in the western part of the Chukchi peninsula, in the east up to Vankarém River inclusive, sporadic, probably nesting farther up to Kolyuchin Bay, and absent from the eastern and southern parts of the Chukchi peninsula. Straggles to Wrangel Island.

The white-fronted goose nests very rarely on the banks of Anadyr Bay (Portenko 1939b, vol. II, p. 82). V.É. Yakobi found it in the nesting areas near Uél'kal'. Stray pairs were seen on June 4, 1961. On June 16, he collected a female from a nest with

[1]Nomads knowing only the Chukchi language call all these geese "eitu". At the same time, there is similarity between this name and "yaptu", the name for goose in the Yamal'sk languages.

eggs. In the fall white-fronted geese were spotted more often as they flew in pairs and flocks. However, neither L.O. Belopol'skii (1934) nor P.T. Butenko and I found it in Krest Bay.

N.F. Kallinikov reported (1912, p. 151) that the geese were rather few to the east of Krest Bay because of the local conditions. None of the ornithologists who visited Providence Bay, including I.O. Olenev and P.T. Butenko, who wintered there, found the white-fronted goose.

E.W. Nelson (1883, p. 93) at first erroneously reported that the white-fronted goose nested on St. Lawrence Island but later (Nelson 1887, p. 83) more accurately pointed out that geese chicks on the island were seen in the summer of 1881. In May, 1937, a specimen was caught near Gambell (Friedmann 1938). F.H. Fay and T.J. Cade (1959) came to the conclusion that this goose was found on St. Lawrence Island irregularly and did not nest there. A lone bird was noticed on May 29, and four were seen on June 26, 1953. Many of the younger residents of Gambell had not even seen this bird. According to a report by E.G.F. Sauer (Sauer and Urban 1964) a white-fronted goose was noticed on June 7, 1960, on a lakelet north of Boxer Bay. H. Friedmann (1934a) found the metacarpal bones in two 1,000-year-old excavations at the southeastern and northwestern tips of the island.

E.W. Nelson wrote that the white-fronted geese nested on the Siberian coast of Bering Strait but this very general reference was not supported by actual observations or specimens. More recently É.V. Schmidt did not find the white-fronted goose in Mechigmensk gulf, Lawrence Bay or Uélen at all. According to my findings, these geese were absent not only from the coastal areas of Uélen but also farther inland in the valleys of the Rivers Kol'oam-Véem and Utte-Véem. In the summer of 1914 at Cape Serdtse-Kamen' some flocks of white-fronted geese were reportedly noticed by F.S. Hersey, but he did not collect any specimens and could have erred since the specific identification of flying geese is not always easy. For Kolyuchin Bay there is a reference to a record made by the *Vega* expedition (Palmén 1886) along with some other doubtful observations. On June 19, 1879, a female white-fronted goose was brought from Dzhenretlen. Later this specimen was exhibited in London (*The Ibis*, 1883, p. 348). An egg brought on June 29 was initially assumed to be that of a white-fronted goose but V. Meves later identified it as that of a brent goose. On July 8 E.K. Brusevits shot a goose, identification of which was not accurate.

According to the information I gathered in 1934, the white-fronted goose was regarded as a great rarity in Vankarém. According to the observations of A.A. Kishchinskii, in Vankarém this goose did not occur because of the absence of a suitable habitat but slightly westward and southward the white-fronted goose was fairly common. Between the lagoons of Vankarém and Nutauge, Kishchinskii shot four broods with downy chicks and apart from them, adult geese were shot on July 17 and 18, 1970. At first sight, the white-fronted goose was much rarer there than around Ukouge lagoon, where a sample section of 48 sq km held 30 to 35 geese regularly in June and the first half of July, 1970. They nested mostly. Kishchinskii and his assistants found six nests with clutches from June 17 through 30 (Fig. 18).

In 1956, I found a pair nesting in the tundra near the 91st km. From the beginning of June there were a few pairs and some lone birds on the Amguema. On June 25 and 30 I saw one flock of five birds, evidently single birds. The small number of geese was evidently to be explained by the unrestricted fall hunting. According to the information gathered by É.V. Schmidt, the white-fronted goose predominated among other species of goose on the Amguema. According to the observations of Kishchinskii, in the Amguema estuary it was even more common than in Ukouge lagoon. Four nests with clutches were found there on July 3 and 4, 1970.

Near Cape Schmidt there were not many geese; in the spring of 1915, a specimen was collected by A.A. Savich (Artobolevskii 1927). In June, 1935, in the nearest lagoon, a goose was collected by V.Ya. Isaev. He found it with a brood in a lake on the lower reaches of the Ékiatap River close to the mountains. According to É.V. Schmidt the geese were very numerous in the Kuvét River mouth; on the Apapyl'-gyn River 15 km to the east of Cape Pevek the white-fronted goose was more numerous than other species.

Even A.I. Argentov (1861a) cited a goose which was unusually large in the Trans-Lena region, i.e. on the tundra from Chaun Bay to the lower reaches of the Kolyma. But the information as to nidification was unfortunately mixed up with that on other geese. N.F. Kallinikov also wrote in very general terms that the white-fronted geese joined the other species of Chukchian geese at Chaun and on the Kolyma.

S.G. Pavlov caught a white-fronted goose in Chaun Bay on June 20, 1933. É.V. Schmidt gave Portenko detailed information covering the 30s of this century. According to him, innumerable geese came to the Mlelyu-Véem River, to the Chaun lowlands, all the low-lying shore of Chaun Bay, to the Karchyk peninsula, to Aiok Island, to the lower reaches of the Baranikha and Kolyma, and farther to the west up to Alazei, i.e. up to the limit of the territory covered by his observations. V.D. Lebedev and V.R. Filin (1959) caught four specimens from May 22 through 24, 1958, on the west coast of Aiok Island from a flock gathered for molting. They saw the molted geese on the west coast of the Karchyk peninsula in flocks of up to 50 birds each in the first 10 days of August. From July 22 through 24 molted flocks were sighted on the west shore of Chaun Bay and on Nagleinyn Mountain. In 1956 F.B. Chernyavskii saw broods time and again in the broad valley of the Yarak-Véem River, in the eastern part of the north Anyui Range.

According to K.N. Yakovlev the white-fronted goose was found on the coastal tundra from the Bol'shaya Baranikha to the Kolyma in the same places as the bean goose, but more frequently than the latter.

There was only a chance find on Wrangel Island. On the night of June 13/14, 1939, A.I. Agapov, the physician, shot a lone white-fronted goose on the tundra at Rodgers Bay. It flew in from the north and had probably lost its way. Another wintering resident assured me that he saw two flights of these geese.

From the zoogeographic viewpoint it is important to notice that the nesting range of the white-fronted goose falls short of Bering Strait. It nests on the lower reaches of the Pakhach, Apuk and Anadyr rivers but is absent east of Krest and Kolyuchin bays. Nor is it seen on St. Lawrence Island.

Arrival—According to the observations of A.I. Argentov, the first arrivals of geese in the Trans-Lena region are on June 20 by the old calendar. Argentov did not distinguish the different species although not all of them arrived at the same time. According to É.V. Schmidt who studied the geese in the same region from Chaun

Bay to the Kolyma, the white-fronted goose was seen later than the bean goose and its mass flight occurred at least a day later. It may be recalled (Portenko 1939b, vol. II, p. 83) that N. Gondatti pointed out a similar time lag in the arrival of geese in the Anadyr region. According to V.D. Lebedev and V.R. Filin, in 1958 the white-fronted goose in flight was noticed on May 22 in Gizhiga, on May 22 and 27 near Pevek and on May 30 on Aiok Island. Molting there evidently took place in the latter half of July and early August.

Breeding—According to my observations, on the Amguema in 1956, the white-fronted geese were very active until mid-June. They wandered in different directions and their disyllabic cry "kavgák" was often heard. On seeing me these geese could become very agitated and their calls would rise to a very high pitch. On June 10 a lone male was seen constantly in flight in the neighborhood calling for its lost mate. After the 16th I did not see these geese and assumed that they had deserted this turbulent area, but on July 8 I found the nesting area thanks to a wolf. In the distance I saw a pair of geese crying and circling a place and later sighted a huge wolf scouring the tundra. When I approached the geese flew off and settled far off. On June 25 and 30 a flock of five birds flew past the knoll. Probably they were beginning to flock before molting.

According to the observations of V.É. Yakobi, in 1961 the white-fronted geese on arriving settled in an area of water 700 × 600 m free from ice. On July 16, on another lake 300 × 200 m still covered with ice, tiny leads were formed to an islet on which a nest was found with six poorly incubated eggs. The female, which was shot down, revealed a large brood patch. The male was standing not far away. On August 29 white-fronted geese were found in pairs and flocks. On September 7 a flock flew over Uél'kal' in a southwesterly direction following the wind.

Remaining information is given along with that for the bean goose.

Weight—The female caught around a nest 2 km from Uél'kal' weighed 2,299 g.

Economic importance—Being common in the western part of the peninsula, the white-fronted goose is caught there to the same extent as the bean goose.

Systematics of the subspecies—As already pointed out (Portenko 1939b), the white-fronted goose does not form a subspecies throughout the Eurasian North. The concepts of subspecies in North America and Greenland have undergone significant changes in the last decade or so. At present, four subspecies are recognized:

1. **Anser albifrons albifrons** Scop. Relatively small goose of bright color with a pinkish-white beak. It inhabits the Eurasian tundra from Kanin and Novaya Zemlya to Kolyuchin Bay, Krest Bay and the lower reaches of the Anadyr.

2. **Anser albifrons frontalis** Baird. A bigger bird with a very long neck and beak. The plumage is more brownish than grayish. It occurs in Alaska as far east as the Mackenzie.

3. **Anser albifrons gambeli** Hartl. This is a very large goose, darker than the preceding one, with very narrow feather tips. The eyelids are yellow. It probably nests on Victoria Island but the precise nesting ground is not known.

4. **Anser albifrons flavirostris** Dalg. and Scott. In size, it occupies a midpoint between the subspecies *A. a. gambeli* and *A. a. frontalis*. It is darker than the rest with narrow feather tips. The color of its beak is orange. It nests on the west coast

of Greenland.

Only one specimen of the subspecies of Chukchian white-fronted goose and some specimens and measurements given in the works of I.A. Palmén (1887) and V.M. Artobolevskii (1927) (Table 10) are available to judge the characteristics of the subspecies.

A comparison of measurements given in Table 10 with those given earlier by the present author (1939b, vol. II, p. 87, Table 11) leads him to conclude that all three specimens were females and of small size. Hence they could not be placed in the larger subspecies *A. a. frontalis*.

Specimen—Chaun Bay, June 20, 1933, ○, Pavlov.

Table 10. Measurements of bills and wings of white-fronted geese, cm

Locality, date and sex	Bill from forehead	Height above beak	Wing measurement
Chaun Bay, June 20, 1933, ○	5.14	2.37	41.2
Dzhenretlen, June 19, 1879, ○	4.70	—	41.2
Cape Schmidt, spring 1915, ○ of second year	4.75	—	38.5

13. Anser erythropus (L.)—Lesser White-fronted Goose

Distribution and status—Found in the migratory flight period in the westernmost parts of the Chukchi peninsula; does not cross to east of Chaun Bay. Perhaps nests. Extremely few in numbers.

Even F.P. Wrangel (1841, p. 199) wrote that the residents of the lower Kolyma distinguished the lesser white-fronted goose as a separate species. While listing the species of geese, A.I. Argentov (1861a, p. 493) referred to "a small white-fronted goose", but did not provide details of its distribution. I am obliged to É.V. Schmidt for accurate information on the occurrence of this species in the Chukchi peninsula.

He noticed the lesser white-fronted goose only at Chaun Bay in spring flight, saw some flocks, and collected one bird in the fall. That goose perhaps nested along the Chaun River; it appeared early in the spring on its lower reaches. In the spring flight the lesser white-fronted goose was noticed in the Karchyk peninsula and on Aiok Island, but was not found in summer, at least on Aiok Island. It was noted more often in the estuary of the Kolyma; after the spring Schmidt took five to eight of them, which comprised 5 per cent of all of the specimens collected.

Flight—According to É.V. Schmidt the lesser white-fronted goose is seen in spring after the bean and white-fronted geese.

Economic importance—Because of its small numbers, it has no special importance in hunting and is bagged in goose hunts along with bean and white-fronted geese, especially with the latter.

Systematics—There is only one race of lesser white-fronted goose throughout the area from Novaya Zemlya to the Anadyr region (Portenko, 1939b, vol. II, p. 87, Table 6).

14. **Melanonyx fabalis serrirostris** (Swinh.)—**Bean Goose**

Distribution and status—Species nesting and migrating in the winter, absent from the eastern part of the Chukchi peninsula from Cape Bering and Vankarém. Is common toward west, from Krest and Chaun bays. Enters St. Lawrence Island very rarely and is not found on Wrangel Island.

The bean goose is numerous in the maritime zone of the Anadyr region. L.O. Belopol'skii (1934) found broods during his travels from Krest Bay to the Anadyr lagoon and saw a pair on May 24, 1931, between Krest Bay and Cape Bering. However, V.É. Yakobi never found bean geese in Krest Bay and I.O. Olenev and P.T. Butenko did not see it in Providence Bay. N.F. Kallinikov wrote (1912, p. 151) that there were not many of these geese to the east of Krest Bay; only flocks of them were to be seen flying in the spring from time to time. For the south coast of the Chukchi peninsula there is no further information about the bean geese, nor is there any information for the east coast.

At St. Lawrence Island a young male with a pink band on the beak was found on the ice floes north of Gambell on May 8, 1952, as a rare exception (Fay and Cade 1959).

This goose is altogether absent from the interior of the eastern half of the peninsula. I did not find it in the valleys of the Utte-Véem and Kol'oam-Véem rivers. It was not mentioned for Kolyuchin Bay by the members of the *Vega* expedition (Palmén 1887).

The bean goose nested on the Amguema. E.M. Meller found a clutch near Pereval'naya Station and in 1956 I found a pair around the 91st km several times. It was taken by hunters in Vankarém but V.Ya. Isaev did not report on nidification near Cape Schmidt. Only once, in mid-June, 1935, was a bean goose bagged from a flock in flight. In the words of É.V. Schmidt, bean geese were still few around the Kuvet River. The Chukchians said nests were found from time to time in the tundra near Nol'de Bay. The bean goose was quite common on the Apapyl'gyn River (15 km east of Pevek). Stray nests were found on the Rautan. J. Koren (Thayer and Bangs 1914) found this goose in smaller numbers on marine tundras east of Cape Shelagskii than in the area from Chaun to the Kolyma. According to K.N. Yakovlev bean geese were found in very large numbers southeast of Cape Shelagskii along the lakes and river estuaries.

On the western side of Chaun Bay, according to an eyewitness account by É.V. Schmidt, the bean goose represents 20 to 30 per cent of the total number of geese caught. This ratio was established as a result of hunt in the Karchyk peninsula and on Aiok Island. V.D. Lebedev and V.R. Filin (1959) regarded the bean goose in these areas as a fairly common bird. On Aiok Island, in the summer of 1958, some nests with clutches were found, nesting birds were collected and flocks gathering for molting observed. On the west shore of Chaun Bay broods accompanying females were noticed. Similar broods and molting bean geese were seen on the Kozmina River and its tributary, the Tikhaye, in the Karchyk peninsula.

To the west of Chaun Bay the bean goose was long regarded as a very common bird. This is recorded in old references from the time of J. Billing's expedition which, after July 16, 1787, found this species for certain around Baranov-Kamen'.

G.A. Sarychev (1802, vol. I, p. 90) writes that in the lakes he passed there were many large, wild graylag geese, called bean geese, which were molting at that time and could not fly. They were shot in large numbers. In the travel records of F.P. Wrangel we find many references to innumerable geese. Unfortunately the species were not identified on each occasion and the geese were referred to according to the species recognized by the locals (Wrangel 1841, vol. II, p. 199), i.e. bean goose, common wild goose and very large graylag goose. On July 21, 1822, the Wrangel expedition approached a network of lakes between Malyi and Bol'shoi Baranov Kamen' which served as a shelter for the molting geese. Wrangel writes (1841, vol. II, p. 198) that they quickly bagged 15 birds which, according to their guides, was a very good shoot considering the season of the year. Formerly goose hunting was usually very good in this area but for some time the geese seem to prefer the coast of Indigirka, where the local residents kill them in thousands as food for the dogs and store them for the winter. The following day (July 22, 1822) the expedition's bean goose hunt extended to the sea coast 15 versts to the east of Bol'shoi Baranov Kamen'. In the estuary of the Zemlyanaya rivulet a large number of geese were observed. With much honking they threw themselves into the sea, swam through the opening onto the ice and were soon concealed from view.

On August 1, 1822, in the Berezova river valley, i.e. Malaya Baranikha, on a lake five versts from the sea, Matyushkin's party was aroused by a loud honking of geese splashing around in innumerable numbers (ibid, pp. 243 and 244). In a short time 75 geese were killed with sticks. The following day, moving farther east along the sea coast, the travelers continued to hunt for the geese, going around the marshy outlets of rivulets and brooks.

On August 15, 1844, A.I. Argentov (1875b, p. 43) rode with a caravan of pack horses along the tundra from lower Kolyma to Baranikha, roughly a day's journey from the Arctic Ocean, and saw molting geese on a small lake. Some dozens of them were sitting on the sand bank. The hungry travelers began a frenzied hunt. The men were possessed with a passion to destroy the geese. The beat, caught, shot, stabbed, chased and stamped on them, and called it goose hunting. The trophies of this slaughter were 27 bean geese.

According to the legends of É.V. Schmidt, molting flocks of bean geese were noticed on the lakes between Bol'shoi and Malyi Anyui. Along these lakes, bean geese were the only geese to be seen, as on the Omolon. Along the edge of the forest on the Kolyma this species predominated over other species of geese. This is understandable since the bean geese everywhere penetrated the forest deeper than the white-fronted goose. In 1965, F.B. Chernyavskii found broods in the Yarak-Véem River basin in the eastern part of the north Anyui Range. In N.P. Sokol'nikov's manuscript, which I processed, it is pointed out that many bean geese molt 50 versts beyond Eropol up the Anadyr. In general, however, the bulk of the bean geese nest on the lower course of this river (Portenko 1939b, vol. II, pp. 90 and 91). According to an eyewitness account by K.N. Yakovlev, in the so-called East tundra between Chaun Bay and the Kolyma, though the bean geese were numerous, they were fewer than the white-fronted geese. J. Koren (Schaanning 1954) collected two males of *Melanonyx fabalis serrirostris* in the Kolyma delta on June 8 and July 14, 1916 and three downy chicks and a clutch of three eggs on July 1, 1917. He also shot a male on June 5, 1916, which H.T.L. Schaanning identified as *M. f. sibiricus* (Alph.).

On Wrangel Island the bean goose has not yet been collected but it quite possibly flies there.

Habitat—F.P. Wrangel's expedition found geese, especially bean geese, in the valleys of rivers and around lakes. A.I. Argentov writes (1861a, p. 486) that the geese usually nest in the elevated dry clearings around water and J. Koren notes that the bean goose, compared to the white-fronted goose, evidently prefers elevated dry tundra. For example, it does not nest on the depressed islets in the Kolyma delta used by the white-fronted goose.

V.D. Lebedev and V.R. Filin (1959) found a nest on Aiok Island on the slope of a ridge among sedge-cotton-grass hummocky marsh tundra 300 m from the river and two nests on similar, but wet, tundra. I could never make out any significant difference between the site preferences of white-fronted and bean geese for nidification.

Arrival—A.I. Argentov writes (1861a) that the first geese arrived on May 2 in the Trans-Lena region and the most massive arrival along the coasts of the Arctic Ocean was on May 19, 20 and 21 (pp. 484 and 485, old calendar). According to the observations of É.V. Schmidt, from Chaun Bay to the Kolyma the first geese to appear everywhere were the bean geese. They were followed by the white-fronted geese and only then by the lesser white-fronted geese. The first flocks of bean geese came 10 days before the mass arrival and sometimes even earlier. V.D. Lebedev and V.R. Filin (1959) noticed four flying bean geese near Pevek on May 26, 1958. In 1931, L.O. Belopol'skii saw the first geese in Krest Bay on May 15 and at Cape Bering on May 18. The mass flight was in the last 10 days of May. On May 24 he also saw bean geese which were already paired, between Krest Bay and Cape Bering.

Nidification—It is now well known that geese, like many other birds of the North, do not reproduce every year and mostly remain single in their second year. This was noticed even by A.I. Argentov (1861a, see about swans).

He writes that the best time for collecting swan and goose eggs is from May 21 through 31; they have already been laid in the nest and what is more they are fresh and not yet incubated. A nest with two pecked eggs was found by J. Koren at Cape Bol'shoi Baranov on July 6, 1912. The eggs were later taken on board the ship and put around a stove. On the following day chicks emerged from them. As reported by V.D. Lebedev and V.R. Filin, a nest with four eggs was found on Aiok Island on June 12, 1958, and two nests with three and five eggs on June 23. The chirp of chicks still inside unpecked eggs could be heard on June 30. A nest with a clutch of four eggs was found by E.M. Meller near Pereval'naya on June 10, 1939. It was found in a depression between mounds near a small brook and was covered with feathers. The incubating goose flew off 30 m from the nest on Meller's approach. The embryos in the eggs had just begun to develop a vascular network. The sizes of the two eggs were 5.87 × 8.84 cm and 5.84 × 8.73 cm, and their weight 13.50 and 13.85* g, respectively. The color was dull milk-white.

*An obvious error in the original. Should read 135.0 and 138.5 g respectively—General Editor.

On July 10 and 11, 1958, V.D. Lebedev and V.R. Filin saw broods accompanied by females in the Karchyk peninsula and on July 19 and 21 in the sea at Chaun Bay. On August 19, 1931, on the tundra between Krest Bay and the Anadyr lagoon, L.O. Belopol'skii found a brood of seven still nonflying but fully plumed chicks.

Molting—V.D. Lebedev and V.R. Filin saw flocks of 30 to 40 bean geese gathered for molting on the south coast of Aiok in mid-July.

Some idea of the molting period can be had from the scattered notes of G.A. Sarychev, F.P. Wrangel and A.I. Argentov.

In the first half of August molting was in full swing, judging from the fact that many geese were caught. In the travel records of F.P. Wrangel (1841, vol. II, p. 246) it is pointed out that molting of geese was complete by August 13, in 1822, but Matyushkin found a whole flock of molting geese on August 15.

A.I. Argentov (1857a) reports that the sedentary Chukchians hunted for molting geese at the end of June and in the first half of July (old calendar) and caught the geese right up to Assumption Day, i.e. up to August 27. He was himself present at a hunt for molting bean geese on August 15 (3), 1844. V.D. Lebedev and V.R. Filin found pairs of molting bean geese in the Karchyk peninsula on August 18, 1958.

Migration—On August 13, 1822, Matyushkin noticed the migration of innumerable flocks 10 km east of the Baranikha estuary. On September 6 he came out of Malyi Anyui and saw two flocks of flying geese. On August 27, 1958, V.D. Lebedev and V.R. Filin noticed the last pair of bean geese on the northwestern coast of Aiok Island. F.B. Chernyavskii found huge flocks flying above the north Anyui Range from September 10 through 15, 1965.

Economic importance—There is no doubt that in bygone days hunting of molting bean geese was of vital importance for the residents of the tundra and the riverine areas west of Chaun Bay. G.A. Sarychev (1802, vol. I, p. 90) writes that Kolyma Cossacks drove large flocks of geese into a stretched net, beat them with sticks and threw them without further processing into a pit dug in the ground. Argentov writes (1857a, pp. 97 and 98, and 101) that the sedentary Chukchians used dogs to hunt the molting birds. They also pierced the geese with spears and mostly killed them with sticks but did not drive them into a net or tent as the Tungus and Yakutians did at Kolyma. N.F. Kallinikov (1912, p. 151) was told that there were so many geese at Chaun and on the Kolyma that the residents killed them in large numbers and preserved them. In the 30s, according to É.V. Schmidt, the Kolyma residents set off specially to hunt geese on the lakes between Bol'shoi and Malyi Anyui. Yakovlev, the professional hunter, told me that only amateur hunting of bean goose has developed among the Russian public.

A.I. Argentov (1857b) also refers to the recovery of marrow. The wings of geese containing the marrow were dressed for this purpose. It is well known that in the initial stages of molting the tubular bones of wings are filled with marrow which evidently was considered a delicacy.

Systematics of the subspecies—Recently the systematics of the subspecies of bean geese have undergone a review, first by H. Johansen (1945) and later by J. Delacour (1951). In any case, the Chukchi peninsula is characterized by the presence of the subspecies *Melanonyx fabalis serrirostris* (Swinh.) which is very well distinguished by the shape of the bill and size (Portenko 1939b, vol. II, p. 101, Table 7). The range of distribution extends from the lower Lena to the western part of the Chukchi peninsula, the Anadyr basin and Koryatz Zemlya.

Unlike J. Delacour (1954, vol. I, p. 92), I am not inclined to include the bean goose in the group of grayleg geese which covers *Anser anser* (L.), *A. albifrons* (Scop.), and *A. erythropus* (L.). I regard the bean goose as an Arctic variant of the Canadian *Branta canadensis* (L.). Incidentally, the black color on the beak is a vestige of the black covering large parts of the neck and head among the ancestors of the bean goose.

It is not just an accident that the western subspecies of the Canadian geese resembles the bean goose in the form of the body and color while the sharply differing subspecies (especially in size) are characteristic of east and northeastern North America. Moreover, the downy chicks of Canadian geese, like those of bean geese, are yellow. In other geese of the genus *Branta* the fledgelings are gray in color without any yellow.

Biological collection—Two eggs from a clutch in the vicinity of Pereval'naya, June 10, 1939, Meller.

15. **Philacte canagica** (Sewast.)—**Emperor Goose**

Local name—Chukchian: Ítlikhléut, idlidljaut in the records of the *Vega* expedition (denoting "white-headed"). In Eskimo: lekhlépik at Providence Bay and lŏkh'-lŭk on St. Lawrence Island. It is interesting that the Russian settlers in Alaska called it "Caeser's goose" (Turner 1886, p. 153).

Distribution and status—Species nesting and migrating in the winter, spread almost exclusively through the eastern part of the Chukchi peninsula and in the west up to the Amguema. They only rarely fly to Wrangel Island.

The nesting zone of the emperor goose beginning at Cape Navarin covers the maritime belt of the Anadyr Range farther to the north, where this species is not rare (Portenko 1939b, vol. II, p. 102). In Krest Bay it was found in spring flight by L.O. Belopol'skii (1934), who saw flocks many times in early June, 1931, and collected a specimen from Meechken Island. This bird was also noted by P.T. Butenko in fall flight in 1937 near Uél'kal'. On June 8, 1956, I saw a flying flock of five birds not far from Égvekinot and on September 13, 1939, in Providence Bay. Though the emperor goose was common in this bay it was not prolific. W.S. Brooks (1915) quite often saw it in June, 1913. According to I.O. Olenev the emperor goose nested, and was not a rarity, all around Providence Bay and nearby, for example near Kivak village. At the apex of the bay Olenev found a large number of feathers and droppings. In September, 1931, he noticed a flock of 30 to 40 birds probably gathered for molting. On May 26 or 27, 1932, he collected a male flying over Istiget village. P.T. Butenko, who also wintered in Providence Bay, noticed emperor geese only a few times, specifically on May 25, 1938, in Sireniki. He collected a female on June 11 in Istiget and a male on June 24 in Providence Bay. Add to this the fact that Brooks secured a male on June 5, 1913, at Cape Chaplin (Indian point), and we have all the information on the occurrence of the emperor goose on the south coast of the Chukchi peninsula.

Information on finds of emperor geese on St. Lawrence Island has long remained vague and contradictory. At the time of the visit of the *Vega* expedition to the island (Palmén 1887) from July 31 through August 2, 1879, a specimen was offered for sale. O. Nordquist heard the call of this goose in the northwestern part of the island. E.W. Nelson (1883, p. 95) first writes that on June 24, 1881, he noticed on the northwestern tip of the island a considerable number of emperor geese on daily forage journeys. But later (Nelson, 1887) he reports that this species was found in large numbers on the southwest coast. The captain of the *Corwin*, K.L. Hooper (1884, p. 23), also mentions that many large flocks were noticed near the island. They flew away in a southwesterly direction. W.S. Brooks (1915) found the emperor goose abundant on the south coast of the island. J. Dixon (1916, p. 373), riding with Brooks, noticed that the goose did not nest there in spite of its abundance. On June 25, 1913, he saw flocks of seven to 20 birds totaling more than one hundred but the dissected specimens did not reveal any signs of breeding. F.S. Hersey (1916), who was on St. Lawrence Island on July 24 and 26, 1914, also heard that the geese molted in large numbers on the south coast. In 1921, in the first week of July, R.W. Hendee (Bailey 1925) daily noticed this goose on the north coast and collected a nesting female close to Savunga village. On June 28, 1921, A.M. Bailey saw seven emperor geese near Kukuliak village and five next day near Gambell village. On July 8, 1928, F.L. Jaques (1930) observed two near the island. On September 18 and 21 and also on October 2, 1930, H.B. Collins (Friedmann 1932a) bagged birds in flight near Gambell. O.J. Murie (1936) made a collection of 20 specimens, mostly of young birds with dark-colored heads. According to a report of O.W. Geist thousands of emperor geese gathered annually in July to molt on the south coast. Miles of coast were covered with nonflying, molting geese, which had found adequate food there. According to the observations of E.G.F. Sauer and E.K. Urban (1964), large flocks were seen on the coasts from Kangi to Boxer Bay on June 14, 1960. During June the emperor geese fed and rested on the sand banks in this bay, on the wet tundra in the plains and in the valley of the Boxer River. In July they disappeared and flocks of molting geese numbering up to 57 birds were seen in August on inaccessible marshes in the eastern part of the Boxer River delta. Finally, F.H. Fay and T.J. Cade (1959) explained that the emperor geese nested in the central and southeastern parts of the island, where there were many lakes. In the spring flights were commonly seen on the west coast and thousands of immature nonpaired birds molted in summer on the south coast. In his much later work, F.H. Fay (1961) comes to more precise conclusions. The emperor goose, according to him, is a very common and characteristic species of swimming wild bird in the summer season on St. Lawrence Island. On the south coast and in some lagoons on the north coast, 10,000 to 20,000 nonbreeding birds spend the summer and gather in large flocks for molting. T.J. Cade correctly reckoned that St. Lawrence Island was the main assembly ground for the molting of single emperor geese from both the American and Asiatic sides of the ocean. The number of birds nesting locally on the island was hardly one-tenth the number of single birds.

H. Friedmann (1934a) found very few bones of the emperor goose in his archaeological excavations. They were mostly metacarpal bones or pieces of breastbone and coracoids, mainly at the southeastern tip of the island.

The crew of transport ship the *Shilk* (Cherskii 1915) obtained a female in Senyavin Strait on September 28, 1909. In a letter preserved with me N.P. Sokol'nikov writes to Prof. M.A. Menzbier that many emperor geese molted in a narrow section of Mechigmensk Gulf in the early 1900s.

According to A.P. Kuzyakin, who studied the coast from Lawrence Bay to Dezhnev settlement, the emperor goose was so rare that many of the local residents did not even know about it. But he found two nests on the tundra between Uélen and Dezhnev. In July, 1881, E.W. Nelson found a few birds (1883) near Cape Dezhnev. In 1934, I made several observations in the neighborhood of Uélen. Emperor geese were common there in spring but were found in relatively small numbers. I confirmed nidification, at least in the immediate vicinity of Uélen, but few geese molted there in the summer. In the fall huge flocks sometimes gathered. The proximity of the villages was no doubt responsible for the reduction in the population of these birds. In the interior they were common in the nesting areas. I found them on the Kol'oam-Véem and Utte-Véem rivers. I saw two broods on the former and caught two broods on the latter. Flocks gathered to molt and molting birds were commonly found in groups of up to 20 birds. Much larger flocks were rare. On August 9, 1934, in the delta of the Kol'oam River, I counted about 200 birds in one flock. On August 18, I found a large amount of goose droppings on the shore of Lake Kool'ong. From the feathers shed, it could be said that the emperor geese frequented that area. On July 4, 1934, specimens in flight were shot at Mitkulen during the day and P.T. Butenko saw two flying geese there on May 20, apparently of this species. In June and early July, 1970, V.V. Leonovich noticed small flocks near Énurmino. Some of them contained 20 to 30 birds.

The members of the *Vega* expedition (Palmén 1887) quite often found emperor geese in the area adjoining Kolyuchin Bay to the east. During a trip from June 13 through 17, 1879, E.A. Almquist saw some inland. The hunter P. Johansen shot a specimen on June 17 around the winter anchorage of the ship and the Chukchians brought a pair from Dzhenretlen on the 19th. On June 22 a goose was seen and on the 24th another was shot by E.K. Brusevits. On June 27, O. Nordquist saw a pair on the lagoon at Dzhenretlen and on the 30th Johansen found a nest at Pitlekai. On July 1 a goose was again seen and three eggs were obtained from Neshkan. A bird was shot near the *Vega*. The following day E.K. Brusevits and A.A.L. Palander brought an unusually small specimen. On July 5 six eggs were brought from Irgunnuk. On July 9 T.A. Bostrem returned from a hunt with two geese and four eggs taken from under a female. Finally, on July 17, on the eve of the freeing of the *Vega* from the ice floes, some emperor geese were seen by A.E. Nordenskjöld, Almquist and Nordquist. All of these data point beyond doubt to the emperor goose having been abundant in Kolyuchin Bay, at least in those years. During J. Koren's journey (Thayer and Bangs 1914) along the north coast of the Chukchi peninsula this goose was seen only rarely; it was even more rare to the west of Kolyuchin Bay.

According to the information I have been able to gather, emperor geese were found in summer in large flocks in the neighborhood of Vankarém. According to a report by É.V. Schmidt they reached the Amguema estuary in the west. In 1970 A.A. Kishchinskii (1971) found them in large numbers in the nesting areas around the Ukouge lagoon. Not more than 200 birds of this species gathered from June 5 through 20 on the coast from Vankarém to the Amguema. On June 22, on the

Ukouge lagoon, several hundreds were seen and about 2,000 from June 25 through 27. In the first 10 days of July most of them disappeared. Judging from the abundance of old droppings, the emperor geese gathered there every year, perhaps after flying over much of the coast. At the end of July large collections of single and juvenile birds were found on the lagoon. Flocks of four to 15 birds were seen in July in different places from Vankarém to the mouth of the Amguema. V.Ya. Isaev did not see one emperor goose near Cape Schmidt. N.F. Kallinikov (1912) writes that the "imperial" goose is found along with other species of geese on the Chaun and Kolyma. According to the information collected by E.P. Spangenberg (1960), in 1959 the "white-necked" bird was well known to the people on the lower Kolyma, was found in pairs, and nested in small numbers at Cape Darovatyi. On June 8 he noticed a pair in the neighborhood of Mikhalkino village and on June 30 a pair flying over the sea. Another was seen over the Kolyma on July 3. The geese flew away in the direction of Cape Darovatyi. E.P. Spangenberg was justified in believing that the emperor goose appeared on the lower Kolyma only relatively recently. I believe this bird may come there periodically.

This bird reaches Wrangel Island as a straggler. On June 8, 1929, G.A. Ushakov (Bannikov 1941) was given a specimen which later was handed over to the Moscow Zoological Museum. The eskimos said the goose was flying low along the coast.

It is well known that emperor geese go down the American coast as far as California for wintering. One of the ringed birds recovered there was probably an emperor goose of Chukchi origin, though this is a guess. In an article (1948) J.A. Neff reports that a ringed goose was shot around Gridley on November 21, 1940. Enquiries showed that the ring with the mark "510 H—Moskwa—131528" was applied by Capt. G. Grinberg working at Uélen in 1938 and 1939. He died in the war. The place where the bird was ringed and the exact species were unknown. Nor did the hunter who shot it in California give any useful information. According to him it was a whitish goose with patches of some creamish color, the wings without black fringes, weighing about five pounds, and different from the other geese he had seen.

Habitat—According to its biology the emperor goose is a marine bird. But it is not strictly confined to the coast, since it goes fairly deep inland.

I encountered a brood with downy chicks in a hill stream in the Utte-Véem river valley 30 km from the sea. I and my party were traveling in a tiny leather canoe using a towline against the current as the shoals became increasingly difficult to negotiate. Under these conditions the brood was coming down the river toward us. Somewhat lower down the river we found a lone male on a pebble spit. Later, 10 km farther down the stream, another brood, also with tiny chicks, was caught in the swift flow of the strong current.

Thus emperor geese can cope with mountain stream habitats though they evidently nest there in small numbers. On a coast with sand dunes I found the shell of an egg. In the lower reaches and estuaries of rivers flocks of nonnesting birds were often found.

In August 1934, I repeatedly found emperor geese on the Kol'oam River, in fact more often on its lower course, and a huge flock at the mouth. I found tracks even on the shore of Lake Kool'ong, which is drained by a river of that name. Later I saw these geese or heard their calls on lakes away from the river.

According to the observations of É.V. Schmidt, the emperor goose nested in the eastern part of the Chukchi peninsula on the rocky, depressed tundra along the banks of lakes and rivulets. According to a description by A.P. Kuzyakin, a nest was found 2 km south of the Uélen lagoon on wet sedge-cotton-grass tundra far from the lowland of a small rivulet and lake on a flat elevation overgrown with grass and moss. There were only two small puddles of thawed water around. A path about 100 m away in the form of high earth mounds was used by people crossing the tundra from Uélen to Dezhnev settlement.

Emperor geese also nested on the banks of lagoons. I.O. Olenev told me that they nested on the banks of the lagoon linked to the sea near Kivak village. P. Johansen found a nest with a clutch in a freshwater lagoon at Pitlekai. Later some clutches were brought from nearby areas. From all this it may be concluded that the section of the coast to the east of Kolyuchin Bay with a nearly endless series of lagoons was very favorable for the habitation of emperor geese.

On St. Lawrence Island, according to the eskimos, these geese nested on the moist tundra in the central and eastern parts of the island.

Along the stretch from Uélen to Mitkulen I never saw this bird settle on the coast, though I noticed pairs and flocks flying over it. On the morning of July 4, 1934, the ice floes drifted toward Mitkulen and the neighborhood was wrapped in dense fog. In this weather eiders are usually seen on the coast. To my surprise a flock of emperor geese flew toward the hunters, though they were not to be seen in clear weather in the summer.

At the feeding places I most frequently saw these geese on the wet, grassy banks of small lakes or lagoons or in the depressed spits at the mouth of rivulets with a dense cover of low but very fresh green grass. On August 30, 1933, in the delta of the Téeyu-Véem River near Uélen, I found a huge flock. The emperor geese, along with two lesser snow geese and a small flock of brent geese, enjoyed themselves on the flat shoal of sand and gravel crossed by meandering shallow river courses full of stagnant water. In the silted sections of the shoal there was low grass which shone brightly after the intense frost. It no doubt served as the main food for the geese which, as could be judged from the large heaps of droppings and shed feathers, were there in large numbers throughout the summer, as also in the adjoining sections of the lagoon and tundra lakelets. The picture I beheld on August 30 was as magnificent as it was rare. Against the general background of the yellowing tundra and a most colorful lowland the dense flock of emperor geese in fresh plumage stood out like a bright blue wedge. The orange claws blended in total harmony with this typical multicolored background.

On the south coast of St. Lawrence Island, according to O.W. Geist, the emperor geese gathered in thousands to molt on the sand spit separating the lagoon from the sea. The spit extends for about 50 miles and is only 100 yards wide. When disturbed, they took shelter in the lagoon or the sea.

Around Uélen, I noticed emperor geese from the time of arrival on marshy lowland filled with meltwater and grass.

Arrival—In early June, 1931, L.O. Belopol'skii saw flocks of emperor geese many times in Krest Bay flying east-west. Judging from the fairly late date, it was a mass arrival. In Providence Bay the first few birds were seen in the last 10 days of May. In 1932 I.O. Olenev collected a male on May 26–27 at Istiget village. P.T. Butenko noticed the first few emperor geese in 1938 on his way to Sireniki on May 25. On St. Lawrence Island, according to a report by F.H. Fay and T.J. Cade, the first arrivals were sighted on or about May 10, and somewhat earlier on the south coast. In the first week of June flocks of up to 20 birds were a common sight on the shore ice on the west coast.

Around Uélen, in the spring of 1934, I noticed the first pair only on June 1. The birds from the tundra flew straight north out to sea. On June 2 four emperor geese flew past the knoll out to sea and four more were seen after some time. On June 3 two geese were seen on the same course. Only on June 4 did I see some sitting pairs around the tundra; in one case, there were six pairs together.

On May 1, 1934, the wintering personnel at Cape Schmidt saw a flock of geese flying over the sea. This date was very early for any type of goose but a small flock of geese, namely emperor geese, was also seen in Vankarém on May 1. On May 20 P.T. Butenko saw a flying pair of geese near Énmitagin village but in the blinding brightness of the arctic spring he may have erred. In any case, they were not brent geese.

At Kolyuchin Bay, in the spring of 1879, the emperor geese were noticed very late. E.A. Almquist saw some on his expedition inland from June 13 through 17, collected one at Pitlekai on the 17th and a pair on the 19th at Dzhenretlen.

I saw emperor geese after their arrival in the feeding areas around Uélen. They loved to walk on the grass. Their call, though not loud, could be heard from afar. The geese were very alert, took off when approached to within 250 to 300 feet and later settled farther away.

Breeding—Of the two June males caught at Uélen on June 26, 1934, the testes were just about twice as long as normal (Table 11), which showed that the bird was in the initial stage of breeding. The males with much shorter testes obtained

Table 11. Size of testes of emperor geese, mm

Date	Left	Right	Locality
June 24, 1938	15×7	14×7	Providence Bay
June 26, 1934	26×15	17×9	Uélen village
July 4, 1934	15×5	10×4	Mitkulen village
July 7, 1934	15×7	10×6	Utte-Véem River
July 7, 1934	15×6	11×5	—do—
July 10, 1934	15×8	14×7	—do—

Table 12. Structure of ovaries of emperor geese

Date	Ovary structure	Locality
June 11, 1938	Coarse-grained	Kivak village
June 26, 1934	Largest follicle, 8 mm	Uélen
July 4, 1934	Fine-grained	Mitkulen village
July 7, 1934	—do—	Utte-Véem River
July 10, 1934	—do—	—do—

from Providence Bay on June 24 were possibly single birds. The July geese which had reared young had small gonads roughly of the same dimensions. The females showed a fairly uniform fine-grained ovary structure (Table 12).

They were devoid of any subcutaneous adipose layers, whereas on arrival all the emperor geese with one exception had had appreciable adipose layers. An October male from Uél'kal was also emaciated. A female collected on June 19, 1879, near Dzhenretlen had a thick adipose layer; the largest follicle size in the ovary went up to 3.7 cm; it was 0.8 cm in females caught in Uélen on June 26, 1934.

Six eggs were seen in a nest found by A.P. Kuzyakin (1965) on June 29, 1957. The goose sat on them so stubbornly that it took off only when approached to within 15 to 20 paces. It could not be seen at all while it pressed its head to the ground. It rose suddenly, flapping its wings strongly and stretching its neck. The nest pit was 29 × 32 cm and about 6 mm deep without any ridge along the rim. It was generously lined with down mixed with feathers, stalks, moss fragments and lichen. Four eggs were found slightly incubated, and two were addled. In mid-June of the same year, 1957, a local eskimo traveling from Dezhnev to Uélen found a nest with eight fresh eggs, which he ate.

The *Vega* expedition gathered five clutches which were later measured by V. Meves (Table 13).

F.H. Fay and T.J. Cade give the photograph of a nest of the emperor goose with four eggs taken on June 23, 1954.

According to É.V. Schmidt the emperor goose never nested in colonies. Once on a small island about three hectares in area he happened to find seven nests but they were some distance apart. Community care of chicks, as with brent geese, was not detected in the case of emperor geese. When the female is killed the eggs invariably perish.

According to A.A. Kishchinskii incubating females were always found in two nests found near the Ukouge lagoon (Figs. 27 and 28). The male stood aside or fed not far away. The chicks all hatched in one day, on July 13, 1970, and began to peck about in a day or two.

According to my observations the emperor goose has a strong bond with its young. On July 7, 1934, when P.T. Butenko and I were going up the upper course of the Utte-Véem River, we suddenly came across a brood with five tiny chicks floating downstream (Fig. 26). Taken unawares, the male and the female did not attempt to fly away but struggled to reach the bank and began staring at the chicks, which could hardly keep up with their parents.

On July 10, equally unexpectedly, we found a second brood with similar tiny chicks floating in the stream. Having noticed us, the male and the female turned upstream but were easily overtaken. They did not attempt to fly away even when approached to within a few meters. The male did not attempt to protect itself though his wings were slightly spurred.

On July 7 we came across a lone male on the pebbled spit. Probably the incubating female was somewhere around and that could be the reason he did not show the wariness so common at other times. P.T. Butenko collected him without difficulty.

Table 13. Dimensions and weights

Locality and date	Length, mm						Width, mm	
Pitlekai, June 30, 1879	82.0	84.5	85.0	81.0	—	—	53.5	53.0
Neshkan, July 1, 1879	81.5	77.5	77.5	—	—	—	52.5	53.0
Pitlekai, July 2, 1879	84.5	79.0	80.0	78.0	76.5	—	53.0	53.0
Irgunnuk, July 5, 1879	83.0	84.5	80.0	82.0	79.0	76.5	51.0	52.5
Pitlekai, July 9, 1879	78.5	79.0	77.0	77.0	—	—	54.5	54.5
Uélen, June 29, 1957	82.0	81.2	80.4	80.0	80.0	79.0	53.2	53.3

Note: Def. = Defective.

The females obtained had brood patches; brood patches were not found on the males.

In the color of their down emperor goose chicks resemble those of the brent goose more than those of the white-fronted goose or the bean goose because there is no lemon-yellow tinge. The back is bright ash gray, noticeably darker around the eyes. The base of the beak is surrounded by a bright area, whitish in the anterior forehead and even more so on the chin. The cheeks are grayish, the throat and the ventral aspect of the neck, breast and mid-abdomen grayish-white. The claws and beak are blackish, the beak tip whitish.

On August 23, 1934, I came across two broods on the shore of a tundra lake beyond the lagoon at the mouth of the Kol'oam-Véem River. The young birds differed from the adults only in their small size and in the dark color of the neck and head. They were so wary that they could not be caught.

F.H. Fay saw broods with two and three downy chicks on St. Lawrence Island on July 15 and 29, 1953. On August 22 he saw a nonflying goose which was completely plumed but for the neck and head.

More often, I came across emperor geese which were not breeding that year. They were still in pairs or flocks from the spring, mostly in even numbers. Throughout the summer these birds, not burdened with the care of offspring, made daily journeys, assembling for rest on the river or lake spits, usually in flocks of 20 birds.

Molting—My diary does not contain any notes on this species from July 11 through August 10, 1934. Evidently the emperor geese then were in the process of molting and were not conspicuous. As in other species of goose, nonnesting individual emperor geese invariably gathered for molting. In 1933, arriving at Uélen in mid-August, I got the news that the geese had already molted. On the Téeyu-Véem River I found a mass of discarded feathers which included some half-grown new feathers. There were some whose tuft had not completely dropped off from the hemp. Evidently someone had badly frightened the geese there. Running away, molting geese nevertheless flap their wings. It is said that they can be chased and caught only by men who are good runners.

On St. Lawrence Island, according to F.H. Fay (1961), the eskimos caught molting geese between June 17 and August 7. On a southern lagoon on July 21, 1960, not more than 10 of a flock of over 5,000 birds could fly but nonflying birds could be seen even on August 15.

of emperor goose eggs

Width, mm				Weight of shells Nos. 1 to 5 latched, and of No. 6 unlatched, g					
53.5	54.5	—	—	11.11	11.47	10.50	11.56	—	—
53.5	—	—	—	10.76	10.55	Def.			—
53.0	53.0	54.0	—	13.75	10.69	9.93	10.71	Def.	—
51.5	52.5	50.5	51.0	8.77	11.50	10.37	10.50	10.42	11.28
54.0	53.0	—	—	Def.	10.47	Def.	10.22	—	—
53.4	53.2	52.6	53.7	11.7	11.5	11.45	11.2	11.15	11.8

After molting the emperor geese remained in their places for a long time and I did not notice extensive fall wanderings.

Migration—On August 24, 1933, at Uélen, P.T. Butenko saw a flock leaving the tundra and flying over the lagoon to the north out to sea, i.e. in the same direction as in the spring. It was the beginning of migration, caused by the onset of cold snaps and the associated deterioration in the food value of the vegetation the geese eat. On August 28, I made an excursion over the tundra around Uélen. The low-flying plane frightened the local feathered population, which took to flight in different directions. Two flocks and a lone emperor goose flew toward me. On August 30 I again saw two flocks and encountered a huge flock at the mouth of the Vtoraya rivulet. However, only three birds were to be seen on August 31. Near Uélen on that day small flocks flew in a northeasterly direction, bypassing on the north the knoll adjoining Cape Dezhnev.

In the fall of 1934, in the delta of the Kol'oam River, I saw a huge flock of about 200 birds gathered before migration as early as August 9. The geese rose when I was 300 paces away from them and later settled one-fourth of a kilometer off. On August 10 I found perhaps the same flock in the same place, but slightly reduced; some brent geese had been added to it. Being frightened, it broke into small groups which wandered from place to place. When the party was going up the river, pairs and small flocks flew toward us. Sometimes we saw birds pastured on the meadows. Their honking was often heard from afar. On the way back, on August 23, we found three and two emperor geese in the lower reaches of the river and saw a very big flock with some brent geese in the estuary itself. The flock flew away in a southeasterly direction in the early morning of August 24 and only one pair remained on a small rivulet close by. On September 2, over the lagoon at Uélen, a flock flew over in an easterly direction. It consisted of about 20 emperor geese. Having flown up to the knoll the birds were somewhat confused, but then turned south toward Dezhnev village. On that day the observers were back aboard the ship, having completed their field observations.

On September 13, 1939, I saw a small flock of emperor geese flying south over Émma Bay. In the morning young shore ice and plates were to be seen but they began thawing by midday. It was beyond doubt the frost that drove the geese south. As could be anticipated, on the south coast of the Chukchi peninsula the migration occurred later than around Uélen. On St. Lawrence Island frosts began in mid-

August and almost half of the emperor geese had deserted the island by early September. According to F.H. Fay (1961), between August 10 and 22 the geese were found migrating north along the coast and over the tundra or knolls, and by the end of August in the reverse direction. By September 1, in the western half of the island, almost the entire population of juveniles had disappeared. Some old birds along with yearlings persisted until early October. According to the old eskimos, the emperor geese gathered around the southeast cape, some remaining even up to December.

Habits—In external appearance and behavior the emperor goose differs widely from the common features of geese. It is built compactly with noticeably short neck and wings; compared with the bean and white-fronted geese, it appears more sluggish and rather heavy, quieter and more timid than the lesser snow goose. A.P. Kuzyakin remarked that it was a very wary bird, honked little, rarely took off, and covered quite long distances on foot. In places where the geese walk more and make paths they avoid using the old track but walk next to it. I noticed that the emperor geese love to fly low over the land or water. I never saw them flying very high, but they fly very fast. Their call resembles the honk of the white-fronted goose. The cackling was a disyllabic or trisyllabic gak-gak, fairly high-pitched.

Food—Field observations on emperor geese and a study of their stomach contents showed that they survived on grass, at least in the summer. The stomachs of seven specimens including three downy chicks that I collected from June 26 through July 7, 1934, showed only stalks of herbaceous plants; the stomachs of chicks showed fragments of leaves (in one case, the shoot of a horse-tail), with much sand in all of them. The stomach of the females caught at Cape Dzhenretlen on June 19, 1879, also contained some grass and sand. According to F.H. Fay and T.J. Cade, the geese arriving on the west coast of St. Lawrence Island fed on aquatic plants and rubbish cast up by the surf. L.M. Turner showed that this species fed on molluscs in the late fall at low tide. Evidently its food habits change with the season and the bird is more active from late fall to early spring.

Weight—A fatty female caught on June 24, 1938, in Providence Bay weighed 2.27 kg.

Economic importance—In a letter N.P. Sokol'nikov wrote that many molted emperor geese were killed with sticks in a narrow section of Mechigmensk Gulf. This was the picture at the beginning of this century. Formerly the eskimos on St. Lawrence Island caught large numbers of molting juvenile geese. I did not hear of mass hunting nowadays anywhere in the Chukchi peninsula. It is shot only rarely because of its great alertness.

According to L.M. Turner and W.S. Brooks, the eskimos entice the emperor goose by lying on their back, waving their hands, feet and cap and imitating the call of the bird. The unusual movements often attract different birds (see for example my observations on pine finches and wagtails in *Fauna of the Anadyr Region*, 1939b, vol. I, pp. 61 and 90).

Systematics—I compared the Asiatic specimens with the American but could not find any differences in the subspecies. The emperor goose is monotypical not only in the genus but also in the species.

Being endemic to the Bering Sea coast, it occupies a special position among many other geese with respect to several distinctive features.

N.A. Severtsov (1879) drew attention to a possible philogenetic affinity of the emperor goose to the Indian variety. In giving his views with respect to mutual genetic affinities he mentioned the group of South American geese of the genus *Cloephaga*. Based on anatomical studies of North American geese of the genera *Anser*, *Chen*, and *Brants*, the Hawaiian geese *Nesochen* and the genus *Cloephaga*, A.H. Miller (1937, p. 60) came to the conclusion that though *Cloephaga* stood largely apart, nevertheless the emperor goose was much closer, if there was any affinity, to the genera *Branta* and *Philacte*, especially to the latter.

I think it would be logical to look for genetic affinities of the emperor geese in the northern part of the Atlantic Ocean also. There are geographic variants among several animals inhabiting the northern parts of the Atlantic and Pacific oceans. They include, for example, the marine sandpiper, common eider, puffin and others. *Branta leucopsis* (Bechst.) was a unique endemic North Atlantic goose. It is hard to imagine that two endemic geese in the northern parts of the Atlantic and Pacific oceans evolved totally independent of each other, especially when species of birds whose affinity is beyond doubt were living among them.

As far as the affinity of *Philacte canagica* with *Branta leucopsis* is concerned it is to be seen especially in the color of adult birds and downy chicks. The differences in the body proportions are appreciable but they are subject to wide fluctuations among the geese. Suffice it to mention the differences that are found even between the subspecies of Canadian geese *Branta canadensis canadensis* (L.), *B. c. occidentalis* (Baird) and *B. c. minima* Ridgw.

I am in full agreement with A.H. Miller that the genus *Philacte* is much closer to the genus *Branta* than to the genus *Anser*. I find no basis to deny the affinity between *Philacte* and *Cloephaga*.

Specimens— 1) Wrangel Island, June 8, 1929, ○, G.A. Ushakov; 2) Meechken Island, June 13, 1931, ♀, Belopol'skii; 3) village Istiget, May 26 and 27, 1932, ♂, Olenev; 4 and 5) Uélen, June 26, 1934, ♂♀, Portenko; 6 and 7) Mitkulen village, July 4, 1934, ♂♀, Portenko; 8) mouth of Utte-Véem River, July 5, 1934, ⊙, Portenko; 9 to 14) midcourse of Utte-Véem River, July 7, 1934, ♂♂, ♀, and 3 pull., Portenko; 15 to 18) same place, July 10, 1934, ♂♀, and 2 pull., Portenko; 19) Uél'kal' village, October 18, 1937, ♂, Butenko; 20) Kivak village, June 11, 1938, ♀, Butenko; and 21) Providence Bay, June 24, 1938, ♂, Butenko.

16. **Branta bernicla nigricans** (Lawr.)—**Brent Goose**

Local name— Chukchian: Aàying in Uélen, uédliuitti in the records of the *Vega* expedition and vel'vittsy in the records of A.G. Velizhanin on Wrangel Island. In Eskimo: lekhlekh takhkél'guk in Providence Bay and tŭ-géthl′-quk on St. Lawrence Island.

Distribution and status—Common in the nesting areas of the Chukchi peninsula but sporadically encountered elsewhere. At places forms appreciable colonies, being rare or altogether absent from other places. Quite often seen in flight. Nests on Wrangel Island in large numbers (Fig. 29) but numerically much less common than the lesser snow goose.

The brent goose is common in Krest Bay, where it nests and gathers in flocks for molting. According to a report by T.P. Shevareva (1961b), a bird ringed on July 28, 1951, in the Yukon estuary, Alaska, was caught in Égvekinot on June 23, 1956.

Portenko found a flock of 10 birds around Notapenmen village on August 6, 1932. L.O. Belopol'skii (1934) noticed flocks in flight and caught a female on June 1, 1931, on Meechken Island. Several score molted geese were brought there by the Chukchians from the Kurimul' River, east of Krest Bay. Along the rocky south coast of the Chukchi peninsula this goose is nowhere numerous. N.F. Kallinikov (1912, p. 151) noticed that the geese were few from Krest Bay to the east. The topography there was rocky and tundra rivers few and hence there was only an occasional flock of bean or brent geese in the spring. I.O. Olenev and P.T. Butenko, who wintered in Providence Bay, did not find one brent goose but one was sighted there by W.S. Brooks (1915) and myself. On June 19, 1913, Brooks saw a flock of 20 birds in the western part of the bay and caught some specimens. On August 25, 1932, I saw seven brent geese flying over the spit from the eastern shore of the bay. I saw some flying over the bay itself on the 26th.

On St. Lawrence Island the brent goose is seen only occasionally and nests even more rarely. According to a report by O.W. Geist (Murie 1936) a specimen was caught there in August, 1929, and another on July 26, 1932. O.J. Murie had in his collection males and females from Savunga village caught on September 16, 1933, and 10 specimens from Kukuliak village caught on September 5 and 6, 1935. According to F.H. Fay and T.J. Cade (1959) flocks of five to 15 brent geese might be seen at the end of May or early June along the west coast. A small flock was noticed on May 1, 1954, at Southeast Cape. Three nests were found on the Kuzata lagoon in 1953 and five nests in 1954. Later Fay (1961) came to the conclusion that brent geese flew along the south coast of the island with halts. On June 7, 1960, E.G.F. Sauer (Sauer and Urban 1964) noticed a lone brent goose flying above Maloe Lake at Boxer Bay. H. Friedmann (1934a) found the metacarpal bone of this species among archaeological remains.

S.M. Uspenskii (1959 and 1963a) believes that this goose regularly flies along the south coast of the Chukchi peninsula in the spring and evidently in the fall too. My data contradict the fixed flight course as charted by Uspenskii in this section.

According to É.V. Schmidt, in spite of steady, intense persecution the brent goose still nests in large numbers in Mechigmensk Gulf. He was aware of two colonies of roughly 70 and 300 nests each. In 1938, residents of the cultural base gathered about 1,500 eggs and in 1939 up to 2,500 from these places. The brent geese migrate from Mechigmensk Gulf to other places for molting. The brent goose also nests in Lawrence Bay. A sizeable nesting colony was found at the same time halfway along the shore of the bay but was destroyed by the visitors. A big colony of brent geese was regularly seen in the islands of the delta of Mamka River entering Lawrence Bay. On August 19, 1932, P.T. Butenko saw a flock flying over the south coast at the entrance to the bay. It was perhaps in the form of 16 brent geese that the Chukchians paid their dues to O.E. Kotsebue's associates in August, 1816 (Kotsebue 1821, vol. I, p. 149; and Choris 1822, Kamchatka, p. 19). T.P. Shevareva (1959) reported a young brent goose being ringed in the Yukon delta on

August 9, 1952, and shot in early 1953 near Lawrence Bay (Chetpakaergin village). In 1957, A.P. Kuzyakin studied a nesting colony on the lagoon banks at Poutyn. On June 26 six nests were found there with clutches and, apart from these nesting birds, a flock of nearly 20 birds was found. According to V.V. Leonovich the last of the migratory single birds was seen at Lawrence Bay on June 14 and 23, 1970.

On June 3, 1958, K.W. Kenyon (Kenyon and Brooks 1960) noticed a flight of 10 birds on Malyi Diomede Island. On June 9 a lone young bird settled on the slope of the northern settlement.

According to a report by A.P. Kuzyakin, two specimens were collected on the south bank of the lagoon at Uélen.

In the immediate vicinity of Uélen, I did not find brent geese in the nesting areas in the interior of the Chukchi peninsula along the Kol'oam-Véem or Utte-Véem rivers. Around Uélen it was commonly seen in flight. On Inchoun lagoons and around Mitkulen, I came across them in the summer but could not find direct evidence of their nesting. On July 11, 1934, I noticed a lone brent goose flying over the southernmost lagoon of Inchoun and a small flock above the ice near Mitkulen on July 20. On August 10 and 23 in the Kol'oam estuary I saw some brent geese attached to a flock of emperor geese. J. Koren (Thayer and Bangs 1914) found a pair on Inchoun lagoon at the end of the fall flight on October 7, 1912.

Farther to the west where the coast is high and rocky the brent geese do not build nests up to Cape Serdtse-Kamen'. In June-July, V.V. Leonovich found flocks at Énurmino. In one flock, he counted up to 60 brent geese. According to É.V. Schmidt very few of them nest in the lagoon at Énmelin, Neshkan and Tjapka. The *Vega* expedition (Palmén 1887) collected a male at Neshkan on July 1, 1879, i.e. in the nesting period; in July one specimen was collected and some clutches were found near Pitlekai. Judging from the information gathered by S.M. Uspenskii, collections of brent geese occur even today at Neshkan. On July 3, 1889, the *Vega* expedition was given a female brought from the interior. Probably these geese nested in Kolyuchin Bay. T.P. Shevareva reported a young female ringed on July 29, 1950, between the estuaries of the Yukon and Kuskokwim rivers in Alaska and caught on July 20, 1951, in Kolyuchin Bay.

According to J. Koren the brent goose is rare on the arctic coast of the Chukchi peninsula. According to my information its distribution is very uneven. I was told that these geese were found in Vankarém while, according to É.V. Schmidt, there were many of them on the lower reaches of the Amguema. According to A.A. Kishchinskii's data, in 1970 the brent geese nested only at two places, in very small numbers, on the north coast from Vankarém to the Amguema. Flocks of single geese consisting of five to 30 birds were found in June and July in the marine lagoons everywhere but were not found on the tundra far from the coast or even 2 to 4 km from the lagoon. Four brent geese were collected. The information given by S.M. Uspenskii about the collection of brent geese on the Amguema must relate to the lower reaches of the river since the flight of this species was not noticed along the valley in the interior of the country.

A.A. Savich (Artobolevskii 1927) collected specimens on Cape Schmidt in spring, 1915. The brent geese were common in the spring but only a small number of them remained there to raise their young. According to V.Ya. Isaev the brent goose was common at Cape Schmidt only in flight; it was not found at the end of summer. He found a nest with eggs in the valley of rivulets to the east of Cape Schmidt. According to the information gathered by T.P. Shevareva (1959) some brent geese ringed in Alaska in 1951 were found from June 20 through July 24, 1952, near Cape Schmidt. A young female ringed in the Yukon delta on August 1, 1951, was found at Cape Schmidt on August 24, 1952. According to the observations of the workers at the Polar Station (Uspenskii 1959), at Val'karai, west of Cape Schmidt, brent geese were not encountered as reported by other observers. The members of the *Vega* expedition found them during their visit to one of the Chukchi settlements between Schmidt and Yakan capes on September 9, 1878.

According to É.V. Schmidt brent geese nested in fairly large numbers in the Kuvet River delta but there were not many along the Chaun Bay shore. They were mostly encountered on the northeastern coast. In the Karchyk peninsula they nested in the northeastern part right on the sea; they were in large numbers there. On Aiok Island only flying broods were seen but V.D. Lebedev and V.R. Filin even found a nest and collected a brood with five young in the Karchyk peninsula. In the southwestern part of Chaun Bay and in the estuary of the Chaun River the brent geese gathered in thousands before the fall migration. S.M. Uspenskii's assumption that the fall flight of brent geese was not known on the north coast of the Chukchi peninsula does not correspond with the available information. A.I. Argentov (1861a) refers to this marine bird as wandering in the spring and fall but on August 12, 1912, J. Koren found a nest in the valley some 30 miles east of Cape Bol'shoi Baranov and also collected chicks and adults. According to a report by É.V. Schmidt the brent goose nested in the Baranikha estuary but apparently in small numbers.

According to A.I. Mineev brent geese nested in thousands on Wrangel Island though in smaller numbers than the lesser snow geese. In the fall of 1932 he noticed such a congregation of old and young geese in the Nasha River estuary that it could well be compared to anthills. In Mineev's time this goose nested even on the coastal tundra at Rodgers Bay.

I found it in the nesting sites along the banks of the Mamontovaya and Nasha rivers. It was very common in spring flight and most numerous in the fall. In the second half of August, 1938, I noticed it in Tundra Akademii in flocks of several dozens and even hundreds of birds. In 1881, E.W. Nelson (1883 and 1887) did not find brent geese either on the Chukchi coast or on Wrangel though, on the latter, he found evidence of the presence of some geese. According to C.L. Hooper (1884), the Captain of the *Corwin*, goose droppings were found on the slopes of knolls near the Klér River estuary in such a large quantity that it must have been a resting place for goose flocks in the very early part of the year. It is more probable, I think, that brent geese halted there.

In June, 1955, a bird was caught on Wrangel Island that had been ringed on August 14, 1952, in the Yukon delta. On August 7, 1955, a male was shot that had been ringed right there on July 29, 1953. In 1960, S.M. Uspenskii and R.L. Bëme (Uspenskii, Bëme, and Velizhanin 1963) found lone brent geese and pairs in the southern part of Wrangel Island as well as in Tundra Akademii. On July 23 a flock was sighted from the plane over Cape Florence. It contained 50 to 70 birds.

On July 26 six nonflying geese were seen in a flock of molting lesser snow geese. In the same year, 1960, as identified by A.G. Velizhanin (1965) the brent goose was a fairly common bird. On July 1 he saw these geese caught by hunters on Chicherina spit. In June geologists shot them in the Klér River estuary. According to the reports of the hunters, brent geese nested near the Gusinaya River. In 1964, S.M. Uspenskii determined the number of brent geese on Wrangel Island at 1,000 to 2,000 pairs. A gathering of single birds was found in mid-July in the northern part of the island. The flocks consisted of a few hundred birds and the molting birds numbered up to 10,000. As far as could be surmised from the plumage, the flocks included two age groups.

De Long (1883) recorded in his diary that at midnight of May 21, 1880, a huge flock, probably of wild geese, was seen from the *Jeannette*, which two days before had been at 73°28′19″ north and 178°51′45″ east. The birds flew southeast-northwest. Unfortunately the species could not be identified exactly and they could as well have been eiders.

Judging from the enquiries made by S.M. Uspenskii, in the 50s there was an appreciable reduction in the population of this species on the northeastern coast of the USSR, though it was being seen every year.

Habitat—Although generally a marine bird the brent goose nests mostly in river valleys. J. Koren found a nest in a valley on a small grassy islet in a lake on the tundra. V.D. Lebedev and V.R. Filin also found a nest on an islet among shallow lakes on the south coast of Aiok and V.Ya. Isaev found one not far from a lake in the valley of a rivulet. Brent geese love the lowlands and river deltas. É.V. Schmidt found nesting colonies on the islands of the Mamka River delta, in Lawrence Bay and on similar islands in the delta of Mechigmensk Gulf. A.A. Kishchinskii found two nests on a lagoon in the Amguema estuary. In the middle of it was an islet not more than 80 × 20 m in area overgrown with *Elymus* grass. Herring gulls numbering up to 70 pairs, a few glaucous gulls, common eiders, king eiders and two pairs of brent geese nested in a colony on this islet. The nests of brent geese were at a distance of 25 m from each other and five to seven m from those of gulls. The nesting female geese were caught on Nutauge lagoon west of Vankarém. In the Karchyk peninsula the geese nested on the islets of shallow lakes located in the northeastern part right on the sea coast. In the colony at Poutyn studied by A.P. Kuzyakin the nests were located on the broad sandbank separating the lagoon from the sea and in the mouth of a small river. On the bank there were broken ridges of sand, partly covered with grass. There were lakes between them, some with grassy-mossy islets. The rivulet at the entrance to the lagoon formed a broad delta with flat islets covered with moss and sand spits. The locality therefore provided diverse conditions for the birds to build nests, feed and rest. Not only the nesting pairs but even flocks of single birds found it comfortable there.

On Wrangel Island, I found nesting colonies along river banks under conditions of hilly topography, in the clearings and on terraces at a height of a few score meters above the river level. Nesting areas were perhaps likely at a much higher level in the central part of the island. In Somnitel'naya Bay I found nesting areas on a flat lowland plateau with large lakes.

Brent geese perform noticeable daily as well as seasonal migrations. According to the observations of É.V. Schmidt, they love to feed in the marine meadows and on the shoals along the Chukchi peninsula, where they nibble *Phipsia*, but were never found on berry plantations. They mostly rest on the shoals. Even in the feeding grounds they were invariably quite close to the water. These geese love water very much and quite often a flock is found sitting in the water before approaching land. On Wrangel Island the arriving brent geese mostly sat in meltwater along the pebble spits. Around Uélen, another striking feature was that they flew without apparent reason from the tundra out to sea, taking totally inexplicable directions. At sea they did not settle but nevertheless found some advantage flying over the waves or the ice rather than over land. When I pursued brent geese along the low bank of a lagoon at Notapenmen they gradually moved away toward the bay, finally entered the water, swam and became airborne from the water.

Before molting began brent geese often flew over the lagoons, where they later gathered in flocks and molted all of the time. On being pursued, the molting birds escaped by swimming and, what is more, remained in the water for a long time. Compared with other geese brent geese have a much stronger affinity to water and the seacoast.

There was yet another characteristic of brent geese under the conditions on Wrangel Island. They never paused before crossing a hill or several hill ranges of relatively low height, one after another. They nested under conditions of mountainous terrain and regularly crossed through the mountains during local movements. In this respect they were inferior to lesser snow geese but superior to eiders, of which only very few crossed the lowest of passes.

At the end of summer on Wrangel Island brent geese gathered on level plateaus where there was sufficient grass, independent of the type of tundra, but mostly in the valleys of rivulets and brooks. In their fall flight in the eastern part of the Chukchi peninsula they held to the coastline and circumvented the Dezhnev knolls from the north or flew above them from Uélen in the east. If they stopped it was on the lagoons and in the delta of the Téeyu-Véem River (Vtoraya rivulet). On September 25, 1933, a brood of young brent geese consisting of five birds landed in Uélen on the pebbles near Chukchian skin tents.

Arrival—The brent geese arrived relatively late, in the last 10 days of May and in early June. On this count alone, A.F. Middendorf (1874, p. 1149) erred in assuming that the "black ducks" that F.P. Wrangel saw over the ice around 71.5° north to the east of the Kolyma on April 18 were brent geese. It is strange that I.A. Palmén (1887) never mentions this error. Only A.A. Birulya (1907) pointed it out much later.

According to F.H. Fay (Fay 1961), brent geese were usually seen on St. Lawrence Island between May 20 and 29, along with the lesser snow and emperor geese or pintails but after the eiders, and traveled in a northwesterly direction to the Chukchi peninsula. Therefore they were first seen at Southeast Cape where they arrived as early as May 1 in 1954. Conversely, at Northwest Cape not a single bird was seen until May 28. Evidently they lingered on the south coast.

In the spring of 1931, in Krest Bay, L.O. Belopol'skii saw the flight of brent geese at the end of May and beginning of June. The flight was from east to west. On Malyi Diomede Island K.W. Kenyon saw a flock flying to Bol'shoi Diomede on

June 3. In 1934, they were seen at Uélen in the very last days of May in stray pairs. On May 31 I saw two and three birds; on June 1, two birds; and on June 2, a flock which crossed the spit in the morning mist, taking a northerly direction out to sea. In the evening a pair was found sitting on the lagoon. I noticed two pairs on June 3 and two more pairs along with emperor geese on the 7th; a lone bird was seen flying east over the sea on the 12th. On June 14 three flocks flew along the knolls from the Uélen lagoons out to sea and this completed the flight which was very uncoordinated. My observations at Uélen were that the local geese had by then appeared in pairs and could be seen flying in different directions. The flying birds quickly formed flocks and proceeded in a northerly direction; they crossed the low isthmus of the land to the west of the Dezhnev knolls.

In 1879, Brusevits noticed the first brent goose at Pitlekai on June 15. Two of the specimens noticed were no doubt already localized. In the spring of 1915, at Cape Schmidt, A.A. Savich noticed the first pair on May 20; two days later, on May 22, there were already many of them on the tundra on the island; there was intense flying activity on the 24th and 26th, which ceased by the 29th. Similarly, according to the observations of workers at the Polar Station at Cape Schmidt (Uspenskii 1959), brent geese were already seen around the 20th of May.

G.A. Ushakov noticed the first arrivals on Wrangel Island (Bannikov 1941) on May 25, 1927, and May 15, 1928, and a mass arrival from May 28 through 30, 1927, and June 1 through 3, 1928. The brent geese arrived from the southeast in flocks of six to 20 birds, sometimes up to 50. A.I. Mineev told me that they began to appear in inconspicuous numbers and in any case in an uncoordinated manner. In the spring of 1939, I myself drew attention to the fact that unlike the lesser snow geese, the brent geese arrived a few at a time. Only on June 2 did I sight them for the first time after the winter. Small flocks passed to the west and northwest, in particular through the Mamontovaya River valley. Next day one pair flew to and fro past my tent: the birds had evidently settled immediately on arrival. On June 4 the survivor of a pair circled for a long time above a dead goose while small flocks were flying in a westerly direction throughout the day. On June 5 they were commonly seen around my tent to the south of the Mamontovaya River and on the 7th along the banks of the river, mostly in pairs. I saw only pairs on June 9. Even on June 8 flying flocks were seen but by then the geese were few, having dispersed about the island.

The first brent geese to arrive were quite often heard calling to each other though they were silent at other times. This call, dull, constrained and rather unpleasant resembles that of an eider; in its general character it was more that of a duck than that of a goose. In any case, brent geese do not honk like many other geese.

In the course of the first few days after arrival the brent geese wandered about in all directions. Many of them were probably looking for places convenient for nesting. At this time, the pairs were avidly attached to other breeding pairs or flocks of nonbreeding brent geese and even to geese of other species: to emperor geese in the Chukchi peninsula and lesser snow geese on Wrangel Island.

Breeding—As a rule brent geese nested in colonies. This would no doubt explain the sporadic finds of nests. In Mechigmensk Gulf É.V. Schmidt knew of two colonies of 70 and 300 nests each. As a result of persecution by man these colonies have shifted. In 1938, in the first colony, the number of nests rose to 300 with a concurrent reduction in the second colony. In 1939 brent geese again nested in large numbers on the second island. According to A.I. Mineev, not more than 200 eggs were gathered in the independent colonies of brent geese on Wrangel Island: the strength of the colonies did not exceed a few dozen nests. In the Nasha River valley I found two very small colonies separated by a rocky cape. Unfortunately, before my visit the colony had fallen victim to destruction by man, and I had only five nests to examine. In my view, under such conditions the colony is spread over a considerable area so that it is quite difficult to find the nests. Even lone nests are not rare. In small meadows in the Mamontovaya River valley I put up some pairs which perhaps had settled from the time of arrival in small, isolated nest zones. J. Koren found a lone nest at Cape Bol'shoi Baranov. But Mineev only once found a lone nest outside a colony.

It has been established beyond doubt that the brent goose often builds its colony in the immediate vicinity of the nests of predators which do not threaten the geese. This cohabitation is one of the interesting phenomena in the life of the North and I was not a bit surprised when I saw it with my own eyes. On the Nasha River a nest of the snowy owl would be found as a rule on a headland and nests of brent geese would be located on the same terrace, the closest of them not farther than 150 paces from the owl's nest. The owls and the brent geese were equally agitated by my visit and neither gave the other away. The behavior of the geese was altogether different upon the appearance of a moderate-sized jaeger, which they chased. In my presence a female goose flew straight at a jaeger and chased it for some time. It was an altogether uncommon sight since geese are accustomed to flying straight in a given direction at a fixed level. In the present case, however, the brent goose pressed the jaeger hard, slowed down in flight, swooped, soared, and wheeled right and left, close behind the retreating enemy.

According to A.I. Mineev, brent geese on Wrangel Island, like the lesser snow geese, generally nested in the immediate vicinity of the nest of a snowy owl. In one case the distance was 250 to 300 m and in another only 100 m. In a mixed colony of lesser snow and brent geese one nest of the latter was literally 7 m from that of the owl. In very large colonies of lesser snow geese he found only a few nests of brent geese.

According to the observations of F.B. Chernyavskii (1967), in 1964 the brent geese built a nest on the Mamontovaya River in the neighborhood of an owl and lesser snow geese.

Even more interesting is the cohabitation of geese in colonies of polar foxes. In a large colony in Mechigmensk Gulf É.V. Schmidt found the burrow of a fox and even saw the fox itself as it dived into the burrow. However, on the islands occupied by the brent geese the foxes did not burrow every year. According to Schmidt, near Chaun the geese nested alternately with glaucous or herring gulls but did not leave their nests unprotected.

Before nesting, pairs of brent geese fly about in different directions, the birds staying closer to each other than when searching for food, but I did not notice any particular courtship ceremonies.

The gonads of birds arriving just then were of maximum size (Tables 14 and 15). All of the old birds that I collected were characterized by appreciable subcutaneous adipose layers, which were absent in the young birds.

The nest is in the form of a small depression covered with down. There is so much of it that the eggs are virtually buried in down. It is dark gray and of a cleaner shade than that of eiders, whose down has a brown tinge. The nest also contains large feathers and a mixture of moss and stalks is common in the nests of brent geese as well as of eiders. In its cohesive properties, the down of brent geese is much inferior to that of eiders. It also retains its form and is not blown by the wind; to the touch, it is somewhat coarser than that of the eider. Coming out of the nest, the brent goose can cover an egg even when a man is nearby (Fig. 30). The gray color of the down is easily missed against the background of hill tundra and cannot be seen even five or six paces away.

Of the nests examined by A.P. Kuzyakin, the first was at the entrance of a gopher burrow. One of the two eggs in the clutch had rolled 10 cm deep inside the burrow. The second nest was on a shallow pit on a flat islet and was profusely covered with down. There were four highly incubated eggs. Three nests were found on the mossy banks of the delta: one near the water, another a few meters from it and the third quite far off on sedge-cotton-grass tundra. The colonization of the brent geese there was very sparse: the distance between nests was almost 0.5 km. The trough area in the two nests was 10 × 12 and 11 × 12 cm; the cross section of the downy cover was 22 × 25 and 22 × 23 cm, respectively. Two clutches comprised four eggs each and one five. The eggs (June 26, 1957) were only slightly incubated with the exception of a fresh clutch.

Table 14. Size of testes of brent geese, mm

Date	Age	Left	Right
June 3, 1939	Adults	23 × 11	19 × 10
June 4, 1939		20 × 11	16 × 8
June 9, 1939		20 × 10	15 × 10
June 29, 1939		15 × 10	12 × 8
Aug. 31, 1933		7 × 5	6 × 3
Sep. 25, 1933	Yearlings	8 × 2	7 × 2
Sep. 25, 1933		4 × 2	3 × 2
Sep. 25, 1933		4 × 2	3 × 2
Sep. 25, 1933		4 × 2	3 × 2

Table 15. Size of ovaries of brent geese, mm

Date	Age	Ovary length	Biggest follicle
June 4, 1939	Adults	56	30
June 4, 1939		48	36
June 4, 1939		36	25
June 18, 1934		—	5
Sep. 25, 1938	Yearlings	Strip-like	

According to A.I. Mineev the clutches comprised not more than six eggs, often less. In some nests that I observed on Wrangel Island, including ones from which the eggs had been removed by hunters before my visit, there were not more than four eggs.

On June 28, 1879, clutches of brent geese eggs were given to members of the *Vega* expedition, and again on July 1, 2 and 8 (Table 16).

The eggs are laid in the first 20 days of June. In the clutch found by A.I. Mineev on June 12, 1932, one egg was unincubated but blood vessels were developed in the rest. In another clutch taken on June 14, 1932, embryos had already developed heads. In the eggs of a clutch found on June 23, 1932, blood vessels were seen. In another the eggs were very unevenly incubated: one egg showed the rudiments of blood vessels while another showed a fairly developed network of them. In the third the head and eyes of the embryo had formed. In a clutch of four eggs that I found on the Nasha River unequally developed chicks were found.

A.I. Mineev and A.P. Kuzyakin found large brood patches on the incubating females. According to Mineev the bird sits on the nest extending her legs backward, not under herself, and hence cannot turn around while sitting on the nest. On the

Table 16. Dimensions and weights of brent geese eggs

	Length, mm (in decreasing order)	Width, mm (corresponding to previous column)	Weight of shell, g (corresponding to first column)
Vega expedition, measured by V. Meves	73.5, 73.5, 73.0,	47.5, 46.5, 47.0,	6.46, 7.40, 7.60,
	72.0, 71.0, 71.0,	46.0, 48.0, 47.0,	6.00, 6.22, 6.39,
	69.5, 60.0, 69.0,	47.5, 47.0, 47.0,	6.70, 6.85, 6.62,
	69.0, 67.0, 66.5	42.0, 47.0, 46.0	7.30, 6.60, 7.05
L.A. Portenko, Wrangel Island	74.1, 73.6, 72.3,	48.2, 47.8, 47.7,	7.0, 6.0, 6.7, 6.8,
	70.8, 69.3, —,	47.2, 47.3, —,	6.0, —, —, —
	—, —,	—, —	
A.I. Mineev, Wrangel Island	74.2, 73.9, 72.1,	47.5, 45.6, 48.2,	6.8, 5.93, 6.85,
	71.0, 70.8, 70.7,	49.1, 47.5, 47.5,	6.55, 6.4, 6.0,
	70.5, 70.3, 69.9,	48.3, 47.8, 46.6,	6.4, 6.4, 5.9,
	69.3, 69.2, 68.8,	48.6, 45.5, 45.5,	7.25, 6.0, 6.1,
	66.8, —, —,	45.7, —, —,	6.15, —, —,
	—	—	—
			Weight of slightly and moderately incubated eggs, g
A.P. Kuzyakin, Poutyn	77.8, 76.3, 75.1,	45.7, 46.8, 46.9,	81.0, 83.5, 84.0,
	74.6, 73.5, 73.3,	47.9, 47.8, 46.9,	85.5, 84.5, 84.0,
	71.5, 71.4, 70.7,	46.5, 47.5, 45.7,	80.5, 84.5, 77.0,
	—, —, —	—, —, —	—, —, —

approach of a man, brent geese fly away from the nest sooner than lesser snow geese do. According to my observations, however, brent geese in all cases were less wary than the lesser snow geese.

On June 29, 1939, I visited a colony on the middle course of the Nasha River. On the right bank was a terrace with a plot of shrubbery at a height of 40 to 50 m above the level of the water. Nearby several brent geese were moving about in the herbage fringing a mountain stream. As I approached the plot an owl came to meet me. The small flock of geese began to withdraw steadily. Only some pairs and lone birds remained in their nests. Then they, too, began leaving the nests and finally took to their wings, settling not farther than 100 to 120 paces from me. As soon as I withdrew the geese walked back, sat and came so close that they could have been shot without difficulty. Later they flew off to the river, returning after some time. Some birds tried to withdraw bending close to the ground and running. Others remained in pairs and cried restlessly. They drove away a marauding jaeger.

Beyond the headland, 300 m upstream from this colony, on a moderate-sized plot only 15 to 20 m above the water, I found another group of nests. The brent geese selected small dry ridges on shrubby tundra for nesting. Since the nest of the owl was behind the headland its presence could not have been absolutely essential for the nesting of brent geese. An incubating bird which I failed to notice in the grass flew away from the nest when I was just 10 paces from it. The nest contained four eggs and the goose could not cover them up. The disturbed geese flew to and fro in pairs along the river.

On July 12, 1912, J. Koren found a nest in a valley 30 miles east of Cape Bol'shoi Baranov on a tiny shrubby islet in a tundra lake. It contained five downy chicks which had just hatched out, one of them not yet completely free of the shell. Close by was a pair of adult birds, which were collected.

On July 15, 1939, I found a brood with three downy chicks on a lake in Somnitel'naya Bay. They attempted to escape by swimming but they were ill at ease on the water and ultimately the chicks had to return to the bank (Fig. 31). The parents flew about with a low, uneasy honking until Tayan shot them. I was not a bit surprised when the latter explained that he decided to kill the parents because the chicks would find new fosterparents. As a matter of fact, an hour or two later when we passed that lake again we saw the chicks already following a new pair which did not show as much uneasiness as the real parents. Tayan was very happy to find proof of his statement but I was still skeptical until É.V. Schmidt narrated similar instances from personal experience. He also said that even if brent geese from a nest with eggs were killed other birds would incubate the eggs. In at least one colony where geese were shot chicks emerged from all of the nests. If gulls attacked the chicks other geese protected them.

Before our arrival a huge flock of nonbreeding brent geese was removed from a lakelet at Somnitel'naya but the hunters found three more downy chicks nearby. On July 16 some downy chicks were taken in the Nasha River valley. The goslings grew very rapidly; in early August, they were already feathered and at migration time the young under-one-year-olds could be distinguished from the adults in all the broods. Moreover, in the flocks arriving in spring immature geese of the previous breeding season could be distinguished without difficulty among the adults. On

Wrangel the broods stick to pastures, mixing at times with lone molting birds. The nesting birds no doubt molt late and separately from the massive flocks. On August 16, 1938, I found a lone goose on one of the big lakes near the Krasnyi Flag River estuary. It remained there for a few days along with a female eider. This bird was molting late. On August 17 the eider was seen on a neighboring lake and the molted lone goose had joined a large flock.

It is evident that brent geese do not nest every year. From the beginning of their arrival on Wrangel the life of the lone birds passed in a characteristic way. In the spring of 1939 the arrival concluded in the first 10 days of June. At the end of this period the nesting geese were seen in pairs while the single birds, on the contrary, were in flocks. On June 12 I found pairs and small groups to the west of Akatylanva and put up some geese sitting together with eiders on the 13th at the mouth of one of the rivulets entering Somnitel'naya Bay. They were found even farther to the east. On June 26 I found a flock of 14 birds at the eastern end of Rodgers Bay and another on June 29 halfway up the Nasha River. In the last 10 days of June and the first 10 days of July flocks of brent geese kept flying past Rodgers Bay, this being a daily routine.

Molting—During July a gradual increase in the flocks and a reduction in daily flights were noticed. The flocks usually moved over the lagoons and rarely above the tundra at any time of the day. I saw sitting flocks, for example on a lake near the mouth of the Amerikanskaya River and in Somnitel'naya Bay. On July 22 I noted in my diary the sighting of the last of the flying flocks. The wintering personnel at the Polar Station organized the hunting of a huge flock of molting geese on the Ozero lagoon on August 2. A very large number of birds succeeded in crossing the spit and escaped into the sea but nevertheless 89 birds were caught. I examined the entire quarry. In some the shafts on the wings had just begun to grow while the wing feathers of others had already grown from 10 to 15 cm. In the middle of August, the brent geese on Wrangel Island began flying.

On August 8, 1938, hunters caught more than 30 flightless molting brent geese at Bruch spit. On molting, the geese remained in large flocks. On August 12 a huge flock was seen flying in an easterly direction above Rodgers Bay. On August 13 I noticed some geese over the sea north of Cape Uéring. On August 14 I encountered some large flocks in Tundra Akademii south of Bruch spit; some of them comprised hundreds of birds. Some were alone and others joined flocks of lesser snow geese. On August 16 and 17, on the tundra along the Krasnyi Flag River, brent geese flew in flocks. They differed from the lesser snow geese in their restlessness. Characteristic wanderings before migration became conspicuous.

Not much information is available about molting in the Chukchi peninsula. On July 17, 1879, the *Vega* expedition found a flock flying past Pitlekai. They could have been brent geese gathered before molting. According to L.O. Belopol'skii (1934), on July 8, 1931, the Chukchians caught a few dozen molting geese on the Kurimul' River east of Krest Bay. They were probably lone birds since Belopol'skii himself killed a goose (possibly a nesting bird) with undeveloped wing feathers on August 17, 1931.

Migration—According to É.V. Schmidt, after molting daily flights were noticed among brent geese. In the mornings they would set off to the marine lagoons and fly to the shoals for rest. The flocks formed for migration remained long in one place though the wanderings of flapping broods could extend from the Chukchi mainland to Aiok Island. I saw some brent geese in a flock of emperor geese in the Kol'oam-Véem River estuary on August 10, 1934, and again at the same place on August 23.

The migration on Wrangel Island began earlier than in the Chukchi peninsula. G.A. Ushakov noticed mass flights from August 15 through 20, 1926, August 20 through 25, 1927, and August 18 through 20, 1928, invariably in a southwesterly direction. My observations are too few to confirm this phenomenon as definitely as in the case of lesser snow geese.

According to A.I. Mineev, brent geese migrated gradually. In the fall of 1938, on the north coast of the island, I noticed huge flocks ready to migrate as early as August 17. At Bruch spit, on August 26, brent geese had settled on the tundra bank of the lagoon. In the evening of August 27 two huge flocks were seen flying in the direction of Cape Uéring. On September 9 a lone brent goose, the last of 1938, flew past the Polar Station. In 1939 the migration began on August 16. On the morning of that day I noticed a flock not far from the Station, around the knolls. After midday a huge flock flew along the coast eastward. On August 22 a flock passed over the Nasha River. The geese flew at a moderate height in a southwesterly direction. On August 24 a flying goose was bagged. No more were seen up to the 28th, when I left Wrangel Island.

É.V. Schmidt drew my attention to the fact that brent geese in the Chukchi peninsula migrated later than other geese. Around Uélen in the fall of 1933 the first flying birds were seen on August 24. I noticed different-sized flocks on August 30 in the lagoons and at the mouth of the Vtoraya rivulet (Téeyu-Véem). Some flocks moved about leisurely not far off. The flight continued in the first few days of September. It had ceased by the 10th. On September 25 five young geese flew into Uélen, and a flock of 12 to 15 birds was noticed on the 27th above the knoll close by. Finally, on October 1 the last of the flocks went by. I saw three flocks with six, 11 and 26 birds. The flying flocks usually took an easterly direction. In the fall of 1934 there was no movement of local brent geese throughout August.

I did not see other species in large flocks of brent geese any more than brent geese could be seen in flocks of lesser snow geese migrating from Wrangel Island. The small brent goose could not of course fly alongside the large species because of differences in flight capabilities.

Habits—The brent goose is a very wary bird though in this respect it is inferior to the emperor and lesser snow geese. When beside its nest it comes within range of a rifle shot but in the spring and fall it is hardly possible to approach a pair or a flock closer than 200 paces in the open. Without noticing a hunter, it may fly very close. If one of a pair is killed the companion circles above and can easily be shot. Attachment to wounded members is also noticed in the flocks. An entire brood flying over Uélen village was killed because the young geese did not desert those that had been shot.

A.I. Mineev assured me that brent geese invariably flew like ravens, in an amorphous flock, and not in ranks or formations. Sometimes just a few brent geese would fly in single file. This is not correct. Brent geese do form ranks and formations but frequently change the order. In fact, they differ in this behavior from the larger species of geese.

Food—The stomachs of specimens collected on Wrangel Island revealed the following contents: 1) June 4, 1939. Ground mass of leaves of sedge *Carex lugens* Holm. and fine sand. 2) June 9, 1939. About 0.25 g fine sand. 3) June 9, 1939. Thin rootlets of sedge. Ground plant mass occupied three-fourths of the stomach volume, the rest being occupied by sand. 4) June 13, 1939. Three berries, two flowers, 50 seeds of cloudberry, 20 grass shoots, 4 g ground plant remnants, 2 g fine sand. 5) June 29, 1939. Ground remnants, about 50 whole blades of grass *Dupontia fischeri* R. Br. and fine sand. 6) July 16, 1939. Highly digested shoots of grass *Dupontia fischeri.*

The stomach of a downy chick collected on July 16, 1939, also showed highly ground remnants of grass *Dupontia fischeri* occupying one-half of its volume, and fine sand. According to A.G. Velizhanin the brent goose in captivity ate groats and wheat, and grasses not so avidly.

Weight—A male caught on Wrangel on June 9, 1939, weighed 1,552 g. An adult female shot on June 13 weighed 1,470 g.

Economic importance—The brent goose is a beautiful bird of the wilds. It grows very fat; for example, all the birds I collected in June, 1939, on Wrangel Island were characterized by a compact subcutaneous layer of fat. Its flesh is more tender than that of the much larger species of goose and is devoid of any marine aftertaste. Therefore brent geese are hunted at every available opportunity. The molting birds are killed by the dozen in the Chukchi peninsula and on Wrangel Island. Down and eggs are collected from the breeding grounds. The new hunters pay no heed to preserving the nesting colonies and often ruin incubated clutches for no apparent reason, which the Chukchians of course never do. It is quite clear, therefore, that large colonies should be brought under protection and the killing of molting birds permitted only when absolutely essential.

Systematics of the subspecies—Three distinct subspecies inhabit USSR territory:

1) **Branta bernicla hrota** (Müller). Form with a bright belly. The anterior aspect of the body—head, neck, upper back, and breast—are black and differ sharply from the grayish-brown, relatively pale hind part of body. It is grayish-brown on top with diffuse bright fringes gradually disappearing farther back. The rump is darker and the upper tail coverts are almost black. The large outer tail feathers are of a bright nut-brown color with broad whitish fringes. The breast and the anterior part of the abdomen are a pale grayish-brown with white fringes. The lower abdomen and the undertail coverts are pure white.

In the winter dress the back is of a more bluish shade, the fringes being less prominent. In the young birds the fringes are seen even in the flight feathers; in general, they are broader and whiter at the ends with a patchy appearance. On the underside of the body there are bright roundish spots. Twelve birds were studied.

The nesting zone extends from the Parry archipelago (arctic Canada) through Greenland and Spitsbergen to Franz Josef Land. A.F. Middendorf collected a flying specimen on June 16, 1843, in western Taimir. I would not be surprised if this subspecies later turned out to be nesting Severnaya Zemlya. The extension of the subspecies to Novaya Zemlya calls for a detailed study.

2) **Branta bernicla bernicla** (L.). Bluish-gray form. The black anterior of the body stands out quite prominently compared to the very bright remainder of the body, which is characterized by a brownish-gray color with a characteristic slate-blue tinge. The upper parts are somewhat darker than in the preceding subspecies; the fringes are less distinct. The general tone is not a nutty shade but blue. The underparts are of a brownish-slate color; each feather has a brownish edge. The fringes on the slate-brown sides are less than 0.5 cm in width, while in *B. b. hrota* they are almost 1 cm wide in the hindmost lateral feathers. The lower abdomen and the undertail coverts are white. The white band on the neck is only slightly bigger than in *B. b. hrota*.

The young birds are much brighter and more bluish-gray in color than the adults. The underparts are noticeably darker than in the young birds of *B. b. hrota*, from which they differ primarily in their bluish, not brownish color. Eighteen birds were studied including nesting birds from western Taimir and Khatanga and migratory birds from Finland. The nesting zone extends from Kolguev and the southern island of Novaya Zemlya to Khatanga, inclusive.

3) **Branta bernicla nigricans** (Lawr.). Blackish-brown form. The black color on the anterior body is less prominent against the very dark color of the rest of the body. The upper parts are dark nut-brown with slightly brighter feather fringes fading to a dark horn color. The flanks are brown but the bright edges are broader and whiter than in *B. b. bernicla*. In this respect some similarity to *B. b. hrota* is noticed but the fringes are much narrower in the anterior part of the sides and broaden only toward the rear. In the two preceding subspecies, this transition from narrow to broad fringes on the sides from front to rear is more gradual. The breast and the abdomen are of a very dark grayish-brown with narrow, even darker edges. The dark color of the abdomen runs farther back than in *B. b. bernicla*. The anal and subcaudal portions are white. The white band on the neck is broader than in the preceding two subspecies and is invariably closed in the front.

The entire color of the winter dress is darker. The feathers fringing the back are hardly paler than the main background tone. In the young birds they are whitish. The black color on the crop merges more smoothly with the dark background of the breast than in the adult birds. The general color, compared with the young of *B. b. bernicla*, is a much darker slate-brown. Thirty-three specimens were studied.

This subspecies is distributed from the Lena in the east to Bering Strait and from Alaska to Parry River in arctic Canada.

Even before my collections on Wrangel Island entered the Institute of Zoology, Academy of Sciences of the USSR, A.Ya. Tugarinov (1941) described the black-cropped goose from northeast Asia under the name *B. b. orientalis* Tug. It was found from the Lena to the Anadyr and differed from the American goose in its brighter color. After preparing the manuscript for the publication *Fauna of Anadyr Region*, I again carefully studied the entire series of black geese preserved in the Institute of Zoology, Academy of Sciences of the USSR, with the additional specimens that I had from Wrangel Island, and came to the conclusion that the characteristics listed by A.Ya. Tugarinov for his *B. b. orientalis* were only individual variations. The American specimen in the collection of the Institute of Zoology, Academy of Sciences of the USSR, is dressed in the winter plumage and for this reason was already darker than the rest. The extension of this dark color onto the abdomen farther back is explained by the technique of stuffing. A.Ya. Tugarinov explained to me that he described the new subspecies without seeing my Wrangel series. Ten years later, J. Delacour and J.T. Zimmer (1952) revised the subspecies of black brent geese based on the material available in American museums. Like me, they did not recognize the differences pointed out by Tugarinov.

It would appear that the name *B. b. nigricans* should be retained for the Chukchian and Wrangel geese, but Delacour and Zimmer proposed another solution for the problem. They differentiated one more subspecies, also with a dark abdomen but of large size, from northeastern Canada. Only three birds of this form are known in the collections, which Delacour (1954, p. 191) himself regarded as somewhat mysterious. If the name *nigricans* is retained for this form, the name *orientalis* should be left for Chukchian geese according to the rules of nomenclature.

Nevertheless, I am not certain about the large form in spite of the fact that it was recognized by American hunters and eskimos. Therefore, until the problem is thoroughly solved, I would, as before, call my Chukchian and Wrangel brent geese by the name *B. b. nigricans*.

Specimens— 1) Rodgers Bay, June 21, 1931, ♂, Mineev; 2) southeastern part of Wrangel, June 23, 1934, ♀, Mineev; 3) Uélen, August 30, 1933, ○ 1° anno, Portenko; 4) same place, August 31, 1933, ♂, Portenko; 5 to 9) same place, September 25, 1933, ♀♂♂♂♂ 1° anno, Portenko; 10) same place, May 31, 1934, ○ Portenko; 11) same place, June 18, 1934, ♀, Portenko; 12 to 16) Bruch spit, August 8, 1938, ○ ○, Portenko; 17) Akatylanva landmark, June 3, 1939, ♂, Portenko; 18 to 21) same place, June 4, 1939, ♂ and ♀♀♀, Portenko; 22) same place, June 7, 1939, ○, Portenko; 23) same place, June 9, 1939, ♂, Portenko; 24) same place, June 13, 1939, ♀, Portenko; 25) Nasha River, June 29, 1939, ♂, Portenko; and 26 to 29) same place, July 16, 1939, pull., Portenko.

Biological collection— 1) Clutch of four eggs, upper reaches of Mamontovaya River, June 12, 1932, Mineev; 2) clutch of three eggs, Atternon hill slope, June 14, 1932, Mineev; 3) clutch of three eggs, Rodgers Bay, June 23, 1932, Mineev; 4) clutch of four eggs, same date, Mineev; 5) one egg, Nasha River, June 27, 1939, Portenko; and 6) nest with a clutch of four eggs, June 29, 1939, Portenko.

Branta canadensis minima Ridgw.—**Cackling Canada Goose**

So far not one of the cackling goose forms has been found either in the Chukchi peninsula or on Wrangel Island. E.W. Nelson (1883, p. 94) erred when he assumed that *Branta canadensis leucopareia* (Brandt) was undoubtedly found on the Siberian coast though some stray arrivals there are possible.

According to a report by F.H. Fay and T.J. Cade (1959), a local resident shot a cackling goose on May 10, 1956, near Gambell and another lone bird was sighted on June 3, 1957, over the village.

In his treatise on archaeological discoveries of birds on St. Lawrence Island H. Friedmann (1934a) mentions two instances: 1) coracoid bones and 2) a pair of beaks excavated from the upper formations in the ancient village of Kaiélegak. The excavations are around one thousand years old. This is an interesting document which shows how rare it is to find the cackling goose on the west side of Bering Strait.

17. **Anas platyrhynchos platyrhynchos** L.—**Mallard Duck**

Very rare migratory species.

A male was collected around Égvekinot on July 2, 1959; the year before, on September 26, 1958, this bird had been ringed in the southwestern part of Saskachewan, Canada, 2 miles from Simley (51°35′ north and 109°25′ west). A. Dzubin (1962), who reported sighting a mallard entering Krest Bay, correctly gauged that it was hardly of local origin and more probably American. I believe it could, for example, have followed flocks of pintails wintering in North America.

When I visited Cape Schmidt in May, 1934, the Director of the local factory, M.S. Venediktov, told me that in July, 1933, male and female mallards were brought to him and that he was acquainted with the species in more southerly latitudes. Since Venediktov was not a hunter I am not certain of the identification: he could have mistaken the male scaup for a male mallard. In the Anadyr region (Portenko, 1939b, vol. II, p. 105) a migrating female mallard was collected on June 17, 1933, on the Vtoraya brook near Anadyr village. Hence, later flights into the Chukchi peninsula from the Bering Sea are possible. In Alaska this duck nests as far north as Kotsebue Bay, though it is rare in some parts of the country adjoining Bering Strait.

18. **Nettion crecca crecca** (L.)—**European Common Teal or Green-winged Teal**

Distribution and status—Species nesting quite often in the westernmost part of the Chukchi peninsula adjoining Chaun Bay. Probably migrates only east: found in the spring in the southern and eastern parts of the peninsula.

Only two reliable finds are known for the south coast of the Island: P.T. Butenko collected a male in Providence Bay on May 30, 1938, and W.S. Brooks (1915) reported shooting a male on June 6, 1913, at Cape Chaplin (Indian point). According to É.V. Schmidt, this teal was found in Mechigmensk Gulf. K.W. Kenyon (Kenyon and Brooks 1960) noticed a female on June 10, 1958, on the drifting ice off Malyi Diomede Island. The subspecies of the bird, however, could not be identified. On June 12, 1970, a migratory male was collected by A.A. Kishchinskii around the Ukouge lagoon. As reported by É.V. Schmidt, this teal nests nearly everywhere in the Chaun region though it is less numerous than the Baikal teal.

According to a report of I.N. Gabrielson and F.C. Lincoln (1959), the nominal form of European teal occasionally flew past the Pribylov peninsula but in the Aleutian Islands it has been replaced by the much larger subspecies *Nettion crecca nimia* (Friedm.). If the random finds are excluded, the area from Chaun Bay to Anadyr Strait south of the Anadyr Range may be regarded as the northeastern limit of the distribution of this teal.

Reproduction—The testes of the male collected by P.T. Butenko were already enlarged, the left and right ones measuring 11 × 31 and 10 × 28 mm, respectively. It was a plump specimen with subcutaneous adipose layers but small in size. It weighed only 280 g.

Specimen—Providence Bay, May 30, 1938, ♂, Butenko.

Nettion crecca carolinensis (Gm.)—**American Green-winged Teal**

Arrivals on Lawrence Island established.

Stray records are possible on the south coast of the Chukchi peninsula. E.W. Nelson (1883, p. 97) thought that this form of teal nested on St. Lawrence Island but found no actual record. According to H. Friedmann (1938) a male was collected on May 16, 1936, near Gambell. F.H. Fay and T.J. Cade (1959) reported that a male was taken on May 28, 1953, on the north coast of island.

19. **Nettion formosa** (Georgi)—**Baikal Teal**

Distribution and status—Nests in the Chukchi peninsula and is common in the western part; sporadically inhabits the eastern part, being mostly absent or rare. Comes to Wrangel Island, or even spends the summer there, but does not nest.

On July 23, 1937, H. Collins (Gabrielson 1941) collected a pair at Savunga on St. Lawrence Island. Only a few summer records are known in northwestern Alaska although nesting has not been conclusively established (Maher 1960).

I have some information from É.V. Schmidt about the distribution of the Baikal teal on the east coast of the Chukchi peninsula. According to him, it was common in Mechigmensk Gulf and was found on Lawrence Bay in small numbers. I did not find it at all around Uélen or along the Kol'oam- and Utte-Véem river valleys. This species was not seen even by the *Vega* expedition at Kolyuchin Bay. Evidently it becomes quite common much farther west.

A.A. Savich collected a male in breeding plumage at Cape Schmidt on May 26, 1915 (Artobolevskii 1927). There the Baikal teal was not a rarity since I found some stuffed heads of this duck among bird skins in the local factory in the spring of 1934. Farther west, in the Chaun region, this teal is numerous, according to É.V. Schmidt. It nests, particularly, in the Karchyk peninsula and on Aiok Island. On the Kolyma, it is one of the most common of ducks. J. Koren (Schaanning 1954) collected downy chicks on the lower Kolyma on July 24, 1915, and took three clutches in 1915 and 1916: seven fresh eggs on June 19, seven three-day incubated eggs on June 24 and eight fresh eggs on June 25.

It is remarkable that the Baikal teal has been repeatedly seen on Wrangel Island. On May 28, 1934, a pair was shot in the southeastern part of the Island and given to V.E. Vlasova. On August 16, 1938, I put up a pair, a female and a male in summer plumage, near the Krasnyi Flag River estuary on the northern tip of Wrangel. I noticed a female or two on the lagoons east of Predatel'skaya Bay on June 9 and 12, 1939. The ducks were very wary: On June 9, I put up three ducks from a long distance and two at the same place on June 12. On the latter occasion I confirmed with the binoculars that they were female teals along with a pintail. During the Eastern High Altitude Expedition A.P. Andriyashev collected a female teal on August 13, 1946, off the ice north of Wrangel at 72°03.7′ north and 179°21.5′ west.

Habitat—The teals found on Wrangel were confined to the lakes in the northern and southern parts of the island, as could be anticipated for freshwater ducks. A specimen from Andriyashev was collected in a 10-point ice environment.

Economic importance—The fact that the head skins of male teal were cured at Cape Schmidt shows the possible utilization of the beautiful plumage of this duck, even if on a small scale. Collars, rugs and other articles could find a market instead of simply throwing away the heads.

Specimens— 1 and 2) Cape Schmidt, 1933 (headskins), ♂♂, Portenko; 3 and 4) southeastern part of Wrangel, May 28, 1934, ♂♀, Vlasova; and 5) Chukchi Sea, north of Wrangel Island, August 13, 1946, ♀, Andriyashev.

20. **Dafila acuta acuta** (L.)—**Pintail**

Local name—In Eskimo: Nī′-vŭ-ghă mtă'-thlūk on St. Lawrence Island.

Distribution and status—Nests in the Chukchi peninsula and is numerous in the western part up to Cape Schmidt. Farther to the east, up to Bering Strait, is found in summer, being not particularly rare, but nidification not established. Comes to St. Lawrence Island.

L.O. Belopol'skii (1934) noticed pintails in Krest Bay in spring flight. On May 18, 1954, a male was caught there that had been ringed on December 9, 1951, in Arkansas on the northwest shore of the Bay of Mexico (Shevareva 1959). According to the observations of V.É. Yakobi, it was the most numerous of river ducks around Uél'kal' in 1961. Flocks of 20 to 30 birds flew in the spring and fall. The flight directions in the spring were north and northeast. On June 30 a flock of 25 birds passed to the south at a height of about 150 m; thus began the migrations of non-paired birds gathering for molting. I.O. Olenev saw pintails in spring flight over Émma Bay but P.T. Butenko did not find them even once at Providence Bay.

On St. Lawrence Island in the summer of 1881 E.W. Nelson (1883) saw some pintails. In August, 1930, G.P. Collins collected a young male. O.J. Murie (1936) gathered some females on August 29 and September 24, 1934, and also on August 16, 1935. As reported by F.H. Fay and T.J. Cade (1959), a male was taken on June 30, 1950, and another was sighted in 1952. In 1953 and 1954 pintails constituted an appreciable proportion of the island's avifauna. Two nests were found in 1953 and four in 1954. In 1953 a female with a brood was seen. In June, 1960, E.G.F. Sauer and E.K. Urban (1964) often encountered pintails, usually in pairs, in the valley of the Boxer River in the southwestern part of the island. In general, F.H. Fay (1961) came to the conclusion that their population on St. Lawrence Island was highly variable and might even exceed one thousand nesting birds, while the nonpaired birds were only about one-half of this number. The spring flight in small numbers occurred in a northwesterly direction. H. Friedmann (1934a) found a basidigital bone in the archaeological excavations.

According to information gathered by the Bird Ringing Center a young pintail was obtained on Arakamchechen Island on June 20, 1935; it had been ringed on January 8 of the same year in Los Banos, California. According to É.V. Schmidt the pintail was noticed in the summer in Mechigmensk Gulf and on the tundras near Lawrence Bay. A male was collected in this bay on May 25, 1953. It had been ringed on April 5, 1952, in Idaho State. I did not see pintails either in Providence Bay or in Lawrence Bay; nor did A.P. Kuzyakin.

In the spring of 1958 K.W. Kenyon (Kenyon and Brooks 1960) often sighted pintails on Malyi Diomede Island. On May 18 an adult male circled the village and a pair was sighted on May 23 in the ice leads at the southern end of the island. On June 9 an adult male flew past the village northward along the coast. Finally, a young male was shot on the knoll beyond the settlement. This was a bird with enlarged testes: 7 × 25 mm.

I did not find pintails around Uélen or on my trips up the Kol'oam-Véem River but found them in large numbers on a lake in the middle reaches of the Utte-Véem River. They were found singly and in flocks, one such flock comprising 18 birds. The day before, P.T. Butenko collected a female. The conditions under which the pintails were found proved beyond doubt that they were not nesting but only lone birds which evidently gathered for molting. Pintails were not sighted at all near the winter anchorage of the *Vega* on Kolyuchin Bay.

E.M. Meller collected a female on June 7, 1939, at Pereval'naya and I found some pairs in the course of summer, 1956, on the Amguema around the 91st km. E.W. Nelson (1883, p. 96) wrote that they were also found on the north Siberian (i.e. Chukchian) coast and were in fact sighted just about wherever they landed on the coast, where the country provided a suitable marshy habitat for the birds. In mid-June, 1970, A.A. Kishchinskii noted some pairs around the Ukouge lagoon. In the last 10 days of June and early July hundreds of flocks of males which had begun molting were found by its banks.

V.Ya. Isaev only once, in mid-June, 1935, found a male pintail at Cape Schmidt, but É.V. Schmidt told me that the breeding grounds of pintails extended from Chaun Bay at least up to Cape Schmidt along the tundra plain. In Chaun Bay Schmidt himself collected many birds, including young ones, and sighted large flocks in spring flight. He found broods even on Aiok Island but more rarely than in the Chaun lowland. Toward the east this duck became even less numerous, though according to Schmidt it could be regarded as common even in the eastern part of the Chukchi peninsula. T.P. Shevareva (1959) reported the recovery of a ring from a two-year-old female ringed in North Dakota on September 10, 1952, and shot on May 31, 1953, about 35 km from the Lelyu-Véem River estuary (69° 28′ north and 171°22′ east). J. Koren (Thayer and Bangs 1914) shot a young pintail some miles south of Cape Shelagskii. A.I. Argentov (1861a) cited a pintail among the local ducks on the north coast from Cape Yakan to the Kolyma. According to S.A. Buturlin (1906b, p. 3), pintails were found every few yards in the lower reaches of the Kolyma. J. Koren's collection (Schaanning 1954) contained two clutches from the lower Kolyma: six eggs incubated for two days, on June 23, and seven eggs incubated for four days, on June 30, 1916.

On June 12, 1939, I saw a female pintail on Wrangel Island, east of Predatel'skaya Bay.

The ringing of birds has clearly shown that pintails, like scaups, brent geese and lesser snow geese, fly to the southwestern parts of North America for wintering.

Habitat—Under the conditions of the interior of the Chukchi peninsula the pintail is evidently confined, as in Anadyr, to the lakes adjoining the rivers. Residents of Markovo village called it a river duck (misspelt due to a printing error in my *Fauna of Anadyr Region*, vol. II, p. 108), to differentiate it from sea ducks, but is in fact a lake duck by habitat. The lake on which I found the pintails near the Utte-Véem River was on the tundra not far from the river but there were no stagnant water puddles. There was two to three hectares of tundra, of circular form, with stunted shrubs on one side and dead branches and stubs jutting out from the water. But the local atmosphere was not maritime at all. In fact, old squaws and female common eiders were found on the lake because of the proximity of the sea. On Wrangel Island I found a pintail flying from one freshwater lake to another. A migratory pintail was noted even on a saltwater lagoon by V.Ya. Isaev at Cape Schmidt, though it was confined to lakes in the adjacent tundra.

Arrival—In 1953 the first flocks of three to 10 birds appeared in the tundra near Gambell on St. Lawrence Island in the last week of May before the ice thawed on the lake. F.H. Fay gave May 19 as the date of arrival at Northwest Cape.

In the Chukchi peninsula pintails arrived late, at least those wintering in America. In 1932, I.O. Olenev saw migratory flocks on June 2 and 3 at Émma Bay. In 1931, L.O. Belopol'skii found the first four birds on June 1 at Krest Bay; the ducks flew from east to west. According to V.É. Yakobi, around Uél'kal' in the spring of 1961, flocks of pintails in flight were seen on June 5, 7, 19 and 20.

On the day I arrived at the Amguema (June 10, 1956) I saw a small number of pintails already flying in pairs. It is possible that in the western part of the Chukchi peninsula they came earlier from the side of the Asian wintering sites.

Breeding—On St. Lawrence Island a nest with eggs was found between June 15 and 23. There were six freshly laid eggs in a nest on June 21, 1954. A female with a brood was seen on August 15, 1954. On August 27, 1912, J. Koren collected a fully grown young pintail south of Cape Shelagskii.

Summer residence—Lone as well as non-breeding birds spend the summer in the Chukchi peninsula and on St. Lawrence Island. In June, 1954, on the Kuzata lagoon on the south coast of St. Lawrence Island, 75 per cent of the pintails sighted were males. On July 10, 1934, on a lake near the Utte-Véem River, I found flocks of lone pintails in large numbers. But I never found massive gatherings anywhere. In summer, 1956, I frequently saw three pintails living together on the Amguema throughout June. They did not build a nest. On June 17, 1970, according to A.A. Kishchinskii, flocks of pintails consisting almost exclusively of males regularly flew along the sea coast at the Ukouge lagoon in a northwesterly or southwesterly direction. From June 22 hundreds of flocks were noticed on the lakes around the tundra. Among the males, which evidently gathered for molting, females were also found. They were often lone birds probably in the second year, partly from destroyed nests. The autopsy of a female collected on June 23 revealed signs of recent activity of the ovary and oviduct. Observations continued up to July 12 but the pintails probably remained there much longer.

Migration—According to the information gathered by V.É. Yakobi, flocks of pintails flew away from Uél'kal' from August 17 through 29.

Food—The stomach of a female collected on July 9, 1934, showed fragments of two larvae, evidently *Plecoptera*, bits of bacilli and heads of roughly 10 river larvae, 15 bivalve mollusks, and about the same number of other mollusks, about 100 tiny seeds, pieces of shoots and rootlets, and finally tiny pebbles. Judging from the diverse feed intake, the birds had no reason to starve. A horse-tail was found in the crop of a bird collected by E.M. Meller while its stomach showed the remains of various marsh plants, insect larvae and tiny pebbles.

Systematics of the subspecies—Based on a study of nearly 100 males from the Paleoarctic and only five birds from America, I came to the conclusion (1939b, vol. II, pp. 111 and 112) (1) that *Dafila acuta tzitzihoa* (Vieill.) was actually a distinct subspecies and (2) that the characteristics of the subspecies *D. a. tzitzihoa* and of the five American male specimens available to me could not be seen in all of the Paleoarctic series[1]. Later American ornithologists stopped recognizing the subspecies *D. a. tzitzihoa* because pintails with the characteristics of both the subspecies formerly recognized were found in North America. At the same time it became clear that pintails arriving from northeast Asia wintered in North America. Two questions therefore arise: (1) why the ducks with the characteristics of *D. a. tzitzihoa* are not encountered in the Paleoarctic and (2) whether the American ornithologists actually found pintails that had come from northeast Asia; whether nesting of *D. a. acuta* (L.) occurs in northwestern North America. I cannot answer these questions in the absence of a good series of breeding males from different parts of North America and a series of Chukchian specimens.

Collection of males in breeding dress from the Chukchi peninsula and Wrangel Island is therefore very desirable. H. Friedmann and O.J. Murie called the pintails on St. Lawrence Island *D. a. tzitzihoa* (Vieill.) but Friedmann had with him only a young male while Murie had a lone female. It is impossible to determine the subspecies from them. In this case we have to resort to the common practice of American ornithologists of assigning difficult subspecies to one of the American forms.

Specimen—Middle reaches of the Utte-Véem River, July 9, 1934, ♀, Portenko.

21. **Mareca penelope penelope** (L.)—**Wigeon**

Nonbreeding species in the Chukchi peninsula noted from time to time on the western and more rarely on the eastern side. Not found on Wrangel Island.

On May 28, 1931, L.O. Belopol'skii (1934) collected an adult male near Uél'kal' village. It was no doubt a migrating bird. The wigeon was never seen in Providence Bay and only one record was reported on St. Lawrence Island (Friedmann 1932a) in Gambell village. É.V. Schmidt reports seeing wigeons many times in Mechigmensk Gulf, more often on the Chaun River, on Aiok Island and even on the Kolyma, where it was fairly numerous. Its numbers were smaller than those of pintails, at most one-fourth or one-fifth.

Specimen—Near village Uél'kal, May 28, 1931, ♂, Belopol'skii.

22. **Spatula clypeata** (L.)—**Shoveler**

Two instances known of the arrival on the south coast of the Chukchi peninsula and its interior.

[1]According to I.N. Gabrielson and F.C. Lincoln (1959, p. 153, footnote), a pintail collected in spring, 1936, at Cape Chaplin nearly conformed to the characteristics of *D. a. tzitzihoa.* The duck had been ringed on January 3, 1936, in Los Banos, California. Since the identification of the subspecies was not absolutely exact, I do not list it among the Chukchian birds.

According to Tayan, he happened to kill a male shoveler in Providence Bay in 1922 or 1923. His sketch and description leave no doubt whatever that it was indeed *S. clypeata.*

As reported by F.H. Fay and T.J. Cade (1959), a shoveler was collected only once in the last 30 years near Gambell on St. Lawrence Island.

On June 26, 1956, I saw a pair in a large old stagnant pool on the Amguema near the 91st km. The birds were unusually wary and probably came there on being frightened by hunters.

In northeastern Asia the nearest breeding grounds of shovelers lay relatively far away: in Kamchatka and Kolyma. They are much closer in Alaska, where this duck is found up to Kotsebue Bay as a sporadic nesting bird.

23. **Aythya fuligula** (L.)—**Tufted Duck**

A single instance of arrival on Wrangel Island established.

On May 28, 1939, I was given a male shot in Rodgers Bay from out of a pair. The birds were sitting on a tiny thawed pool. Ice still covered the lagoon. This pair was noticed as early as May 3. These ducks, which are unusual for Wrangel Island, flew over the bay and tundra and surprised the eskimos who sighted them.

The tufted duck is very rarely seen in flight in the western part of the Anadyr region, nests in Kamchatka, evidently on the Commander Islands, and on the Kolyma is found up to 69°4′ north according to S.A. Buturlin (1935, vol. II, p. 128). J. Koren (Schaanning 1954) had with him four downy chicks collected on the lower Kolyma on June 27, 1915.

Specimen—Rodgers Bay, May 28, 1939, ♂, Portenko.

24. **Aythya marila mariloides** (Vig.)—**Greater Scaup**

Distribution and status—In the Chukchi peninsula, some wandering and non-breeding pairs or molting males that stray off course, but rarely in the western parts. Nests, eggs or chicks not found anywhere so far but mating calls heard. Not reported on Wrangel Island.

Around Krest Bay, L.O. Belopol'skii (1934) did not encounter the greater scaup though it was common in the nesting areas in the Anadyr basin. In Uél'kal', V.É. Yakobi found a flock and pairs in flight in 1961 and later saw the birds in mating ceremonies; specimens were also collected. Farther east along the south coast of the peninsula this duck was not encountered at all.

E.W. Nelson (1883, p. 97) writes that the greater scaup was found on St. Lawrence Island. According to O.J. Murie (1936), a male was shot in summer dress on October 28, 1935, on the north coast of the island. According to F.H. Fay and T.J. Cade (1959) a pair was collected on May 28, 1954, south of Gambell and another on June 17, 1954, on the Kuzata lagoon, where two more pairs were noticed on June 23; their mating ceremonies were also observed. In the museum at Berkeley a pair collected on May 26, 1932, has been preserved. In his archaeological excavations H. Friedmann (1934a) found a breastbone which could be classified as of this species.

For the entire east coast of the Chukchi peninsula I have only the reference by É.V. Schmidt, according to whom two birds were collected in Mechigmensk Gulf. In the immediate neighborhood of Uélen, I did not see this duck but I found a flock on July 6, 1934, in the interior of this peninsula on the Utte-Véem River. A few days later, on July 12, it was perhaps the same flock that was again seen flying over the lagoon in the interior of Inchoun. It consisted of nine males which had evidently gathered for molting.

On the Amguema I saw perhaps the same pair twice on June 20 and 26, 1956. The pair was confined to the lakes and was very timid.

There is no information about the occurrence of the greater scaup on the north coast to the west of Cape Schmidt. On June 29, 1915, a flying male was collected there by A.A. Savich (Artobolevskii 1927). A.I. Argentov (1861a) found a "white-sided bird" among the local waterfowl. According to É.V. Schmidt, the greater scaup was bagged in flight on the lower reaches of the Chaun River. It evidently nested there and hence was found only in pairs. It was sighted rarely to the north in the Karchyk peninsula and on Aiok Island.

According to V.D. Lebedev and V.R. Filin (1959) a female was collected on July 15, 1958, on the north coast of the Karchyk peninsula from a flock of Steller's eiders. Lone birds were noticed on July 13 on the west coast of the peninsula and on July 21 on the west shore of Chaun Bay.

This duck was numerous in the taiga zone of Kolyma but rare on the open tundra.

Arrival—According to the observations of V.É. Yakobi, around Uél'kal' in 1961 the greater scaups arrived only on June 15 when the first flock of 15 birds was noticed on the lagoon. On June 16, around a small lake, a male with poorly developed testes was collected. On June 17 the mating calls of scaups were heard; the birds met breast to breast, splashed, flapped their wings and dived. When the female was shot, one of the three males in the group flew toward her and was also collected.

Weight—The weight of two males was 960 and 858 g and of a female 837 g.

Systematics of the subspecies—Having collected a series of spring males on the shore of Olyutor Bay I had occasion to review my former subspecies of greater scaup (Portenko 1939b, vol. II, p. 18).

The geographic variations could be successfully traced only in the adult males. Here the brown feathers on the sides which are characteristic of immature birds are totally absent. The juvenile characteristics as also those of adulthood vary widely in individual juvenile males and females.

Retaining the old names, I group the subspecies in a slightly different way as below:

1) **Aythya marila marila** (L.)—There is a pattern of fine wavy vermiculations on the back and shoulders. The shoulders appear whiter than the upper back (Fig. 36). The development of the white area on the shoulders varies in individual birds. In some, with much whiter shoulders, only the spots of the design remain. The purple shade on the head and neck is poorly developed but this character depends on the incidence of light on the feathers and its assessment for diagnostic purposes is difficult. The wing length on the average is greater: it was less than 21 cm only in

one case (Table 17).

I have a series of 13 spring males collected from Karelia in the west of Taimir.

Table 17. Wing length of male greater scaups, cm

Subspecies	Maximum	Minimum	Mean	No. of birds
Aythya marila marila (L.)	22.28	20.80	21.45	13
A. marila mariloides (Vig.)	22.05	20.07	21.25	26

2) **Aythya marila mariloides** (Vig.)—The pattern on the back and shoulders is coarser, i.e. the vermiculations forming the pattern, are broader; they are also blacker. This difference is important in this series and is highly conspicuous (Fig. 36). Such white shoulders as in the nominal form are not seen in the eastern subspecies. The purple shade on the head and neck is more intensely developed, especially in Kamchatka specimens. Specimens with much shorter wings predominate. Among the 26 birds studied, the wing was shorter than 21 cm in seven.

Spring males collected in Kolyma, in the Anadyr region, Koryatz Zemlya, Kamchatka and Bering Island, as also migratory and winter birds from Sakhalin in the Ussuriisk region and Japan were studied.

3) **Aythya marila nearctica** (Stejn.)—The backs and shoulders are much darker than in *A. m. mariloides*. The purple patch on the head is very restricted while the green patch is hardly larger than in *A. m. marila*. Unlike the two former subspecies, tiny spots are noticed on the white flanks even in adult birds.

It inhabits Alaska, Cape Prince of Wales and the Aleutian Islands up to the Mackenzie basin and Lake Athabasca.

4) **Aythya marila affinis** (Eyton)—The pattern on the back and shoulders is coarse. The metallic shade on the head and neck is purple. The size is small. It occurs from the interior of Alaska to Hudson Bay and as far south as Oregon, Utah, Iowa and Wisconsin. The distribution in Alaska partly coincides with the breeding zone of *A. m. nearctica*. Hybrids among them, if any, cannot be recognized because of the great similarity between the two forms. American ornithologists regard them as species.

Bucephala clangula (L.)—**Common Golden-eye**

L.O. Belopol'skii (1934, p. 27) writes that on May 23, 1931, on the tundra by a lake between Uél'kal' and Red'kin, he saw a duck which in size and plumage closely resembled the common golden-eye. This observation cannot be regarded as reliable (Portenko, 1939b, vol. II, p. 120).

25. **Clangula hyemalis** (L.)—**Old Squaw**

Local name—Chukchian: Àchek, ásek, and àsyakh; ♂—pójgatschek and ♀—atschak in the records of the *Vega* expedition. In Eskimo: kaunghak, aìgrak (in dark plumage) in Providence Bay; kăng-wŏk′ on St. Lawrence Island.

Distribution and status—Breeds in relatively small numbers in the Chukchi peninsula; common but distributed unevenly. Innumerable in both flights. Lone birds and males which have completed the mating period gather in large numbers, often in thousands, for molting on marine lagoons. Spends the winter partly on east and south coasts of the peninsula. Nests very rarely on Wrangel Island. Males come for molting in thousands of flocks.

Before going into the details of the distribution and status of old squaws, some preliminary observations require to be made. Most if not all of them do not breed in their second year and later do not necessarily breed every year. Further, the males are almost twice as many as the females. As a result, there is invariably an abundance of lone birds which live in a characteristic way, holding themselves aloof from the nesting birds, sometimes at a distance of several hundred kilometers. Therefore the distribution and status of the breeding and nonbreeding birds will have to be considered separately.

Distribution and status of breeding squaws—L.O. Belopol'skii (1934) did not report their nesting in Krest Bay. V.É. Yakobi caught a female with an egg inside around Uél'kal'. The squaw could be called one of the most numerous birds in the maritime zone but it is quite difficult to determine the number of nesting birds. The nesting of this duck has not been established in the hilly sections of the south coast of the Chukchi peninsula. I.O. Olenev told me that squaws did not nest in Providence Bay, which tallies with P.T. Butenko's and my own observations.

Squaws nest in large numbers on St. Lawrence Island. E.W. Nelson (1883) saw them when he visited the island in June and July, 1881. H. Friedmann (1932a) refers to a specimen collected there on July 13, 1899. W.S. Brooks (1915) in 1913 and A.M. Bailey (1925) in 1921 brought clutches. According to O.W. Geist (Murie 1936) old squaws nested along the north coast of the island. T.J. Cade (Fay and Cade 1959) saw dozens of broods on the lakes along the west coast between Gambell and Boxer Bay on August 8 and 9, 1950, and in the same month often found families on the Kuzata lagoon (south coast). In another work, F.H. Fay (1961) recalls two nests found on July 15 and 17. On St. Lawrence Island it was one of the more common of birds though a massive concentration of nests was not seen, any more than elsewhere.

According to É.V. Schmidt, old squaws were many in Mechigmensk Gulf but few at Lawrence Bay since there are few lakes around the latter. A.P. Kuzyakin also ascribes the small number of squaws in this part of the peninsula to the lack of suitable lakes.

In 1884, E.W. Nelson (1883, p. 99) found the old squaw common at Dezhnev settlement (East Cape). It does not nest on Bol'shoi Diomede Island because of the local conditions and I am convinced of this after my own visit to the island. According to my observations old squaws nest in small numbers on the plain tundra very close to Uélen. At different times in three summer seasons I spent near Uélen I met with only one nonflying brood, though in the early summer of 1934 I saw many pairs engaged in mating ceremonies. The old squaws in the nearby interior of the peninsula are by no means more numerous. I found only one brood on my expedition up the Kol'oam-Véem River from the estuary to Lake Kool'ong and back, and only one nest in the estuary of the Utte-Véem River during another trip.

The old squaw was similarly found few in numbers in the nesting areas at Kolyuchin Bay near the winter anchorage of the *Vega* expedition (Palmén 1887). In 1879 three clutches from Pitlekai and Neshkan were brought to the members of this expedition. In mid-July, 1909, J. Koren (1910) found old squaws in the freshwater lakes on the western side of Kolyuchin Bay. On Kolyuchi Island, as he himself verified, this duck was absent because of the topographic conditions.

In the middle reaches of the Amguema in June, 1956, I saw stray pairs. In 1970, according to A.A. Kishchinskii, old squaws were numerous in the breeding grounds along the north coast from Vankarém to the Amguema. V.M. Artobolevskii (1927) assumed that old squaws were numerous in the nesting areas at Cape Schmidt but he was evidently relying on June observations by A.A. Savich, which could have included single birds. V.Ya. Isaev told me that old squaws were numerous on the tundra near Cape Schmidt but he could not confirm this by actual observations either. A.I. Argentov saw a "white-headed duck" (1861a) among the local ducks on the north coast between Cape Yakan and the Kolyma. According to É.V. Schmidt the old squaw was numerous in the Chaun region. V.D. Lebedev and V.R. Filin (1959) refer to a female collected on June 15, 1958; there was a nearly complete egg in her oviduct. On June 28, on the south coast of Aiok Island, five nests were found. Females with chicks were found on July 21 and 22 on the west coast of Chaun Bay and on August 1 in the western part of the Karchyk peninsula.

Old squaws nest very rarely on Wrangel Island. A.G. Bannikov (1941) cites an egg found by G.A. Ushakov, but the conditions under which it was found are not reported. S.A. Skurikhin, the hunter, told V.F. Vlasova that he found a nest only once after eight years' sojourn on the island. A.I. Mineev (1936) writes that downy and older chicks have not been reported. He mistakes the molting old squaws for young birds when he reports a large number of young pintail ducks that were just beginning to fly.

In the spring of 1939, even before the mass appearance of male flocks, I found two pairs separately east of Predatel'skaya Bay. Later I saw a pair east of Somnitel'naya Bay but could not confirm that it was breeding there. Eskimo hunters told me that they found old squaws in the nesting areas but very rarely. A.G. Velizhanin (1965) writes without any substantiation that old squaws nested in the lakes of Tundra Akademii.

Distribution and status in spring flight—In June, 1961, V.É. Yakobi observed innumerable flocks consisting of 15 to 20 birds each around Uél'kal'. Their shrieks could be heard everywhere. The total sojourn depended on the coastal ice conditions. Old squaws in spring flight were noticed by L.O. Belopol'skii on the tundra near Cape Bering. Farther east on the south coast by the sea the phenomena of arrival and spring migration are lost in the local migrations at the end of wintering. I.O. Olenev had nothing to report about the mass spring flight in Providence Bay, nor had P.T. Butenko about this bay and Cape Chaplin.

On St. Lawrence Island W.S. Brooks found old squaws very common on June 2, 1913. Since they were not only in pairs but also in small flocks their flight or at least their arrival could be regarded as having begun. According to T.J. Cade from mid-May to mid-June pairs and small flocks were usually seen along the entire coast and everywhere in open freshwater lakes. According to E.G.F. Sauer and E.K. Urban (1964), in early June, 1960, flocks of old squaws were common in Boxer

Bay. On June 14 they were found in abundance at sea on the way to Kangi. K.W. Kenyon (Kenyon and Brooks 1960) saw pairs and small flocks in the 1958 spring flight past Malyi Diomede Island to the north or east.

On May 24, 1934, I noticed a few old squaws on the shore ice at Cape Dezhnev. No clear signs of flight were visible: the ducks swam, screamed and flew among flocks of murres in no definite direction. Evidently, the old squaws advance from Bering Strait to the north very gradually as leads form in the ice, but ultimately they can be found very far from the land. H.U. Sverdrup (Schaanning 1928) in his diary records old squaws (Hansen saw four and collected one) on June 10, 1923, at 75°01′ north and 165°05′ east, i.e. on the way to Novosibirsk archipelago.

Apart from the sea flyway through Bering Strait I believe the old squaws breeding on the north coast of the Chukchi peninsula have another flyway which for the most part is continental. In the spring of 1934 I noticed that most of old squaw flocks at Uélen were flying over the sea from west to east. It was a mass flight and not a local migration that depends on the opening or otherwise of leads in the ice. I also saw local movements there, but later on. Furthermore, the flocks were already of a smaller size and they flew leisurely in different directions, whereas the migrations were sometimes massive. It is also interesting that the first appearance of old squaws in spring, 1934, was registered at Cape Serdtse-Kamen' a week earlier than at Cape Dezhnev. It is hardly a coincidence that in the spring of 1879 at Kolyuchin Bay, according to the observations of A.A.L. Palander (Palmén 1887), the first large flocks of old squaws flew along the coast from west to east. The question naturally arose as to where this stream of old squaws flying from the west was bound for. According to my observations at Anadyr, in spring, 1932, the old squaws flew in large numbers around Markovo when the lakes in the central and eastern parts of the Anadyr basin were still covered with ice. The birds possibly came from the direction of Penzhinsk Bay. According to É.V. Schmidt in the spring a few old squaws flew to the lower reaches of the Kolyma but they flew in huge flocks to middle reaches of the river. I have no doubt that old squaws have been found in the spring in the northeastern part of Asia to the east of the Kolyma after crossing land. Pausing at the breaks in hill rivers that have opened up early, the old squaws proceed toward the seacoast, following the rivers east. Judging from the fact that members of the *Vega* expedition noticed large flocks at Kolyuchin Bay at the beginning of their flight and for a long time afterward, old squaws were numerous there. A.A. Savich often records them in his diary for Cape Schmidt throughout the sojourn of the *Kolyma* from September 18, 1914, through June 30, 1915, i.e. until the end of the spring flight.

A.I. Mineev and V.F. Vlasova observed the spring flight on Wrangel Island. In the spring of 1939 I established the arrival of some stray pairs which probably also nested there later. I was able to track the second appearance of old squaws particularly clearly, not pairs and not nesting, but large flocks arriving for mass molting. In 1960, according to the observations of A.G. Velizhanin, lone squaws were seen until mid-June on the south coast of Wrangel Island but flocks of a few hundred birds were common by the end of that month.

Distribution and status of nonpaired and molting old squaws—Flocks of lone old squaws arrive later than those coming to breed. They appear in something like a second wave in the Chukchi peninsula and on Wrangel Island. Later males that have been through the mating phase and are leaving the females in the nests join the flocks.

Innumerable flocks noticed by V.Ya. Yakobi around Uél'kal' in early June, 1961, consisted mainly of lone birds. On June 11 he saw both lone birds and pairs simultaneously. On the approach of a man the big flocks would only shift but not fly away altogether, this being highly characteristic of lone birds moving leisurely in the nesting areas. I found only three lone birds on a small lagoon at Notapenmen village on Krest Bay on August 6, 1932.

According to I.O. Olenev old squaws flew in fairly large flocks of 50 to 100 birds at Providence Bay in early July. I have no information about the mass gathering of these birds for molting on the south coast of the Chukchi peninsula.

The members of the *Vega* expedition often noticed nonbreeding old squaws gathered for molting on the coast of St. Lawrence Island between July 31 and August 2, 1879. According to F.H. Fay and T.J. Cade, the number of lone old squaws on the island was roughly equal to the number of nesting birds. In the course of the summer they could often be seen in flocks numbering anywhere from 10 birds to more than 100. At the end of June flocks of up to 300 birds were seen on some occasions on the lakes and lagoons. H. Friedmann (1934a) found the bones of old squaws in 12 excavations. In all probability they were of nonbreeding birds, which were often caught.

N.F. Kallinikov (1912, p. 150) writes in general terms that the white-headed duck like all of other ducks remained especially long in the bays and straits on the east side of the Chukchi peninsula. É.V. Schmidt told me that innumerable molting flocks of old squaws gathered in the northwestern corner of Mechigmensk Gulf. At the end of June, 1957, A.P. Kuzyakin noticed flocks consisting of a few dozen birds on the coast between Lawrence Bay and Uélen. In 1934 I did not see migratory flocks of old squaws gathered for molting near Uélen but at the western end of the Uélen lagoon I found innumerable birds which were already molting. One such flock counted upward of 1,000 birds. I encountered similar flocks farther west on the Inchoun lagoon. There is a reference in N.P. Sokol'nikov's unpublished manuscript to old squaws molting in large numbers at Uélen settlement, where it was caught in thousands. On June 27, 1909, crossing the ice floes to Cape Serdtse-Kamen', J. Koren often found large flocks. According to the observations of O. Nordquist (Palmén 1887) some large flocks of old squaws, evidently gathered for molting, were seen in the last 10 days of July, 1879.

In July, 1970, A.A. Kishchinskii observed large groups in the sea on the Vankarém-Amguema traverse. The flocks consisted of males and a very small number of females.

In early August, 1938, I saw large and small flocks at Cape Schmidt. According to V.D. Lebedev and V.R. Filin, large flocks of old squaws were sighted from early June until the end of August, 1958, on Aiok Island and in Karchyk peninsula. Around August 10 flocks of molting birds were seen on the sea off the west coast of Karchyk and on the River Kozmina.

V.F. Vlasova and A.I. Mineev also told me that thousands of flocks, mostly of males, gathered on Wrangel Island for molting. In my very first excursion from

Rodgers Bay to the Ozero lagoon on August 11, 1938, I found flocks on the shore and huge flocks on the lagoons. I saw similar flocks on August 13 at Bruch spit and on August 15 in a lagoon fed by the Krasnyi Flag River. From August 21 through 27 some hundreds of birds could be counted in flocks near Bruch spit.

In 1939, I saw the arrival of a distinct second wave of birds, i.e. the arrival of flocks of males for molting immediately after the first migratory pairs were noticed. Initially they came in small flocks: on July 11, I counted 100 or more males in one such flock. Later, from July 22 through 28, in this same Rodgers Bay, they were to be seen swimming in huge flocks. At each stage only males were to be seen. In 1938, watching flock after flock through the binoculars, I sighted a female only once. On July 15, 1939, in Somnitel'naya Bay, I fired into a flock and killed a female bird. V.F. Vlasova's collection includes a female collected on October 11, 1931. Female old squaws from Wrangel Island were somewhat of a collector's item.

The seasonal segregation of the sexes and also of the breeding and nonbreeding old squaws is dramatic: these groups are separated by considerable geographic distances even though all of them originate from one and the same country. Thousands of male old squaws molt on Wrangel Island when their females are occupied at their nests in the Chukchi peninsula or even farther south. Almost 200 years ago N.S. Pallas was aware of this geographic separation, which is not widely known now. In *Zoographia* (vol. II, p. 277) he writes that when the females settled down around the more boreal lakes and marshes the males were off to the Arctic Ocean to change their plumage. They swam there in such huge flocks that they covered the entire bay and some of the sea beyond.

Distribution and status in fall flight—On September 2, 1932, P.T. Butenko noticed flying old squaws on his way from Uél'kal to Olovyannaya Bay by ship. According to V.É. Yakobi, old squaws were seen in large flocks at Uél'kal' from August 17, 1961, to the end of that month.

The mass fall flight was not observed at Providence Bay. Local migrations were seen from early August (I.O. Olenev's observations) to December (P.T. Butenko's observations). Evidently it was wandering flocks that I saw at Émma Bay on September 7, 1934, and September 11, 1939. A.M. Bailey reported seeing old squaws at Providence Bay in considerable numbers without indicating, however, the time or conditions of the sighting.

According to F.H. Fay (1961), old squaws were rare or altogether absent on St. Lawrence Island in October and November. E.W. Nelson writes (1883, p. 99) that this bird was common at Cape Dezhnev (East Cape). A.M. Bailey also saw old squaws in considerable numbers there. According to F.L. Jaques (1930) these ducks (assuming that there was no error of identification) were accidentally found in August, 1928, in Bering Strait and northward in the Arctic Ocean.

I saw wandering flocks of birds at Dezhnev village on August 14, 1932, and a mass flight at Uélen on September 23, 1933, counting over 1,000 birds in each of three flocks. The number of old squaws in flight later decreased steadily. In the fall of 1878 a vast flight was noticed by the members of the *Vega* expedition when the ship was anchored at Cape Schmidt. On September 16 E. Almquist saw innumerable old squaws flying east. On September 18 O. Nordquist noticed huge flocks flying from the west and north, also to the east; on September 19 he saw birds in countless numbers some miles to the east flying past for a long while from 3.00 in the afternoon. They were heading northwest toward the coast. They evidently continued the flight south-southeast along the coast and overland. A.P. Andriyashev sighted huge flocks at sea west of Cape Shelagskii. They counted a few hundred birds. But on September 27, 1946, he saw flocks within sight of the coast. According to É.V. Schmidt, around the west coast of Aiok Island many weaned broods were found along with the males, which indicated flocking together of the birds for migration.

The fall flocks of old squaws are a common phenomenon all along the Chukchi coast. There are some general references to the occurrence of old squaws on the north coast of the Chukchi peninsula partly in the period of migration and partly just before. N.F. Kallinikov (1912, p. 151) reports that old squaws, like other ducks, occur in large numbers everywhere and in especially large numbers on the Arctic Ocean coast. E.W. Nelson (1883, p. 99) writes that this duck was encountered in abundance on the Siberian (i.e. Chukchian) coast and was particularly common along the north coast. J. Koren (Thayer and Bangs 1914) regarded the old squaw as common along the entire arctic coast of Siberia, i.e. from Bering Strait to the Kolyma. In 1915, Copley Amory, Jr. (Riley 1918) saw old squaws in large numbers along the Chukchi coast and in the Kolyma delta. They were very common among all the ducks noticed. K.N. Yakovlev, the hunter, told me that old squaws predominated quantitatively over all other species of duck in Chaun and the eastern tundra regions. But this is not applicable to the east and south coasts of the Chukchi peninsula.

On Wrangel Island flocks of different sizes gathered before migration, some flocks being larger than those seen in spring and summer. On September 14, 1938, I noticed only one such flock at Cape Proletarskii. It covered a field of several hectares; there were some more large flocks flying over the sea. The bulk of the migrating birds were first seen in small flocks until the end of September, and later singly. In the accession register of the Zoological Museum of the Academy of Sciences of the USSR, serial number 448 of 1912 has a list of birds brought by the freighter *Vaigach*. It includes a male old squaw collected in the southwestern part of Wrangel Island (70°53′ north and 179°15′ west) on September 17 (4), 1911. I would also place in this species the ducks entered in De Long's diary (1883) for October 6, 1879, without exact identification. At that time the *Jeannette* was drifting north of Herald Island though the latter was still visible from the ship. It was recorded in the diary that R.L. Newcomb shot 28 ducks.

Distribution and status in the wintering areas—Old squaws winter on the southern and eastern coasts of the Chukchi peninsula according to the ice conditions, which vary greatly from year to year. L.O. Belopol'skii noticed small flocks around Bering Cape on March 20, 1931. I.O. Olenev, who wintered in Providence Bay in 1931/1932, did not see old squaws wintering at all. But in 1937/1938 P.T. Butenko traced them wintering in Providence Bay and on Cape Chaplin. The population varied depending on the formation of leads in the ice, on the increase or decrease in their size and finally on the proximity or otherwise of the edge of the ice. On January 11 and 12, 1938, old squaws predominated over other species of duck at Cape Chaplin.

According to the data of F.H. Fay and T.J. Cade, an aerial survey in January and March, 1956 and 1957, established the presence of hundreds of thousands of old squaws wintering on St. Lawrence Island. During a short evening flight over Gambell in January, 1956, over 20,000 of them could be counted. In a separate article, F.H. Fay wrote that aerial observations showed that up to 500,000 old squaws wintered around the island every year. They were incessantly in motion, flying over the ice from one lead to another. When the ice floes came right inshore as a result of a change in the wind the ducks would take off, cross the island or fly around it and settle on the opposite coast on newly formed leads.

According to J. Koren old squaws remained in the Diomede Islands throughout the winter of 1912/1913. I do not rule out their occurrence in the winter on leads, even farther to the north, but I did not see them in the winter of 1933/1934 around Uélen even when ice leads opened up.

Habitat—Being a typical marine bird, to some extent even an oceanic duck, the old squaw is confined for seven to eight months in the year to the shallow water zone along the coasts and edges of the ice by the food availability factor. Old squaws in flight are common even over land-locked water. They behave like typical tundra birds right from the beginning of nesting: females at the time of nesting and rearing of chicks and males in a much shorter mating season. But even in the nesting period, the habitation of this mobile duck is not limited to any lakelet.

In the spring of 1934, around Uélen, I noticed the first arrivals of old squaws around an opening in a tiny strait joining a large lagoon to the sea. The opening had formed there earlier than at other places as a result of a strong current under the pressure of meltwater entering the lagoon. The old squaws were later seen successively around openings that formed first on the large lagoon and later in the lakes on the tundra. On June 7, I saw some pairs on a large lake and a lone bird on a tiny lake. From June 13 pairs of old squaws became a common phenomenon on water of any size. In spring, 1939, on Wrangel Island, I noticed a newly arrived pair on a tundra lake and another on a lakelet linked to the lagoon east of Predatel'skaya Bay. Later I saw a pair in one of the lagoons to the east of Predatel'skaya Bay and still later a pair on one of the lagoons east of Somnitel'naya Bay.

In the spring of 1879, the thawing of openings on Kolyuchin Bay was evidently delayed. On June 22 old squaws in pairs were confined to the lagoons on which the ice had just begun to break up. From July 11 they flew in pairs or singly (evidently in pairs when the female had begun the clutch) to feed by the sea in leads between Tjapka and Neshkan, and to the nesting sites on the tundra.

I happened to locate a nest only once on a tiny lakelet in the Utte-Véem River delta. The members of the *Vega* expedition were given eggs from the neighboring lagoons near Pitlekai and Neshkan. On the tundra adjoining Cape Schmidt, according to a report by V.Ya. Isaev, old squaws nested near any lakelet on the plains. On Aiok Island V.D. Lebedev and V.R. Filin found nests on islets in a shallow tundra lake. According to É.V. Schmidt, on the lower reaches of the Kolyma the preferred nesting place was depressed marine tundra. The absence or extreme rarity of nesting on Wrangel Island is explained no doubt by the lack of suitable lakelets because of the predominance of hilly or rocky terrain in that locality and the presence of the polar fox, an enemy of these ducks. This would also apply to such tiny islands as Kolyuchi and Diomede and the rocky sections of the south coast of the Chukchi peninsula.

Lone old squaws arriving to molt on the coasts of the Chukchi peninsula and Wrangel Island continue to behave like birds at sea or on the coast, almost without reference to the tundra. Males that have completed their mating period join them later for molting. This whole bird population, not linked to any breeding site, has not yet shed its wing feathers. It forms into flocks of constantly varying size. According to my observations around Uélen, flocks of old squaws were confined to lagoons of different sizes before molting. As the birds' flying ability declined, the flock size would increase, and they would confine themselves to the largest of lagoons where they were less liable to be persecuted. The sojourn of a flock mainly depended on the factor of food availability. I found most of the molting old squaws in Kuét Strait joining the lagoon fed by the River Kol'oam with the larger Uélen lagoon. An abundance of tiny aquatic organisms gathered here in streams of varying salinities and perhaps different oxygen concentrations served as food for the ducks. This fact of abundant aquatic fauna in the estuary sections of lagoons and coasts is well known.

In the early summer of 1939 on Wrangel Island, when the lagoon had not yet opened up, incoming old squaws were confined to the surf break in the shore ice at estuaries, singly or in very small numbers. They were fewer than the eiders. The ice floes have an important influence on the sojourn of old squaws. The freshwater streams from the thawing ice floes bring with them abundant aquatic organisms. When the wind drove the ice inshore the old squaws gathered at the water openings between the floes. I invariably found innumerable old squaws in such tiny straits leading from the lagoon to the sea when the shore was piled with washed up ice floes. On the night of July 1, 1879, O. Nordquist found huge flocks of old squaws settling down on the floes on a lagoon at Tjapka.

According to my observations Rodgers Bay was 60 per cent free of ice on July 11, 1939. Between the floes that remained intact after the winter and those drifting in from the sea, small flocks were to be seen swimming. Along the rim of the pack ice, flocks in the form of a long chain would settle down to rest. In my very first trip along the south coast of Wrangel Island on August 11, 1938, I came across small flocks resting on the ice. In the second half of August the ice floes drifted close in to the north shore of the island. The molted old squaws would fly from the ice-free lagoon to the openings in the sea. There, I saw small flocks and single birds along with murres. All birds no doubt fell upon the abundant food in the fresh openings in the ice field, especially in the shallow zones. But this natural enticement turned out to be a trap. The ice leads would gradually close up and ultimately the birds were left on such narrow strips of water that they could not take off. Their anxious shrieks could be heard from the ice floes.

In the fall of 1924 (around October 1), Hansen (Schaanning 1928, p. 16) found four dead young birds on the ice one mile north of Chetyrekhstolb Island. The death of old squaws in the steadily shrinking ice leads is evidently not a unique phenomenon. The birds are attracted by the concentration of food in a limited area and the food is easily accessible.

On extensive water surfaces the sojourn of old squaws largely depends on weather factors. In total calm they gladly spend time on the shore but they desert it when the waves develop. On large lagoons, even in a relatively light wind, the old squaws gather on the leeward bank and are sometimes confined to a very narrow surf-free zone. For this, they choose a section of fairly high bank perpendicular to the direction of the wind. When the wind blows along the coast the birds take shelter in quiet little bays, taking utmost advantage of the winding coastline. With big waves the ducks stop feeding, become mostly lethargic, and bob passively in the water. In foggy weather, especially when fog envelops the incoming ice, old squaws migrate from place to place like eiders. In early August, 1938, I noticed diurnal migrations at Cape Schmidt. There a narrow pebbled spit joining the rocky Cape Kozhevnikov with the mainland separates adjacent shores. When the feeding conditions became unfavorable in one section the old squaws would fly to the other. When the coast wind changed in the course of the day and there were high and low tides it was easy to fathom the periodicity in the migration of old squaws over the spit. Unfavorable weather conditions may drive the birds even onto water areas inland. On August 20, 1934, I saw groups of lone birds on the innumerable tiny lakelets around big Lake Kool'ong, which they had temporarily deserted because of large waves. In the same year, 1934, on July 10, I found old squaws together with lone pintails on a large lake near the Utte-Véem River estuary. On ice-strewn Somnitel'naya Bay, Wrangel Island, I saw flocks of old squaws flying over small tundra lakes. Under all other conditions, however, old squaws gathered for molting, the molting birds being confined mainly to the lagoons, rarely to the shoreline.

On molting, the old squaws wander from the lagoon to the sea and back. Throughout the winter they behave even more like marine birds living on the sea. In the fall of 1931 I did not see large flocks on the Anadyr at all. Even such a large river as the Anadyr cannot offer long-term shelter for them in the migration period. In the fall of 1939, when I was sailing from Wrangel through thin ice, it was quite clear that the old squaws were confined to the coastal waters closest to the island. Their sojourn there in the period of migration evidently depended on the ice conditions.

According to V.F. Vlasova and A.I. Mineev, thousands of flocks of old squaws molting in the bays were later confined to the openings among the ice floes. According to my observations, on Wrangel and near Uélen, the old squaws usually flew away from the lagoons long before they iced over and even before shore ice appeared, or film ice began to form on much of the water surface. When necessary, the old squaws would settle on the smallest of rivulets. On September 23, 1933, the sea around Uélen was covered with ice and large flying flocks landed on the lagoons. But I noticed three old squaws floating on a very tiny opening among the ice floes on the coast. On October 3 tardy flocks rested on a large lagoon partly covered with thin ice.

When the *Vega* was ice-bound at Kolyuchin Bay old squaws were seen in the openings until October 4. J. Koren confirmed that in the 1912/1913 winter old squaws were frequently seen on Diomede Island in small leads in the ice. According to the observations of P.T. Butenko, in the 1937/1938 winter old squaws were not to be seen in Providence Bay for a month until the ice appeared and covered the bay. But they were again seen in the winter, on December 22, 1937, when the ice in the bay was broken by the south wind and leads opened up for a few hours.

In the same winter at Cape Chaplin, the old squaws disappeared for some time and appeared again depending on the weather and ice conditions. They could be seen in the open water along the shallow shoreline and among the ice, depending on its movement. This movement was a function of the tides and the direction and force of the wind. From January 11 through 13, 1938, the north wind was so strong that one Chukchian was carried out to sea on an ice floe. The drifting floes piled up on the surf side of the coast and there was intense movement of ice to the south. Under such stormy conditions at sea the ducks were restless even on the leeward coast and constantly flew over the ice for short distances northward. If they settled on the water they were quickly carried south. In two weeks' time the weather changed: on January 30 east wind blew, bringing in small amounts of snow. The ice moved back from south to north, the ducks also flying along with it. After another two weeks, on February 14, a north wind got up, clear, cold weather set in and the old squaws disappeared in a southerly direction.

Arrival—According to the observations of V.É. Yakobi, flocks of old squaws were seen in Uél'kal' in early June, 1961, when the ice moved away from the coast to a distance of 2 to 3 km. On June 11 the wind drove the ice quite close inshore and the ducks shifted to inland lakes, which were partly ice-free. Pairs and lone birds were seen in small openings in the sea, where they fed on water bugs and other invertebrates. On June 30 an opening of 350 × 100 m that had formed offshore contained a huge flock of lone birds. They flew away when the ice again closed the passage.

According to the observations of L.O. Belopol'skii at Cape Bering in 1931 the first old squaws were found at the end of May. Since they were noticed not on the sea but on the tundra this date may be regarded as the time of arrival.

In Providence Bay and at Cape Chaplin, old squaws did not nest at all or did so only rarely. Hence P.T. Butenko could not establish the arrival of local birds. In his diary the spring dates on which these ducks were seen on the sea are nearly one month apart: at Cape Chaplin on March 23, April 23 and May 2 (on the last of these dates, the birds were seen only from time to time), and near Sireniki village on May 27, 1938. Only the last of these dates can be regarded as that of the spring flight: all the others relate to winter-spring wanderings.

According to F.H. Fay, on St. Lawrence Island pairs and small flocks were confined to the coast from mid-May through mid-June from the time of arrival. As soon as the ice opened up on the lakes at the end of May or early in June the old squaws began to migrate inland and very few of them remained on the coast. According to the observations of E.G.F. Sauer, in 1960 pairs of old squaws began separating from the flocks and spreading out over the central plateau and the surrounding valleys in mid-June.

On May 14, 1958, K.W. Kenyon saw the first pair on a lead at the southern end of Malyi Diomede Island. In spring, 1934, I received the first report of the appearance of old squaws not at Uélen but at Cape Serdtse-Kamen, where this duck was collected on May 18. Only on May 25 did I see flying old squaws at Cape Dezhnev. I observed the arrival of pairs and small groups of local birds of this species near Uélen only on May 31. On the afternoon of May 31 there was a migration of large flocks from west to east over the sea. This was because fog had developed. They continued to fly in the same direction even on June 1. On the afternoon of June 3 the fog dispersed, the old squaws flew in pairs and small flocks and the flights ceased. On June 4 pairs were already seen in the open water in the lagoon. Judging from the lively calls, the mating period of old squaws was in full swing.

In spring, 1879, according to observations of members of the *Vega* expedition, this duck was first seen on a large lead opposite Kolyuchin Bay some miles from the winter anchorage of the ship. In the snowy weather on the morning of May 14 large flocks passed along the coast from the west. Stopping short of the ship, the birds turned back westward. Later on the same day O. Nordquist saw huge flocks, probably of old squaws, flying past Cape Dzhenretlen from southeast to northwest. On May 31 and June 1 large flocks of old squaws swam and flew to and fro above the lead that had formed not far from the ship, which was up to 50 or 60 m wide at places. After this such flocks were seen daily.

When I reached the Amguema on June 10, 1956, there were already large openings on the river. There were 10 old squaws on one of them. When the birds dispersed it was always in pairs. Sometimes single males flew over the river. On June 14 the river opened up over a long stretch and from then on only individual pairs were seen.

In the spring of 1939, on June 9 on Wrangel Island, I noticed two separate pairs for the first time. On June 12 I saw two more pairs in different places somewhat to the east, and one pair still farther east on June 14. My impression was that pairs gradually migrated from west to east. According to V.F. Vlasova and A.I. Mineev, old squaws were seen in spring flight in early June immediately after the eiders. I did not see flocks flying over the ice at Wrangel. This can probably be explained by the ice conditions in the spring of 1939. They were noticed even farther north by the members of the *Maud* expedition (Schaanning 1928): in spring, 1923, the first few birds were seen on June 10 at 75°01′ north and 165°05′ east and in 1924 on June 11 at 76°15′ north and 145°51′ east. In 1925 the first of these birds were noticed on May 29 on Chetyrekhstolb Island.

From these periods of the appearance of old squaws it is clear that this duck is not seen before mid-May on the coast of the Chukchi peninsula or in the Anadyr basin and the Kolyma estuary. On Wrangel Island the arrival starts in the first 10 days of June though it usually commences in the last 10 days of May. At the end of the island and farther north and northwest it begins on June 10 and 11.

Breeding—The breeding behavior of old squaws begins to manifest even in the wintering grounds. F.H. Fay noticed them on April 25 on St. Lawrence Island.

According to my observations, on May 31, 1934, the old squaws were around Uélen in pairs or small groups easily separable into pairs. Quite often a few males gathered around the females. The air was rent with shrieks which intensified with each advancing day. On June 5, I saw some pairs on the thawing lakes. Males quite often pursued the females or followed them closely. From then to the middle of the month mating and laying of eggs occurred. Measurements of gonads are shown in Tables 18 and 19.

The gonads, which remained dormant while wintering at least from November through February, revealed signs of growth only in May when the testes of males and the follicles of females enlarged. During July and August the size of the testes gradually decreased. The subcutaneous adipose layers in females evidently did not undergo significant changes but the males obtained in the wintering sites were mostly emaciated. After arrival, both sexes were characterized by the formation of significant adipose layers.

Table 18. Testis sizes of old squaws, mm

Date	Left	Right	Locality
Nov. 12, 1937	7×2	8×2	Plover Bay
Dec. 22, 1937	7×3	7×3	—do—
Dec. 22, 1937	7×2	6×2	—do—
Feb. 20, 1938	8×2	7×2	Cape Chaplin
May 18, 1938	15×5	13×4	Cape Stoletiya
May 27, 1932	30×14	31×13	Fort, middle reaches of Anadyr
May 31, 1934	31×15	28×14	Uélen
June 2, 1932	27×14	25×13	Markovo
June 6, 1932	32×16	29×13	—do—
June 6, 1932	30×12	20×10	—do—
June 9, 1932	29×15	24×17	—do—
June 19, 1934	34×15	30×14	Uélen
June 21, 1939	30×20	35×20	Rodgers Bay
July 10, 1931	25×10	—	Tumanskaya River estuary, Anadyr region
Aug. 26, 1938	15×4	10×4	Bruch spit

Table 19. Ovary dimensions and structure of old squaws

Date	Ovary length, mm	Ovay structure	Locality
Nov. 11, 1937	22	—	Plover Bay
Nov. 11, 1937	19	Filmy	—do—
Nov. 15, 1937	16	—	—do—
Dec. 22, 1937	—	Filmy	—do—
Feb. 20, 1938	20	—do—	Cape Chaplin
Feb. 20, 1938	16	—do—	—do—
May 27, 1932	—	Maximum follicle, 15 mm	Fort, middle reaches of Anadyr
June 18, 1934	—	Dense, not granular	Uélen
July 15, 1939	19	Maximum follicle, 19 mm	Somnitel'naya Bay

V.É. Yakobi collected a female around Uél'kal' on June 16, 1961; its oviduct contained an egg without a shell.

On St. Lawrence Island, according to F.H. Fay, nidification began in early June but on July 15 and 17 he found nests with clutches that had been incubated for only a week. In the first of these there were four eggs and in the second six. W.S. Brooks noticed a pair and tiny flocks of old squaws on June 2, 1913. A clutch of six unincubated eggs was taken on June 25. A.M. Bailey gathered a clutch of five eggs on July 9, 1921. According to O.W. Geist, one old squaw nest was located only a few paces from occupied houses in Kukuliak village. When leaving the nest the duck covered its seven eggs with down but ultimately lost it when it was submerged by torrential rain.

In the delta of the Utte-Véem River, I found a nest of old squaws on a tiny islet close to nests of eiders, Temminsk's stints and arctic terns. Colonial cohabitation has long been noticed by observers but old squaws often nest singly too.

In spring, 1879, at Pitlekai, the cyclic phenomena in the life of old squaws were delayed. The ovary of females shot on May 31 contained about 70 follicles, the largest being 6 mm in size. But even on June 22 these ducks were noticed for the most part in pairs on the lagoons near Kolyuchin Bay, where the ice was just breaking up. On June 30 a nest was found with two eggs on one of the lagoons, and two clutches were brought in on July 1.

The clutches found on Aiok Island by V.D. Lebedev and V.R. Filin contained different numbers of eggs: two of them had four eggs each; there were six in one and nine each in two more. J. Koren (Schaanning 1954) found a nest among driftwood on a grassy islet in the Kolyma delta on July 17, 1917. It contained four eggs incubated for about 16 days. According to my observations, along the Utte-Véem River, even after the females began incubating the males continued to visit the nesting sites and meet the females, though they were increasingly becoming lone birds in the lagoon and on the shore. Late in the evening of July 2 I noticed in the foothills of the Inchoun uplands lone males flying from the tundra to the sea. On July 6 males single or in pairs with females were seen in tundra lakelets in the lowlands of the Utte-Véem River. On July 20, above a tiny strait at Inchoun lagoon, I saw males flying not only in flocks but also singly. The females leaving the nests for feeding did not stay away for long, and I did not see them flying to the sea.

On August 15, 1934, on the upper course of the Kol'oam River, I encountered a female with eight downy chicks. The brood evidently was migrating somewhere. My party and I, in a light canoe, easily overtook the birds swimming desperately against a strong current. Another day a female flew past us, evidently agitated on seeing us. I often noticed that the ducks left their broods to track the course of a hunter.

On August 30, 1933, on a group of tiny islets near Uélen, I came across a brood of feathered chicks, each sitting on a different lakelet. They still could not fly and escaped by diving. The female was absent for some reason. I found a lone young bird again on one of these lakelets even on September 9. I did not see more of the fall emergence of broods and they probably moved away immediately to the south without gathering on the north shore of the sea.

Molting—The life of males gathering for molting is entirely different. They are seen in flocks much after the arrival of nesting birds but long before the beginning of molting.

According to I.O. Olenev lone males were seen twice in Providence Bay in summer, 1932: in early July and later in early August. In 1934, only on July 10 and 11 did I see flocks that had gathered for molting on the lagoon and the lake near the Utte-Véem River estuary. On July 12, I saw large flocks of flying and swimming old squaws in the southern parts of Inchoun lagoon. I noticed them there again on my return journey on July 20 and 21. In the adjacent Kuét Strait a multitude of old squaws were found swimming on July 9. Some of them escaped by diving. But on August 24 they swam away without taking off *en masse*.

On August 20, my party and I visited Lake Kool'ong from which molting old squaws were wandering to neighboring lakelets.

From spring, 1879, flocks began wandering at Kolyuchin Bay. On June 22 a large flock flew past Pitlekai. Nesting old squaws were seen at that time in pairs. Later some large flocks were seen on June 27 and small flocks on July 17.

I easily traced the arrival of males for molting on Wrangel Island in 1939. On July 2 I saw a flock flying high above the ice past the Ozero lagoon and another near Rodgers Bay. On July 11 small and large flocks were seen in the bay. My hand gun disturbed the old squaws resting on the spit but not all of them, which showed that the wing feathers were still incomplete. On July 14 and 15 flocks of different sizes flew over Somnitel'naya Bay, but on July 22 molting old squaws were found swimming in hundreds in Rodgers Bay. I saw only three birds flying over the coast near the Nasha River estuary. On July 24 and 26 flocks were seen on the lagoons, those flying were very few. The wings of birds shot at the end of July were completely bare and the feather shafts were just beginning to grow on those obtained from August 3 through 7.

The end of molting was traced in 1938. From August 11 through 15 most of the old squaws on Wrangel could not fly. Only some stray ducks were seen flying from August 21 through 27. In the last few days of August the old squaws began rising on their wings but not readily and then only some among them.

Toward the end of molting the surf carried a mass of feathers onto the lagoon banks. Where goose feather heaps are mixed with excreta old squaw feathers were free of it, first because they defecated in the water and secondly because their feces was very thin owing to their diet.

The tail feathers were shed much later than the wing feathers. At the end of August some males still had their long summer tails. Among others, Copley Amory, Jr. (Riley 1918) collected three males on July 22 and 23, 1915, on Bol'shoi Baranov Kamen'. They had already shed the long central tail feathers; the remainder were very worn out. Scapular feathers had been thoroughly shed and the feathers on the back were fading. On September 14, 1938, I thoroughly surveyed through the binoculars the composition of a huge flock from the vantage point of lofty Cape Proletarskii above the coast. The flock consisted exclusively of males. Almost all of them were speckled with white winter plumelets but the tail was still relatively short in most of them. Only two or three birds stood out in their white winter plumage and only one had totally molted. Large flocks were flying over the sea. On my approaching, the old squaws sitting on the shore swam away. Others dived, were agitated and uttered growls or shrieks but did not take off *en masse*.

Nesting females molted very late, later than the males. For example, H.B. Collins (Friedmann 1932a) collected a molting male at Gambell village on St. Lawrence Island in August, 1930, and a molting female only on September 17. In the museum of Alaska University there is a young male from St. Lawrence Island which only began molting in its winter dress. The male preserved in the museum of the University of British Columbia still had its winter plumage on April 18, 1953.

Migration—In 1938 I thoroughly investigated the migration of old squaws on Wrangel Island. In early September small flocks remained in Rodgers Bay but when the bay began to freeze over on the 13th the number of old squaws decreased noticeably. They were again assembled on the sea from where their calls could be frequently heard. On September 14, as already stated, I noticed a huge flock at Cape Proletarskii. The bulk of old squaws migrated a few days later. On September 26, I saw a flock flying out of Rodgers Bay and a lone male on the 29th. Tayan reported seeing five old squaws even on October 31. A.I. Mineev's collections contained a female obtained on October 11, 1931. According to the observations of A.G. Velizhanin, in 1960 there was a mass migration of old squaws on Wrangel Island in early September. On September 3 and 4 a flock of about 5,000 birds was found on the Davydov lagoon. Stray flocks were noted around the island until the first few days of October. A.P. Andriyashev noticed huge flocks of migratory old squaws on September 27, 1946 at Cape Shelagskii. They were sitting on the still water and did not take off on the approach of a ship but only fled flapping their wings on the water, or dived. A reference has already been made to the intense fall flight past Cape Schmidt from September 16 through 19, 1878. After the *Vega* was stuck in the ice in Kolyuchin Bay old squaws began to be noticed right up to October 4.

According to my observations, at Uélen, beginning from the last few days of August, 1933, old squaws were encountered in flocks of different strengths. On the evening of September 18 the weather changed sharply, stormy northwesterly winds with snowstorms prevailed and intense cooling set in, after which the general scene was wintry. On the very first clear day after the storm, September 23, there was a mass flight of old squaws. Three huge flocks flew over the sea at a height of about 1,000 m going due south. On sighting the lagoon they descended very steeply. With a noise like the drone of an airplane the mass of ducks landed in the water, churning it up. It was one of those scenes in the life of northern birds which without exaggeration may be called spectacular. Only the aerobatics of lesser snow geese or ravens at the time of courtship ceremonies could be compared with it. Small groups and flocks were noticed on the last few days on the lagoon (the sea was covered with ice). On October 1 and 3 I saw males mostly with white heads. I noticed an old squaw for the last time on October 3 when the lagoon was covered for the most part with ice or film ice.

On August 14, 1932, I noticed the flight of old squaws above Dezhnev village. They flew south at a height of over 1,000 m. I could not understand the reason for such an early migration.

According to F.H. Fay, old squaws on St. Lawrence Island migrated in September. They were absent or rare in October and November.

P.T. Butenko made fall observations on the south coast of the Chukchi peninsula in 1937. He noticed old squaws in large numbers on the coast beyond Uél'kal' village on October 14 and 17. Later he saw them on October 18 in Olovyannaya Bay, on October 24 at Notapenmen village, and from October 29 through November 12 in Providence Bay, where he continued his observations until the end of that year.

Wintering—As stated above, on December 22, 1937, the south wind broke the

PLATE III

Age-wise plumage of male king eiders *Somateria spectabilis* (L.): *top*—nesting bird; *bottom*—summer old males; *left* (*1st*)—breeding; *left* (*2nd*)—first summer; *right* (*1st*)—second winter; *right* (*2nd*)—first winter. Pic. by L.A. Portenko.

ice in Providence Bay and the old squaws appeared a few hours later. From January 11, 1938, observations were made at Cape Chaplin. In the first few days, January 11 through 13, P.T. Butenko saw very many old squaws; they disappeared later and could be seen only at intervals. From January 14 through 25 Butenko was absent from Cape Chaplin and did not find them on his return. They were, however, seen on January 30, to disappear again on February 14. After an interruption of observations from February 18 through March 15 the birds were recorded in the diary on March 16, 17 and 23, April 23 and May 2 and 27.

According to a report by L.O. Belopol'skii, in winter, 1931, the old squaws were seen on March 20 around Cape Bering. On the Chukchian south coast they sometimes came close in during the winter and at other times went far out depending wholly on the ice conditions at sea.

According to O.W. Geist, old squaws wintered in large numbers near St. Lawrence Island in the openings among extensive ice fields. They changed locale with the changing environment caused by tides but evidently found large enough open water surfaces. F.H. Fay wrote that old squaws were seen around the island simultaneously with the ice drifting in from the north and remained until the middle or end of April, making for a very large population of wintering birds. The males remained separate from the females but mixed flocks were often seen by the end of the month.

Voice-Habits—The call note of the male old squaw sounds like "av-avlýk" or "au-aúk". Late in the fall, I described it as "av-avuáu" but it usually sounds different depending on the distance. The bird itself alters its voice depending on the nature of the stimulus.

Old squaws are incomparably more vociferous than many other ducks and occupy the first place in this respect among arctic species. The male voice could be heard at any time of the year even in the wintering places and during molting though much less often than in the mating period or before migration.

Old squaws are rarely found in the company of other sea ducks but I once noticed them on the shore along with murres. They returned together to the coast. Quite often murres fly with geese in a single line and the old squaws would form links in the general chain of flocks.

I had some occasion to witness the unusual vitality of old squaws. At the end of August, 1938, returning from a hunt on Wrangel Island along with Tayan, we began unloading the dead ducks from our whaleboat on the shore. On being thrown onto the beach one of them regained consciousness as a result of the impact and with exceptional agility, literally in an instant, rushed to the water and dived. I could clearly see it paddling under water with its wings in exactly the same way as the murres "fly" underwater. The resuscitated bird appeared in the water a few dozen paces away and dived again, this time traversing a very long distance underwater.

Food—The results of examinations of stomach contents were rather vague. Along with a mass of highly digested food which could not be identified sand or gravel not more than 5 mm in diameter was invariably found.

Weight—The males obtained by P.T. Butenko in Providence Bay weighed 890, 780, 745, 700, and 680 g. The weight of the females was 820, 770, 730, and 725 g.

Specimens weighing more than 800 g were characterized by significant subcutaneous adipose formations. The rest either did not have such layers at all or they were very thin. On June 11, 1961, at Uél'kal, V.É. Yakobi shot a male weighing 784.5 g and a female weighing 673.9 g.

Economic importance—The importance of old squaws is not the same in the different parts of the territory. Under the conditions of the Far North on Wrangel Island where fresh meat is invariably in demand it cannot be ignored in spite of the availability of better game like geese and eiders. The massive concentration of molting males made it relatively easy to catch them for use. In different years, including the period of my stay on the island in 1938–1939, many dozens, perhaps even hundreds, of old squaws were caught daily.

In the Chukchi peninsula such large concentrations of old squaws as on Wrangel are not usually seen. Where they are few, hunting for them does not justify the effort and ammunition, especially as their meat is not exactly first-grade. But where old squaws are abundant and can be easily bagged, hunting by all available means is practiced. Hunting is nowhere on the commercial scale.

A general reduction of water fowl is inferred in the present case also. In the manuscript notes by N.P. Sokol'nikov, I found a remark pertaining to the early period of this century to the effect that the bird molted in large numbers on the Arctic Ocean at Uélen settlement. There it was killed with sticks in thousands near the shore. During my stay at Uélen I found that the local residents had never heard of such a hunt.

According to the accounts of F.H. Fay, over 1,000 old squaws, mainly wintering birds, were secured on St. Lawrence Island every year, and perhaps quite a number of them are consumed by predators like gyrfalcons and snowy owls.

Old squaws are hunted with very varied techniques and means. On the north coast of Wrangel I hunted with Tayan from a motorized whaleboat. On approaching the flocks of molting ducks which were gathered on the lagoon we used a heavy shot. The frightened birds often dived and had to be shot from a long distance. As frequently happens when hunting for diving birds, the shot did not hit the old squaw but the ripples formed where it had dived. After using up a large amount of gasoline and ammunition we brought back a few dozen ducks in a day. It was more economic to hunt from the shore in sections shielded from the wind. By stealthily coming from behind the rubble bank we could shoot a few ducks with the first few shots. In the narrow confines of the lagoon, we fired at old squaws hiding behind the ice. Hunters experienced in ice conditions run from one ice floe to another and overtake the birds caught in the narrow leads that cannot take to their wings. According to A.I. Mineev, late in the fall when the molting old squaws were on the polynyas they were chased into a cul-de-sac where they could not take off. Eight birds were bagged with one shot. Mineev even shot birds swimming close inshore from the window of his house. According to A.G. Velizhanin, in the 50s, the polar residents on Wrangel collected the birds by driving them into a net from a boat.

At Cape Schmidt, I witnessed the hunting of old squaws flying daily through the spit leading to Cape Kozhevnikov. There was no such hunting at Uélen since the old squaws did not fly either over the village or nearby. During my stay there, the bird was hunted in very small numbers. Teenagers sailing in a skin canoe with an outboard motor usually engaged themselves in hunting in the fall. I hunted with them many times. The hunting technique was as follows: With the motor ticking over the hunters would approach the birds and wait until the agitated ducks dived. When the birds appeared on the surface again quite close to the boat we would gun the motor. Temperamental hunters tended to scare the birds with shouts and sudden movements, so that they would dive before we could fire. I think one must aim at the point where the birds are likely to surface while they are still under. If the old squaws take to their wings rather than diving, it is best if one has approached against the wind so one can shoot them head-on. Sometimes I sat in ambush on the shore, noticing how the light wind gradually drove the birds resting on the exposed lagoon banks toward me. On other sections of the Chukchi coast where the old squaws fly in flocks, the local residents, especially in the past, would use a device called an eplicathet, which is discussed in the section on eiders.

According to O.W. Geist, hunting old squaws on St. Lawrence Island paid off for some weeks at the end of winter and early spring when the birds were performing local migrations to the leads and back. They flew very low in large flocks. This not only let the hunters shoot them by the hundred but also let young boys catch them with eplicathets.

Systematics of the subspecies—Old squaws do not form geographic races throughout the circumpolar region in which they occur.

Specimens— 1) Cape Dezhnev, September 29, 1910, ♂, juv., Starokadomskii; 2 to 4) Providence Bay, July 16, 19, and 20, 1912, ♂♂, Starokadomskii; 5) same place, August 1, 1914, ♀, Starokadomskii; 6) Kolyuchin Bay, August 19, 1914, ♀, Starokadomskii; 7) Uélen, June 5, 1927, ♂, Sheneberg; 8) Wrangel Island, July 15, 1929, ○, Ushakov; 9) Rodgers Bay, October 11, 1931, ♀, Vlasova; 10) same location, July 23, 1932, ♂, Vlasova; 11 and 12) Uélen, August 29, and October 3, 1933, ♀, juv. and ♀, Portenko; 13) same place, May 21, 1934, ♀, Chechulin; 14 to 16) same place, May 31, 1934, ♂♀♀, Portenko; 17 to 19) same place, June 18 and 19, 1939, ♂♀, Portenko; 20 to 26) Providence Bay, November 11, ♀♀, November 12, ♂, November 15, ♀, and November 22, 1937, ♂♂♀, Butenko; 27 to 29) Cape Chaplin, February 20, 1938, ♂♀♀, Butenko; 30 and 31) Cape Stoletiya, May 18 and 30, 1938, ♂♂, Butenko; 32 and 33) Wrangel Island, August 20, 1938, ♂♂, Druzhinin; 34 and 35) Bruch spit, August 26, 1938, ♂♂, Portenko; 36) Rodgers Bay, June 21, 1939, ♂, Portenko; and 37) Somnitel'naya Bay, July 15, 1939, ♀ Portenko.

26. **Histrionicus histrionicus pacificus** Brooks—**Harlequin Duck**

Local name—In Eskimo: ka-ghā'-nĭk on St. Lawrence Island.

Distribution and status—Found in the interior and on the south coast of the Chukchi peninsula where it no doubt nests, though sporadically and in small numbers. Lone and molting harlequin ducks in large numbers occur in summer habitation on the south coast. Big spring flights recorded at Krest Bay. Not found on north coast or on Wrangel.

Distribution in the nesting period—On June 18, 1956, I found a male harlequin duck on an old stagnant pool on the Amguema near the 91st km. The bird was sitting on snow in the mouth of a rivulet flowing swiftly past the escarpment of the high bank. On seeing me it entered the water, paused to catch something and later hid between the chunks of snow. From the behavior of the bird it was evident that the female was in the nest somewhere close by. In any case, it was not a migratory bird.

In summer, 1931, L.O. Belopol'skii (1934) found lone harlequin ducks and pairs around Meechken Island. He thought the ducks were nesting not far away. On July 13, 1938, I found a brood in Providence Bay.

O.W. Geist (Murie 1936) thought that the harlequin duck nested in the southwestern part of St. Lawrence Island. One fall two broods were noticed in Boxer Bay. F.H. Fay and T.J. Cade (1959) referred to a female collected on July 25, 1950, on the River Ikaluksik at the western tip of the island.

The above records help demarcate the boundary of the breeding area of harlequin ducks in northeast Asia. It extends from the middle reaches of the Amguema to Krest Bay, Providence Bay and the western part of St. Lawrence Island.

Distribution of nonbreeding and molting harlequin ducks—Like the nonpaired and breeding old squaws gathering north of their breeding grounds for molting, the harlequin ducks gather for the same purpose in appreciable numbers along the fringe of their breeding grounds on the south coast of the Chukchi peninsula and on St. Lawrence Island. In spring, 1931, L.O. Belopol'skii saw large flocks numbering 40 to 60 birds in Krest Bay. Since the harlequin ducks did not nest there in large numbers, nonpaired birds alone constituted the flocks there, evidently for the forthcoming molting. In the summer he saw small flocks around Meechken Island. Both nesting and lone harlequin ducks could be seen in Providence Bay in the summer. Therefore W.S. Brooks' record (1915) in June, 1913, has no significance. But A.M. Bailey (1925) saw seven males in 1921, suggesting a flocking tendency at that date. On July 20, 1912, L.M. Starokadomskii collected two males, of which one was a two-year-old juvenile, in Providence Bay. On August 26, 1932, on the southeast coast of Providence Bay, I found a huge flock. Apart from this I saw only lone birds and some pairs. In the very early summer, in mid-July, 1938, I happened to see flocks numbering up to 30 males and smaller flocks consisting of males and nonbreeding females. The autopsy of seven males showed that they were all nonbreeding birds.

F.H. Fay and T.J. Cade called St. Lawrence Island the molting ground of male harlequin ducks (like Wrangel Island for the flocks of molting old squaws). Small flocks were seen along the west coast. They usually comprised 10 to 20 birds but many more in stormy weather. On St. Lawrence Island harlequin ducks were noticed by different observers. On June 27, 1921, A.M. Bailey saw three of them. F.S. Hersey (1916) saw two or three to the east of the island. H.B. Collins (Friedmann 1932a) collected a molting female in Gambell on June 27, 1930. According to O.J. Murie (1936) a male in breeding plumage was collected there on June 2, 1933. E.G.F. Sauer and E.K. Urban (1964) often noticed a flock of 13 harlequin ducks floating in the tiny bay to the west of Boxer Bay. According to F.H. Fay (1961) harlequin ducks were found in groups of 5 to 10 birds along the rocky southwestern coast of the island. H. Friedmann (1934a) established the presence of the shoulder bones of harlequin ducks in archaeological excavations.

The harlequin duck does not occur for certain on the east and north coasts of the Chukchi peninsula. É.V. Schmidt, who collected in Meechigmensk Gulf and Lawrence Bay, did not find this duck. Without providing factual data, E.W. Nelson (1883, p. 98) writes that the harlequin duck was found along the northeast coast of Siberia and that it visited the islands in the Bering Sea in the summer. But it was not encountered by the *Corwin* expedition to the Arctic where, even if it were found, it would be as a stray or very rare summer bird.

Flight sightings—I.O. Olenev in 1932 and P.T. Butenko in 1938 found very few harlequin ducks in the spring flight in Providence Bay, mostly non-breeding birds. It is interesting that on June 2, 1958, K.W. Kenyon (Kenyon and Brooks 1960) saw a flock of nearly 10 harlequin ducks flying northward over a lead off the southern tip of Malyi Diomede Island. Two more pairs were seen beside the shore ice to the north of the settlement.

In the fall this duck was found in Providence Bay and on St. Lawrence Island but no one sighted a massive flight. In the northern extreme of the habitat of the species this is quite understandable.

The harlequin duck does not winter in the Chukchi peninsula.

Habitat—In Providence Bay harlequin ducks nested near the sea and led the life of sea ducks. I saw broods swimming offshore. It is probable that the brood was raised on the bank of a rivulet flowing from the highlands near Cape Stoletiya. Here I noticed many old squaws flying in from the sea every day. One flock passed over the bay while others fed on the shore, sometimes in the company of eiders. It is interesting that solitary birds as well as flocks were confined to the surf life. The harlequin ducks bobbed on the waves like floats but did not deviate from their course. They swam along the shoreline one behind the other, single file, sometimes catching something in the water.

On July 7, 1938, I happened to see a male harlequin duck floating alone in the sea. I was on a ship just within sight of the Kamchatka coast as we passed Cape Africa. With the exception of eiders I never saw any other duck in the open sea so far from the coast during the summer.

Flight—In the spring of 1931, L.O. Belopol'skii observed the flight of large flocks at Krest Bay at the end of May and early June. According to P.T. Butenko's records, in the spring of 1938 he found the first harlequin ducks on his way from Providence Bay to Sireniki village on May 25.

Breeding—Judging from the measurements of testes, what I collected were only nonbreeding males (Table 20).

Table 20. Size of testes of harlequin ducks, mm

Date	Left	Right	Locality
June 10, 1938	15×8	14×7	Plover Bay
July 12, 1938	11×4	9×3	Cape Stoletiya
July 12, 1938	10×4	8×3	—do—
July 12, 1938	9×3	8×3	—do—
July 12, 1938	8×3	7×3	—do—
July 12, 1938	8×3	4×3	—do—
Aug. 5, 1938	10×4	8×3	—do—

As could be anticipated, freshly arriving June males had appreciable subcutaneous adipose layers. Later the males used them up or conserved them to varying degrees. Most of the July birds were emaciated.

On July 13, 1938, I saw a female with a brood of four or five young ones off the coast not far from Cape Stoletiya. The young were only slightly less grown than the adult bird. At that time of the year the harlequin ducks were performing daily migrations from the sea into the valley of the rivulet in flocks comprising both sexes.

Molting—The feathers on the upper and posterior parts of the head, neck and shoulders were shed in a male obtained on August 5, 1938. According to an eyewitness account by H. Friedmann, a female taken in Gambell on June 27, 1930, was in a state of molt. On August 26, 1932, I found molting harlequin ducks east of Cape Plover. It was an unusual sight. In the dark twilight the birds were swimming in a dense flock along the surf and approached within 10 paces of where I lay in ambush. After I fired the harlequin ducks escaped by diving or fled across the water splashing with their wings, being in no shape to take off.

Migration—L.M. Starokadomsii collected a female in Providence Bay as early as September 25, 1912. H.B. Collins evidently got a female on St. Lawrence Island on September 2, 1930.

Habits—The calls uttered by harlequin ducks feeding on the surf line mark them out from the silent eiders. At other times the harlequin ducks too are silent birds.

Weight—The weight of a male was 690 g.

Economic importance—Hunters arriving in Providence Bay noticed the regular daily movement and set out to hunt the harlequin ducks on a rivulet near Cape Stoletiya. I happened to be present on one such hunt. Oblivious, the harlequin ducks flew low over the water and were an easy target. On a successful evening the hunters shot from 10 to 15 ducks. It was not difficult to shoot the harlequin ducks on the surf from behind the pebble banks but it was nearly impossible to retrieve the birds under such conditions. In any case, these ducks were only of secondary interest for hunting, the eiders being the prime trophy.

Systematics of the subspecies—I have with me only three specimens of typical *Histrionicus histrionicus histrionicus* (L.) but I can distinguish them from Anadyr and Chukchian *H. h. pacificus* Brooks since the latter have a much longer wing and a more prominent beak. Color differences can be seen from specimen to specimen. The sizes of white and russet patches vary widely.

Specimens— 1 and 2) Providence Bay, July 20, 1912, ♂♂, Starokadomskii; 3 and 4) same place, September 25, 1912, ♀♀, Starokadomskii; 5) Meechekn Island, June 13, 1931, ♂, Belopol'skii; 6) same place, Plover Bay, June 10, 1938, ♂, Butenko; 7 to 11) same place, rivulet at Cape Stoletiya, July 12, 1938, ♂♂, Butenko; 12) same place, August 5, 1938, ♂, Butenko; and 13 and 14) same place, August 12, 1938, ♂♂, Butenko.

Melanitta nigra americana (Swains.)—**Black Scoter**

Distribution and status—Not found for certain on Wrangel Island or in the Chukchi peninsula. Could yfl into the interior or western part of the peninsula since it is common on the Anadyr. Lone birds noticed in spring and summer in Bering Strait and on St. Lawrence Island.

In his diary A.A. Savich writes (Artobolevskii 1927) that on June 28, 1915, a pair of black ducks was collected at Cape Schmidt. It is difficult to determine now what those birds were. Among the names of ducks listed by A.I. Argentov (1861a) for the coast of the Arctic Ocean from Cape Yakan to the Kolyma are "black sea ducks, arriving from east" and "black river ducks arriving from south". It is possible that one of these names, especially the latter, pertained to the scoter but this reference still does not mean that the range of the bird reached Yakan. I never saw scoters and heard nothing about them from Chukchian hunters or from the eskimos on Wrangel Island. As experienced a hunter as É.V. Schmidt did not find the scoter either on the east coast of the Chukchi peninsula or around Chaun Bay, but he hunted it on the Kolyma. According to him the black scoter wandered along the lower Kolyma but in smaller numbers than the surf or white-winged scoters. He managed to shoot only a few while up to 38 surf or white-winged scoters were bagged in one night. Farther north at Zaimka Kolyma, opposite the Omolon estuary, he did not find the black scoter even once.

According to E.W. Nelson (1883, p. 102, and 1887), in the late summer of 1881 when the *Corwin* sailed along the Siberian coast to the south of Bering Strait black scoters were noticed along with innumerable surf or white-winged scoters. In 1922, in Bering Strait, A.M. Bailey (1925) noticed the black scoter from time to time. Some birds along with king eiders were noticed on May 8 and tiny flocks on May 17. One male was collected on May 19. It is explained that in Bering Strait black scoters and chicks unrelated to any brood were seen in the open sea from spring through fall. But evidently the black scoters did not remain on the Chukchi coast or approached it rarely, since no one found them on the coast or near it.

According to F.H. Fay and T.J. Cade (1959), on June 4, 1953, three black scoters were noticed among drifting ice to the northeast of Gambell. A month later a solitary bird was noticed at Cape Siknik. Two were put up on the Kuzata lagoon on June 25, 1954. E.W. Nelson (1883, p. 102) writes that the black scoter was found on St. Lawrence Island in moderate numbers. H. Friedmann (1934a) established the presence of black scoter bones in five 1,000-year-old archaeological excavations at the southeastern tip of the island.

Melanitta fusca stejnegeri Ridgw. —**Hook-nosed Scoter**

Distribution and status—Not a single reliable record is known for the Chukchi peninsula or Wrangel Island. Solitary birds sighted in summer in Bering Strait and on St. Lawrence Island.

E.W. Nelson (1883, p. 102) writes that at the time of the *Corwin* expedition this scoter was noticed around Kotsebue Bay and in the Arctic up to the Siberian (i.e. Chukchian) coast; it was further noticed in appreciable numbers on a rock at Cape Vankarém on August 7, 1881. Later in the summer, when the *Corwin* was sailing down the Chukchi coast to the south of Bering Strait, appreciable numbers of these scoters together with black scoters were noticed in the sea far from land, though a month before none was to be seen there. In his 1887 report E.W. Nelson writes of finding the hook-nosed scoters on both shores of Bering Strait and in Kotsebue Bay, where they nested. They were also noticed in small numbers along the Chukchi coast to the northwest of the strait. These unreliable references are characteristic of some of Nelson's observations, which were casual, given the conditions of his journey. He identified the birds at great distances "on sight" and mistook them for birds he had seen on his southern travels. In any case, his sketch of these scoters at Cape Vankarém Kamen' appeared meaningless to local residents. This reference should therefore be ignored.

A.I. Argentov (1861, p. 492) very accurately referred to a hook-nosed black scoter but only for the lakes along the border of the northern forests between Alazeey and the Kolyma. É.V. Schmidt did not find the hook-nosed scoter in the eastern part of the Chukchi peninsula or in the Chaun region. I noticed a dark-colored duck in a flock of old squaws on June 13, 1956, but because of the distance could not accurately establish whether it was a female scoter or a king eider. I have no other sightings to report.

According to a report by F.H. Fay and T.J. Cade (1959) a male hook-nosed scoter was collected on St. Lawrence Island on July 2, 1929. On August 2 and 3, 1946, five or six birds of this species were noticed around Gambell. During June, 1953 and 1954, groups of two or three scoters totaling around 20 birds were noticed between Boxer Bay and Siknik and two scoters around Savunga.

27. **Melanitta perspicillata** (L.)—**Surf Scoter**

Distribution and status—Only one case of positive nidification known on the east coast of the Chukchi peninsula.

On August 8, 1843, I.G. Voznesenskii collected a young male in Mechigmensk Gulf. Since the bird was young, it remained unidentified for a century.

E.W. Nelson (1883, p. 102) writes that some birds of this species were noticed in the sea off the northeastern coast of Siberia at the end of August, 1881, when the *Corwin* left the Arctic. The surf scoter was also noticed together with the hook-nosed scoter on the rocks by Cape Vankarém on August 7, 1881. Later, Nelson (1887) wrote that he found this scoter quite commonly on both shores of Bering Strait. These reports of Nelson, which are neither accurate nor consistent, cannot be regarded as totally reliable. The different types of scoters behave like sea birds outside of the nesting period and their occurrence in the southern and eastern parts of the Bering Sea is beyond doubt.

H. Friedmann (1934a) differentiated a bone of this scoter in 1,000-year-old kitchen middens on the southeastern tip of St. Lawrence Island.

Specimen—Mechigmensk Gulf, August 6, 1843, ♂, 1° anno, Voznesenskii.

28. **Polysticta stelleri** (Pall.)—**Steller's Eider**

Local name—Chukchian: Kataàtl'gyn; káttaadlin in the records of the *Vega* expedition. In Eskimo: aglỳkysigak in Providence Bay and ăghă-lĭk-sĭ-ghăk on St. Lawrence Island.

Distribution and status—Nests on coasts of Chukchi peninsula but only at certain places and in small numbers. During summer residence, before and during molting, it is quite common, though encountered sporadically and in varying numbers; sometimes in very large flocks. Common in spring and relatively rare in the fall flight, but does not winter. Occasionally flies over Wrangel Island during migrations.

Distribution during the nesting period—Though Steller's eider cannot be called a rare bird, information on its nidification in the Chukchi peninsula, as in most other parts of its range, is scattered and incomplete. In 1914, W. Percy (Phillips 1926, vol. IV, pp. 67, 70 and 71; Percy 1958) reportedly found a nest on Litke Island and in the adjoining section of the shore of Lawrence Bay, but the Chukchians destroyed them. On July 6, 1934, in the lower reaches of the Utte-Véem River, I saw a lone male flying over a stagnant pool. Since the other males at that time were in flocks it could be assumed that the Steller's eider had not yet deserted the female. On July 6, 1879, E.K. Brusevits (Palmén 1887) shot a male during an excursion inland to the south of the *Vega's* anchorage. On July 8, near Pitlekai, he bagged a male and a female. Finally, on July 11 a male and a female were seen flying from the lagoon to the sea. They were mostly breeding birds and were not gathering for molting. A.A. Kishchinskii could not find a single nest of this bird in June and July, 1970, on the tundra from Vankarém to the Amguema. É.V. Schmidt told me that a pair was collected on Aiok Island.

I saw a pair of Steller's eiders on Wrangel Island on June 12, 1939, near a lagoon to the east of Predatel'skaya Bay. After a few shots the birds returned to the spot they were occupying before they were disturbed. Perhaps it was this pair together with another bird that was noticed on June 14 east of Somnitel'naya Bay. At that time the hunters saw pairs of Steller's eiders in Rodgers Bay but the birds later disappeared.

E.W. Nelson (1883) reports that in the first few days of July, 1881, he found the Steller's eiders nesting in small numbers on St. Lawrence Island. But later he explains that it did not nest there regularly. F.H. Fay and T.J. Cade (1959) recalled only one record of a female with two downy chicks collected near Naskak on July 7, 1954.

Distribution and status of lone and molting Steller's eiders—Non-breeding birds were found in flocks at certain points on the Chukchi coast. The birds were not confined to one particular place.

During summer, 1931, L.O. Belopol'skii (1934) many times found Steller's eider at Krest Bay. At Providence Bay E.E. Arngol'd and L.M. Starokadomskii collected innumerable summer birds at different times in 1912 to 1914. Copley Amory, Jr. (Riley 1918) obtained a female on August 8, 1914, at Émma Bay. In the first week of July, 1921, A.M. Bailey (1925) found a small number of these eiders there. In August, 1932, I found Steller's eiders in Providence and Émma bays in very small numbers. I.O. Olenev, who wintered there in 1931/1932, has nothing to report about this bird. During my visit to Providence Bay from July 11 through 14, 1938, I did not find a single Steller's eider but saw them in Émma Bay in September, 1939. In the summer of 1939 P.T. Butenko collected some. On August 23, 1932, I found a small number of them at Cape Chaplin.

W.S. Brooks (1915) saw large flocks, mostly of males, on June 25, 1913, on the southern side of St. Lawrence Island. They were in such concentrations in the shallows offshore that the water was not visible. This could be explained by the accumulation of food there. F.S. Hersey (1916) found the Steller's eider common but R.W. Hende (Bailey 1925), who spent a week on the island in 1914, did not see it at all. O.J. Murie (1936) collected a series of 12 males in Kukuliak village on August 9, 1935, but the collection of such a large number of males showed that they were nonbreeding birds. I.N. Gabrielson (Gabrielson and Lincoln 1959) saw Steller's eiders at Southwest Cape on August 3, 1946. E.G.F. Sauer and E.K. Urban (1964) noticed flocks on the shores of Boxer Bay in June, 1960. F.H. Fay and T.J. Cade noticed that the summer population consisted mostly of two-year-old birds or very old males. In the archaeological excavations of kitchen middens, H. Friedmann (1934a) identified very few bones of Steller's eiders: pieces of thigh, scapula and synsacrum; but later thigh bones were found in the oldest of excavations. I.G. Voznesenskii collected a female on July 3, 1843, in Bering Strait on his way from St. Lawrence Island to Norton Bay.

In August, 1855, W. Stimpson (Cassin 1863, p. 323) collected a specimen in Senyavin Strait. Steller's eider was found by the *Vega* expedition during its brief trip along the east coast of the Chukchi peninsula. In particular, on July 30, 1879, molting males were found on an expedition into the hinterland at Kon'yam Bay. É.V. Schmidt told me that he did not encounter this species of eider in Mechigmensk Gulf but then he did not do much collecting at sea. Two males were taken by the *Vega* expedition on July 21, 1879, near Nunyamo village at the entrance to Lawrence Bay. I.N. Akif'ev (1904) obtained a male on July 30, 1900, and F.S. Hersey found a large flock in summer, 1914, in the same bay near Litke Island. The sand was peppered black and white with the innumerable birds on it. Whalers told him that their teams fed on these ducks. In June, 1914, W. Percy saw a flock numbering 400 to 1,000 birds on the shores of the bay, but the females formed less than 5 percent. At rest or when feeding they gathered in very dense groups. When W. Percy fired at a female spectacled eider coming in his sight, 11 Steller's eiders fell dead. In summer, 1957, A.P. Kuzyakin did not find Steller's eiders at all on the coast from Lawrence Bay to Uélen but procured a specimen in Uélen.

On July 12, 1922, A.M. Bailey and R.W. Hendee made a collection in Uélen and saw many flocks of eiders flying in clear weather from the north during the morning hours. It is possible that the eiders had left the Arctic Ocean ice to molt in the Bering Sea. All the four species of eiders took part in this migration. It included Steller's eiders in the same proportions as the other birds, the males predominating. This presumption is confirmed by the 1928 observations of F.L. Jaques (1930). On July 27 he noticed a solitary male at Diomede Island. He saw 30 Steller's eiders in brown summer plumage on September 3 at Bol'shoi Diomede. He shot two at Bering strait. A summer specimen of a Steller's eider from Uélen was given to M.A. Menzbier by Sheneberg. On August 16, 1948, V.N. Lyubin obtained a female that had been shot there.

During my one year's stay at Uélen, I regularly saw flocks of Steller's eiders only in the summer of 1934. The eiders wandered along the coast from Uélen to Mitkulen. They could be regarded as common but innumerable birds of that species could be observed only near Mitkulen and Inchoun. Though they were somewhat fewer in numbers than king eiders there they outnumbered the common and spectacled eiders. On July 24, 1934, I saw huge flocks of Steller's and king eiders near Inchoun. I could not locate the place where they molted. O. Nordquist (Palmén 1887) noticed some floating Steller's eiders on the lagoon by Ryraitynop on July 9, 1879, near the winter anchorage of the *Vega*. This was a unique summer observation. In mid-July, 1909, J. Koren (1910) daily noticed hundreds of Steller's eiders with other species of migratory birds near the coast on the west side of the entrance to Kolyuchin Bay.

Steller's eiders did not nest there. According to the observations of E.W. Nelson (1883, p. 99), in 1881 they were especially numerous on the north coast of the Chukchi peninsula. Thousands of flocks were seen in the first few days of August around Cape Vankarém, roughly in the same numbers as king eiders. The quantitative distribution, specieswise, in mixed flocks of eiders varied constantly because of rearrangements and regroupings of flocks. The eiders rose in an apparently unbroken flight three or four miles long when the *Corwin* was at Vankarém. Nelson called this part of the Chukchi coast the great summer residence of Steller's eiders. They occurred there in thousands when not one could be found on the north coast of Alaska. In his 1887 report Nelson (1887, p. 76) writes in very general terms that in the summer of 1881, when the *Corwin* made some expeditions along the Chukchi coast northwest of Bering Strait, these birds were found in huge flocks in the extensive river estuaries and on the lagoons. In his description of his Vankarém visit K.L. Hooper (1884) reports that innumerable eiders were found, including some Steller's eiders. In June, 1970, A.A. Kishchinskii found them several times on the tundra near the Ukouge lagoon. Females were encountered very rarely. In all, there were not more than five of them. Probably they were nonbreeding birds since no nests were found. In July, on the seacoast from Vankarém to Ukouge, there were hundreds of flocks consisting exclusively of males.

On August 13, 1914, Copley Amory, Jr., saw large flocks at Cape Schmidt and collected four females. According to V.Ya. Isaev, large flocks of Steller's eiders were constantly noticed in the summer flying along the coastline at Cape Schmidt. According to my observations, in July-August, 1938, male Steller's eiders were found in flocks of ducks that were performing diurnal migrations along the spit joining Cape Kozhevnikov with the mainland. In numbers they were fewer than the old squaws as also common eiders. É.V. Schmidt told me of encountering a flock of 30 birds on Rautan Island near Pevek. He saw a flock on Aiok Island too. According to the observations of V.D. Lebedev and V.R. Filin (1959) flocks of Steller's eiders consisting exclusively of males numbering 30 to 40 each were found in July, 1958, in the sea off the east coast of the Karchyk peninsula and on the west coast of Aiok Island. They were in small numbers on the north coast of Karchyk; 19 males fell into the net on July 10, 1958. In 1911 and 1912, J. Koren (Thayer and Bangs 1914) found this eider everywhere along the north coast of the Chukchi peninsula. S.A. Buturlin (1906b) saw it only occasionally in Kolyma delta.

On Wrangel Island I saw a flock of three males and three females on June 26, 1939, at the eastern extremity of Rodgers Bay. Probably it was from this very flock that a female was shot on June 30 but later no one saw these birds. According to me they wandered on the island at the very end of the spring migration but later spent the summer somewhere else. No one had seen molting Steller's eiders on Wrangel Island.

Distribution during migratory season—L.O. Belopol'skii found innumerable flocks during the spring flight on Meechken Island and later at the end of the winter migrations between Pervyi and Vtoroi Red'kin, as also at Cape Bering. According to the observations of W.S. Brooks Steller's eiders were very common and to be found in flocks during the first three weeks of June, 1913, at Providence Bay. S.G. Pavlov obtained a spring specimen there. In 1939 P.T. Butenko tracked the spring flight in Providence Bay. There is no doubt that the male taken by H.B. Collins (Friedmann 1932a) on June 8, 1930, at Gambell village on St. Lawrence Island should be regarded as a migratory bird.

W.S. Brooks saw migratory flocks on June 7, 1913, at Cape Dezhnev. According to my observations in spring, 1934, at Uélen, Steller's eiders in relatively small flocks were common in flight though they were not encountered on all my expeditions. It is not without significance that observers on the *Vega* expedition (Palmén 1887) did not notice the spring flight in 1879 at Kolyuchin Bay. At Cape Schmidt a spring male was collected by A.A. Savich (Artobolevskii 1927) in 1915. J. Koren, who tracked the flight of birds in spring, 1912, around the lower Kolyma, saw o Steller's eider only once. At Zaimka Kolyma É.V. Schmidt found two large flocks of up to 50 to 70 birds flying low along the river on one occasion.

Steller's eiders were found everywhere in small numbers in the fall flight. On September 17, 1911, hunters on the freighter *Vaigach* shot a male southwest of Wrangel Island at 70°53′ north and 173°15′ east. Nevertheless, no one has recorded any regular fall flight there. V.F. Vlasova and A.I. Mineev (Portenko 1937b) saw only three pairs in different years during their five-year sojourn at Rodgers Bay. Tayan informed me that a flock flew past the bay in 1937.

É.E. Arngol'd collected a female on September 2, 1911, at Cape Shelagskii. In the fall of 1933, I found a brood in Uélen only once and some specimens among other species of eiders brought by the Chukchians. In the fall of 1938, P.T. Butenko noticed Steller's eiders and shot them in Providence Bay. On September 14, 1939, I sighted molting Steller's eiders in Émma Bay. On St. Lawrence Island O.J. Murie collected a male and a female at Savunga village on September 25, 1935, and a male on November 7, 1935.

Habitat—It was pointed out above that the likely breeding sites were near the lagoons and estuaries of rivers feeding them. E.W. Nelson found Steller's eiders in small numbers in early July, 1881, in the brackish lakes on St. Lawrence Island. On July 8, 1879, E.K. Brusevits shot a male on a shallow lakelet. É.V. Schmidt collected a pair by a pool on Aiok Island. I found a pair on Wrangel Island on June 12, 1939, on a tundra lake near a lagoon. Under conditions where the Steller's eiders lived in pairs, before or during nesting, they were to be found on shallow water on the maritime tundra. Apart from nidification the Steller's eider is a purely marine bird confirmed to the coasts and almost a stranger to the land.

L.O. Belopol'skii saw Steller's eiders near Cape Bering in ice-free parts of the sea on their early spring movement to the north. According to my observations in spring, 1934, in Uélen, these eiders were more attached to the sea than other species.

On a very big flight the flocks extended over the sea. When the flight paused the flocks would fly about locally. Quite often they crossed the isthmus between Dezhnev village and Uélen. But unlike the common and king eiders, Steller's eiders avoided flying over the village and the Chukchians had to hunt them on the spit along the Uélen lagoon.

Even later, in the summer, I did not see flights of Steller's eiders at Uélen settlement but A.M. Bailey gives a very picturesque description of a massive movement that occurred on July 12, 1921. Flocks of eiders including Steller's eiders flew in from the north and followed the bank of the Uélen lagoon. Then they wheeled and flew over the village. I suggest the Steller's eiders were attracted by the great stream of other species of eider. Once on August 13, 1934, in the middle reaches of the Kol'oam-Véem River, I saw a flock of Steller's eiders flying low in perfect formation over a stretch of water. Evidently they were migrating from Lake Kool'ong, if not from Lawrence Bay, to the north coast.

In all other cases, from Cape Dezhnev to Mitkulen, I saw Steller's eiders in the sea among the ice floes. Sometimes they were feeding by a tiny strait linking Uélen lagoon with the sea. Many sea birds gathered to feed there. On my trip to Bol'shoi Diomede Island at the end of June, 1934, I became convinced that Steller's eiders were confined to the coast, which was then covered with thin ice, but were absent both from the strait and from the shores of Diomede Island. Near Naukan and Inchoun, Steller's eiders floated around the rocks. They were seen on the lagoons when the ice was close inshore or in a strong wind. In the latter case, they would take refuge in tiny bays protected from the wind. In the fall flying young birds were noticed in the lagoons at Uélen. At Providence Bay I noticed daily movements from the sea to the shores of the bay. On September 14, 1939, a very large number of Steller's eiders were serenely swimming in Émma Bay on a still surface in calm weather. According to V.Ya. Isaev's observations, at Cape Schmidt these eiders would fly over the sea along the coast but not over the lagoons where other eiders and old squaws would be encountered.

Spring flight—Steller's eiders do not winter on the Chukchi coasts but when there is no ice they are to be seen very early on the south coast. L.O. Belopol'skii found a flock between the Red'kin villages and at Cape Bering in March, 1931. P.T. Butenko, who tracked the wintering of other eiders at Cape Chaplin did not find Steller's eiders in the winter of 1937/1938. They came only in May. The first bird was noticed at Cape Stoletiya and collected on the night of May 17/18, 1938. The next specimen was taken there on May 30. According to F.H. Fay (1961) Steller's eiders were seen on St. Lawrence Island in large numbers around May 15.

In 1934 spring, I tracked the flight near Uélen. I noticed the first flock consisting of a few pairs near Cape Dezhnev on May 25. They flew north in a long chain along with murres. On May 31 flocks in small numbers were flying over the spit of Uélen lagoon and above the sea. On June 1 my party hunted at the edge of the shore ice opposite Uélen. In a small group that flew toward us females predominated. Small flocks continued to fly on June 3 but later the movement was much reduced.

A migratory specimen was collected by J. Koren on the lower Kolyma on June 9,

1912, and another by the *Maud* expedition (Schaanning 1928) at Lake Chetyrekhstolb on June 12, 1925.

Breeding—I measured the gonads in a very large number of birds collected at different times of the year (Tables 21 and 22).

Table 21. Testis dimensions of Steller's eiders, mm

Date	Left	Right	Locality
May 18, 1938	15×4	15×3	Cape Stoletiya
May 30, 1938	12×5	11×5	—do—
May 31, 1934	21×8	19×7	Uélen
June 1, 1934	12×8	10×7	—do—
June 1, 1934	10×7	9×6	—do—
June 7, 1932	—	17×9	Markovo
June 17, 1934	12×6	10×5	Uélen
June 26, 1934	11×4	9×4	—do—
July 4, 1934	12×5	10×4	Mitkulen
July 4, 1934	12×5	8×4	—do—
July 4, 1934	10×3	8×2	—do—
July 4, 1934	8×2	—	—do—
July 29, 1934	10×4	7×3	Uélen
Aug. 8, 1938	10×2	9×2	Cape Stoletiya
Nov. 11, 1937	8×3	7×3	Plover Bay
Nov. 19, 1937	13×6	11×5	—do—
Nov. 30, 1937	8×2	7×2	—do—

Table 22. Ovary structure of Steller's eiders

Date	Ovary structure		Locality
May 31, 1934	Length of largest follicle,	7 mm	Uélen
June 1, 1934	—do—	8 mm	—do—
June 17, 1934	—do—	6 mm	—do—
Nov. 19, 1937	Granular structure		Plover Bay
Nov. 30, 1937	Filmlike structure		—do—

Judging from testis measurements and ovary structure, perhaps only one male collected at Uélen on May 31, 1934, and three females seen there could have bred in the early summer. All the others were nonbreeding birds.

A study of the subcutaneous adipose layers showed that during the migratory season the birds were well fed and plump. At the end of this period, however, the birds no doubt became emaciated. It is very interesting that the males in summer plumage collected on August 8, 1938, at Cape Stoletiya were very fat. F.S. Hersey also drew attention to the fact that the specimens he took in Lawrence Bay were very plump in spite of molting. The November birds had thin adipose layers. Almost all the females were emaciated but one of them collected on June 1, 1934, at Uélen had appreciable adipose layers. Compared with the others, her ovaries contained the biggest follicle. According to W. Percy the males he saw at Lawrence Bay in June, 1914, were attempting to utter the mating call, characteristically stretching and throwing back the neck, but he did not hear a full-throated call.

Usually the males sat on the ground or on the ice floes in a somewhat erect posture holding the head and neck almost horizontally. Their beautiful color gives them a foppish look. In June, breeding females were constantly flying from the sea to the tundra. At the end of June most of the females incubated and a few birds, either nonbreeding or from destroyed nests, were seen on the shore. In Clarence Port, Alaska, on July 24, 1879, the *Vega* expedition caught three chicks which still had the embryonal down over the growing feathers. The back, wings and part of the chin had only down and no feathers. In the fall of 1933, on the lagoon at Uélen, I noticed the first emergence of young ones on September 18. Judging from this belated date, it may have been a wandering and not a local brood.

Molting—At the end of the spring flight nonbreeding birds remain in small flocks which gradually grow and sometimes reach huge proportions. In 1934, above Uélen, Steller's eiders could not be seen for two successive weeks in the first few days of June. On June 17 P.T. Butenko found very few (4+6) around the rocks; I saw flocks flying in different directions or resting on the ice floes on June 20 and 21 on my way from Uélen to Naukan and around the latter area. In July, Steller's eiders were innumerable around Inchoun and Mitkulen; I also sighted some huge flocks on July 21.

According to the observations of A.A. Kishchinskii, the first flocks of males were found in 1970 in the Ukouge lagoon on June 25. On July 7 he counted about 150 of them. On July 8 there were from 500 to 600 birds along the seashore. In all, during July, some tens of thousands of birds traversed. Signs of molting were noticed on July 7 and 8. Males of mixed winter and summer plumage were noticed from July 17 through 19. In one case there were only four females among 1,500 male birds counted, yearlings being altogether absent.

In the summer of 1934, around Uélen, I noticed as early as July 21 that the head of many males was dark-colored. In 1932, up to the end of August, I saw only dark-colored males in Providence Bay and at Cape Chaplin. Specimens collected by P.T. Butenko in Providence Bay on August 8, 1936, still did not sport the full summer plumage as they had not shed the flight feathers. Where and when the molting took place could not be established.

In Lawrence Bay the *Vega* expedition noticed males in winter plumage as late as July 21, 1879, but molting birds were sighted on July 30. F.S. Hersey collected molting Steller's eiders there on July 26, 1914. According to the observations of W. Percy (Phillips 1926 and Percy 1958), in the same year, 1914, the first signs of molting of males in Lawrence Bay were detected on June 25. Many of them lost their scapulars by July 8 and were in a condition of heavy molt by July 15. On July 16 a specimen collected had completely molted into summer plumage. By July 27, most of the males were molting though some were still flying up to August 11, when Percy stopped observing. On the last few days of July and in early August, according to him, huge flocks of eiders were continuously flying south over Bering Strait. Among them Steller's eiders were also seen in small numbers and in much smaller flocks. Evidently, they were nonbreeding birds gathered for molting but the molting ground of Steller's eiders outside of Lawrence Bay and to the south of Bering Strait is still not clearly known.

Migration—In the fall of 1933 around Uélen, apart from the brood noticed on

September 18, already referred to, I did not see any more Steller's eiders. Hence I am of the view that their migration follows a path out to sea, far from the coast. In the fall of 1937, P.T. Butenko was in Krest Bay on October 14 and in Providence Bay on October 29. But he saw Steller's eiders only from November 11. In about three weeks they were almost the commonest of ducks. They were sighted and collected for the last time on November 30. Evidently the Steller's eider migrates late. Being a sea duck, it can negotiate the ice conditions on the coast, where innumerable flocks of nonbreeding birds spent the summer.

Habits—Steller's eiders fly at different altitudes, in large and small flocks, and in different formations. Large flocks, according to my observations, do not rise as high as the flocks of common or king eiders. Small groups or single birds sometimes fly low over the water. From afar a huge flock resembles a cloud, sometimes swelling, sometimes shrinking. Tiny flocks quite often form single rows or are stretched out in a chain. The male flies behind the female, the next pair flying in the same way behind the first. The chain sometimes includes some links of murres. Sometimes, on the other hand, the flocks form echelons. For the most part, such rows fly very low. Steller's eiders were to be seen in flocks of common eiders, old squaws or murres, independent of the size of the flocks, briefly or for long periods. Nevertheless, they prefer to hold themselves separate.

In an account of hunting when the birds were making daily flights above Vankarém village E.W. Nelson posed the question why eiders repeatedly follow the same course even if they incur losses from the flock every time. He put this down to the use of silent eplicathet devices, where guns with their loud reports would have frightened the birds. I have another explanation. The flocks began their flight under favorable conditions and were not alert. When the flock reached a dangerous place it was already too late to alter speed or direction. For a large flock it is quite difficult to dodge swiftly aside or alter formation. In this respect it follows some special principles, such as are characteristic of large flocks of mammals.

Sighting danger, Steller's eiders utter an indistinct, dull call note from anxiety and fright. I have heard this call only once or twice.

W. Percy noticed how the feeding flocks swam in a very rapid current. The rear birds dropped behind but later overtook the ones in front or chased them. I did not see anything like this among swimming birds. The flock did not break up in this process. According to Percy, the noise made by the wings in flight is so loud that in fog it is heard before the eiders are sighted.

Food—The stomach of females killed from July 10 through 12, 1879, at Pitlekai revealed insect larvae, as also *Asellus* and *Gammarus*. In the food contained in 44 stomachs of Steller's eiders collected by W. Percy in Lawrence Bay in June and July, 1914, *Amphipoda* and bivalve molluscs predominated. Equally abundant were the sea ducklings; but there were only stray specimens of marine worms, crabs and sea urchins, and only traces of alga. In the stomachs of specimens obtained by me at Uélen on June 17, 1934, remains of crustaceae were found in dozens. In a specimen shot there on June 26, remains of some dozens of mollusks were found. Tiny pebbles were abundant in all the stomachs.

Weight—The weight of males collected by P.T. Butenko in November was 840, 810 and 800 but also 680 g, and of females 865 and 820 g.

PLATE IV

Common eider *Somateria mollissima* var. *nigrum* Gray.
Atternon mountains in the background.
Pic. by L.A. Portenko.

Economic importance—The Steller's eider is caught by the local people as also new hunters when the birds perform their diurnal migration over the coast. I knew of hunting with the eplicathet and guns during these migrations at Uélen, Inchoun, Mitkulen, Vankarém and Cape Schmidt. It is not as though the eiders chose a path through the settlements for their diurnal movements but the latter happened to be advantageously situated for hunting. I will discuss the hunting of these eiders when dealing with the common eider. E.W. Nelson long ago described (1883, p. 99) mass hunting using eplicathets at Vankarém. Later a hunt at Uélen with eplicathets and guns was described by A.M. Bailey. Guns have been in use there for some decades but the eiders continued to fly over the village just the same.

Because of their small size and small numbers, Steller's eiders are caught in smaller numbers than common or king eiders, but some hunters prefer them for their tasty meat.

Systematics—I compared Chukchian with American specimens and with those originating from the far western parts of Siberia, but found no geographic variability.

From an examination of the male Labrador eider *Camptorhynchus labradorius* (Gm.) preserved in the collection of the Institute of Zoology, Academy of Sciences of the USSR, I came to the conclusion that this species, which became extinct around 1875, represented a geographic vicariate of the Steller's eider. In their very small size, shape of beak and color pattern, these two eiders should be set apart from the others and placed in a single genus *Camtorhynchus.*

Specimens— 1) Bering Sea, between St. Lawrence Island and Norton Bay, July 3, 1843, ♀, Voznesenskii; 2) Lawrence Bay, July 30, 1900, ♂, Akif'ev; 3) Diomede Island, June 1, 1905, ♂, Thayer; 4) Cape Shelagskii, September 2, 1911, ♀, Arngol'd; 5) southwestern part of Wrangel Island, September 17, 1911, ♂, freighter *Vaigach*; 6) Providence Bay, July 17, 1912, ♀, Arngol'd; 7 to 10) same place, July 18, 1912, ♂♂♂♀, Starokadomskii; 11 and 12) same place, September 24 and 25, 1912, ♂♂, Starokadomskii; 13) same place, September 26, 1912, ♂, 1° anno, Arngol'd; 14 and 15) Émma Bay, July 20 and 24, 1913, ♂, Starokadomskii; 16 and 17) Providence Bay, August 12, 1914, ♂♂, Arngol'd; 18) Uélen village, July 7, 1927, ♂, Sheneberg; 19) Wrangel Island, without date, ♂, Vlasova; 20) Providence Bay, without date, ♂, in spring plumage, Pavlov; 21) Uélen village, September 18, 1933, ♀, Portenko; 22 to 24) same place, May 31, 1934, ♂♀♀, Portenko; 25 to 28) same place, June 1, 1934, ♂♂♂♀, Portenko; 29 and 30) same place, June 17, 1934, ♂ ♀, Portenko; 31) same place, June 26, 1934, ♂, Portenko; 32 to 36) Mitkulen village, July 4, 1934, ♂♂, Portenko; 37) Uélen village, July 29, 1934, ♂, Portenko; 38) Providence Bay, Plover, November 11, 1937, ♂, Butenko; 39 and 40) same place, November 19, 1937, ♂ ♀, Butenko; 41) same place, November 25, 1937, ♀?, Butenko; 42 and 43) same place, November 30, 1937, ♂♀, Butenko; 44 and 45) Cape Stoletiya, May 18 and 30, 1938, ♂♂, Butenko; 46 to 50) Providence Bay, July 6 and 21, 1938, ♂♀, Butenko; 51) Kivak village, July 22, 1938, ⊙, Butenko; 52) Chechen village, July 25, 1938, ⊙, Butenko; and 53 and 54) Cape Stoletiya, August 8, 1938, ♂♂, Butenko.

29. **Arctonetta fischeri** (Brandt)—**Spectacled Eider**

Local name—Chukchian: Lilèkel' (lilèkelet plural); lilekedlin in the records of the *Vega* expedition. In Eskimo: lelàkali in Providence Bay and ēv́-ghăn on St. Lawrence Island. "Motley-eyed" on the Kolyma, according to Bogoraz.

Distribution and status—Found nesting only on the north coast of the Chukchi peninsula, in small numbers; nests sporadically, not in the same place every year. Nest found not long ago on St. Lawrence Island. Lone birds noticed in summer on different parts of the coast but in flocks only on St. Lawrence Island and on the section of the seacoast from Bering Strait to Kolyuchin Bay. Numerous in spring flight in Bering Strait and rare on other parts of the coast. In fall flight, nowhere found on the coasts in large numbers. Does not winter. Two cases of arrival on Wrangel Island established.

Distribution in breeding period—On March 8, 1879, a Chukchian from Mama brought a female spectacled eider to the *Vega* expedition and reported killing it on his way not far from the shore. This account gave rise to justifiable doubts as to when the bird was collected because the flight of spectacled eider occurred only in May and the tail and flight feathers of the bird were not fully formed. It is difficult to say whether it was a nesting or only a molting bird but in any case it was evident that the Chukchian had preserved it from the fall. The wing span totaled 18.0 cm while in other females taken by the *Vega* expedition it reached 25.5 to 26.0 cm (Palmén 1887, p. 441). More conclusive information on the nidification of spectacled eider near Kolyuchin Bay is not available.

The same would apply to my explorations near Uélen. The lone reliable record of nidification in the Chukchi peninsula was made by J. Koren (Thayer and Bangs 1914), who sighted two broods that still could not fly on September 18, 1912, on the River Tenkergin east of Cape Schmidt; one bird was collected.

S.A. Buturlin (1910) writes that the spectacled eider is more common than any other eider between the estuary of the Indigirka and Chaun Bay. In a later work, he (1935, p. 142) does not mention Chaun Bay at all but states that the spectacled eider nests on the south coast of the Chukchi peninsula, where he chanced to see skins of this bird with the local people in 1925. I have no doubt that the specimens were collected when the birds were still in the migratory period. In 1914, W. Percy (Phillips 1926) could not find nests of spectacled eider in spite of a thorough search along the lakelets on the coast from Lawrence Bay to Cape Dezhnev.

According to an eyewitness account by F.H. Fay and T.J. Cade (1959), a nest was found on July 7, 1954, near Naskak on St. Lawrence Island.

Distribution of nonbreeding and molting spectacled eiders—Spectacled eiders are found on the south coast of the Chukchi peninsula, but rarely, in summer before and probably during molting. According to I.O. Olenev, they were found in small numbers in Providence Bay. A two-year-old male specimen that he gave me was collected on June 29, 1932, in Émma Bay. P.T. Butenko did not see the spectacled eider at all during one year's stay in Providence Bay.

W.S. Brooks (Brooks 1915) reported collecting three specimens on the south side of St. Lawrence Island on June 25, 1913. F.S. Hersey (1916) found eiders there on July 24 and 25, 1914, in small numbers. According to Fay and Cade, this species was rare on the island outside the migratory period. On June 4, 1929, a male was collected on Southwest Cape. On the north and west coasts specimens were sighted and secured in May and early June, 1952 and 1953. From June 18 through 22, 1954, four males were noticed on the south coast. One of them accompanied a female and the other accompanied a flock of juveniles. According to E.G.F. Sauer and E.K. Urban (1964), on June 14, 1960, a female was shot in Kangi. Among the bones found in archaeological excavations, H. Friedmann (1934a) placed three scapula and four coracoid bones as of this species.

F.S. Hersey found a small number of spectacled eiders in Lawrence Bay on July 26, 1914. W. Percy (1958) collected a molted male in summer plumage there in the summer of 1914. On June 23, 1914, he (Phillips 1926) saw a flock of 100 to 150 birds in a dense cloudlike formation on his way from Lawrence Bay to Cape Dezhnev.

On Malyi Diomede Island, K.W. Kenyon (Kenyon and Brooks 1960) was given a male on May 11, 1958, and according to hunters these eiders were sighted in small numbers even later. F.L. Jaques (1930) saw some at the end of summer, 1928, north of Bering Strait.

A.M. Bailey (1925) collected three molting males at Uélen on July 12, 1921. In the summer of 1934 I sighted nonbreeding spectacled eiders on the coast around Uélen only once on my way to Naukan, and only a small flock at that. The Chukchians accompanying me spotted these birds from far off because they were very rare after the spring flight. I was given an almost completely molted three-year-old male and a two-year-old non-breeding female on July 29. V.N. Lyubin procured a spectacled eider at Uélen on August 15, 1948.

On July 3, 1934, I sighted a flock flying by the rocks near Inchoun village and on July 4 a large flock over the strait to the west. Later I found a small flock of spectacled eiders around Mitkulen, where I collected only three specimens, even with the help of some hunters.

In 1909, J. Koren (1910) found spectacled eiders only once, on June 27 while traversing the ice along the coast to Cape Serdtse-Kamen'. The birds were so unsuspecting that he was able to shoot three from the schooner.

In 1879, at the *Vega's* winter anchorage (Palmén 1887) near Kolyuchin Bay, only males were sighted from the very early flight period. From this it was evident that they had gathered there for molting. After the flight males were found successively on June 4 at Neshkan, July 11 at Pitlekai and June 13 at Irgunnuk. Females were later collected on June 25 and July 11.

In June and July, 1970, A.A. Kishchinskii only twice saw solitary males on the tundra from Vankarém to the Amguema estuary. They were clearly not associated with any nidification.

V.D. Lebedev and V.R. Filin (1959) collected three males on June 6 and 12, 1958, on the south coast of Aiok Island and sighted six males there on July 2. J. Koren (Thayer and Bangs 1914) found a large number of spectacled eiders 30 miles to the east of Bol'shoi Baranov Kamen' on July 12 to 15, 1912, but found neither the nests nor any other signs of breeding. Evidently the birds gathered there for molting.

Distribution during spring flight—L.O. Belopol'skii (1934) writes that, according to the eskimos, the spectacled eider was to be encountered from time to time in Krest Bay. It is a very vague reference, most probably concerning spring migration. In 1925 S.A. Buturlin evidently saw the skins of spring birds with the residents of

Providence Bay since the skins were prepared in the spring when the eider sported colorful plumage. The collection of Academician M.A. Menzbier contains a male specimen obtained by N.P. Sokol'nikov at Cape Chaplin on April 23, 1902. According to Sokol'nikov, his companion who collected the eider drew attention to the plumage characteristics, which distinguished it from a majority of other eiders. This bird was a rarity. It was recorded unusually early. P.T. Butenko, who hunted at Cape Chaplin in the winter of 1938, did not find the spectacled eider though he collected many other birds.

On St. Lawrence Island a spring pair was secured on May 27, 1953, and some were noticed in king eider flocks on the north and west coasts in May and in the first week of June, 1952 and 1953. Finally, O.W. Geist (Murie 1936) took a specimen on June 4, 1929.

Judging from the number of heads of this eider that I have seen with one person on Lawrence Bay, it was common there in spring flight. A.P. Kuzyakin saw a pair of spectacled eiders, probably caught in the spring, with a Chukchian on his way from Uélen to Yandagai. The captain of a ship wintering in the ice 30 miles south of Cape Dezhnev (East Cape) told A.M. Bailey that in the spring of 1922 literally thousands of spectacled eiders flew past on some days. The Chukchians told Bailey that at Uélen these eiders flew north in large numbers every spring. In 1934, according to information I was able to gather, the flight of eiders around Uélen was much reduced by the ice conditions. Ice piled up in front of Dezhnev settlement because there were no northerly winds. Therefore the eiders could not gather on the sea before Dezhnev and did not fly through the low isthmus connecting Dezhnev knoll with the mainland. Nevertheless, I saw very many spectacled eiders among the eiders shot by hunters at Uélen. Their mass flight concluded even before my return from a journey along the north coast. I saw flocks only at the very end of May, and then high over the sea. According to the Chukchians, spectacled eiders flew past Uélen every year but sometimes there were very few of them. I was given specimens collected during the 1940 spring flight at Uélen.

In the summer of 1970, according to V.V. Leonovich, two dead specimens were found near Énurmino. Probably these migratory birds fell victim to hunters.

In May, 1879, some males obtained in the villages near Kolyuchin Bay were given to *Vega* expedition members. On two of my visits to Cape Schmidt no one could tell me anything about spectacled eiders. In my view the birds flew over the sea, bypassing the Cape because of the local ice conditions.

Unfortunately, I could not decipher all the names of ducks mentioned by A.I. Argentov (1861a) as used on the coasts of the Arctic Ocean from Yakan to the Kolyma. But it is quite probable that the spectacled eider is covered by one of the names, such as marine drake or marine motley duck, which Argentov used to describe the various migratory birds. É.V. Schmidt told me that he collected a pair on Aiok Island during their spring flight.

In the spring, I chanced to sight a migratory pair on Wrangel Island in the estuary of the Amerikanskaya rivulet. A few years before, Tayan had succeeded in collecting a spectacled eider.

Distribution during fall flight—The spectacled eider is now rare everywhere. In the fall of 1933 I found it sometimes around Uélen and even collected some specimens. L.M. Starokadomskii caught a molting female on September 25, 1912, in Providence Bay. O.J. Murie had with him two fall specimens from St. Lawrence Island: a young bird from Punuk islet taken on September 1, 1934, and an adult female found on September 19, 1935.

Habitat—According to an eyewitness account by J. Koren, the spectacled eider nested on tiny tundra lakes. I saw young birds in the fall flight around Uélen on a broad lagoon. In all other cases, however, spectacled eiders not associated with breeding were sighted only at sea. This eider is a more marine bird than the others and has a special affinity for ice floes. Experienced Chukchian hunters drew my attention to the latter phenomenon. In Mitkulen, it was explained to me that spectacled eiders appeared in large numbers along with the ice floes in the summer, lived among them, loved to rest on the floes, etc. These ducks, like many other sea birds, avoid ice packs. For this reason the spectacled eider is not found in flight over sections of the coast that are lined with very broad shore ice. A.M. Bailey heard a similar explanation from the eskimos on the Alaskan coast.

At Uélen, spectacled eiders appeared in a truly winter environment in the spring flight and tried to move toward open water. Near the wintering station of the *Vega* in Kolyuchin Bay they were collected from the ice leads. I.O. Olenev found a bird on June 24, 1932, in Émma Bay when the ice had not yet opened up. In the 1933 fall flight at Uélen I noticed adult males far out to sea when storms drove the ice out from the village.

Spring flight—The earliest record of the spectacled eider in the Chukchi peninsula was on April 23, 1902, at Cape Chaplin. This was an exception. It represented an early northward movement of wintering marine birds which is caused by unusual conditions and often leads to their return. F.H. Fay (1961) gave May 13 as the date of arrival at Northwest Cape on St. Lawrence Island. In spring, 1934, around Uélen, the flight of spectacled eiders occurred in mid-May and ended a few days later. I saw the last flocks over the sea on May 31. Local Chukchians told me that spectacled eiders, like Steller's eiders, flew not only over the village but also westward, crossing the spit.

In 1879, at the *Vega's* anchorage, the first spectacled eider was shot on May 18. It was a male which settled on the thawed patch around the ship. Between then and June 11 the Chukchians brought six males to the expedition. From them it was gathered that only nonbreeding birds stopped there, while breeding birds proceeded farther west some distance inland from the coast. Though the expedition secured two females on June 25 and July 11, the period was so late that they could hardly be regarded as migratory birds. Evidently the flight of spectacled eiders was very uncoordinated, and without any relation to their arrival on the coast. It could easily be missed if not looked for on the beaches.

On the morning of June 15, 1939, in the estuary of the Amerikanskaya rivulet on Wrangel Island, active local wanderings of common eiders were noticed. Among them was found a tiny pair of spectacled eiders which were wandering there after the flight. The female, which appeared to be two years old, was bagged and the male did not come back for her.

W. Percy thought that spectacled eiders flew north even during June in East Siberia. I think such late dates for the Chukchi peninsula could only apply to nonbreeding birds, which perform local migrations during the summer. In particular, flocks are seen on the coast when the ice floes drift inshore. I noticed that in these cases there was quite often a fog and the spectacled eiders, like other marine birds, began wandering restlessly. In foggy weather lasting many days such local migrations occurred periodically at definite hours. They would be of massive proportions in the early morning hours. I noticed the spectacled eiders most often flying at a height of 5 to 7 m in flocks of different numbers.

Condition of gonads and amount of fat—The sizes of testes in males that I collected from June 26 through August 29, 1934, were roughly identical: 1) 14×7 and 10×6, 2) 12×6 and 8×4, 3) 12×5 and 8×4, 4) 10×4 and 6×3, and 5) 12×4 and 10×3 mm. These values could not be regarded as large since they were only slightly smaller, at 7×4 and 6×3 mm, in a young male found on September 18, 1933. Judging from the size of the testes, these summer males were nonbreeding birds. A two-year-old female from Wrangel Island had a 23 mm long ovary with a maximum follicle diameter of 5 mm.

Specimens obtained on arrival were not noticeably fat. A male from Irgunnuk collected on May 22, 1879, was very emaciated but a female taken on June 25 was moderately fat. My male specimen of June 26, 1934, was emaciated, while the males collected on July 4 and 29 possessed very thin adipose formations. A two-year-old female collected on June 15, 1939, on Wrangel Island was very fat. From among the young fall birds one female was emaciated but others had subcutaneous adipose layers.

Molting—Males collected at the end of June and in early July possessed worn-out plumage. Thin summer plumage had just begun to form. On the head of one a narrow border of growing dark plumelets was seen below the green caplet. In another, they appeared on the crown, neck and throat. A third was speckled more heavily. The dark feathers were seen around the rear half of the eyes, on the crown, cheeks, throat and to some extent even on the back. A two-year-old male collected by I.O. Olenev in Providence Bay on June 29, 1932, was in a state of molting from the first winter dress and in eclipse. A three-year-old male given to me in Uélen on July 29, 1934, was almost completely in the second summer plumage. The plumage of these two specimens has been described in detail in a special article (Portenko 1952, pp. 1119 to 1121).

J. Koren saw many spectacled eiders in female plumage from July 12 through 15, 1912, 48 km east of Bol'shoi Baranov Kamen'. They were swimming on the lake and flying: evidently they had not shed their flight feathers. A male of July 29, 1934, also had not changed his flight feathers and thus molting in winter plumage occurred late. On October 22 and 23, 1933, I noticed even white-headed males at Uélen.

The plumage of a female collected on September 25, 1912, in Providence Bay is of much interest. In spite of the late time of year she was in a condition of molting, having changed much of her fine plumage, but the flight feathers had not grown completely. The wing span measured 24.2 cm, against 26 cm in an unmolted female from Uélen obtained on July 29, 1934. Evidently molting was delayed. I feel that it was a lone female which had spent the entire summer at Providence Bay.

Broods—On September 18, 1912, J. Koren noticed two broods on the River

Ténkérgin; they were not flying yet and followed the adults in the water. Around Uélen I encountered on a lagoon three fully grown young spectacled eiders on September 18,1933. They probably belonged to the same brood though they were seen apart in the society of young king eiders. Later I was given young spectacled eiders on September 25 and October 1.

Migration—In the fall of 1933 I saw spectacled eiders around Uélen for the last time on October 22 and 23. They were adult males.

Habits—W. Percy, who observed this species several times in the Chukchi peninsula, confirmed that the spectacled eider was the most confiding of marine ducks and became more alert only in the period of molting. Further, it was more awkward in its behavior than the other eiders; before diving it would open its wings and start splashing. According to Percy's own observations, the spectacled eider kept itself aloof from other species; however, 9 or 10 birds were once noticed together with two or three king eiders. On another occasion a lone male was seen in a flock of Steller's eiders. According to my observations, the spectacled eider is not particularly confiding and is in fact less wary than other eiders; it keeps itself aloof but does not avoid the company of king eiders. In external characteristics and behavior the spectacled eider is closer to the king and common eiders than to the Steller's eider.

Food—The stomach of a male collected around Uélen on June 26, 1934, showed only eight pebbles. That of a female obtained on Wrangel Island on June 15, 1939, revealed 40 tiny pebbles 2 to 8 mm across and some bits of plant stalk. A study of the stomachs brought by the *Vega* expedition gave the following results:

1) Irgunnuk, May 22, 1879, ♂. Some tiny pebbles. The intestine contained yellow-green mucus and a large amount of intestinal worms. 2) Same place, May 19, 1879, ♂. Some stones up to 1 cm in diameter. A very large number of worms found in the intestinal mucus. 3) Same place, June 13, 1879, ♂, Parts of *Hyas aranea* and shells. 4) Water around the *Vega*, June 25, 1879, ♀. One specimen of *Trochus* and tiny stones. 5) Same place, July 11, 1879, ○. Unidentified remnants of small crustaceae, slime and plant remnants.

According to J.C. Phillips (1926), the stomachs of two spectacled eiders from Lawrence Bay contained the remains of a small number of molluscs.

Weight—According to the weighing by the members of the *Vega* expedition, one male weighed 1,743 and another 1,445 g. A two-year-old female from Wrangel Island weighed 1,324 g.

Economic importance—It is strange that this bird, which is rare even in the collections of large museums, is fully exploited in the regions where it is common. The heads of spectacled eiders are gathered by the local people for their beautiful color and feather structure. They are made into decorative articles, mainly the collars of ladies' overcoats and rugs. Processed skins of heads have an average size of 15 × 10 cm. After removing the flesh by the home technique they are stitched along the line from the beak to the ear. During my visit to Lawrence Bay in 1932 I saw a topcoat with collar and cuffs decorated with about 40 to 50 of them. For an ornithological collector such a costume was almost a museum piece. In spring, 1934, at Uélen, this local dress was grabbed by some visiting ladies. The Chukchians and eskimos do not use the heads of spectacled eiders in their dress. W. Percy acquired a small rug incorporating 10 heads of king and common eiders. F.S. Hersey referred to different decorations made by local residents using the heads of spectacled and common eiders together. S.A. Buturlin saw dressed bird skins in providence Bay. Similar articles were also in vogue on the Alaskan side of Bering Strait.

It goes without saying that this industry cannot enjoy extensive development because of the scarcity of spectacled eiders. From the viewpoint of preservation of this rare arctic bird it should not be encouraged. Modern ladies' wear avoids the bulk use of the skins of rare birds.

Systematics of the subspecies—I have with me 10 adult males and one two-year-old male and some young birds. A preliminary examination reveals the striking green coloration of the head of specimens from Indigirka and Yana, having a deep, dark shade, especially under the eyes. On the other hand, a single specimen from Alaska (brent type by description) was characterized by a remarkably long wing. It is difficult to find any perceptible geographical variability in the very limited material available with me.

The wing span of measured males is as follows (mm):

Alaska, Norton Sound, 1844	27.3				
Chukchi peninsula, my collection	26.7,	26.7,	26.6,	26.4,	25.3,
	25.2,	25.0			
Yana and Indigirka estuaries	27.0,	26.3,	26.2		

In the young specimens I noticed that the rust-colored fringes on the upper side of the body were broader, brighter and more colorful in the males than in the females: the latter appeared faded and gray.

A.M. Bailey, among others, referred to an adult male collected on June 9, 1922, in Wainwright. This bird had a V-shaped patch on the throat as in king eiders or in the Pacific subspecies of common eider, but it was brighter in the spectacled eiders. If this pattern does not turn out to be a random growth of summer feathers this characteristic could be of interest as a common genetic feature of eiders.

Specimens— 1) Cape Chaplin, April 23, 1902, ♂, Sokol'nikov; 2) Providence Bay, September 25, 1912, ♀, Starokadomskii; 3) same place, June 29, 1932, ♂, 2° anno, Portenko; 4) Uélen, September 18, 1933, ♂, 1° anno, Portenko; 5 and 6) same place, September 25 and October 1, 1933, ♀♀, 1° anno, Portenko; 7 to 10) same place, May, 1934 (heads); 11) same place, June 26, 1934, ♂, Portenko; 12 to 14) Mitkulen village, July 4, 1934, ♂♂, Portenko; 15 and 16) Uélen, July 29, 1934, ♂, sen., ♀, 2° anno, Portenko; 17) Wrangel Island, Amerikanskaya rivulet, June 15, 1939, ♀, 2° anno, Portenko; and 18 and 19) Uélen, May, 1940, ♂♂, sen., Portenko.

30. Somateria spectabilis (L.)—King Eider

Local name—Chukchian: Nakuatle; jekadlin in the records of the *Vega* expedition. In Eskimo: Amàgutak (collective sense) or knanalek (meaning "big-nosed") in Providence Bay; kăng-ă'-lik on St. Lawrence Island.

Distribution and status—Nests in small numbers on Wrangel Island and found commonly in the breeding areas on the north coast of the Chukchi peninsula.

In summer the nonbreeding birds join up to form huge flocks along the north and east coasts of the Chukchi peninsula and gather in very small numbers on the south coast, but not on Wrangel Island. In the spring flight it is quite common but very rare in the fall. It winters partly in Bering Strait, partly on the south coast of the Chukchi peninsula and in small numbers by the sea on St. Lawrence Island.

Distribution in the nesting period—Information on the nidification of king eiders is unfortunately incomplete and unreliable. As a rule, most observers regard the occurrence of king eiders in the nesting period as sufficient to confirm its nidification. Though this assumption would be in order for some birds, it would be erroneous in the case of most of the ducks, especially under the conditions of the Chukchi peninsula. The king eider nests in its third or fourth year. Consequently the number of juvenile nonbreeding birds is relatively high. Therefore the recording of a nest with a clutch or a brood or nonflying chicks can alone serve as proof of nidification.

L.O. Belopol'skii (1933 and 1934) writes that king eiders evidently nest in Krest Bay, though in smaller numbers than the common eider. He does not report any actual observations. According to I.O. Olenev the king eider evidently did not nest in Providence Bay. P.T. Butenko and I came to a similar conclusion based on our own observations. S.A. Buturlin (1935), who visited the Bay during his 1925 journey, reported seeing nonflying broods. Though it is more difficult to contradict than confirm it, I nevertheless do not regard this reference as reliable.

There are some references to nidification on St. Lawrence Island. These, too, are unreliable because of the absence of accurate data on nests or chicks. F.S. Hersey (1916) does not doubt the nesting of king eiders. The same is affirmed by J.C. Phillips (1926, p. 117) based on the unpublished data of the U.S. Biological Services. He writes that they nested on St. Lawrence Island in small numbers. F.H. Fay (Fay and Cade 1959) did not find nests and in the first two weeks of June, 1953, saw in all only three pairs of adult birds in breeding plumage. But the residents of Gambell said that they found the nests occasionally.

A.P. Kuzyakin did not find any nests of king eiders when traveling up the coast from Lawrence Bay to Uélen in 1957. I could not establish its breeding either in Lawrence Bay or around Uélen though I was experienced in locating its nests in Novaya Zemlya. During the breeding season at Uélen I made autopsies on some dozens of birds but could not detect gonad activity in any of them.

S.A. Buturlin (1935, vol. II, p. 142) writes that the king eider is a common breeding bird along the north coast of the Chukchi peninsula but does not provide any complete or reliable data. The Chukchians told the members of the *Vega* expedition (Palmén 1887) that this eider did not nest around Kolyuchin Bay. I did not find it on Kolyuchi Island. According to A.A. Kishchinskii, the king eider was a common nesting bird in the marine tundra from Vankarém to the Amguema not farther than 5 to 10 km inland from the shore or the lagoon. From July 15 through 18, 1970, he noticed a female on the tundra between Vankarém and Nutauge lagoon. He found a king eider with downy chicks on July 18 near Nutauge. Around the Ukouge lagoon, up to 50 king eiders inhabited a sample area of 48 km². Of them, evidently 22 pairs nested although only two nests were in fact found. In July, a brood was noticed and the ovary of a female showed signs of recent activity. Similar females were obtained in the lower course of the Amguema from July 3 through 6. Around the tundra Kishchinskii found pits with feathers and lumps of down, evidently from nests that had been destroyed. On one lake a king eider persistently returned to an islet and probably had its nest there. Two nests were found with clutches belonging to three females on an island in the Amguema lagoon. According to Kishchinskii, in the coastal belt that he examined the king eider was the most common desting duck after the old squaw.

V.M. Artobolevskii (1927) believed the king eider nested at Cape Schmidt since A.A. Savich collected a male and a female there in spring, 1915. According to V. Ya. Isaev the king eider in fact nested there, though in small numbers. He found at least four nests.

A flock of eiders including nonflying chicks was sighted by the members of the *Vega* expedition from September 9 through 11, 1878, not far from Cape Yakan. But the species of the eiders could not be conclusively established. According to É.V. Schmidt the king eider did not nest on Aiok Island or in the Karchyk peninsula. V.D. Lebedev and V.R. Filin (1959) did not find it in the nesting sites there either. It is difficult to understand A.I. Argentov's account (1861a) since he does not use the word "king eider". He calls the male a "motley hook-nosed marine scoter" and the female a "marine black duck" and classes them as migratory birds in the subdivision of arriving birds. Argentov writes (1861a, p. 495) that the hook-nosed motley scoter should also be placed in this division.

S.A. Buturlin regarded it as a common nesting bird in the tundra part of the Kolyma delta. J. Koren (Thayer and Bangs 1914) found a nest on one of the delta islands.

According to I.N. Gabrielson and F.C. Lincoln (1959), the zone of abundant nesting king eiders in Alaska begins only at Cape Barrow. As on the Asiatic side of the Bering Sea, information on nidification on the Alaskan coast is scanty and unreliable for the most part.

The king eider nests on Wrangel Island in very small numbers. On August 12, 1881, E.W. Nelson (1883) noticed a female with a chick swimming away from the shore near the Klér River estuary. In August, 1911, Capt. F.E. Kleinschmidt collected a king eider on the south coast of the island. According to G.A. Ushakov (Bannikov 1941) it was not a regular feature but it did nest. A clutch of two eggs and a young bird still in down with the wing feathers sprouting was taken on August 11, 1929. During his five-year sojourn on Wrangel Island A.I. Mineev did not see this eider at all in the nesting period. Tayan, however, told me that he was aware of at least two cases of nesting. On August 14, 1938, I noticed two females in Tundra Akademii under conditions that could be regarded as favorable for nidification. Later, on the south coast between Rodgers Bay and Krasnaya Glina, I found two broods of king eiders. Though the bird caught could already fly, it was so young that it could hardly have flown in from afar. The young female collected by N.M. Vakulenko on October 27, 1934, at Rodgers Bay was evidently a local bird.

Distribution of nonbreeding birds—A very large number of king eiders spend only the summer on the Chukchi coast. At Cape Gek, south of the Anadyr estuary, I sighted very small numbers of lone king eiders in the summer. According to L.O. Belopol'skii, they were more common on the north coast of Anadyr Bay. V.É. Yakobi told me about a male collected on June 30, 1961, in Uél'kal' from a mixed flock of males and females. In Providence Bay king eiders were common in the early summer but their numbers later gradually decreased. In July, 1912 and 1913, L.M. Starokadomskii and E.E. Arngol'd collected a single adult male there as an exception and more than 10 birds of two years which were undoubtedly lone birds. In early June, 1913, W.S. Brooks (1915) found king eiders very common in Providence Bay. A.M. Bailey (1925) observed them in Émma Bay in moderate numbers in the first week of July, 1921. According to I.O. Olenev there were almost no king eiders in Providence Bay in the summer of 1932. In 1938, I found them from July 11 through 14 in much smaller numbers than the common eiders. I found small flying flocks in which males predominated; on July 22, P.T. Butenko obtained two king eiders. I.N. Akif'ev (1904) brought a July male from Cape Chaplin.

Evidently king eiders were common in the summer on St. Lawrence Island, as E.W. Nelson reported. According to the observations of W.S. Brooks, they were common on June 2, 1913, near Cape Chibukak, where they had gathered in pairs and flocks. Again the presence of pairs in this case does not prove nidification. W. Percy recorded seeing juvenile eiders on the island. O.J. Murie (1936) gathered a whole series of 14 males and three females collected from August 6 through 9, 1935, in Kukuliak village. One of the four males obtained there on July 18 was evidently two years old. On August 13, 1934, a female was shot in Savunga. Sexual activity was not detected in any of the specimens. According to F.H. Fay and T.J. Cade, large flocks of two-year-olds were sighted from time to time at the end of June and in July, 1953, near Cape Tatik and in Savunga, and some near Kuzata lagoon. According to E.G.F. Sauer and E.K. Urban (1964), in June and early July, 1960, groups of king eiders in different numbers were found along the shore of Boxer Bay. On July 2 a pair was noticed in the valley of the Mogovelik River northwest of Puvupak hill. F.H. Fay (1961) thought that at least 2,000 lone two-year-old birds and a very small number of adult birds gathered in the sea and in the lagoons of the south coast in summer. They lived in flocks of up to 200 birds. H. Friedmann (1934a) found the bone remains of king eiders in 37 archaeological excavations which, in his opinion, proved its abundance in prehistoric times. He explained the absence of remains in Gambell village by a recent reduction in the population of king eiders. It is hardly possible to subscribe to these explanations and O.J. Murie was quite correct in rejecting them.

In mid-August, 1855, W. Stimpson noticed (Heine 1859, vol. III, p. 169) that king eiders were not very common in Sanyavin strait. The new species found among them were lone king eiders in complete breeding plumage; one specimen was collected (Cassin 1863, p. 323). According to É.W. Schmidt the king eider was collected very rarely in Mechigmensk Gulf. Summer males were collected by members of the *Vega* expedition on July 21, 1879, around Nunyamo village at the entrance to Lake Lawrence. In 1881, E.W. Nelson found large flocks in the bay. In 1921 the local residents told A.M. Bailey that this eider was encountered there in large numbers. Most recently, P.V. Ushakov gave a summer two-year-old male from there to the Institute of Zoology, Academy of Sciences of the USSR. However, according to Schmidt, who visited Lawrence Bay and Mechigmensk Gulf from 1913 through 1935, the king eider was encountered in small numbers even in Lawrence Bay. W. Percy (Phillips 1926, p. 120) reported that many nonbreeding king eiders were found on the coast from Lawrence Bay to Cape Dezhnev. His observations were made in

1914. In the summer of 1957 A.P. Kuzyakin found king eiders almost all along the coast from Akkani to Uélen. They were common though everywhere in smaller numbers than the common eiders. They were found in small flocks of a few dozen birds, independently and along with common eiders. Two-year-old birds predominated.

Large numbers of lone king eiders were found around Uélen. On July 20, 1879, the members of the *Vega* expedition (Palmén 1887) were given two males there; judging from the description, they were undoubtedly two-year-old birds. According to E.W. Nelson, king eiders were common on the Siberian shore of Bering Strait. Interesting information on bird populations is given by A.M. Bailey, who noticed a mass migration of king eiders at Uélen on July 12, 1921. According to him it was impossible to have any idea of the bird population as flocks were to be seen all of the time during some morning hours. They included all four species of eiders, king eiders abounding. A Capt. Cochran confided to A.M. Bailey that this abundance was nothing to what he had seen on his earlier expedition to Lawrence Bay. On August 1, 1928, F.L. Jaques (1930) saw stray flocks of male common or king eiders flying over the sea south of 68°30′ north on the Cape Dezhnev meridian. According to my observations at Uélen in 1933 and 1934, nonbreeding king eiders in flocks were to be seen day in, day out throughout the summer over the village. It was therefore a most convenient place for hunting almost any day, competing in this respect with Vankarém and Ryrkaipiya. These summer migrations, unlike the true spring and fall flights, involved flights in different directions. They are especially intense in foggy weather when the ducks appear restless. The migrations also depend on the condition of the sea and especially of the ice floes. Over Uélen, king eiders flew most often from the south, from the direction of Dezhnev settlement, and sometimes from the west. Passing over the long Uélen lagoon and turning toward Dezhnev settlement, they would circle the rocky cape and continue the journey over the sea. Mostly the flocks consisted of king eiders alone, sometimes with an admixture of common eiders but in a considerably smaller number. According to my observations, in the summer of 1934 lone king eiders predominated over all other species of eiders along the coast from Uélen to Mitkulen. My diary has many entries like "innumerable king eiders", "several flocks", "huge flocks", etc. King eiders did not gather on the Uélen waterfront because they were intensely persecuted there but innumerable lone eiders were found west of Mitkulen and south of Uélen between Dezhnev settlement and Lawrence Bay. Very large numbers of king eiders flew constantly past Mitkulen village and over Uélen settlement. Before the commencement of molting males predominated in the flocks; from mid-August females were abundant because the males were away to molt.

On June 27, 1909, J. Koren found a large number of eiders on the ice along the coast on his way to Cape Serdtse-Kamen'. They were so unsuspecting that a king eider was shot from the schooner. On July 9, 1881, E.W. Nelson noticed king eiders in considerable numbers at Cape Serdtse-Kamen'. W.S. Brooks also found huge flocks there on July 16, 1913. He was certain (Phillips 1926, p. 126) of having seen millions of them that day. However, it was an exaggeration and could not have been confirmed by actual count. J.C. Phillips rightly suggested that, in that particular case, the males and the nonbreeding females were on migration. W.S. Brooks noticed that the flocks were flying eastward but in mid-July, 1914, he noticed a few flocks of males flying westward over the arctic coast of Alaska at Cape Demarcation. More recently American ornithologists, especially A.M. Bailey, have established the summer migration of king eiders at the end of June and in July, the males mostly flying in large flocks from Cape Barrow to the southwest. It is not clear how far south this migration continues. My own observation on the Chukchi coast was that flocks of king eiders constantly flew over Mitkulen in an easterly direction. However, along the entire north coast of the Chukchi peninsula no one noticed any mass or planned migration in the summer from west to east. Evidently restricted local migrations took an easterly direction and the birds would later return over the sea far from the coast.

In the first half of the summer of 1879 king eiders for some reason were not noticed at all by the observers of the *Vega* expedition near Kolyuchin Bay. According to E.W. Nelson (1887, p. 79) these eiders were abundant in the summer of 1881 near Tjapka village and formed innumerable flocks along with Siberian eiders. In mid-July, 1909, J. Koren noticed hundreds of eiders flying daily over the coast from the western shore of the entrance to Kolyuchin Bay. He could not work out where such a large number of eiders nested and this confirmed the mass summer residence of lone birds.

In the last 10 days of July, 1938, on Kolyuchi Island I noticed flocks of king eiders, sometimes over the strait separating the island from the mainland. The Chukchians caught them as a matter of routine. E.W. Nelson (1883, pp. 99 and 101) very picturesquely described the abundance of king eiders together with other eiders which were sighted by the members of the *Corwin* expedition on August 5, 1881, during their visit to Vankarém. C.L. Hooper (1884, p. 61) writes that this place is full of eiders, especially king eiders. Evidently, I.C. Rosse (1883, p. 168) had this in mind when he referred to the incredible number of eiders on the Siberian coast. According to Nelson, king eiders together with Steller's eiders formed the bulk of the large flocks constantly flying over the estuary at Vankarém, coming back and so on. A considerable number of king eiders were presented by the Chukchians, who caught them using the eplicathet device. During my stay at Vankarém in spring, 1934, I was given to understand that the daily migrations of eiders at Vankarém exceeded those well known to occur in Uélen. In July, 1970, A.A. Kishchinskii found flocks of lone king eiders of different strengths among the ice in the sea between Vankarém and the Amguema 500 to 1,000 m from the shore, where common eiders also lived. One flock contained dozens of birds and another hundreds. All of them gradually moved southeast. Flocks of lone king eiders were also encountered at Cape Schmidt. References to this are found even in the works of A.I. Argentov (1861b, p. 9, footnote 2), who writes that large numbers of black ducks were seen on the Chukchi coast at the beginning of summer. In particular, they were hunted in Ryrkaipiya, where the black ducks moved along the sea coast and crossed through the low isthmus of a cape jutting into the sea. There is no doubt that the reference here is to a rubble spit joining Cape Kozhevnikov with the mainland. During my visit to Cape Schmidt in early August, 1938, there were daily hunts at this spit. But these did not interrupt the daily flights of birds. There the king eiders were in smaller numbers than all the other species of marine duck. J. Koren noticed many adult king eiders on the Ryrkaipiya River (Karpe River) on September 1, 1912. Copley Amory, Jr. (Riley 1918) saw large flocks there on August 13, 1914.

Two females, probably lone, were collected by Amory on August 18, on Aiok Island but he did not sight any eiders farther to the west. According to V.D. Lebedev and V.R. Filin (1959) flocks of females together with males were found throughout the summer of 1958 on the west shore of Chaun Bay, in Malyi Chaun Strait and on the west coasts of Aiok Island and the Karchyk peninsula.

In mid-July, 1912, J. Koren found large flocks of king eiders in female plumage on Cape Bol'shoi Baranov, especially in the broad valley 30 miles eastward.

On August 11, 1881, when the *Corwin* was approaching Wrangel Island, E.W. Nelson noticed king eiders sitting on the ice and coming within 50 or 60 paces of the ship. They later threw themselves into the water or flew away. There is no doubt that they were summer lone birds. According to the observations of V.F. Vlasova and A.I. Mineev, and according to my information, the king eider did not gather on the Wrangel coast or close to it for summer molting; however, a group of hunters who sailed far out to sea found two flocks of males on July 22, 1939. A female collected on July 15 of the same year near a tiny hut on Somnitel'naya Bay turned out to be a lone two-year-old bird.

According to S.M. Uspenskii and R.L. Bëme (Uspenskii, Bëme, and Velizhanin 1963) flocks of five to six females were sighted in Tundra Akademii on July 18 and 19, 1960. A bird collected turned out to be a juvenile, evidently a yearling. A.G. Velizhanin (1965) regarded the king eider as a fairly common species on the island. It was collected in June near the Klér River estuary; one was shot at Cape Chicherin and some in Rodgers and Somnitel'naya bays.

Distribution in spring flight—I have reported elsewhere (1939b, vol. II, p. 134) that the king eider was common in flight over the shores of Anadyr Bay. From there the eiders turned north in a straight line through the mountains. On June 8, 1956, I saw a huge flock of eiders flying over the knolls at Égvekinot and on June 13 noticed three female king eiders over the Amguema at the 91st km. Only small channels had begun to open up in the river. There I also noticed from afar a female king eider in a flight of old squaws. As will be seen later, the king eiders crossed the Anadyr Range overland. A special study of their course would probably throw some light on the island's position in the eastern part of the Chukchi peninsula in the geological past.

L.O. Belopol'skii collected two males and a female in a spring flight on Meechken Island. In Providence Bay, surrounded by the hills, no massive spring flight was noticed though the king eiders were not rare there in the spring. At Cape Chaplin P.T. Butenko noticed very early, brief spring flights. Evidently it is difficult to track the mass flights there because of local migrations at the end of winter. There is no doubt that in some cases a flock progresses northward off the Alaskan coast and in others nearer to the Chukchi peninsula. G.A. Hill's notes (1923, pp. 103 and 104) contain a reference to mass flights from April 10 through May 5, 1915, 30 miles from Nom. Flocks consisting of some long chains of birds following one another closely gave the impression of a continuous procession. This would go on for hours during the first week or 10 days in spite of the fact that there was no letup in the winter and the birds should have died in the snow-bound icy environment.

The photograph of a dead king eider illustrating Hill's article depicts a three-year old male. According to K. Kenyon (Kenyon and Brooks 1960) flocks of king eiders numbering four to 35 birds were sighted from Malyi Diomede Island between May 14 and June 2, 1958, in some cases flying low over the leads in the ice. The eskimos often caught them in the early spring and even in winter. J.W. Brooks noticed that in May, when the king eiders were flying in the north in large numbers at Cape Prince of Wales, they were relatively few in numbers on Malyi Diomede Island.

Near Uélen, according to my observations, the spring flight was in two waves: first the king eiders hurrying to their northern breeding grounds; then the non-breeding birds. In spring, 1934, an appreciable number of flying eiders was seen in the first wave only in two cases in the immediate neighborhood of Uélen: about 200 birds on May 1 and huge flocks on May 9. Evidently Uélen falls on the main flight course. King eiders either crossed the Bering Strait in the east or reached the Arctic Ocean after crossing the land mass and the Anadyr Range. In May, 1934, I followed the sled route along the north coast of the Chukchi peninsula and twice saw flocks heading for the sea from the direction of the mountains inland to the south: on May 11 in Vankarém and on May 17 above the estuary of the Nétte-Véem River between Neshkan and Énurmino. Probably the spring of 1934 was an exception: the flight of eiders overland was caused by the fact that the southern part of Cape Dezhnev was long snow-bound in 1934. At least, the Chukchians in Uélen complained that the flight of eiders there that year was very poor because of the ice conditions, as they put it. The few king eiders seen by W.S. Brooks at Cape Dezhnev on June 7, 1913, and a specimen collected by Sheneberg at Uélen on June 4, 1927, were perhaps still migratory birds.

According to the observations of the members of the *Vega* expedition, king eiders in flight were not a rarity near Kolyuchin Bay in spring, 1879. A reference has already been made to my observations in Vankarém. According to V.Ya. Isaev the king eider was commonly seen in flights at Cape Schmidt. According to a report by É.V. Schmidt it was common in spring flight on Aiok Island and adjoining the Karchyk peninsula; it was sighted in flights even over the lowlands of the Chaun River, though rarely. Depending on the ice conditions, the flight was sometimes close inshore and sometimes over the sea farther out. I believe the two references by F.P. Wrangel (1841) could be to the flight of king eiders over the ice field between Chaun Bay and the Medvezhii Islands. The first observation was on April 30 (18), 1822, around 71°18′ north and 4°4′ east[1] reckoning from Bolshoi Baranov Kamen', i.e. roughly one degree north of Aiok Island. In travel records (Wrangel, vol. II, p. 171), it is said that the signs of approaching spring were evident at night: a large flock of black ducks (*Anas nigra*) flying NW often covered huge ice floes drifting off northern Siberia. The second observation was at 70°54′ north and 3°12′ east, reckoned as before. It was on May 6 (April 24). On p. 176 of his work, we read that innumerable flocks of black ducks high overhead stretched to the west in the evening. I have already stated[2] that black ducks should be understood to mean female

[1]Argentov (1861b, p. 8), referring to this place, gave the longitude as 4° 36′ east from Bol'shoi Baranov Kamen'.

[2]A.F. Middendorf, however, was of a different view (1869, Travels in North and East Siberia, part II, Section V, Siberian fauna, p. 874, footnote). According to him the black ducks seen by

king eiders and that A.I. Argentov reckoned king eiders among the migratory birds of the Chukchi coast to the west of Yakan.

King eiders in spring flight are encountered every year on Wrangel Island. According to G.A. Ushakov they were common in flight. On the south coast, according to A.I. Mineev, they were sometimes seen in flocks flying over the sea past Rodgers Bay, but were generally rare. In the spring of 1939, hunters saw them in Somnitel'naya Bay initially in small and later in large flocks. Later they were seen at different times over the shore of Rodgers Bay but remained rare. I did not see a single bird in the spring. The Chukchians and eskimos told me that king eiders flew mostly along the northern coast of the island and in fairly large numbers of flocks of different sizes. The eiders and ducks in flight mentioned without further identification of their species in De Long's account (1883) of the drifting of the *Jeannette* from Herald to Jeannette and Henrietta islands can for this reason be regarded justifiably as king eiders. On April 30, 1880, a flock of about 20 eiders of unknown species was noticed north of Wrangel around 73° north. The birds, flying high to the west were, as De Long confidently puts it, proceeding toward some land. Next year, on May 6, 1881, to the southeast of Henrietta Island, a flock of some ducks was noticed flying to the west. On May 14 the reference was even more accurate: eiders of unknown species were noticed flying in flocks in the same westerly direction until midday. Next day the *Jeannette* was at 76°43′20″ North and 161°53′45″ East. At midday on May 29 a huge flock of up to 500 ducks flying low to the north utterly surprised the observers. It was still closer to Henrietta Island: two days before the ship was at 77°14′45″ North and 159°16′ East. It is a shame that no precise identification of the birds was made.

Distribution in fall flight—No large fall flight has been noticed so far on Wrangel Island.

Along the north coast of the Chukchi peninsula, in the fall, the king eiders fly sometimes close inshore, sometimes far out to sea, depending on the ice conditions. In the large flocks of eiders noticed by the members of the *Vega* expedition between Chaun and Kolyuchin bays, king eiders were also present. V.Ya. Isaev told me that this eider was very common at Cape Schmidt in both flights. I did not notice a mass fall flight at Uélen. In the fall of 1933 the population of king eiders gradually decreased and there was no flocking before migration. There were more eiders in the summer than in the fall.

The fall flight was altogether slight on St. Lawrence Island. O.J. Murie collected only some migratory specimens: six in September, a female in Kukuliak village on September 20, 1934, five males and three females in October and November, 1935, and finally a male on November 6, 1935.

On the south coast of the Chukchi peninsula the fall flight was not seen. As may be judged from the observations of I.O. Olenev and P.T. Butenko, king eiders appeared in Providence Bay from the north quite late for wintering in open water in-

Wrangel should be regarded as brent geese, all the more because they are generally called ducks and not geese in northern Siberia. The fact that Kiber referred to them as *Anas nigra* does not mean anything since there is positive proof that he would assign the most impossible zoological name. The early date of F.P. Wrangel's observations means they could not refer to late-arriving brent geese.

shore. On August 26, 1932, I found in a bay a small flock of females probably spending the whole of the summer there.

Distribution during wintering—This depends on the condition of the ice floes. King eiders sometimes winter even in the northern part of Bering Strait. According to J. Koren, in 1912/1913 they wintered in considerable numbers together with old squaws on the Diomede Islands. However, in 1932, I could not find a single eider after the winter set in for keeps in Uélen.

F.H. Fay (1961) wrote that the water surrounding St. Lawrence Island represented a large area for the wintering of king eiders. In February, 1953, for example, flocks numbering up to 15,000 birds were noticed.

In the exposed part of the sea along the south coast of the Chukchi peninsula king eiders represented a fairly constant feature in winter. According to P.T. Butenko's observations, in early 1938 they were as frequent at Cape Chaplin as common eiders and old squaws. According to the local eskimos they wintered there regularly. As established by I.O. Olenev and P.T. Butenko, king eiders were also found in winter in Providence Bay when the ice opened up there. According to L.O. Belopol'skii, they wintered in large numbers near Cape Bering. On March 14, 1931, around Vtoroi Red'kin Bay, he found a flock comprising king and common eiders numbering 2,000 to 2,500 birds.

Habitat—According to A.A. Kishchinskii, around the Ukouge lagoon pairs of king eiders made their homes at the lakes on the tundra right from the time of arrival, more often on rocky mossy-sedge than on wet, grassy tundras. In July, broods were found on the lakes near the Nutauge lagoon and on the lower course of the Amguema. King eiders nested on the islets in the lake or in the lagoon. They gathered in groups at the feeding grounds and small flocks of birds that had lost their clutches were seen on the lakes. V.Ya. Isaev told me that he found a nest near a place where there were nests of common eiders. A nest found by J. Koren in the Kolyma delta was located 10 feet from the shore of a small lake on one of the islands in the delta. On August 14, 1938, on Wrangel Island south of Bruch spit, I saw two instances of females flying low over the tundra from the rivulet to the islets. Evidently they also nested near the lakes. The locality very much resembled the one where I found a nest in July, 1930, on Novaya Zemlya in Belushaya Gulf.

Nonbreeding king eiders live like true marine birds in the summer. L.O. Belopol'skii correctly pointed out that the king eider rarely went beyond the strait running deep inland, containing freshened water. According to É.V. Schmidt, in the summer nonbreeding king eiders lived not so much in Lawrence Bay as on the adjoining open sea. On the lagoons at Uélen I did not find king eiders in the summer as I had on the lagoons at Cape Schmidt, but they abounded on the shore. Nevertheless, in response to ill health caused by molting the king eiders would penetrate to the lagoon at the end of the summer to escape inhospitable winter. On August 24, 1934, I found a small number of king eiders on a lagoon fed by the Kol'oam-Véem River. They were sheltering from the strong wind in the tiny protected bays along with flocks of old squaws just beginning to molt. A few king eiders were swimming on the large Uélen lagoon, staying near the banks protected from the wind. On finding more abundant food near the ice floes king eiders, like other marine arctic birds, are drawn to the ice. They perform local migrations depending on the ice conditions. This phenomenon is also seen during the spring flight but it should not be concluded that the flight itself consists only of migrations following the ice drift. On the contrary, as stated earlier, king eiders are not deterred by land masses. They pass through mountain ranges and fly long distances over compact ice until they find a convenient polynya. There is no doubt that some king eiders migrate north along with the ice if the latter does not settle down as stable pack ice because of unfavorable weather conditions. On May 25, 1934, near Cape Dezhnev, I saw a huge male swimming among the ice floes and evidently somewhat delayed in his northward journey. I noticed how well the complete breeding plumage of the king eider merged with the pale blue hummocks, snow and greenish sea water. According to I.O. Olenev king eiders were found in Providence Bay as long as the ice remained there.

During the fall flight, I found young birds almost alone on a large lagoon at Uélen. They were mainly confined to the banks, avoiding the waves in the middle of the lagoon. In the fall of 1938, on Wrangel Island, I often found young king eiders on the coast between Rodgers Bay and Krasnaya Glina. They were also found right on the shore.

According to P.T. Butenko's observations, in the fall of 1937, the king eiders arriving for wintering remained more than one month in the hinterland of Providence Bay until the ice formed. In the winter he noticed king eiders at Cape Chaplin, where the birds were confined to the thin ice with leads, avoiding the pack ice. They were found comparatively rarely in the open sea. King eiders were seen in large numbers when the south wind set the ice in motion, driving it north. According to J. Koren, in the 1912/1913 season, king eiders wintered on the Diomede Islands in the polynyas among the floes. L.O. Belopol'skii noticed that king eiders wintered on the open water near Cape Bering.

Spring flight and arrival—The commencement and duration of the spring flight on the south coast of the Chukchi peninsula are difficult to determine since the wintering grounds are also located there. On Meechken Island, positively migratory birds were found by L.O. Belopol'skii on May 14, 1931. In his 1938 diary P.T. Butenko recorded sighting king eiders regularly at Cape Chaplin from January through March 23. They were not seen again until April 23, when they were sighted along with ravens, gulls and ducks of other species on the same day. In Plover Bay, Providence Bay, a migratory male was collected much later, on May 17.

According to F.H. Fay, after the old squaws the king eiders were the earliest and most common of migratory birds on the west coast of St. Lawrence Island. They were seen in abundance around April 25 and were flying north over the ice, with interruptions, for a month.

In the spring of 1934 the arrival of king eiders coincided with my journey from Cape Schmidt to Uélen. Therefore my observations cover the entire section of the north coast of the Chukchi peninsula that I traversed. On April 7 I was informed at Uélen that two flocks of eiders had been sighted that day flying north-south. This direction quite elearly indicated a late winter migration. On May 1 the news broke at Cape Schmidt that the "geese" had been seen flying over the sea in the morning. I had no doubt that they were eiders. As we learned later, on the same day eiders were sighted in Vankarém. What is more, about 200 of them were seen flying east at Uélen. On May 2 P.T. Butenko saw a flock and a solitary eider on a lead in the ice at Uélen. On the evening of May 8 three eiders flew overhead along the shore at Vankarém. The sea was still completely covered with hummocks and snow. On the 9th a flock flew over the sea. At Uélen that day a huge flock of eiders was seen in continuous flight from Dezhnev settlement to the north. On the evening of May 11 at Vankarém I saw a huge flock flying in from the south. In the preceding instances it was not known which species of eider was involved, but on May 11 I was able to ascertain that the flock consisted of king eiders, most of them males. Before reaching Cape Serdtse-Kamen' on May 17 I saw a huge flock of king eiders flying in from the south over the Nétte-Véem River estuary beside the sea. Finally, approaching Uélen on May 21 I noticed from time to time how the eiders flew over the spit. But when I came specially to the spit on May 24 to collect them I could not find one. The flight of king eiders had ended around the 20th. The flight of eiders at Uélen was very scanty in spring, 1934, but among the fowl obtained by the local hunters in that season I found quite a few king eiders. At the end of May I came across mostly solitary birds; on May 25 a male bird was found swimming among the ice floes at Cape Dezhnev. On May 31 a male was seen flying over the strait cutting across Uélen spit. On June 1 another solitary bird was seen swimming off Uélen far out to sea.

In the spring of 1879 observations were made on bird arrival by the members of the *Vega* expedition near Kolyuchin Bay. On May 8 six female eiders were noticed flying east. A Chukchian reported that he saw a large number of king eiders on May 9. Some species of eider was sighted on May 14; it is possible that some lived among the large flocks of old squaws flying on the same day. Next day F.R. Chel'man saw a pair flying past the ship. On May 22 the members of the expedition were presented with a male king eider obtained in the interior of the Chukchi peninsula, another from Neshkan and a female from Dzhenretlen; on May 31 this species was accurately recognized among hundreds of flocks of eiders.

O. Nordquist shot a female on a polynya and upon dissection found small follicles in a cluster-shaped ovary. The biggest of the follicles did not exceed 3.5 mm in diameter. In all 110 to 120 of them were counted. Next day the sailors found three males and a female in the same polynya. On June 5 a male was brought from Irgunnuk and on June 11 another from Neshkan, after which king eiders were not seen again. There is no doubt that this abrupt diappearance of the king eiders would not have occurred if they had remained there in the breeding area.

As stated above, on April 30, 1822, the members of F.P. Wrangel's expedition saw a large flock, probably of king eiders, roughly one degree north of Aiok Island. The birds were flying over the ice field in the night in a northwesterly direction. On May 6 innumerable flocks were sighted one degree westward. Flying at a great height in the evening the birds stretched away toward the west. According to É.V. Schmidt, on Aiok Island and in Karchyk peninsula king eiders in spring flight were innumerable up to June 10, but then disappeared.

In spring, 1939, king eiders were seen on May 17 on the Wrangel Island coast, initially in small groups and later in large flocks. They were noticed for several days thereafter but in smaller numbers.

The dates of arrival given above all agree that the first king eiders were not seen before the last few days of April, usually in early May, in the Chukchi peninsula and only in mid-May on Wrangel Island. The flight ceased in the last 10 days of May or in the first 10 days of June.

Migrations and summer residence of nonbreeding king eiders—A little after the completion of the flight of king eiders breeding in the north the nonbreeding birds gradually assembled to spend the summer and molt. According to F.H. Fay (1961) flocks of two-year-old king and Steller's eiders were often noticed in the sea off St. Lawrence Island and also along the southern bank of the lagoons. They remained there from mid-June to early September. In early June, 1934, king eiders were not a regular feature at Uélen since they did not nest on the surrounding tundra. They were seen sometimes during their migration, only to disappear again. Uélen hunters went far out to sea on June 3 and brought back some king eiders including two-year-old males. This was the first confirmation of the arrival of lone eiders. On June 12 I noticed numerous eiders flying over the sea. They were exclusively king eiders. On June 17 both king and common eiders were seen on some open water in the shore ice; there were some Steller's eiders too. On June 20, I observed eiders on my way from Uélen to Naukan and on July 2 on my way from Uélen to Inchoun; the birds were flying in groups in which males predominated.

Flocks consisting exclusively of males were a striking feature. In the early morning of July 3, on my way from Inchoun to Mitkulen, I noticed small flocks of eiders in flight, king eiders more often than other species. In the evening flocks of king eiders continued to fly intermittently over the coast at Mitkulen. From the morning of July 4 there was an intense fog and the movement of eiders became more frequent, king eiders predominating. The groups moved in one direction from west to east; they also flew in the evening in the same direction. The daily rhythm of flights in the early morning and evening, in spite of the bright nights, was obvious. Returning to Mitkulen on July 13, I found the same picture of local movement of eiders, king eiders predominating as before. During daylight on July 20, on my way from Mitkulen to Inchoun, I came across king eiders swimming between the ice floes and resting on them. Next day I returned to Uélen and on my way saw huge flocks of eiders, mostly king eiders, flying in from the sea. On July 28, over Uélen, numerous flocks, king eiders usually predominating, were seen in flight. But what was interesting was that the flocks consisted almost exclusively of males, females predominating only in some flocks. This isolation of the sexes was no doubt due to the differences between the molting periods of males and females; the males at that time not only separated but also gathered in very large flocks. On August 9, I went by boat along the length of the Uélen lagoon. Flocks of eiders were flying overhead without interruption. They included king eiders. In the main each species of bird was flying separately. Returning to the sea coast on August 24, I again encountered king eiders. Some of them were found in the lagoon, perhaps in the course of molting. Above Uélen, eiders were flying as before, mostly king eiders.

In 1933, I arrived at Uélen on August 15 and found the very same picture of daily flights, especially on cloudy, foggy days. King eiders were flying in large numbers but the flocks consisted almost exclusively of females. Males were no more to be seen until the fall was well advanced. I could not ascertain where they had gathered in large numbers for molting.

The above observations on king eiders made in the summer around Uélen convinced me that only non-nesting birds were encountered there. Dissection of a large number of birds and measurement of the gonads fully confirmed this surmise. It may be seen from Table 23 that in January and February the size of testes in adult and juvenile males was roughly the same. With the onset of spring there was no increase whatever in the size of testes of the two-year-old males, that of males three years old and up showed an increase, though slight (compare also with the Table showing the testis measurements of common eiders) and sexual activity was not detected in a single testis (even in enlarged ones). At the end of June and early July a reduction in the size of testes to the normal size was noticed. In an exactly similar way the ovary length in females in winter remained roughly the same in adult and juvenile birds; structural differences in the ovaries were more appreciable (Table 24). In the young birds the ovary surface was fairly smooth but a granular structure was found in the adults. Two-year-old females collected at Uélen on June 12, 1934, had ovaries of fine-grained structure and measuring 26 mm in length. The ovary length in two-year-olds taken from Wrangel Island on July 15, 1939, was 19 mm and the diameter of the biggest follicle was 3 mm. Of several famales dissected, a cluster-shaped ovary structure was detected only in one bird shot at Uélen on October 1, 1933. This confirmed breeding in the preceding summer. The diameter of the biggest follicle in the ovary of this bird was 5 mm. Judging from the advanced time of year, it could have wandered into Uélen with a brood from the far northwestern parts of the Chukchi peninsula.

Breeding—According to the observations of A.A. Kishchinskii king eiders were seen in pairs from June 6 through 8 and especially from June 10 through 12, 1970, around the Ukouge lagoon (Fig. 32). During the latter half of June the males gradually left the females. On July 17 the first flock was noticed wandering from the tundra to the sea; after June 30 males were found in flocks only off the coast. On June 8 N.I. Makurin scared a female from a nest in which there were two eggs but there was no downy lining. The nest was located in a wet, hummocky marsh beside the lake. On June 21 A.A. Kishchinskii found a nest with a clutch of five eggs. It was on flat, fairly wet mossy-sedge tundra 80 m from a lake and was lined with the previous year's down and sedge. The female was incubating but the nest was found destroyed on July 1. From July 3 through 6 a female was seen in a lake on the tundra on the lower reaches of the Amguema. The nest was evidently located on an islet inhabited by a colony of herring and glaucous gulls. On July 3, on an islet in the Amguema lagoon, two more nests were found among a colony of gulls (Fig. 33). On the same islet there were two pairs of brent geese and around 20 female common eiders. Nests of king eiders were found 50 cm from each other and 80 cm from the nest of a gull. They contained four and six eggs. On July 11 Kishchinskii found broods of females and seven downy chicks on a lake near the Ukouge lagoon. From July 15 through 18, around Nutauge lagoon, a group of females which had probably lost their clutches or chicks was noticed. On July 18 a female with three downy chicks was seen. In the Kolyma delta J. Koren found a nest on June 26, 1912. It was built in the grass and contained the broken shells of two fresh eggs' evidently drained by a pair of glaucous gulls which nested nearby. A pair of king eiders was seen swimming on the lake not far away. According to V.Ya. Isaev, who found four nests at Cape Schmidt, there were not more than five eggs in a clutch.

Table 23. Size of testis of king eiders, mm

Date and locality	Older than 3 years		3-year-olds		2-year-olds	
	left	right	left	right	left	right
Jan. 31 through Feb. 14,	12×3	10×2	—	—	14×5	12×4
Cape Chaplin	11×3	10×2	—	—	12×2	10×2
	11×2	10×2	—	—	11×2	10×2
	10×3	9×2	—	—	10×3	8×2
	—	—	—	—	10×3	8×2
	—	—	—	—	10×2	9×2
May 31 through June 16,	22×11	18×9	21×7	16×7	15×3	12×3
Uélen	16×7	14×7	19×11	13×8	14×5	10×4
	—	—	19×6	—	11×3	8×2
	—	—	17×7	14×7	10×4	8×3
	—	—	14×7	12×6	10×4	8×3
	—	—	14×5	11×4	—	—
June 21 through July 4,	16×10	14×8	14×7	10×6	12×3	8×3
Naukan, Uélen and	14×5	10×4	14×6	11×6	—	—
Mitkulen	14×4	10×4	12×5	8×3	—	—
	10×5	8×4	—	—	—	—
	10×3	8×2	—	—	—	—
July 29, Uélen	14×5	10×4	—	—	—	—
Oct. 15, Uélen	—	—	—	—	15×6	14×6

Table 24. Ovary length of female king eiders, mm

Date and locality	Older than 2 years	2-year-olds	Yearlings
June 12, Uélen	—	26	—
Nov. 6 through 19,	—	24	23
Providence Bay	—	—	22
Jan. 30 through Feb. 14,	16	15	—
Cape Chaplin	15	14	—
	—	13	—
	—	13	—
	—	12	—
	—	10	—

My observation on Wrangel Island in the fall of 1938 was that the hatching of the young was much delayed. On September 14 I found some young king eiders at the exit of Rodgers Bay and a brood of four birds later near Krasnaya Glina. A specimen taken turned out to be less than one year old. A month later, on October 15, I came down to the shore by crossing the lagoon on foot—it was already frozen—and later walked to Rodgers spit. Four young unwary king eiders were seen on the shore: the pancake ice prevented them from swimming far. Possibly it was these same four birds that were seen on October 31 flying over the coast from east to west.

Molting—Systematic observations in the summer near Uélen and examination of a large number of specimens which were collected, particularly a beautiful set of winter birds taken by P.T. Butenko at Cape Chaplin, enabled the stages of molting and change of plumage to be traced fairly thoroughly. In males, up to seven molts ending in the third summer and in females up to six ending in the third winter-spring were distinguished. After these there are no changes in the adults with advancing age. I have described in detail all these plumages and the course of molting in a special article (Portenko 1952). The changes in the amount of subcutaneous adipose layers in relation to molting are also discussed in the article.

Fall flight—On Wrangel Island the local broods were invariably late. N.M. Vakulenko collected a young female on October 27, 1934. In 1938, I found a weaned brood for the last time on October 31 but Tayan found a female king eider in Somnitel'naya Bay as late as November 21.

In the fall of 1878 the members of the *Vega* expedition made some observations on the flight of eiders but unfortunately the species was not accurately identified. On September 5 a large flock of eiders was noticed from the ship to the west of of Chaun Bay; some birds were seen on September 7 and 8 around 69°25′ north and 177°40′ east, slightly east of Cape Yakan. Not far from there, from September 9 through 11, a flock of 10 to 15 eiders was seen with nonflying chicks. On the same day thousands of eiders were seen flying along the coast eastward. From September 12 through 16, at Cape Schmidt, there were innumerable flocks of eiders flying in the same direction along with flocks coming in from the north and joining them. On September 18 O. Nordquist saw a different-sized flock. On October 13 a flock was noticed from the wintering station of the *Vega* stretching away to the east. A very large flock of eiders or old squaws was seen flying eastward on October 19.

According to my observations, in the fall of 1933, at Uélen, when the lone males began to wander for molting the females continued to make daily flights over the village. In the first 10 days of September they were still numerous but later their numbers were much reduced, dropping sharply after the cold winds from September 18 through 22. In foggy weather large flocks sometimes flew over the village. In my excursions on the Uélen lagoon on October 1, 3 and 5, young king eiders were found almost exclusively still in broods and rarely in flocks. An eskimo riding into Naukan from Dezhnev settlement reported seeing many eiders on the coast on October 7. Even on October 16 a flock of king eiders flew toward me. From time to time flocks of eiders, sometimes very large ones, were seen even later, but the king eiders could not be identified accurately in a single case because of distance. I was informed of the last flock, consisting of about 50 eiders, on December 4. Some species of lone eider was noticed even on January 4. In general, at the end of October king eiders ceased to be a common feature at Uélen.

On crossing Bering Strait in mid-September, 1881, E.W. Nelson noticed many flocks of this species together with common eiders. According to F.H. Fay, king eiders returned to St. Lawrence Island from the north in December with the ice floes.

In the fall of 1937 P.T. Butenko arrived in Providence Bay on October 29 and saw king eiders there for a month, right up to November 30. This date can be regarded as the migration date. On December 22, a strong southerly wind broke the ice in the bay and the flight of sea birds, including king eiders, was noticed for many hours thereafter. From January 11, 1938, P.T. Butenko visited Cape Chaplin off and on and every time found that the king eiders were spending the winter there on the coast among the ice floes. This species was recorded in his diary regularly until March 23 inclusive. This date exactly marked the end of wintering and the start of the spring advancement northward in 1938.

Habits—W. Percy (Phillips 1926, p. 122) writes that on the north coast of the Chukchi peninsula the king eiders often form common flocks with spectacled but not with Steller's eiders. According to my observations, here as also in Novaya Zemlya, nonbreeding king eiders stayed freely in common flocks with common eiders. In the Chukchi peninsula I never found large mixed flocks of king and spectacled eiders but the joining of king with common eiders to form common flocks was a regular phenomenon.

Eskimo hunters at Cape Chaplin told me that eiders sometimes literally go blind in misty winter weather due to the rime forming on their eyelids.

Food—The stomachs of 10 king eiders that I collected on June 12, 1934, at Uélen revealed the following contents: 1) Tiny pieces of shells of some dozens of molluscs, bits of some leathery formation and about 20 tiny stones. 2) Tiny pieces of shell of some dozens of molluscs and about 10 tiny stones up to 2 cm in diameter. 3) Twenty to 30 molluscs of which about 10 were prosobranchs. Bits of leathery formation and seven tiny stones. 4) About 50 molluscs of which about 10 were prosobranchs. Leathery formations. 5) Amorphous gruel of animal origin containing many needles. About 100 tiny stones up to 1.5 cm in diameter. 6) Some dozens of molluscs, mainly bivalves, of which eight were whole. Three pieces of leathery formation. Three tiny stones. 7) About 10 molluscs, of these two or three bivalves, and fragments of crab legs. Bits of leathery formation. Three large teeth of fish and three tiny stones. 8) Pieces of shell of six molluscs and 14 tiny stones up to 1.5 cm in diameter. 9) Tiny pieces of shell and soft portions of some dozen bivalve molluscs. 10) Pieces of shell and soft portions of about 50 molluscs, mainly bivalves.

The stomach of a king eider collected on Wrangel Island on September 15, 1938, contained the remains of molluscs *Astarte* sp. They occupied three-fourths of the capacity of the stomach. The stomach also contained 4 g of pebbles up to 7 to 15 mm in diameter.

In the gullet of a female collected on May 31, 1879, at the wintering post of the *Vega* O. Nordquist found *Cardium* swallowed whole and parts of molluscs and crustaceans in its stomach. The stomach of a male from Irgunnuk obtained on June 5 contained parts of *Hyas aranea* and shells of *Margarita*. The stomach of a male taken there on July 13 contained parts of *Hyas aranea*, *Pleurotoma* (?) and broken shells of molluscs, among which pieces of *Fusus* style could be identified.

Weight—According to the weights taken by P.T. Butenko, a May male weighed 1,710 g. The females obtained in November and December weighed 1,595, 1,540, 1,510, 1,450, 1,435, 1,375 and 1,370 g. A two-year-old July female from Wrangel Island weighed 1,080 g.

Economic importance—Among the fowl in the Chukchi peninsula king eiders occupy a prime position for eating and hunting. This eider is collected on the sea coast almost everywhere and in some places where there are massive daily movements of nonbreeding birds hunting acquires commercial proportions. It has its own characteristics which are not found elsewhere on the Siberian coast. This hunting has been described in relation to common eiders and is not repeated here. The hunting affects equally the king and common eiders. The best-known places for large-scale hunting during diurnal migrations are Uélen, Vankarém and Cape Schmidt. In the past, hunting with eplicathet devices predominated but now even the local people have largely taken to hunting with guns. Newly arrived hunters apparently could never master the use of the eplicathet. However profitable the hunting may be, it never results in reckless slaughter since the shooting of an eider in flight is certainly more difficult than, for example, stunning a molting bird with a stick after driving it into a net. During my stay at Uélen in the summer a few hundred eiders were obtained. The tempo of this hunting could only lead to scaring the flock away, thereby automatically interrupting hunting. The more diligent of the hunters killed only a few dozen king eiders, mostly for their own consumption. Dressing of meat as practiced here was not very effective but hard bargains were driven and the dead fowl were sold at arbitrary prices by particular people. The need for fresh meat is especially felt by people in the spring after passing the polar winter. King eiders therefore represent a very desirable fowl with tasty meat almost devoid of marine aftertaste or smell. Many people feel that the meat of king eiders is more tasty than that of common eiders.

As soon as leads formed in the shore ice Uélen hunters rushed to the edge. They sat on the ice for hours waiting for the flocks to arrive. Somewhat later the hunters set out in motorized skin canoes and, negotiating the ice, shot everything that moved. King eiders were often their quarry. When walrus approached the Uélen coast, shooting was prohibited in the village and then the field was left to hunters capable of using the silent eplicathets. In summer, around Inchoun and Mitkulen, the local hunters took many eiders which made daily migrations, mostly in foggy weather. Some sailed the skin canoes and others sat on the ice and the shore. The former had to kill the wounded birds and gather the dead ones. Late in the fall the juveniles were hunted by canoe along the lagoons where wandering broods were seen. Young people with a fairly good motorized canoe would stop the motor on approaching the birds. With their patience, perseverance and northern temperament they could come within 40 to 50 paces. These hunts are particularly successful when large areas of the lagoon are covered with ice. The hunters then take advantage of favorable weather (eiders usually take off against the wind) together with the inability of the birds to swim far because of the ice.

At Cape Chaplin winter hunts were organized from the coast under favorable weather conditions ensuring the return of the dead bird to shore with the waves. On the surf line it would be picked up with the hooks used in hunting seal. The king eider is a rare bird only on Wrangel Island.

In the factory at Cape Schmidt I saw some male king eider skins worked up by the local Chukchians into fur garments. It was the fashion even at Uélen, when I was there, to make carpets and collars of eider skins, though the king eider was found in small numbers among numerous spectacled eiders.

Sometimes the local residents, following an Alaskan custom, use eider skins to line mattresses in place of dry hay, which has to be changed often. The bird skin has the advantage that it is impermeable to moisture from below on the fatty flesh side.

On St. Lawrence Island, according to F.H. Fay, not more than 200 eiders of both species were collected in the winter. Nearly as many were eaten by snowy owls and gyrfalcons.

Systematics of the subspecies—I have used the material available in the collections of the Institute of Zoology and the Arctic Institute and studied more than 200 specimens for intraspecific affinities. There has been no attempt so far to describe the subspecies of king eiders. A comparison of the beaks of king eiders from different parts of the Arctic did not reveal any differences either in size or in shape. But there could probably be same local differences in the color and the prominence on the forehead. The wing measurements of 107 male three-year and older birds did not reveal any geographic localization of this character in any arctic sector. In my Chukchi series I have many comparatively short-winged specimens (mean wing

Table 25. Wing span of king eiders, cm

Age	Males				Females			
	Max.	Min.	Mean	No. of samples	Max.	Min.	Mean	No. of samples
3 years and older	29.5	26.3	28.0	107	29.1	26.0	27.3	57
2 years	27.5	24.9	26.1	27	27.1	24.4	25.6	25

span 27 mm) but they are mostly three-year-olds. In most of the old males the wings are long (28 cm or more). Sharp agewise differences are seen not only in the males but also in females (Table 25).

The king eider is no doubt the nearest kin of the common eider, whose subspecies show similarities in some features. The V-shaped patch on the throat characteristic of king eiders is also present in some subspecies of common eider. The shape of the bill in ***Somateria mollissima dresseri*** Sharpe is somewhat similar to that of king eiders. Hybrids between the two species of eiders are known (Portenko 1952).

Specimens— 1) Cape Chaplin, July 12, 1900, ♂, 3° anno, Akif'ev; 2 to 4) Providence Bay, July 18, 1912, ♂♀♀, 2° anno, Starokadomskii; 5) same place, July 20, 1912, ♂, 2° anno, Arngol'd; 6) same place, September 25, 1912, ♀, 1° anno, Starokadomskii; 7) Émma Bay, September 2, 1913, ♂, 2° anno, Starokadomskii; 8 to 10) same place, August 2, 1914, ♂, sen., ♀♀, 2° anno, Starokadomskii; 11) Chukchi peninsula, May 21, 1927, ♂, 2° anno, Sheneberg; 12 and 13) Uélen, June 4 and July 8, 1927, ♀♂; 14) Wrangel Island, June 20, 1929, ○, G.A. Ushakov; 15) Lawrence Bay, July 31, 1929, ♂, 2° anno, P.V. Ushakov; 16 and 17) Meechken Island, May 14 and June 1, 1931, ♂♂, Belopol'skii; 18) Providence Bay, July 1932, ♀, 2° anno, Olenev; 19) Cape Schmidt, without date, 1933, ♂, Portenko; 20) Uélen, September 30, 1933, ♀, Portenko; 21 to 25) same place, October 1, 3 and 15, 1933, 4 ♀♀ and ♂, Portenko; 26 and 27) same place, May 31, 1934, ♂ sen., ♂ 3° anno, Portenko; 28

and 29) same place, June 3, 12, and 16, 1934, 11 ♂♂ and ♀, Portenko; 40) Naukan village, June 21, 1934, ♂, sen., Portenko; 41 and 42) southeastern part of Wrangel Island, June 27, 1934, ♂♀, sen., Vlasova; 43 to 46) Uélen, June 28, 1934, ♂♂, Portenko; 47 to 51) Mitkulen village, July 4, 1934, ♂♂, sen., 3 ♂♂, 3° anno, Portenko; 52 and 53) Uélen, July 29, 1934, ♂♂, sen., Portenko; 54) Rodgers Bay, October 27, 1934, ♀, 1° anno, Vakulenko; 55 to 62) Providence Bay, November 6, 12, 17, 19 and 30, and December 8 and 9, 1937, ♀♀, Butenko; 63 and 64) Cape Chaplin, January 30, 1938, ♂♀, 2° anno, Butenko; 65) same place, February 6 to 9, 11 and 14, 1938, 9 ♂♂ and 7 ♀, Butenko; 81) Plover Bay, May 17, 1938, ♂ sen., Butenko; 82 and 83) Kivak village, July 22, 1938, ○○, Butenko; 84) Wrangel Island, landmark Krasnaya Glina, September 15, 1938, juv., Portenko; and 85) Somnitel'naya Bay, July 15, 1939, ♀, 2° anno, Portenko.

31. **Somateria mollissima** var. **nigrum** Gray—**Common Eider**

Local name—Chukchian: Kòupýky; ♂ kúpuken and ♀ emngi in the records of the *Vega* expedition. In Eskimo: Méthkak or mýtkhak in Providence Bay, mŭt-khăk on St. Lawrence Island.

Distribution and status—Common and abundantly nesting species on the coasts of the Chukchi peninsula, on Wrangel and St. Lawrence islands. Breeding population of eiders noticeably decreases to the west of Cape Schmidt and falls steeply west of Chaun Bay and Aiok Island.

This species is common in flight up to Chetyrekhstolb Island, becomes rare westward, is found up to the Lena estuary and occurs as a rare exception in Khatanga Bay. Huge flocks of nonbreeding eiders spend the summer and molt on the northern and eastern coasts of the Chukchi peninsula and in a small number on the south coast and St. Lawrence Island but not on Wrangel Island, which even the local birds generally leave to molt at the end of the breeding season. Wintering begins on Bering Strait but becomes more or less regular only on the south coast of the Chukchi peninsula and on St. Lawrence Island.

Distribution in the breeding season—According to my observations, this species is common in the breeding grounds, being numerous at places on the shores of Anadyr Bay. In Krest Bay I found broods in the neighborhood of Notapenmen village. V.É. Yakobi noticed the common eider at Uél'kal' as the most common species while L.O. Belopol'skii saw broods in the strait between Meechken Island and the mainland.

In Providence Bay the common eider has been noticed at the nesting sites by nearly all the observers that have visited the bay. On August 12, 1880, T.H. Bean (1883, p. 167) shot large numbers of nonflying young birds in Plover Bay. On June 26, 1881, E.W. Nelson (1883, p. 101) saw some pairs in Providence Bay. L.M. Starokadomskii collected nonflying young ones in the fall of 1912 and gathered some chicks from a nest in the neighborhood of Émma Bay on July 23, 1913. In the same year, 1913, nests with clutches were found in Providence Bay by W.S. Brooks (1915). The following year, 1914, on August 8, Copley Amory Jr. (Riley 1918) caught a downy chick not far from a nest in Plover Bay. According to him this species was very common in Émma Bay. According to an eyewitness account by A.M. Bailey (1925) a damaged nest was found in Émma Bay on July 5, 1921. I.O. Olenev gives much original information on the common eider in Providence Bay. It was numerous in the nesting areas. In the depressed plateau between the hills at the apex of Émma Bay eight nests were found in an area of 2×2 km one day in the summer of 1932. Chicks were later found in the bay itself. I sighted local eiders in Providence Bay several times, specially on July 12 and 13, 1938, and often saw flying females and occasionally pairs over the valley of the rivulet at Cape Stoletiya. I could not find the nests but saw eggs gathered at that time by the local hunters. P.T. Butenko collected a chick on August 6, 1938.

On St. Lawrence Island, this is one of the most common birds. Among the aquatic birds it is second in numbers only to the emperor goose, but a large number of pairs breed.

The members of the *Vega* expedition (Palmén 1887) noticed females from July 31 through August 2, 1879. The members of E.G. Harriman's expedition saw some eiders on the island on July 13, 1889. On September 21, 1930, H.B. Collins (Friedmann 1932a) collected a young female which was just beginning to grow feathers. O.J. Murie (1936) acquired some specimens in 1934 which were undoubtedly breeding birds. They included two females, in Kukuliak village on August 9, three young ones with remnants of down at Cape Sevu on August 24, a similar young bird on Punuk Island on August 25 and three nonflying young birds around the same time. A six-day-old chick was obtained on July 29, 1935, and a brood was sighted. I.N. Gabrielson (Gabrielson and Lincoln 1959) noticed an eider at Southwest Cape on August 3 and 6, 1946. Later a large series of birds was secured by other collectors from April 26 through December 31. According to F.H. Fay (1961) the breeding summer population on the island runs to 3,500 birds. The most dense colonies of eiders were noticed on some islets, an acre or less in area, in the Kuzata lagoon. In 1953, 200 nests were counted (Fay and Cade 1959) but there were only three-fourths of this number in 1954. On June 24, 1953, 15 nests were found at the fishing site on the Kuzata River. In July, 1950, some nests were recorded in Boxer Bay. In general, nesting sites were extensively distributed throughout the island but not a single nest was found more than 500 yards inland. On some islands in the southern lagoons eiders nested in colonies. Their population density reached roughly 100 pairs per acre.

It is interesting that eiders ringed in summer, 1940, on St. Lawrence Island were later caught on the Siberian coast (Shevareva 1959 and 1960).

According to H. Friedmann (1934a) the common eider is abundantly represented in the bones at 32 archaeological excavations. At present it is more numerous than king eiders on the island but in prehistoric times it was evidently encountered or at least caught by eskimos only in small numbers. O.J. Murie does not agree with these conclusions of Friedmann's.

A flying eider was collected by W. Stimpson in Senyavin Strait in August, 1855 (Cassin 1863, p. 323). On July 28, 1879, the members of the *Vega* expedition collected two females in Kon'yam Bay and saw some in the hinterland of the bay on July 30. Dr. E. Almquist found a nest with eggs. According to É.V. Schmidt the common eider nested in Mechigmensk Gulf in larger numbers than in Lawrence Bay. I visited Lawrence Bay on August 19, 1932, and saw eiders in small numbers there.

I also found downy chicks. V.N. Lyubin secured a female on July 25 and a male on July 30, 1948.

In 1961, A.P. Kuzyakin's colleague found two nests on Balk Islet in Lawrence Bay. Kuzyakin found the males shrieking and flying around the nests to the southeast of the village in the same bay and on his way to Akkani. In Poutyn he found a nest with eggs and about 10 nesting pits.

In early July, 1881, E.W. Nelson sighted a pair of eiders at Dezhnev settlement.

Evidently the common eider does not nest at all on Bol'shoi Diomede Island because of unfavorable local conditions. During my visit to the island I did not find any eiders even on the coast.

Around Uélen, in the early summer of 1934 I often saw pairs but not their nests or broods. This was inevitable because of the proximity of a large village where there were always many hunters and, in the summer, stray dogs. I did not find nesting eiders even in the valley of the Kol'oam River, which was quite far from Uélen. In the neighborhood of Inchoun, however, which is quite a small village compared to Uélen, common eiders nested in large numbers by the banks of the lagoon. On the islet opposite the estuary of the Utte-Véem River, I found a small nesting colony which had been destroyed, probably by a polar fox. During my journey up the river, I often came across lone females and even pairs flying along the river. The pairs clearly indicated nidification. A few kilometers above the estuary I located a nest which had also been destroyed, most probably by a polar fox. On my return journey I found two broods in the southern part of the Inchoun lagoon and two broods on the spit separating it from the sea. In spite of the destroyed nests it was evident that a very scattered colony nested in the neighborhood of the Inchoun lagoon. At places the birds congregated and at other places they nested singly. Eiders were absent from the lagoon system from Uélen to the Kol'oam River because they nested on the Inchoun lagoons.

According to information gathered by A.P. Kuzyakin very many eiders nested between the coastal settlements Chegitun and Énurmino. The residents reportedly gathered basketfuls of eggs there.

Around the wintering post of the *Vega* this species was common in the nesting areas and 21 eggs were gathered. Most of them were collected in the lagoon region from Pitlekai to Neshkan but eggs were also found in Pidlin village on the shore of Kolyuchin Bay. Concurrently eiders were noticed in pairs, some at Tjapka village. I established during my own visit to Kolyuchi Island that eiders did not nest there because of local conditions. E.W. Nelson (1883, p. 101) found the common eider in moderate numbers almost everywhere along the Chukchi coast from Providence Bay to Cape Schmidt. J. Koren (Thayer and Bangs 1914) found this species quite common by the arctic coast from Bering Strait to Vankarém. It was less common farther to the west and seen only occasionally on that side of Cape Schmidt. On July 29, 1909 he (Koren 1910) found a brood in ice-free Vankarém Bay. According to A.A. Kishchinskii it was a common nesting bird on the marine tundra from the Nutauge lagoon to the Amguema estuary. Nests and broods were found there.

In May and June, 1914, according to A.A. Savich's diary (Artobolevskii 1927), common eiders were obtained several times at Cape Schmidt. But it does not necessarily follow that they nested there in considerable numbers. On August 13, 1914, Copley Amory, Jr. collected a feathered young one near Ryrkaipiya. According to V.Ya. Isaev, the common eider nested in the neighborhood of Cape Schmidt but more rarely than king eiders. In the local factory I acquired the skin of a fledgeling. Fledgelings of eiders which still could not fly were sighted by members of the *Vega* expedition from September 9 through 11, 1878, slightly east of Cape Yakan, near 69°25′ north and 177°40′ east, but unfortunately exact identification of the species was not made.

As reported by É.V. Schmidt, this eider was common in Chaun Bay and penetrated 70 km into the tundra up the rivers. It was also common in the Karchyk peninsula and on Aiok Island. The Chukchians reported that on the tiny Ryyanranot islet adjoining Aiok to the north, hundreds of nests were found. Nevertheless, according to Schmidt, the common eider was numerous only to the east of Chaun Bay. On July 26, 1912, on Aiok Island, J. Koren found two females of which one was collected. V.D. Lebedev and V.R. Filin (1959) reported that on June 25, 1958, on the southeast coast of the island, a nest was found with four slightly incubated eggs by a lake. Two broods with 10 to 12 chicks were found in Malyi Chaun Strait on July 29.

According to G.A. Ushakov (Bannikov 1941) the common eider nested in very large numbers on Wrangel Island. According to V.F. Vlasova it was perceptibly less numerous than the lesser snow goose.

According to my observations this eider, though common on Wrangel, does not nest there in very large numbers. On my trip from Rodgers Bay on August 13, 1938, along the east coast in the north part of the island, females flying over the sea were seen only north of Cape Uéring. During my stay on Bruch spit from August 21 through 27 eiders were a common feature. At many places I noted the nesting pits, and the feathers were easily identified as those of common eiders. In one case I found a pit with remains of shells which provided positive proof of nidification. In the interior of Tundra Akademii I did not find common eiders at all. On the south coast of Wrangel Island they were more numerous. In the fall of 1938 I located a brood in Rodgers Bay and Tayan told me of coming across young eiders in Somnitel'naya Bay. In the first half of June, 1939, I noticed many pairs in the valley of the lower course of the Mamontovaya River and along the coast from Predatel'skaya to Rodgers Bay. Later I found some nests in the immediate proximity of the Polar Station on the bank of the Nasha River and on the slopes of knolls in the neighborhood of the Atternon Range. Judging from the numbers of pairs and nonpaired birds flying from the valley of the River Nasha out to sea and back, the number of nests was insignificant within the areas covered on my long-distance expeditions. The nests were located at distances of a kilometer or more from each other. On my automobile trip from Rodgers to Somnitel'naya Bay and back lone females were found dead in a broad zone of tundra adjoining Somnitel'naya Bay. Sometimes when the party stopped to search for nests only a lone one was found. On the pebble spit nests were not found, though Tayan had recorded nests there in earlier years.

At the end of June, 1960, S.M. Uspenskii and R.L. Bëme (Uspenskii, Bëme and Velizhanin 1963) found some nests on the northern slopes of the East plateau more than 10 km from the coast. A.G. Velizhanin (1965) wrote that the common eider was found in all parts of the island. On the northern marine spits eider nests were very numerous and common in Tundra Akademii as well as along the valleys of mountain rivers.

Distribution of nonbreeding and molting eiders—Like king eiders, common eiders do not nest in the second year and most of them do not nest in the third year. Juvenile and nonbreeding birds spend part of the summer away from breeding grounds and part of it there. They are found abundantly on the coasts of the Chukchi peninsula.

On August 6, 1932, I saw a huge flock of up to 1,000 male common eiders together with nonpaired females off the coast at Notapenmen village at the entrance to Krest Bay roughly 2 km from the shore. On September 2, P.T. Butenko noticed eiders near Uél'kal' village. In Providence Bay, I did not see a flock of nonbreeding eiders like other observers who visited the bay, but from July 11 through 14, 1938, I saw a flock of males and small groups of females in the coastal waters adjoining the bay. On August 23, 1932, I saw eiders flying over Cape Chaplin but in small numbers.

At the end of June, 1921, A.M. Bailey saw large flocks of common eiders along the edge of the ice swimming from King to St. Lawrence Island. R.W. Hendee continued to see them in abundance on July 1 and 2 near St. Lawrence Island until the ice withdrew, to be followed later by the eiders. According to F.H. Fay and T.J. Cade, nonbreeding eiders of one or two years formed almost one-half of the entire spring population on the coasts of St. Lawrence Island. In the summer they gathered along the lagoons on the south and east coasts, forming a small part of the local population. According to E.G.F. Sauer and E.K. Urban (1964) common eiders were abundant in Boxer Bay in 1960 and mixed flocks of eiders numbering up to 150 birds were seen at sea off Kangi.

According to É.V. Schmidt there were many molting eiders in Mechigmensk Gulf. N.F. Kallinikov (1912, p. 151) refers to finding eiders, among all other possible species of duck, especially plentiful in the straits and bays at the eastern end of the Chukchi peninsula and along the shores of the Arctic Ocean. At the end of June and in early July, 1957, A.P. Kuzyakin found flocks everywhere on a sea journey between Lawrence Bay and Uélen. The common eider surpassed all the other species of goose in numbers. On August 1, 1928, F.L. Jaques (1930) saw some flocks of male eiders flying south to the north of Cape Dezhnev, at 68°30′ north, but could not determine whether common or king eiders because of the distance. On August 15, 1933, at Cape Dezhnev, I noticed fiom the ship that there were innumerable flocks of common eiders in the strait. It was a large concentration of nonbreeding birds spending the summer there; they made short local migrations, especially in foggy weather. Uélen lay on the path of these daily movements thanks to its geographic position on a low isthmus under the Dezhnev knolls. A.M. Bailey (1925, p. 197), who visited Uélen on July 12, 1921, was surprised at the abundance of eiders of all four species flying over the village. According to him it was impossible even to make a guess at their numbers but their flocks were constantly visible for several hours in the morning. Common eiders took part in these migrations in large numbers. Having visited Uélen for the first time on August 15 and 16, 1932, I brought back many impressions of this typical corner of the Soviet Union; most such impressions were related to the morning hours when I was aroused by the noise of firing at the eiders flying over the village in large flocks. On arriving at Uélen on August 15, 1933, I found similar daily flights of eiders over the village. Only the females took part in these migrations since the males were already molting heavily. Females in flight were seen in abundance at least for a month. On June 2, 1934, I noticed a large flock crossing the spit to the west of Uélen. After a month flocks of common eiders performed daily flights over the village, the males predominating. Massive daily flights of nonbreeding eiders continued until very late. A.P. Kuzyakin (1965) found a particularly large number of eiders at Uélen from June 27 through July 3, 1957. Flocks of 50 to 70 males and females regularly flew low over the housetops. A male obtained turned out to be a two-year-old bird. The ovaries of females examined were found to be undeveloped. Around Inchoun and Mitkulen the common eiders were next in numbers to Steller's and king eiders, at least during the whole of July, 1934.

According to the observations of O. Nordquist and E. Almquist (Palmén 1887), flocks of nonbreeding males began to be seen near Kolyuchin Bay in 1879 when the nesting pairs were with eggs. On July 2 flocks of 30 to 40 males were seen at Tjapka; later large flocks appeared west of Neshkan and a flock of 100 to 200 males was put up on July 9 in the estuary of the Ryraitinop River. Similar flocks were seen on July 17 by the shore ice. During his sojourn on the west side of the entrance to Kolyuchin Bay from July 15 through 26, 1909, J. Koren noticed hundreds of eiders flying by the coast almost daily. He could not understand where such a multitude of ducks nested. As we now know they only spent the summer there.

E.W. Nelson gives a picturesque description of a multitude of eiders flying over the Vankarém estuary and points out that common eiders were few in these flights (Nelson 1883, p. 101). In another place he reports (1887, p. 79) that this eider is becoming very rare on the arctic coast. The captain of the *Corwin*, K.L. Hooper (1884, p. 61), in a description of his landing at Vankarém, also refers to a multitude of eiders including common eiders. According to information I gathered at Vankarém, there were then daily flights of lone eiders which were only slightly smaller in numbers than in Uélen. However, I could not make out how many of them were common eiders. According to the observations of A.A. Kishchinskii, in the first half of June, 1970, hundreds of males in breeding plumage were seen in open water in the isthmus of the Ukouge lagoon. In July hundreds and thousands of eiders, nonbreeding and juvenile, swam in flocks in the sea on the Vankarém-Amguema traverse, gradually advancing southeast. In early August, 1938, I noticed this species in daily flights at Cape Schmidt; among the birds flying in flocks through the spit by Cape Kozhevnikov, common eiders, exclusively males, predominated. Huge flocks sometimes passed above the coast but more often the birds were in small flocks.

E.K. Brusevits noticed a huge flock of eiders on September 5, 1878, west of Chaun Bay. V.D. Lebedev and V.R. Filin noticed flocks of male and female common eiders throughout the summer of 1958 on the coast of Aiok Island and the Karchyk peninsula. This species was most common of all the eiders.

On Wrangel Island juvenile common eiders do not gather in large numbers in the summer or for molting. Leaving the females behind, with very few exceptions the males desert the islands and molt, evidently, on the north coast of the Chukchi peninsula. That is why I did not find one female in early August, 1938, among flocks of common eiders making daily flights at Cape Kozhevnikov.

In 1960, S.M. Uspenskii and R.L. Bëme found nonbreeding females (or ones from nests that had been destroyed) and flocks of six to eight males at Somnitel'naya Bay, Wrangel Island. A.G. Velizhanin wrote that flocks of 10 to 15 eiders, sometimes more, were usually seen. On June 29 he found a flock consisting of 32 birds. On his way from Cape Litke to Chicherin spit he noticed in all up to 500 eiders.

Lone eiders fly far to the west in summer. According to a report by T.P. Shevareva (1959 and 1960), two females ringed in summer, 1940, on St. Lawrence Island were killed in Tikhaya Bay: one in July, 1943, and the other in June, 1946. A third female ringed there was shot in Khatangsk Strait on August 22, 1952. This bird flew at the head of a flock and for this reason could be regarded as a lone female; it could be assumed that the first two did not nest.

Distribution in spring flight and arrival—In spite of the fact that common eiders spend the winter on the south coast of the Chukchi peninsula, the spring flight was tracked. In 1931 L.O. Belopol'skii noticed the appearance of the first few eiders on the west coast of Krest Bay. P.T. Butenko successfully tracked the arrival of eiders in spring, 1938, at Cape Chaplin, based on the fact that there was a break of over a month between the last of his winter sightings on March 22 and the first of his spring sightings on April 23. N.P. Sokol'nikov noticed the massive spring flight of common eiders on the south coast of the Chukchi peninsula in spring, 1902. He reported seeing innumerable eiders at Chaplin and at the exit of Krest Bay, most of them *Somateria* var. *nigrum*.

According to F.H. Fay common eiders were very common in the spring along the west coast of St. Lawrence Island. According to K.W. Kenyon and J.W. Brooks (1960), the eskimos often caught eiders of this species on Malyi Diomede Island. On May 16, 1958, roughly 100 eiders were noticed in the ice leads and later flocks were seen during walrus hunting at sea, but at the end of May not one eider would be seen all day sometimes.

In spring, 1934, the arrival in Uélen was not clearly in evidence. Up to April 23, when I left Uélen, this species had not arrived. Later, I was informed telegraphically that eiders were sighted on May 1; in particular, hunters had bagged common eiders. According to them, in 1934, the flight of eiders around Uélen was very poor because of the ice conditions.

Around Kolyuchin Bay in spring, 1879, the members of the *Vega* expedition could not differentiate the species of eiders in flight. Nevertheless, it became clear when the flight intensified that common eiders predominated in the flocks. From early June flocks of this species were noticed more often, while the king eiders disappeared.

In the spring of 1934 I noticed a distinct flight of common eiders at Vankarém. In one case I came across nearly 20 males and females and on another occasion a huge flock. Judging from the data of A.A. Savich, common eiders were taken many times at Cape Schmidt in May and June, 1914. Even farther to the west a flight, in particular of eiders, was noticed. It later turned toward Wrangel Island. The information provided by G. Maydell (1871, p. 62) in answer to questions put by Acad. K.M. Ber is of greater historical than factual interest. In the references Maydell gives, mention is made of a beautiful species of duck which, from the information provided by the Yukon resident Lykchin, I am inclined to regard as a common eider[1]. En route from Kolyma to Ryrkaipiya Lykchin obtained this species of duck from Chukchian hunters. They were killed before migration to Wrangel Island. It is interesting that, according to available accounts, the birds flew some distance west along the coast before turning north across the sea. According to G. Maydell, a female was collected on May 22, 1870, on the Antoshkina rivulet between Malyi and Bol'shoi Baranov Kamen'. It is quite possible that the black ducks referred to in F.P. Wrangel's travelog, observed on April 30, 1822, flying over the ice one degree north of Aiok Island on May 6 one degree to the west were common eiders. This aspect was discussed in greater detail in the section on king eiders.

According to É.V. Schmidt the common eider is not found in the lower reaches of the Kolyma; nor did S.A. Buturlin find it there (1906b). An altogether reliable reference to the flight of common eiders over Chetyrekhstolb island is found in G.U. Sverdrup's diary (Schaanning 1928): four or five flocks were sighted on June 5, 1925, and a male was collected on June 12.

On Wrangel Island the flight of this bird is not observed since the northern limits of the range of the common eider is on this island. A flying female probably of this species was collected in April, 1880, to the north of Wrangel Island roughly 180° east, as reported by R.L. Newcomb (1888, p. 182), a member of the *Jeannette* expedition.

I clearly recorded the arrival on Wrangel Island gradually building to massive proportions, in spring, 1939. I happened to find a particularly large number of common eiders in the estuary of the Amerikanskaya rivulet. There is no second wave of arrival, i.e. no appearance of nonbreeding eiders on Wrangel Island.

Distribution in fall flight and migration—The migration from Wrangel Island was not a massive phenomenon. Before molting the males left the females in the nests and gradually deserted the island in July. Very few of them, evidently those delayed because of the second clutch, remained to molt. In August lone and unencumbered females gradually disappeared. The broods were the last to leave the island. A.I. Mineev happened to see flocks of common eiders resting and sleeping on the sand spits; quantitatively these birds ran into some hundreds but unfortunately their sex and age composition was not ascertained.

In G.U. Sverdrup's diary eiders are recorded in fall flight on Chetyrekhstolb island. Though specimens were not found, there is nothing unusual in these observations since the common eider has been collected there even in spring flight. Observations of eiders by the *Vega* expedition in the fall of 1878 were not characterized by

[1]According to Lykchin's description, the female plumage was of one color. The male was very smart. These ducks were invariably the first to arrive but they were seen very rarely on the lower Kolyma. They flew over the sea in wide echelons. When Lykchin was shown a dead male king eider he confirmed that the male given him by the Chukchians was not exactly the same but a related species.

accuracy and the information given by I.A. Palmén could refer to any eider species. Nevertheless, it is quite clear that common eiders were seen in fall flight along the north coast of the Chukchi peninsula, at places in considerable numbers, especially northwest of Uélen.

According to my observations at Uélen, the common eiders there, as on Wrangel Island, did not fly away all at once. The first to disappear were the males, heading for a more convenient place for molting, followed by single females. Later the local broods gradually migrated and finally there was the flight of eiders from far northern places. In Providence Bay, surrounded on all sides by mountains, no fall flight was noticed. In October, November and even December the eiders would be seen when polynyas formed, sometimes even in large flocks, but they did not remain for wintering. For Krest and Anadyr bays we have L.O. Belopol'skii's observations (1934, p. 27) that at the end of September and October, with the appearance of ice, the eiders migrated, some to the north and probably some to the south, where they could be found in coastal waters free of ice.

Distribution in winter—According to the observations of J. Koren (Thayer and Bangs 1914) common eiders wintered in the 1912/1913 season on the Diomede Islands. Wintering there cannot be continuous since it is associated with ice conditions, so capricious in this part of Bering Strait. Wintering of eiders on the south coast of the Chukchi peninsula is comparatively regular. In 1938 special observations on wintering marine birds were made by P.T. Butenko at Cape Chaplin. Common eiders were found there throughout the winter up to and on March 23, 1938, sometimes coming close to the cape and sometimes going farther away, depending on the ice conditions. As I.O. Olenev told me, the eider hunting was good near Istiget village in January and February, 1932. According to L.O. Belopol'skii the eider winters in large numbers around Cape Bering. He found a flock near Vtoroi Red'kin Bay on March 14, 1931. It comprised common and king eiders numbering 2,000 to 2,500 birds.

According to information collected by F.H. Fay, the common eider lives in small numbers in the winter months on the south coast of St. Lawrence Island in the company of huge flocks of king eiders.

Habitat—The common eider spends much of the year in the environment of the open sea or ice. It is a purely marine duck. It is confined to the land only at the time of breeding. In the case of females this lasts three or four months and, for males, not more than two or three months. At other times the eiders may only occasionally be seen resting or swimming along the coast.

The eider penetrates far inland only very rarely. Nevertheless, my observations show that eiders traveled overland in the spring across the Chukchi peninsula, even through the Anadyr Range of mountains. On May 7, 1934, to the west of Vankarém, I put up a flock sitting on the snow by the hummocks at the edge of the fall shore ice. Judging from the absence of dark sections on the cloudy horizon there was no open water anywhere in the neighborhood and I think the eiders must have crossed through the Anadyr Range and settled down there for rest as soon as they reached the frozen sea. On May 13 I noticed a large flock of common eiders flying over Vankarém. In my opinion the flock reached the pack ice after crossing through the Anadyr Range.

On the banks of Lake Kool'ong, I found the feathers of the common eider. The birds must have stopped there on their way from Lawrence Bay to Uélen or Inchoun. The lake is in the interior of the Chukchi peninsula and surrounded by mountains.

On Wrangel Island I quite often sighted eiders crossing the low passes in the course of their daily flights from the Nasha River valley to the seacoast. On June 29, 1939, a flock crossed a very high knoll before my eyes in the neighborhood of Atternon hill.

According to É.V. Schmidt, who found many nests in the vicinity of Chaun Bay, the eiders built them quite often deep in the tundra at a distance of up to 70 km inland, but invariably along river valleys. I found a nest on the Utte-Véem River 5 to 7 km from the estuary or 12 to 15 km from the sea. Judging from the fact that stray females were found even farther up the river, the eiders nested there at least 20 km from the seacoast. A nest I found was built right on a patch of shingle on the tow-line.

S.M. Uspenskii and R.L. Bëme found some nests on Wrangel Island on the dry tundra on the northern slopes of East Plateau more than 10 km from the seacoast and 250 to 300 m from the nearest rivulet.

The eiders most often colonized in the immediate proximity of the seacoast, a bay or a lagoon. L.O. Belopol'skii wrote that common eiders nested at the entrance to Krest Bay on the tundra near the seacoast. In 1961 V.É. Yakobi found two old nests with eggshells near Uél'kal' on large mounds on the tundra 200 m from the coast. In the neighborhood of Notapenmen village, I found tiny chicks on tundra lakelets not farther than 100 to 200 m from the sea. I.O. Olenev found a nesting colony at the apex of Émma Bay. There the low plateau between the mountains was crisscrossed by rivulets or mountain streams. The nests were built haphazardly in the grass on moss and rubble, and in one case on a ledge under a cliff. In Lawrence Bay I found a brood on a low section of the coast with lakelets. On the Inchoun lagoon the nest sites varied. In the southern part, in the estuary of the Utte-Véem River, the nesting sites were in a purely riverine habitat. To the north they fell in a marine zone. The nests found by the members of the *Vega* expedition to the east of Kolyuchin Bay were in a lagoon. In one case a nest was found on a grassy mound jutting out of the water in the lagoon.

According to V.Ya. Isaev, in the neighborhood of Cape Schmidt the common eider nested around lagoons and lakes, not in colonies but separately. He found nests, for example, on a mound in shallow water and also on dry tundra. In the neighborhood of Chaun Bay, according to the observations of É.V. Schmidt, the eiders nested in riverine as well as marine habitats. On Wrangel Island, according to my observations, the nesting sites of common eiders for the most part were confined to extensive rubble spits. On the northern side of the island, very rarely visited by man, I located a nest right on the pebble beach, on the north bank of the lagoon separated from the sea by Bruch spit. Tayan did not find a single nest on the spit of Somnitel'naya Bay in 1939 because of the frequent journeys of the settlers along the coast, but eiders nested on the adjoining tundra.

The observations of V.F. Vlasova and A.I. Mineev generally tally with mine: the common eiders on Wrangel Island nest on the tundra in the interior of the island as also on the coastal spits. Sometimes they are found on small sandy islets secure against the attacks of polar foxes. According to A.I. Mineev, however, the foxes even swim out to get at the nests. The marine spits along the north coast of Wrangel are separated by broad lagoons and the nests of eiders on them are numerous (according to observations by myself and A.G. Velizhanin).

The common eider sometimes builds its nests very high up. In the Nasha River valley I found a nest on a high bluff, 50 m above the water. I found another nest on the slope of a knoll near Atternon at a height of almost 100 m. E. Almquist came across a nest in Kon'yam Bay 600 to 700 ft above sea level. According to A.G. Velizhanin, though the eiders mainly nested on marine spits their nests were commonly found along mountain river valleys.

It is generally believed that the Pacific Ocean eiders, unlike those from the Atlantic Ocean, do not nest in colonies. This is not quite true. In the estuary of the Utte-Véem River, on a tiny depressed islet in the delta, I found a colony of some nests. Some nests of terns and one of Temminck's stint were also found there. A reference was already made to a large colony on Ryyanranot islet. According to G.A. Ushakov, nests on Wrangel Island were sometimes so close to one another that they formed a loose colony. On the other hand, on Novaya Zemlya, Murman and in other places, nesting sites of western subspecies in the form of solitary nests are not uncommon.

In this context, a reference may be made to the habit of eiders of nesting around the dens of predators and human settlements; not always of course but under certain conditions. The nest referred to above on the bank of the Nasha River was located in a colony of brent geese in the neighborhood of the nest of a snowy owl, which evidently protected the entire nesting section from the attacks of polar foxes. It did not encroach on the life of the other members of the colony. The brent geese drove away the old squaws. F.B. Chernyavskii (1967) also refers to an instance of eiders nesting alongside a snowy owl.

The eskimos in Alaska told L.M. Turner (1886) that the eiders colonized near the nest of a peregrine falcon. He verified three instances of this cohabitation. According to N.P. Demme, on Novaya Zemlya the eiders sometimes nested alongside glaucousgulls.

Even A.I. Mineev drew attention to the fact that the eiders on Wrangel Island often colonized in the immediate vicinity of a human habitation, evidently to protect the nest from the attacks of polar foxes. During my stay on Wrangel Island dogs were bred in very large numbers at the Polar Station but, in spite of them, in the summer of 1939 I found two nests not far from the Station, one of them just 0.5 km north.

On St. Lawrence Island, F.H. Fay found 15 nests on June 24, 1953, at the River Kuzata hardly 100 yards from a fishing site. Some nests were within 50 paces of a structure on bare rocky soil and one nest 6 in. from its door. For two years running, two nests were also found within 50 paces of a cabin in another village. The birds clearly sought human surveillance but did not get it every year since there were clear traces of interference with them. On the Kuzata lagoon about 50 nests of herring and other gulls were dispersed among eider nests. The eskimos found that the full chicks fed on the eggs and fledgelings of the eiders. The construction of nests in the neighborhood of human habitations or near the nests of predatory birds is explained by the general principle that the eider nests in places where it is not disturbed by the attacks of polar foxes.

The broods with tiny chicks for the most part live on tundra lakes near the sea or on lagoons, but when necessary swim out to sea. L.O. Belopol'skii found broods with downy chicks in the strait between Meechken Island and the mainland. I.O. Olenev found chicks on the tundra and also swimming in Providence Bay. Nonflying chicks of some eiders were sighted by members of the *Vega* expedition on the coast or in the sea east of Cape Yakan. On Wrangel Island I found tiny chicks on the coast at the exit of Rodgers Bay where they lived for a long time. A.I. Mineev also noticed downy chicks not only in the bay but also in the open sea. According to him the eiders as a rule accompany their broods on the water, using the beach sand or drifting ice only for rest.

The females whose nests were destroyed on the Utte-Véem River continued to visit the nesting area for a long time. Later they gathered in flocks on the lagoon near the estuary. Once I found females resting on a large tundra lake close to the estuary in the society of old squaws and such nonmarine birds as pintails and northern phalaropes. In Providence Bay I found nonbreeding females feeding on a steep waterfront but the birds returned to the lakes on Plover spit for rest. On Wrangel Island I found flocks of unencumbered females in Rodgers Bay and on the Ozero lagoon.

The males reverted quite quickly to a marine way of life. On deserting the nesting area they were at first somewhat confined to the shoreline. According to the observations of members of the *Vega* expedition, huge flocks of males were confined in the first 10 days of July, 1879, to the parts of the bay free from ice to the west of Neshkan and in the estuary of the Ryraitinop River. On July 17 they were noticed in a lead near a 500 to 600 ft wide bank. On Wrangel Island such males were found resting right on the shore along the edge of small openings in the ice.

A.I. Mineev saw males before molting resting on the ice in groups of four or five birds. I found a nonbreeding male molting in the tiny strait cutting through Bruch spit. In general, however, before and during molting common eiders are confined to the coast.

During the fall flight and migration the common eiders quite often fly far from the coast and rest on the ice out to sea or are confined to the leads and open water. Nevertheless, they often come close inshore, feed on the surf line and rest on the rubble spits. At Uélen, in the fall of 1933, eiders were found sometimes flying over the frozen lagoons in search of open water. According to the observations of I.O. Olenev, in October, 1931, in Émma Bay, huge flocks of eiders were confined to the edge of ice floes. When the water between the ice and the shore is covered by a layer of thin ice the eiders sat on the shore. According to the observations of P.T. Butenko, in January, February and March, 1938, at Cape Chaplin, common eiders mostly preferred the ice, alternating with open water. They were found in the open sea also. For the most part they followed the drifting ice but flew away when the ice became a solid pack. The eiders were quite often confined to the shoreline, from where they could easily be shot. In exactly the same way on April 10, 1902, N.P. Sokol'nikov saw many eiders swimming quietly 20 paces from the open bank of the

Unyyn spit and 300 paces from a yaranga*. Unfortunately precious little is known about the living conditions of eiders in the winter at sea far from land. On the last few days of June, 1921, A.M. Bailey found large flocks of common eiders along the edge of the ice during his journey from King islet to St. Lawrence Island.

I tracked the transition from marine to coastal conditions of residence in spring, 1934, at Uélen and in spring, 1939, on Wrangel Island. At Uélen, at the end of arrival, common eiders began to appear in open water in the lagoons and tundra lakes, at first singly and later in pairs. Gradually they would pass more time there, and their movement from the sea or lagoons to the lakes became more frequent and regular.

On Wrangel Island in the spring of 1939, traveling along the south coast, I found recently arrived common eiders in meltwater pools and channels in the estuaries of rivulets. They were satisfied with these pools but a flock was also noticed on the exposed bank of the Mamontovaya River. Later I saw them at the thawed fringes of lagoons, and innumerable eiders in the estuary of the Amerikanskaya rivulet. Flowing from the mountains, the meltwaters flooded the surface of the sea ice in the estuary of the rivulet. First thawed patches were seen and later channels, which had to be circumvented by going overland for a kilometer or more. Such places were very dangerous for riding dog sleds but I found eiders on them every time.

The tiny straits draining the excess freshened water from the lagoons into the sea, the estuaries of the rivulets and the thawed patches attract eiders at any time of the year except the winter by the abundance of feed and probably also by the warmer water, in the same way as the spring thawed patches on the surface of sea ice.

Arrival—According to L.O. Belopol'skii the first arrivals of eiders on the western shore of Krest Bay in 1931 were noticed on April 20. In 1902, N.P. Sokol'nikov saw large flying flocks over Red'kin village on May 3. At Cape Chaplin, he wrote, whole flocks of eiders flew very low through Unyyn village uninterruptedly on April 25. P.T. Butenko noted the arriving eiders at Cape Chaplin on April 23, 1938.

According to the observations of F.H. Fay initially a few common eiders flew along the west coast of St. Lawrence Island singly and in small flocks in April and early May; by May 15 there were already many of them. Their spring population touched its peak around June 1. In 1934 I gathered information on the arrival of eiders all along the north coast of the Chukchi peninsula from Uélen to Cape Schmidt. On April 7, at Uélen, I was informed of two flocks of eiders flying north-south. Evidently they were the unlucky first arrivals, which returned on not finding open water in the sea. On May 1 about 200 eiders were seen flying from the east. On May 2 P.T. Butenko saw a flock and a lone eider. On May 9 huge flocks were seen flying all the time from Dezhnev settlement to the north. Unfortunately these observations were not complete for want of accurate identification of the species. According to the local hunters the flight of eiders around Uélen ended in mid-May. I have the impression that the flight had ceased by then. On May 24 I went on an expedition along the Uélen spit with the special objective of seeing and collecting eiders. But I did not find one bird though I went out at 3 p.m. and on the advice of the hunters spent the whole night there. Next day I toured the coastal cliffs

*A portable skin tent—Translator.

right up to Cape Dezhnev and saw tiny flocks of flying males over Bering Strait. Evidently nonbreeding males had begun to arrive to spend the summer on the north coast of the Chukchi peninsula. On June 2, before my eyes, a large flock of common eiders crossed the Uélen spit at a place where I had found most of them on May 24. Even on June 4 small numbers of common eiders flew toward the sea but later all movement northward ceased.

In the spring of 1879 eiders were seen quite late at the wintering post of the *Vega*. Unfortunately, as the above observations at Uélen, the observers at Kolyuchin Bay did not record the species of flying eiders. On May 8, six female eiders of some species were noticed flying east and a flock was sighted on May 14. Next day a pair flew past the ship. Numerous eiders, probably in hundreds, were noticed only on May 31. Later they were noticed more frequently. The first reliable specimens of common eiders were collected only on May 23.

In Vankarém village, in the spring of 1934, the first flocks were sighted on May 1. At 2 a.m. on the night of May 7, I noticed a flock of common eiders somewhat to the west. On the evening of May 9 a flock was noticed over the sea and on May 13 a huge flock flying over the estuary of the River Vankarém. The eiders, roused from the hummocks, flew in a northwest direction. It is quite interesting that the colonized eiders performed their daily migrations mostly late in the evening or at night. At Cape Schmidt, on May 1 of the same year, 1934, I was told that "geese" were flying over the sea in the morning. But I believe that they were some species of eider. G.U. Sverdrup noticed flocks of flying common eiders on June 5, 1925, on Chetyrekhstolb Island.

On Wrangel Island, according to A.I. Mineev, the common eiders arrived late, in early June, which corresponds to my 1939 spring observations. Though the eskimo hunters told me of seeing common eiders to the east of Somnitel'naya Bay as early as May 17 I saw the first flying pair of this species only on June 1. This pair was trying to settle on a hunter's hut east of the Amerikanskaya rivulet estuary. At that time common eiders no doubt were still a rarity. On June 4, I noticed a pair of them flying west from the boundary of Akatylanva. On June 5 I saw many pairs there. From that date the mass arrival began. On June 7, I put up a flock on the Mamontovaya River and the flock scattered in pairs in different directions. On June 8 a significant increase was noticed in the number of eiders. Next day I noticed pairs and groups but only at places, and the eiders began spreading along the coast. On my return journey to Rodgers Bay flocks of eiders were sighted quite frequently. Arriving there on June 18, I noticed active daily movements. Beginning on June 18, the number of eiders began decreasing and this undoubtedly was associated with their dispersal to the nesting areas.

One could not help noticing that from the time of their arrival on Wrangel Island the common eiders were divided into pairs. With the commencement of the breeding season, the males accompanied the females in their daily journeys from the nests to the lagoons. On June 17 I noticed pairs for the first time flying through the passes between the knolls from the Nasha River valley to the sea and on June 29 I saw them for the last time in the same valley. As soon as the females began incubating the males were condemned to loneliness. On June 26 I saw such lone males flying along the Nasha River and considerable numbers of them were assembled in the estuary. Such was the fate of male flocks when breeding activity ceased. Sometimes females would join them, leaving their nests temporarily. I noticed a mixed group of males and females on July 1 in a lagoon at Rodgers Bay and on July 2 in the Ozero lagoon. Later the male and female common eiders lived very differently. In the case of females the way of life of those raising chicks differed from that of females that had lost their clutches.

Breeding-Pair formation—The eiders lived in flocks for a long time after arriving. On June 6, 1961, at Uél'kal', V.É. Yakobi noticed small flocks of five to seven birds. The males and females flew together along the coast and also from the sea to a lake. Later, on June 25, pairs began to be frequently encountered. Still later small flocks consisting of three to five males were noticed and lone females, evidently nesting birds, were seen after July 1.

In 1931, according to the observations of L.O. Belopol'skii, the common eiders at Krest Bay were paired in the first half of June.

On St. Lawrence Island W.S. Brooks found eiders in pairs in the first few days of July, 1921. According to the observations of F.H. Fay the arriving eiders quickly dispersed throughout the nesting areas inland at the end of May and also during the first or second week of June. By that time the freshwater reservoirs were free of ice. In 1954 the ice broke up almost two weeks earlier than in 1952 and 1953 and nesting therefore began correspondingly early.

In the spring of 1934 the common eiders arrived in flocks around Uélen. For some time after their arrival the eiders were confined to the sea. Only on May 31 did I find the first pairs in the open water in the lagoon. Evidently the eiders were initially separated into pairs and later formed colonies on the tundra, lagoon and lakelets. I noticed eiders in pairs through June 13. At that time small groups were seen in the same lagoons and lakelets but they invariably contained an even number of birds and were easily separated into pairs. When I shot down a female from such a flock one male separated out and came back several times, flying close by. Add to this the fact that a single male is constantly seen at the nest and it can be concluded that the eiders form true pairs and that the brood of a female represents the offspring of a single male.

In the spring of 1879, near Kolyuchin Bay, the members of the *Vega* expedition frequently saw flocks in early June. Gradually the common eiders began pairing off. They were in pairs for the most part around June 22 in the lagoons where they were later found with their clutches. Individual pairs were still noticed on July 9; on June 30 and July 4 males were collected from nests but already by then males could be found in flocks. On July 1 pairs and small groups of males not exceeding four in number were noticed around Tjapka. Gradually the male flocks grew. A flock of four females was seen on July 17.

Activity of gonads—As shown by the measurements of gonads (Table 26), the seasonal changes in the enlargement of testes were very considerable. Even in the course of the first winter the testis in young birds was almost the same as in adult males, but it was much reduced by July before molting. In adult males, even in early May, the testes maintained their winter size, but grew abruptly just before the mating period. A similar increase in the males of the third year suggests that at least some of them were ready for reproduction. I collected three-year-old males

Table 26. Size of testes of male common eiders, mm

Date, locality	Older than 3 years		3-year-olds		2-year-olds	
	Left	Right	Left	Right	Left	Right
Feb. 6 through 20, Cape Chaplin	15 × 15	13 × 3	—	—	13 × 4	11 × 3
	14 × 4	13 × 3	—	—	12 × 2	11 × 2
	14 × 3	12 × 2	—	—	11 × 2	9 × 2
	13 × 4	12 × 3	—	—	10 × 3	9 × 2
	13 × 4	11 × 3	—	—	10 × 2	9 × 2
	13 × 3	12 × 2	—	—	10 × 2	9 × 2
	13 × 3	11 × 2	—	—	—	—
	12 × 4	11 × 3	—	—	—	—
	12 × 4	11 × 3	—	—	—	—
	12 × 3	11 × 3	—	—	—	—
	12 × 3	11 × 2	—	—	—	—
	10 × 2	9 × 2	—	—	—	—
	10 × 2	8 × 2	—	—	—	—
May 4, Providence Bay	14 × 5	13 × 5	—	—	—	—
June 1 through 24, Providence Bay, Uélen and Wrangel Island	35 × 15	27 × 14	32 × 15	21 × 10	—	—
	35 × 15	27 × 12	32 × 14	20 × 2 (!)	—	—
	32 × 15	23 × 13	23 × 12	12 × 10	—	—
	30 × 15	27 × 12	—	—	—	—
	29 × 14	27 × 10	—	—	—	—
	28 × 17	18 × 10	—	—	—	—
	28 × 15	16 × 8	—	—	—	—
	28 × 12	—	—	—	—	—
	27 × 13	24 × 14	—	—	—	—
	27 × 15	20 × 12	—	—	—	—
	25 × 14	20 × 12	—	—	—	—
	25 × 13	18 × 9	—	—	—	—
	23 × 13	19 × 12	—	—	—	—
	16 × 7	15 × 6	—	—	—	—
Much emaciated birds	10 × 5	8 × 4	—	—	—	—
July 15 through 18, Cape Schmidt and Wrangel Island	24 × 14	19 × 10	—	—	9 × 4	8 × 3
	22 × 10	20 × 10	—	—	—	—
Sep. 27, Uélen	15 × 6	14 × 5	—	—	—	—
Nov. 4 through 30, Plover Bay	19 × 8	18 × 7	—	—	12 × 3	10 × 2[1]
	14 × 7	12 × 6	—	—	—	—
	14 × 6	10 × 6	—	—	—	—
	14 × 5	13 × 4	—	—	—	—
Dec. 4, Plover Bay	10 × 5	9 × 4	—	—	—	—

[1]Feathered bird.

with enlarged testes at Uélen and even on Wrangel Island. In the middle of July the size of the testes decreased and reverted to the normal size in the period of summer molting.

In young females a homogeneous ovary can be distinguished even in the first fall. It preserves the nongranular external appearance throughout the following year. Its length at this time goes up to 12 to 15 mm. In February an ovary of granular structure enlarged to 18 mm in length was noticed in adult females. In June, the sizes of gonads and developed follicles depended on the activity of egg formation. In July birds the ovary length was 27, 35 and 45 mm and the diameter of the largest follicle 6, 7, 12, 25 and 40 mm. When the length of the biggest follicle was 7 mm, some others were 5 mm in diameter. In July the ovary length was 25 and 35 mm and the diameter of the largest follicle 6 and 7 mm, i.e. the same dimensions as in June.

Laying—On June 18 and 19, 1934, at Uélen, females examined showed eggs ready for laying. In 1938, in Providence Bay, P.T. Butenko found an egg in the ovary of an eider on June 24.

W.S. Brooks and his colleagues found incubated eggs on June 19 and 20, 1913. The eiders at that time were much less timid than now and flew very low; the male flew a few feet behind the female and often with a characteristic sound emanating from the throat. In 1932, at the apex of Émma Bay, I.O. Olenev found eight nests on July 11 and 12. They contained clutches of two to six eggs. The nests with only two eggs were lined with very little down. It may be assumed that they were the second laying since the entire clutches at that time contained six incubated eggs. According to T.J. Cade, on July 8, 1960, in Boxer Bay on St. Lawrence Island, a nest with three incubated eggs was found at the edge of a lake. On July 12 a nest was seen with two eggs on dry soil at the edge of the bird colony. On July 20 another nest with five eggs was found on an elevation among the rocks overgrown with lichen 200 feet from the lakelet to which the female flew every time she was frightened. On the Kuzata River the eiders' clutches contained two to eight eggs, the average being five. Three nests in one of the large colonies contained 10 to 13 eggs, evidently not of one female since in one case the eggs could be clearly separated into two groups by shape and color. According to F.H. Fay (1961), on St. Lawrence Island clutches of eiders contained an average of five eggs. Fresh or slightly incubated eggs could often be found in the course of the first two weeks of July.

On June 26, 1957, A.P. Kuzyakin found a nest with four fresh eggs near Poutyn on a flat mossy-grassy island in the lower reaches of the river entering the lagoon. The nest had a very modest downy bedding. Alongside it and on adjacent islets there were about 10 nest pits and eiders lived around there. Two males rose from the gentle slope of the nearest knoll covered with rock debris; later the females started up from there. On Balk Island in Lawrence Bay, on July 7, two freshly laid eggs were found in a nest. The nest found by E. Almquist in Kon'yam Bay on March 30, 1879, contained four damaged eggs. On June 20, 1970, V.V. Leonovich found a nest in the neighborhood of Lawrence Bay. It was located on a plateau among mountains about 500 m above sea level and 2 km from water. There were four unincubated eggs in it. In the estuary of the Utte-Véem River I found some damaged nests and one clutch of four eggs on July 5, 1934. This was undoubtedly a second clutch. Slightly up river, still in the lower reaches, I found a lone damaged nest on July 6. Since the down was not disturbed and the place was uninhabited this destruction must have been the work of a polar fox. Female eiders were sometimes seen flying very low over the water along with the male in a somewhat leisurely way. One could immediately tell that it was a local nesting duck. I did not hear the call of the eider there.

On July 5, 1970, V.V. Leonovich discovered a nesting colony near Énurmino on an islet among the lakes. In one nest there were four eggs; three nests contained three each and two of them two each; two more had only one egg each. On this islet four pairs of herring gulls also nested.

According to the information gathered by the *Vega* expedition in 1879, the first eggs were found on June 27 at Pidlin where the soil was clear of snow very early. At Pitlekai one egg was found on June 30 and a clutch of four eggs was collected at Neshkan on July 1. Some clutches were obtained from Pitlekai on July 1 and 2 and a slightly incubated one on July 8. On July 4 near the wintering station a male and a female were shot by a nest lined with down containing four eggs.

According to the observations of A.I. Mineev on Wrangel Island the common eiders nested later than many other birds. By June 20 clutches were already found in the nests. In a clutch found on July 4, 1932, one egg was not incubated while the blood vessels had formed in another.

According to A.I. Mineev the eiders usually built their nests on the spits near some conspicuous mark like a boulder, a whale vertebra, wooden plank, etc. which served as some kind of landmark. This was invariably the case and the nests of many birds are placed near prominent local objects. On Bruch spit, among the biggest rubble heaps on the shore, I found round pits left by eiders. They were located for the most part among driftwood protected by some logs, particularly when it was arcuate with the bulge toward the incessant north wind, which protected the bird sitting in the pit. Under the conditions of violent Wrangel storms such pits could serve as daily roosts and hence were built by the birds with the special purpose of protecting themselves. Only in one pit did I find the remains of shells as proof that the pit served as a nest. Some pits were lined with splinters and surf debris. Sometimes I found eider feathers in them but not in one case were remnants of down found. According to A.I. Mineev the nests were profusely lined with down which surrounded the clutch like a ridge. In the nests found on the tundra the down was interwoven with moss which strengthened the structure of the nest. But on the spits where there was no moss the wind quite often scattered the down, which could be found far from the nest in the form of balls. The clutches were located on the bare floor of the pit in such cases.

On June 29, 1939, I found a nest of common eiders at least 1 km from the shore of Rodgers Bay (Fig. 37). The female was away from the nest a few paces from me, having discharged excrement over the eggs out of fright. She kept running to and fro, stumbling and spreading her wings until she was concealed behind the rocks. Coming to the nest at midday, I found it deserted. One egg was emptied, evidently by a jaeger. This nest was of a normal structure, mainly of down mixed with dry lichen, moss, and other plant matter. Its weight in the dry condition after five years was 64 g. It contained five incubated eggs. Another nest I found on the same day on the banks of the Nasha River had apparently been detected by someone else who as an experiment had added the egg of a brent goose to the clutch. On a well-laid bed of down I was surprised to find two eggs of an eider and one of a goose. In spite of this interference, the female continued to incubate. When I approached she flew down to the river but stopped on the snow and sat there for a long time within sight. On July 3, I scared an eider from a nest nearly 0.5 km from the seacoast to the west of Rodgers Bay. The bird initially withdrew to some distance. On my departure she flew back to the waterhole near the nest. There were seven eggs in the nest but when I visited it again on July 6 it was found destroyed, evidently by dogs. I gathered the whole of the downy base of the nest which weighed 120 g on the same day. Finally, on July 15, on the tundra near Somnitel'naya Bay, a nest was found with five eggs.

The clutches are laid about the same time on the south and north coasts of the Chukchi peninsula as also on Wrangel Island, in spite of the differences in latitude. It is not just an accident that the eiders that I disturbed sat on the cold surface of the snow or the waterhole. Evidently the much inflamed skin of the brood patch zone required cooling.

In regard to the eggs brought back by the *Vega* expedition, V. Meves noted that, in general, they were somewhat smaller than those of western forms of eiders but in color could be distinguished with difficulty. In most cases, however, the former were somewhat brighter, i.e. more of a grayish-aquamarine color, while the eggs of European eiders were more olive green. From the biological collection of the Institute of Zoology, Academy of Sciences, USSR, I compared my eggs of *S. m. v-nigrum* with the eggs of *S. m. mollissima* from Novaya Zemlya, the White Sea and Baltic coast. In fact the eggs of western eiders were of a more olive shade but in most cases the difference is imperceptible. A comparison of my measurements with V. Meves' (Table 27) revealed little difference, and it was hardly possible that repeated handlings could have affected them. But Meves was justified in observing that the eggs of Pacific Ocean eiders were smaller than those of western eiders.

For verification, I used the measurements kindly provided by V.V. Rol'nik, who made them individually for clutches found on the Murmansk coast and for clutches from the Kandalaksh Bay islands (Table 28). These showed appreciable differences in the size of eggs in the populations of common eiders on the Murmansk coast and in Kandalaksh Bay.

Broods—L.O. Belopol'skii noticed eight downy chicks with a female in a strait off Meechken Island on July 28, 1931. Around Notapenmen village I encountered females with tiny chicks on August 6, 1932. In Providence Bay L.M. Starokadomskii (1917) found a downy chick and an egg in a nest on July 28, 1913. A chick hatched out of the egg in an incubator after three days of incubation. Both of the chicks ate well for a week and looked satisfactory but died after swallowing cotton from the nest lining. A year before, on September 24, 1912, Starokadomskii caught young nonflying birds there. In size they compared with a wild duck or even bigger but the tips of the primaries reached only the tips of the longest secondaries. On the back and the sides down could be seen and the feathers were yet to grow in the lower back. I.O. Olenev noticed chicks in Providence Bay on July 18 through 20, 1932. Copley Amory, Jr., caught a downy chick not far from a nest in Plover Bay

Table 27. Size and weight of eggs of common eiders in Chukchi peninsula and Wrangel Island

Source	Length, mm (in decreasing order), clutchwise						Width, mm (correspondingly the order of length)						Wt. of empty eggshells, g					
Data of V. Meves	76	74.5	76.5	75	75	78	52	50	49	50	49	48	9.28	7.54	8.15	8.60	7.62	8.27
	74.5	75	—	75	74	—	50.5	49	—	48	49	—	8.59	7.45	—	8.10	7.23	—
	73	74	—	76	75	—	50	50	—	48.5	48	—	8.48	7.84	—	8.35	7.80	—
	—	71.5	—	73	74	—	—	48	—	50	51	—	—	7.47	—	7.61	7.45	—
	—	—	—	73	71	—	—	—	—	50	50	—	—	—	—	7.50	7.56	—
	—	—	—	72.5	71	—	—	—	—	49	50	—	—	—	—	8.18	7.00	—
Measurements by L.A. Portenko	76.7	76.5	74.5	74.4	76.1		48.8	49.1	48.4	50.1	49.2		7.9	9.2	9.25	8.5	Over 8	
	75.5	74.2	—	71.6	74.4		50.4	50.3	—	49.6	48.7		8.05	8.8	—	8.5	8.7	
	74.3	73.5	—	—	73.7		50.6	49.5	—	—	48.5		8.1	9.2	—	—	8.6	
	74.3	72.3	—	—	71.2		47.8	50.8	—	—	49.2		6.66	8.0	—	—	7.7	
	—	—	—	—	67.5		—	—	—	—	46.4		—	—	—	—	7.5	

Table 28. Size of eggs of Somateria mollissima V-nigrum and S.m. mollissima (L.)

Subspecies and locality	Length, mm				Width, mm				Wt. of empty eggshells, g				Wt. of whole eggs, g				No. of eggs in a clutch			
	Max.	Min.	Mean	No. of samples	Max.	Min.	Mean	No. of samples	Max.	Min.	Mean	No. of samples	Max.	Min.	Mean	No. of samples	Max.	Min.	Mean	No. of samples
S. m. v-nigrum, Chukchi peninsula and Wrangel Island	78.0	67.5	74.0	37	52.0	46.4	49.4	37	9.28	9.66	8.07	37	—	—	—	—	—	—	—	—
S. m. mollissima, Murmansk coast	84.7	72.6	78.3	193	54.3	48.0	54.4	193	—	—	—	—	123.0	194.0	109.5	125	6	3	4	222 (71 nests)
S. m. mollissima, Kandalaksh Bay	85.7	73.6	79.4	207	53.3	48.5	51.5	207	—	—	—	—	133.1	103.5	116.1	53	7	3	5	336 (68 nests)

on August 8, 1914. On August 12, 1880 T.H. Bean fired at nonflying young birds there which could dive so well that not one of them was collected. One of the females escaped in the process.

On St. Lawrence Island, O.J. Murie collected a six-day-old chick on July 29, 1935. A brood was led away by a female which left behind two eggs in the nest. One of them turned out to be an addled egg while the other contained a live chick. It emerged from the shell and survived for about six days. On July 27, 1950, a clutch found by T.J. Cade included a chick; the remaining four chicks emerged in the course of the next few days. On July 29, 1952, another brood with downy chicks was seen on the lake. On September 21, 1930, H.B. Collins collected a young female grown to one-third normal size with feathers on the wings, tail, breast and abdomen showing through the down. According to F.H. Fay, females with downy chicks appeared on St. Lawrence Island after July 15.

I came across two downy chicks of the size of teals in Lawrence Bay on August 19, 1932. In the Inchoun lagoon, on May 11, 1934, having moored at one of the capes at the south end, I found on the bank a female playing dead, two other eiders flying around all the while. Since there were no lakelets nearby, the chicks were concealed somewhere on the tundra. Only after waiting for some time did the females lead them to the water in the lagoon. On July 20, I encountered two mixed broods with two females and tiny chicks. As pointed out by A.I. Mineev, two broods of eiders frequently join together on Wrangel Island.

On July 29, 1909, at Vankarém J. Koren noticed an adult eider with ducklings. On August 13, 1914, at Cape Schmidt Copley Amory, Jr. collected a young male whose feathers had begun growing on body sides and behind the shoulders. From September 9 through 11, 1878, the members of the *Vega* expedition found a flock of 10 to 15 eiders at Cape Yakan, with nonflying birds among them. Unfortunately the specific identity was not precisely established.

In the southeastern part of Wrangel Island A.I. Mineev collected recently hatched chicks on August 5, 1932. On the beak the egg tooth could still be seen. According to the observations of A.G. Velizhanin, in 1960, on the south coast of the island, chicks emerged in mid-July. On September 15, 1938, in the isthmus of Rodgers Bay, I found a brood of seven or eight young ones with a single female. All of them dived very expertly. The young bird which was collected was of the size of a duck. Their flight feathers and greater wing coverts had just begun to emerge from the stubs while the tail feathers were completely grown. On the back and bridle the coat consisted of down only. In other places, on the neck and head, down could be seen through a large number of feathers. I found other late broods. Under such tardy conditions, it is not surprising that young eiders were noticed in Somnitel'naya Bay even on October 24. This delay was altogether natural for large birds and the distribution of common eiders far to the west is probably limited by this biological characteristic of the birds. In the far west they are replaced by the smaller species, i.e. spectacled and Steller's eiders, whose chicks grow very rapidly.

Induced second clutch—Observation of eider nests clearly showed how often they were subjected to damage by man or animals like domestic dogs, polar foxes, jaegers and of course gulls. This destruction is reflected in the way of life of the birds affected. Being a widespread phenomenon it could affect the subsequent behavior of eiders. Evidently, very often the affected females set out to lay a second clutch. The latter would explain not only the late broods but also the very late records of lone males in the nesting and adjoining areas. Having been delayed for the second clutch, such males shun the others, which are ready for molting, and at least some remain alone until the fall.

On Wrangel Island this phenomenon was particularly noticed since the males left the females *en masse* and deserted the island for molting. On August 26, 1938, I found a lone molting male on Bruch spit and on September 12 sighted four males in Rodgers Bay already dressed in dark plumage. On September 23 a male and female were seen there. In the summer of 1939 I saw lone males, on July 2 in a flock of females and on July 11 in a large flock of old squaws in Rodgers Bay. Other males at that time were confined to the coast.

In 1934, on the Utte-Véem River, I sometimes saw males accompanying the females even on July 6. There I observed the changes in the life style of the females. On July 2, on my way from Uélen to Mitkulen, I encountered lone females in the sea while the bulk of them sat on their nests. On July 5 females were often seen flying over the Utte-Véem River. On July 8 I saw them there in twos, threes and fives. On July 10 I found a flock of females on a tundra lake and some flocks in the southwestern part of the Inchoun lagoon on July 11 and 12. Finally, on July 21 I noticed near Inchoun a flock of females flying from the sea along the tundra valley. They continued to visit the inhospitable tundra for a long time. Literally before my eyes the females from the damaged nests gradually formed flocks which later increased in size. I cannot say whether they later joined the females that had remained single from the spring, but probably they did not. There is no doubt that a flock of four females noticed by the members of the *Vega* expedition on July 17, 1879, consisted of birds which had lost their clutches. On Wrangel Island, in the summer of 1939, I noticed females leaving damaged nests in mid-July. On July 11 I saw two females above the tundra, and from July 22 through 28 I saw females flying in the valley of the Nasha River and from there to Rodgers Bay. On August 5 they were flying over the coast separately. Probably some of them left their nests for some time but those grouped in twos or threes or more did not incubate.

At the end of summer, 1938, lone old females without chicks were often seen. On August 11 I saw them over the coast on the way from Rodgers Bay to the Ozero lagoon and on August 13 from Cape Uéring to Bruch spit. On August 16, I noticed a lone female together with a brent goose on a small lake near the estuary of the Krasnyi Flag River, a flock of six females at Bruch spit on August 24, and two females in Rodgers Bay on September 13.

Summer residence of nonbreeding birds—The life of nonbreeding common eiders in the Chukchi peninsula and on Wrangel Island differs in many respects from that of king eiders.

From August 6 through 9, 1932, I saw a huge flock on the coast before Notapenmen village. The males were in summer plumage with the lone females along with them but the males were also found in small flocks or in twos. At the end of June, 1961, V.É. Yakobi found flocks of 15 to 20 females near Uél'kal', flying incessantly over one particular lakelet. There is no doubt that they were nonbreeding birds. On the first few days of July, 1921, A.M. Bailey noticed flocks of nonbreeding males

Fig. 32. Pair of king eiders *Somateria spectabilis* (L.). Ukouge lagoon. June 21, 1970. Photo by A. A. Kishchinskii.

Fig. 33. Incubating female king eider *Somateria spectabilis* (L.). Amguema lagoon. July 3, 1970. Photo by A. A. Kishchinskii.

Fig. 36. Subspecies of greater scaups *Aythya marila* (L.): two on left — *A. m. marila* (L.), and two on right — *A. m. mariloides* (Vig.).

Fig. 37. Nest with clutch of common eider *Somateria mollissima* var. *nigrum* Gray. Rodgers Bay. June 29, 1939.

Fig. 38. Subspecies of peregrine falcons *Falco peregrinus* Tunst. Males: Four on left — *F. p. leucogenys* Brehm, and three on right — *F. p. harterti* But.

Fig. 39. Subspecies of peregrine falcons *Falco peregrinus* Tunst. Females: Four on left — *F. p. leucogenys* Brehm, and three on right — *F. p. harterti* But.

Fig. 40. Young peregrine falcon *Falco peregrinus* Tunst. Kol'oam-Véem River. August 11, 1934.

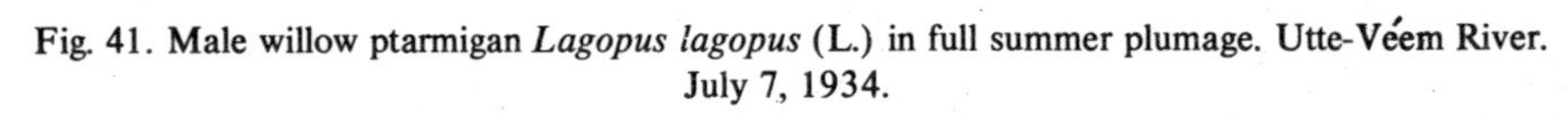

Fig. 41. Male willow ptarmigan *Lagopus lagopus* (L.) in full summer plumage. Utte-Véem River. July 7, 1934.

Fig. 42. Sandhill crane *Grus canadensis* (L.) nestling.
Utte-Véem River. July 8, 1934.

Fig. 43. Gray plover *Pluvailis squatarola* (L.) nestling.
Rodgers Bay. August 2, 1939.

Fig. 44. Female Siberian plover *Pluvialis dominica fulva* (Gm.). Around Amguema by 91st km. June 6, 1956.

Fig. 45. Nest of dotterels *Eudromias morinellus* (L.) with clutch. Yarak-Veém River. June 11, 1965. Photo by F. B. Chernyavskii.

Fig. 46. Ringed plover *Charadrius hiaticula* L. Amguema River by 91st km. July 10, 1956.

Fig. 47. Pair of ringed plovers *Charadrius hiaticula* L. camouflaged against background of shingle. Amguema River by 91st km. July 10, 1956.

g in the sun in Émma Bay.
ding to the observations of T.J. Cade, two-year-
s of both sexes were encountered daily in Boxer
t 8, 1950. On May 13, 1953, a two-year-old male

kin encountered huge flocks of eiders among the
June 3 they were already much reduced. Accord-
in 1934, lone eiders were seen after the arrival of
tion to the north from May 25 through June 4.
n small numbers on the coast between Uélen and
rom Uélen to Inchoun, I found tiny flocks consist-
n which males predominated; some flocks consisted

tkulen, I noticed small flocks. On July 4 a dense
nd there was an animated movement of different
o Mitkulen on July 13 and Inchoun on July 20 I
n eiders in small numbers. On my return to Uélen
breeding eiders over the village a common feature.
Jélen, many flocks consisting almost exclusively of
males predominating only in some flocks. The be-
sexes in the flocks was seen with the approach of
on were no longer to be seen. In August, 1932, at
y as an extremely rare event. They were also innu-
August, 1933, but in mid-September they became
set in on September 18 and ended on September 22,
ver Uélen. From September 23 males were also seen
g was over. Some of them remained separate from
the contrary, formed pairs, or at least two males
. On October 3 a huge flock, half male, settled in the
e in from afar. On October 5 I saw flocks of males,
in pairs. Consequent upon the molting of common
ales are isolated from the females for a period of not
bout July 20, to early October.
rding to the observations of A.I. Mineev, the males
olting flocks. In July when the females were incubat-
four or five together but not more. Based on my own
onclusion that most of the males deserted the island at
d and molted *en masse* elsewhere.
d with females for a second clutch constituted an ex-
1939, during a journey into Somnitel'naya Bay, I saw
the females. The former sat on the ice by the leads.
ter in the estuary of the Amerikanskaya river in the
fter this I did not see any more of them. On July 15,
wo-year-old male in Somnitel'naya Bay. At different
of the tundra at that time I saw flocks of wandering fe-
secured; all of them were devoid of brood patches. The

flock I saw flying over a knoll on July 2 probably consisted of two-year-old females with a non-breeding male. Later I found flocks of females on July 22, 27 and 28, in Rodgers Bay. A flock crossed one of the knolls which was closest to Atternon on July 29. Finally, on August 5 I put up a large flock of females from the Ozero lagoon.

Daily movements—As in many other ducks, daily periodic movements are well developed in common eiders. They are interrupted, apparently, only in birds that are molting, incubating or raising the young. Even the spring flight is the result of daily movements as the eiders arrive in new places at night time, in the hours of daily movements. Massive daily movements around Uélen, Vankarém and Cape Schmidt were referred to above. They occur on Wrangel Island and in Providence Bay to a smaller extent but with the same periodicity. In August, 1932, I noticed very regular daily flights of nonbreeding females from the sea into the apical parts of Providence and Émma bays. At Uélen, the flight in most cases is noticed over the village heading toward the settlement, and not the other way around. This has disastrous consequences for the eiders, which on setting out apparently cannot conceive what awaits them at the end. The most timid and wary birds on reaching Uélen do not attempt to turn back even after the forward ranks of the flock have been shot; they try either to fly faster toward the sea or to gain height. Common eiders usually escape by resorting to the latter course, but not the king eiders.

Molting in common eiders is similar to that in king eiders, the differences being only marginal. The agewise and seasonal plumage have been discussed in a special paper (Portenko 1952, pp. 1114 to 1119) and hence only additional information is given here.

The young males collected on Wrangel Island on September 27, 1932, differed from the young female shot in October by the presence of whitish specks on the large breast feathers.

I could not determine when the molting of the first winter-spring plumage began in the males. Six two-year-old males collected at Cape Chaplin in February had not completed molting by then. It would therefore appear that it begins later than in king eiders. The color of a male taken on Meechken on June 1, 1931, bore the characteristics of great virility. A male from Ryrkaipiya on July 18, 1938, was mostly in the first summer dress. The two-year-old common eiders spent the summer on the south coast of the Chukchi peninsula and south of it; on the north coast, they were a rarity. They were absent altogether from Wrangel Island.

In the second winter-spring plumage the male may be recognized from the brown patches on the anterior part of the wings, from the brown color of the tail tips and its small size. Among the large series of males that I collected on Wrangel Island there was only one with the markings of a three-year-old bird. The size of its testes and body weight were less than in much older males.

In adult males the summer molting began in July. On Meechken Island L.O. Belopol'skii noticed the commencement of molting on July 15, 1931. In 1932, I noticed males with a brownish head still flying from August 6 through 9 near Notapenmen. At Cape Schmidt, in the first few days of August, 1938, almost all the males showed growing summer feathers.

According to A.I. Mineev, on Wrangel Island the males began molting even in

ged plover *Charadrius hiaticula* L. with clutch. Amguema River by 91st km. July 7, 1956.

ith clutch of whimbrel *Numenius phaeopus variegatus* (Scop.). éem River. June 23, 1966. Photo by F. B. Chernyavskii.

July. Two of the males that I took on July 15, 1939, in the estuary of the Amerikanskaya River had a fair quantity of brown summer plumage on the upper side of the body and pinkocherous ones on the breast. On August 26, 1938, at Bruch spit on Wrangel Island, I came across a lone nonflying male in dark plumage which escaped by diving. On September 12, I saw four males in summer plumage in Rodgers Bay. In the fall of 1933 at Uélen, on September 23, the males were still in their dark summer plumage and were still flying. A specimen taken on September 27 had nearly completely grown flight feathers measuring 27.4 cm in length; only the central tail feathers were still growing.

After a month, on October 23, I saw a male which was quite white due to the growth of feathers of the succeeding winter-spring dress. The adult males collected by H.B. Collins (Friedmann 1932a) on St. Lawrence Island on September 27 and October 11 were in the molting condition. The last of the feathers of the dark summer dress disappeared during November. The male collected at Plover Bay on November 4, 1937, still had many brown feathers on its forehead. Some stray brown feathers remained on the cheeks and neck. Some feathers of the summer plumage were retained in males collected on November 15 and 17, but they were no longer seen in December birds.

Stray feathers of the first winter-spring dress were seen on the shoulders of yearling females collected at Providence Bay on November 30, 1937. In February young birds shedding of shoulder feathers was quite advanced. In females obtained on February 20, 1938, the shoulder feathers had been almost completely replaced. In the late broods, molting was correspondingly prolonged. In females obtained at Cape Chaplin on March 22 only some feathers of the winter-spring dress were to be seen on the shoulders, breast and sides. In two-year-olds taken at Providence Bay on July 18 and August 2, 1938, some new tail feathers were growing. The replacement of flight feathers occurred much later.

On June 18, 1934, at Uélen, I collected a female in the second winter-spring plumage. Her inner secondaries (tertiaries) were short and straight, i.e. not flexed crescentwise as in much older birds. Her ovary contained an egg which was ready for laying. Consequently it was not a two-year-old bird. The general color of the plumage was already quite dark: the beautiful broad russet edges of feathers, so prominent in February females, had faded by mid-June to a pale gray.

In the last 10 days of September 1938, at Rodgers Bay, I saw females with underdeveloped flight feathers. An old female obtained in early October still had not molted completely. The eiders obtained by H.B. Collins on St. Lawrence Island on October 12 and 20, 1930, had completely changed their plumage. From the third winter-spring plumage on it is almost impossible to determine the exact age of adult females.

A feathered female that I collected on June 12, 1939, on Wrangel Island and a feathered male shot at Providence Bay on November 30, 1937, were discussed in detail elsewhere (Portenko 1952).

The molting of common eiders as also of king eiders and other ducks affects the health of the birds and the loss of subcutaneous adipose formations. On July 18, 1938, I noticed thin adipose layers only in a two-year-old male, i.e. a nonbreeding bird, in the molting condition. In the fall and in the first half of the winter the adult males were usually devoid of subcutaneous fat but in February, with rare exceptions, the adipose formations were seen in some regions. From that time on, the plumpness of males went on increasing until the end of June. At Uélen three-year-old July males, unlike much older birds, were for some reason deprived of the adipose formations. Individual variations were appreciable. It should be pointed out that on Wrangel Island, at the beginning of summer, the males and females were especially plump. In July, however, the fat formations in the males became quite thin. The fall females were emaciated but a Wrangel female, which had completed molting by early October 1938, was very fat. In December filmy layers were noticed in two-year-old females; this was also the case in one-half of a group of two-year-olds in February. The rest of the two-year-olds in February were either plumper or totally emaciated. The adult females collected in February turned out to be plump. In June their plumpness was at a maximum but it fell sharply in July to film-like layers.

Migration—According to A.I. Mineev, the males flew away from Wrangel Island in the second half of August; according to my observations this happened even in the second half of July. In 1938, I rarely saw males from August 11 when I began my excursions. The females departed much later, depending on the growth of the chicks. According to the observations of A.I. Mineev they stayed there until the end of September and were noticed even in October in polynyas in the ice. My observations in general confirmed these timings. In the fall of 1938, at Rodgers Bay, eiders disappeared *en masse* by the end of September. In the first few days of October, Tayan still saw some in the tiny strait bisecting the Bruch spit, where they remained because of the abundant food supply. Moreover, on October 24 he noticed young eiders in Somnitel'naya Bay. Finally, on October 28, I shot two females which were the last of the flying birds. In 1960 A.G. Velizhanin saw the last of the eiders at Cape Blossom on September 28; there was snow all around by then.

In the diaries of the *Vega* and the *Maud* expeditions flocks of eiders are recorded to the northwest of the Chukchi peninsula in the fall of 1878, 1922 and 1924. But unfortunately no distinctions are made between species and it is not always certain that the flocks contained eiders at all. After the *Vega* became icebound on September 28 at Pitlekai, two eiders were shot on October 9. Even on October 23, when no open water had been seen from the ship for over a week, a lone female flew in and attempted to settle by the fire escape. On being disturbed she descended onto the ice and was shot.

According to my observations, at Uélen in the fall of 1933 eiders were becoming rare by mid-September. The weather turned sharply for the worse from the evening of September 18: there was a strong northwesterly wind and a cold snap set in, causing a general migration of birds. On the morning of September 23, when the weather warmed up and there was a slight drizzle, the eiders again started flying through Uélen and molting males were seen. On September 25, I saw a flock of eiders far away on the ice. On September 27 eiders were seen flying over Uélen in large numbers. On October 1 many eiders were seen on the sea. On October 3, in the lagoon, a huge flock of male eiders, evidently coming from a distance, descended on the water. I also saw flocks of males on October 5. In the last days of September and in early October there was a mass flight and migration of eiders around Uélen when the ice came inshore. The ice crust gradually covered the lagoon concentrically from the banks and on October 8 the entire surface finally froze. The Chukchians told me that the eiders were then in large numbers near Naukan and Dezhnev settlement where there were still some openings in the ice. From time to time they continued to fly over the frozen Uélen lagoon. In my diary I recorded as rare phenomena eider flocks on October 8, 9, 12, 15, 16 and 17, and a lone bird on October 22. When the sea near Uélen again opened up on October 23 I noticed some males and females near the surf. They were very confident birds: some of them slowly flew away while the others dived on my approaching. They apparently came from uninhabited places. On October 25 and 26 eiders flew over the sea in large numbers. Sometimes they turned to the west, probably in search of places with abundant food. On October 27 the ice again came in at Uélen and more flocks were noticed all that day. But later the eiders were seen only on occasion and were confined for the most part to the leads which shrank with every advancing day. On November 10 two or three flocks and two stragglers were seen and on November 16 a flock of females. P.T. Butenko saw eiders resting on the ice. On November 28, I saw a flock heading for Cape Inchoun. On December 4 I was informed that a flock of about 50 eiders had flown east. On January 4, 1934, a lone bird was noticed flying in the same direction. Thus the migration of eiders around Uélen gradually decreased and ceased. They did not winter at Uélen although they were found there for a long time in a totally winter environment.

On St. Lawrence Island O.J. Murie collected a female on October 28 and a male on November 7, 1935.

According to the observations of I.O. Olenev, in October, 1932, before Émma Bay iced over eiders gathered in huge flocks. With the advancing ice crust they gradually moved out to the exit of Providence Bay. In 1934, he visited Émma Bay on September 9. Males and females, perhaps local birds, were seen swimming in the bay. The same picture was to be seen there on September 14, 1939. On November 4, 1937, P.T. Butenko noticed a flock on the shore around the bay but they were probably migrating birds which had come to winter in the neighborhood. They were there throughout November but disappeared in early December. After strong northerly storms, on December 14 the bay began to freeze. On December 22 there was a south wind which broke the ice. After a few hours common eiders along with other marine birds were seen in the exposed leads. On December 28, passages were again formed and eiders came in. Evidently the massive migration of common eiders to the south was in response to the closed bay.

At Krest Bay, I saw eiders on the coast before Uél'kal' on September 2, 1932. P.T. Butenko saw them on October 17 and 18, 1937. On October 13 he sailed through Anadyr Strait and all that day saw only one eider flying over the sea on the traverse of Cape Navarin toward the Anadyr estuary because of the strong wind.

Habits—The eider for most of the year is a very silent duck but in June and July I often heard its bass call note. When the nonbreeding females gathered in flocks in Rodgers Bay their cries could be heard far off as a hoarse clucking.

The eider is very rarely seen walking on land. When it does it stands more upright than other ducks. It runs away quickly but awkwardly from the nest. Starting up abruptly on the approach of a man, the female quite often sprays excreta on the nest.

Eider flocks very often fly without any particular order, especially when there are many birds. Small flocks like to form echelons. Quite often the eiders fly in small flocks but not with such discipline as geese or even cranes. The corners of such flocks are rounded although this is disturbed sometimes. The single file flight is interesting. It is seen with small groups of birds, not exceeding 20. At Providence Bay, I quite often saw female eiders flying in this order, alternately with murres. When the male flew with the female it was always behind and slightly to the right.

The eider is a very wary duck and on being chased panics more than even emperor and brent geese.

Food—Since most of the specimens were collected during migrations to the feeding places stomach contents were obtained only from a few of them. Analysis gave the following results: 1) Providence Bay, August 26, 1932, ♀. Some small bones of tiny fish, up to 100 crustaceae and several pebbles. 2) Uélen, September 27, 1933, ♂. Nine pebbles. 3) Uélen, June 7, 1934, ♀. Fibrous lump of stalks or leaves of grassy plants. Pebbles. 4) Uélen, June 14, 1934, ♂. Shell bits of four large molluscs. Two large pebbles. 5) Uélen, June 14, 1934, ♂. Shell fragments of two large molluscs. Teeth of a large fish. Up to 100 pebbles. 6) Wrangel Island, September 15, 1938, ♂, juv. Digested mass of *Amphipoda* and *Astarte* filling three-fourths of stomach volume; mollusc and about 8 g of tiny pebbles. 7) Wrangel Island, June 8, 1939, ♂. Rounded bits of shells of a bivalve mollusc. 0.5 g of much digested thin gruel and 37 pebbles 3 to 12 mm in diameter. 8) Wrangel Island, June 12, 1939, ♀. 150 pebbles 3 to 8 mm in diameter and sand occupying one-third of the stomach volume. 9) Wrangel Island, June 15, 1939, ♀. Five pebbles 4 to 8 mm in diameter and eight large ones 10 to 18 mm in diameter. 10) Wrangel Island, June 29, 1939, ♂. 50 gnats, 0.25 g of digested plant residues and 150 pebbles 3 to 12 mm in diameter. 11) Wrangel Island, July 15, 1939, ♂. A crab *Chionocetes opilio* Fab. swallowed whole. 12) Wrangel Island, July 15, 1939, ♀. Filamentous alga and about 30 bits of gravel 1 to 4 mm in diameter.

The stomach of a female brought back by the *Vega* expedition from Mama on May 23, 1879, revealed a *Trochus*.

The stomachs of two females collected near Gambell at the end of May, 1952, showed *Gastropoda*: *Neptunea ventricosa* (Carpent.), *Colus spitzbergensis* (Reeve), and *Buccinum normale*; and some *Decapoda*: *Pagurus undosus* (Benedict) and *Hyas coarctatus alutaceus* Brandt.

Weight—P.T. Butenko weighed some eiders that he collected in Providence Bay and at Cape Chaplin and found that their weights varied very widely. Nine males weighed 2,615, 2,370, 2,320, 2,290, 2,250, 2,150, 2,110, 1,900 and 1,750 g. The weight of three females was 2,800, 2,690 and 1,945 g. Unfortunately very few females were weighed but comparison of the weight range of 1,750 to 2,615 (average 2,195) g of the nine males and 1,945 to 2,800 (average 2,478) g of the three females shows that the females were heavier than the males. A male caught on June 24, 1938, at Providence Bay weighed only 1,750 g in spite of appreciable subcutaneous adipose formations. On the other hand, a male obtained at Plover Bay on November 19, 1937, with only adipose films weighed 2,615 g. Evidently these weight variations are simply individual characteristics which cannot be explained by the age of the bird or the season of the year. It will be interesting to compare these average values with the weights taken by S.I. Korobko on Wrangel Island. Twelve males and five females were weighed: males—2,245 to 2,572 (2,407) g and females—2,027 to 2,823 (2,436) g. Thus even in the latter case the females turned out to be heavier than the males.

Economic importance—On the coast of the Chukchi peninsula and on Wrangel Island, after its colonization, this bird has been a very common, widely distributed and popular target of hunters due wholly to its value as an excellent table bird, its size, weight and abundance.

Even before firearms penetrated this area there used to be a special hunt for eiders and to a smaller extent for old squaws using the special device called "eplicathet" in the Chukchian language (Fig. 34). It consists of some bones tied to long cords and bunched together at the opposite end. The following description is based on several specimens that I brought from Uélen. The bones, numbering six (they generally range from four to seven) are shaped from old walrus incisors with a crude axe-like implement. They are shaped like an egg or a plum, resembling a large walnut in color and size. The length varies from 38 to 45 mm and width from 26 to 32 mm. At the broad end a groove is cut and a hole made through it to tie the cord. The cords used to be made of deer tendons but the one available in my collection was made of white 2 mm cotton cord, which is extensively used in making nets in the Far East. The length of each of the six cords is up to 90 cm. At the opposite end they are plaited along with flight feathers which appeared to be of old squaws. Other specimens differ in the better finish of the bones, plaiting of colored rags into the feathers, use of different type of strands, etc. The eplicathet in A.I. Argentov's description (1857a, p. 101) was somewhat different in size. It is usually suspended inside the yaranga and can be carried by any of the menfolk when walking. On foggy days when the eiders may suddenly be sighted in the haze above the yarangas the young boys and the men carry the eplicathet on the head. They hold the cords around the head in such a manner that the bones protrude on the forehead. This practice has imparted to the Chukchians an original and altogether exclusive appearance.

On the approach of a flock of flying eiders the hunter holds the bones in his left hand and the ends of the cords in his right hand and flings the eplicathet upward. This requires strength, dexterity and skill. On attaining a maximum height of a few tens of meters the device turns upside down like a star; the ends of the cords tied together fall in the center and the cords with the bones diverge from it radially; because of centrifugal force these bones fall on the periphery. The moment an eider brushes the cord the bone begins to twist around the body, wing or neck of the bird. Entangled in the cords, the bird falls to the ground. I remember an incident which occurred in front of me when the eplicathet got the wing of an eider. The bird first fell rapidly, as though dead, but landed alive and tried to run away. When used by an expert the cords may entangle two or three eiders, but more often only one. The eplicathet is often hurled by the hunter several times before landing a bird. Nevertheless, the effect of this device is indeed gratifying and the results surprisingly good.

The entire hunting scene is original even from the purely ethnographic viewpoint. When a flock approaches a village the Chukchians raise a weird noise, the shots only adding to the din. The stunned birds gather into a dense flock or even lose height; either of these is favorable for hurling the eplicathet. In clear weather the common eiders in such cases slow down, rapidly gain height and head toward the knolls, bypassing the village and reaching the sea faster; but in a dense fog common, and especially king, eiders fly low over the yarangas and suffer losses

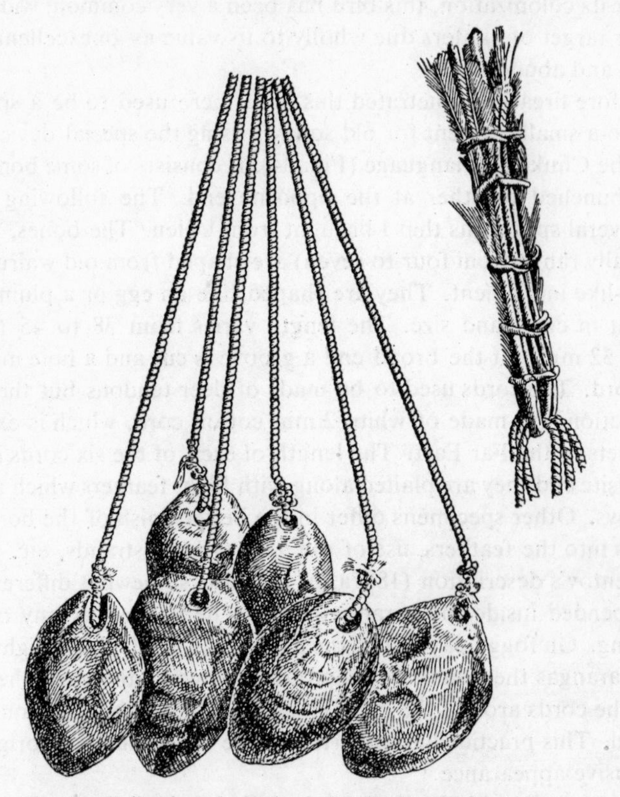

Fig. 34. Eplicathet, device hurled at flock of flying eiders.

from their ranks. The Chukchians immediately raise frightful shouts and yells from their wild hunting throats in the best of traditions. Some run between the yarangas while the others respond to them from inside. On my second day at Uélen, I was woken up in the morning by the unusual noise raised by a hunting party. From lack of experience I at first feared that the entire village was rioting. A.P. Kuzyakin witnessed eider hunting at Uélen from June 27 through July 3, 1957. The local Chukchians, old and young, especially boys from 12 to 15 years of age, shot the eiders with shotguns from the windows of their houses. Since the cartridges were liberally charged with powder the noise of firing gave the impression that some military operation was in progress.

The eplicathet has the advantage that hunting with it is noiseless and the walrus are not frightened; for the local hunters this is essential. The usefulness of hunting with eplicathets evidently depends to a very great extent on the flight of dense, numerous flocks. Hence it is practiced only in places where the ducks gather massively, mostly on the north coast of the Chukchi peninsula, for example, at Vankarém. Having described the local hunting of eiders, K.L. Hooper (1884, p. 61) pointed out that with the help of these eplicathets the young Chukchians could often knock down up to half a dozen ducks from flocks. The eiders falling to the ground are gathered by the hunters and crushed to the ground with the knees in such a way that the blood does not flow out. These same hunters showed great skill in hitting ducks sitting in flocks on the water with a stone from a sling.

As far as I know the eplicathet is not used on the south coast of the Chukchi peninsula. Shotguns were more in use there. N.P. Sokol'nikov writes that on April 25, 1902, there was steady firing as whole flocks of eiders flew very low uninterruptedly, through Unyyn yarangas at Cape Chaplin. Over Red'kin the eiders were as numerous but the residents did not have a single shotgun. According to I.O. Olenev, in January and February, 1932, on frigid moonlit nights, successful hunting of eiders was carried out at Istiget village where a shot into a large flock would bring down seven or eight birds. The frozen eiders were used in very large numbers.

During my stay at Uélen in 1933 and 1934 the Chukchians used shotguns extensively if, under the prevailing ice conditions, the walrus were far out and the shots would not frighten them. In September the eiders were few and the use of the eplicathet became unproductive. Hunters used it only from time to time and resorted to hunting with the gun. For a good scatter of shot and a very sharp strike, which are desirable when firing at flocks flying high, the Chukchians used a very high powder charge. They used guns with the muzzle enlarged at the end like a small bell. The fact that the Chukchians risked shaping their guns in this way showed how extensively they practiced shooting the flocks even at long distances.

On the spit joining Cape Kozhevnikov with Ryrkaipiya village, I saw the hunting of eiders during their daily movements. Places as convenient for hunting and as dangerous for the birds are to be found elsewhere along the coast. In the spring at Uélen I successfully hunted eiders from hides in the tiny strait between the lagoons. I was surprised how much advance aiming was necessary in spite of the fact that the birds were apparently flying slowly.

On Wrangel Island I witnessed a totally different style of hunting nonbreeding females flying in flocks over the tundra at Somnitel'naya Bay. Eskimo Nanaun gave a croak which resembled that made sometimes when hunting male ducks in the spring; the eiders then changed direction, surrounded the party and flew so close that they could be shot. Hunting molting male and other eiders on the sea was so difficult that I saw no point in continuing it for long.

Apart from its meat, the common eider finds practically no use in the Chukchi peninsula and Wrangel Island. Among the heads of ducks processed in the factory at Cape Schmidt in 1933, I found only one of the common eider. I saw few specimens with fanciers for making rugs and collars from eider heads. This rarity is explained by the absence from the heads of common eiders of the variegated colors so characteristic of those of king and spectacled eiders. Down and feathers are

Table 29. Wing and bill measurements in subspecies of common eiders, cm

Subspecies	Adult males				Adult females				2-year males				2-year females			
	Max.	Min.	Mean	No. of samples	Max.	Min.	Mean	No. of samples	Max.	Min.	Mean	No. of samples	Max.	Min.	Mean	No. of samples
Wing length																
S. m. v-nigrum	33.9	29.2	31.5	66	31.9	29.3	30.5	30	29.9	27.5	29.2	9	30.1	27.9	28.8	8
S. m. mollissima	31.6	27.6	30.0	21	30.1	28.4	29.5	7	27.4	27.4	27.4	1	27.2	27.2	27.2	1
S. m. borealis	30.8	29.2	29.9	8	30.9	27.4	28.8	13	28.8	28.8	28.8	1				
S. m. dresseri	29.5	29.5	29.5	1	28.2	28.2	28.2	1								
Bill length from rear end of nostril																
S. m. v-nigrum	4.17	3.24	3.71	66	3.77	2.74	3.51	31	3.92	3.47	3.65	9	3.78	3.36	3.60	8
S. m. mollissima	4.14	3.65	3.93	24	4.11	3.50	3.82	8	3.50	3.50	3.50	1	3.81	3.81	3.81	1
S. m. borealis	3.88	3.54	3.75	3	3.85	3.33	3.56	13	3.93	3.93	3.93	1				
S. m. dresseri	3.65	3.65	3.65	1	3.83	3.83	—	1								
Distance from rear end of nostril to end of lobe																
S. m. v-nigrum	4.64	2.55	3.53	66	3.57	2.21	3.00	31	4.48	2.29	3.45	9	3.82	3.14	3.42	7
S. m. mollissima	3.55	3.03	3.40	24	3.61	2.20	2.99	8	2.99	2.99	2.99	1	3.05	3.05	3.05	1
S. m. borealis	3.28	3.13	3.22	3	3.10	2.37	2.75	13	3.55	3.55	3.55	1				
S. m. dresseri	4.44	4.44	4.44	1	3.65	3.65	3.65	1								
Distance from tip of bill to end of lobe																
S. m. v-nigrum	8.34	6.32	7.20	66	7.26	5.82	6.47	31	7.37	5.82	6.97	9	7.51	6.54	6.90	7
S. m. mollissima	8.02	6.76	7.37	24	7.78	5.82	6.82	8	6.52	6.52	6.52	1	7.09	7.09	7.09	1
S. m. borealis	7.14	6.71	6.99	3	6.83	5.65	6.27	13	7.48	7.48	7.48	1				
S. m. dresseri	8.05	8.05	8.05	1	7.45	7.45	7.45	1								

used occasionally by tourists.

The common eider is hunted for its meat at Uélen in smaller numbers than king eiders, but is shot in larger numbers on Wrangel Island because of the absence of king eiders there. For the wintering personnel at the Polar Station this was a very desirable fowl only inferior in numbers and quality to the lesser snow and brent geese, but superior to murres and alcids. For others the economic importance of common eiders is the same as that of king eiders.

On St. Lawrence Island, according to F.H. Fay, the common eider was hunted by the eskimos in the spring at the rate of not more than 500 every year. In some nesting colonies the eggs are gathered, the number of eggs exceeding 1,000. In the winter season the eiders suffer losses from predators like gyrfalcons and especially the snowy owl. These losses are roughly equal to those caused by man.

Systematics of the subspecies—Within the USSR, I differentiate the following subspecies:

1. **Somateria mollissima borealis** (Brehm). The bare area of beak projecting in the form of a tiny cape above the fillet terminates in a fairly broad, rounded lobe (Fig. 35). The shape of the bill is similar to the nominal form but the size on the average is smaller. The wing length is also similar (Table 29). The beak of males is orange-yellow, as are the bare parts of the legs. The color of the plumage is the same as in the nominal form.

This is distributed from 100° west in Arctic America in the east to Spitsbergen and Franz Josef Land.

In the Fauna of the USSR, A.Ya. Tugarinov (1941) has omitted subspecies *S. m. borealis* since, due to an unfortunate coincidence, the collection of common eiders from Spitsbergen in the Institute of Zoology, Academy of Sciences of the USSR, consists of females and a lone male, the latter in summer plumage. The very limited series from Franz Josef Land consists exclusively of females. I have with me a male collected by N.P. Demme on Hooker Island on June 2, 1933. In it the lobes are so broad, bulging and rounded at the ends that it could by no means be compared with *S. m. mollissima*.

In the summer male specimen of *S. m. borealis* from Spitsbergen the capelike formations on the beak are also very broad but to a smaller extent than in the males from Franz Josef Land. This evidently is to be explained by the same shedding of soft portions of the beak during the summer molt as seen in king eiders. Moreover, I have with me two Greenland specimens preserved in the Department of Zoology of Vertebrates, Leningrad University. In them the skin lobes on the beaks are broad and bluntly rounded as in the male from Franz Josef Land. In one adult male collected in Lichtenfels by Dr. Finster on July 14, 1875, yellow coloration was seen at places on the beak and legs but this darkened in course of time. Another specimen bearing the general label "Greenland" was a two-year-old male. Females from Spitsbergen and Franz Josef Land and also from Greenland did not reveal distinct differences from the nominal subspecies. In Arctic America *S. m. borealis* forms transitions to the subspecies *S. m. v-nigrum*.

2. **Somateria mollissima mollissima** (L.). The lobes on the beak terminate in a narrow and sharp angle (Fig. 35). On the average the beak size is greater than that of *S. m. borealis* and even greater than that of *S. m. v-nigrum*. The wing span is

much smaller than that of *S. m. v-nigrum*. The color of the beak in the males is a greenish-olive and the claws are blackish. The greenish velvety ear coverts and the nape have an ultramarine or bluish shade. The green color stops short of the eyes. The throat is invariably without a patch. The cream color of the breast has a tinge of vinous pink. The black color of upper tail coverts extends far up the back. In the variegated colors of females, there are many black and gray shades and the feather fringe is very bright and ocherous.

This subspecies is distributed in the USSR in the Kola peninsula, on the Bering

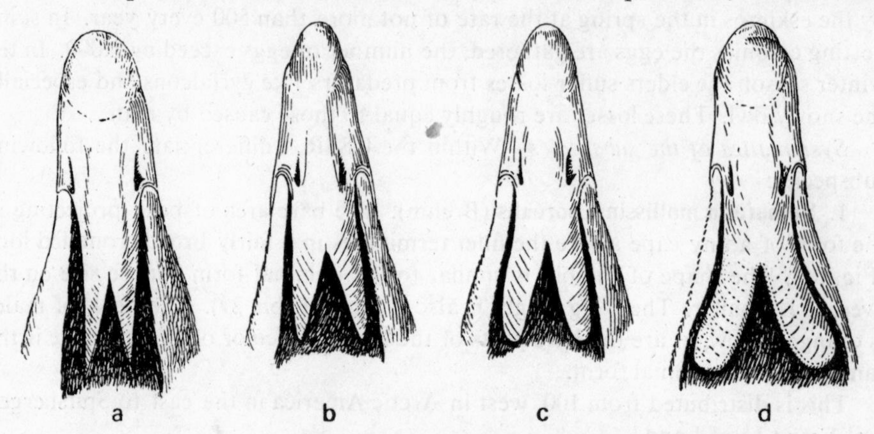

Fig. 35. Beaks of subspecies of common eiders *Somateria mollissima* (L.): a—*S. m. v-nigrum* Gray; b—*S. m. mollissima* (L.); c—*S. m. borealis* (Brehm) and d—*S. m. dresseri* Sharpe.

Sea coast and to the east not farther than Novaya Zemlya and Vaigach. It only flies past farther to the east.

The specimens from Novaya Zemlya and the Kola peninsula are identical in color as well as in size. In Novaya Zemlya, specimens with a much broader lobe on the beak are sometimes seen, being somewhat closer to *S. m. borealis*. The males and females from Kandalaksh are distinguished by their very narrow, sharp lobes.

3. **Somateria mollissima v-nigrum** Gray—The lobes on the beak terminate in a very sharp angle which extends onto the forehead in the form of a parting in the plumage (Fig. 35). When measuring with a compass it is sometimes difficult to find the end of the exposed zone. The shape of bill is somewhat different from that of the preceding subspecies. The anterior part, from the rear edge of the nostril to the tip, is shorter in *S. m. v-nigrum* than in *S. m. mollissima* and *S. m. borealis*. The rear part of the beak from the nostril to the end of the lobe is longer. The wing is considerably longer than in the two preceding subspecies. In males the beak is orange-yellow like the legs. The green velvety feathers have an apple green color. The green color extends under the eyes, as in the Labrador subspecies *S. m. dresseri*. On the throat the black V-shaped patch is usually broad and sharp in outline but sometimes not so prominent or even altogether absent. The cream color of the breast is replaced by a deep yellow ocherous shade. The black color from the rump does not extend as far as in *S. mollissima*. The females have a more russet hue.

This subspecies nests from Wrangel Island and perhaps Chetyrekhstolb Island in the east, along the arctic coast of Alaska and Canada to 100° west and in the south to northern Kamchatka and southern Alaska.

The collection at the Institute of Zoology, Academy of Sciences, USSR, contains a male eider taken by E.I. Plechev in Shkhiperov Bay, Ol'skii region, on the Okhotsk coast. It is characterized by its large size and very long wing span of 33.5 cm; in color it is altogether similar to *S. m. v-nigrum* males but the V-shaped patch is absent from the throat. The hunter who collected the bird remembered that this patch was also absent in the other birds he shot. This led A.Ya. Tugarinov (1941, p. 333, footnote) to posit the existence of a special Okhotsk subspecies. It should be remembered that J.A. Allen (1905) gave two subspecies of eiders: *S. m. mollissima* (L.) for Gizhigi, from where he obtained seven specimens, and *S. m. v-nigra* Gray for Anadyr settlement (Novo-mariinsk) and Cape Chaplin. Consequently he had some basis on which to distinguish Okhotsk from Chukchi-Anadyr eiders.

Very recently A.P. Vas'kovskii drew attention to Okhotsk eiders. He had occasion to study the stuffed males and females exhibited in Magadansk Regional Museum and got the skin of a male bird. He gave me a detailed description of these three specimens and their measurements. At present the following information is available for three males and one female from Shkhiperov Bay:

Wing length, cm

♂, June 20,	1939,	Plechev	33.5
♂,	1938,	Magadansk Regional Museum	32.2
♂, June,	1945,	Vas'kovskii	31.4
♀,	1938,	Magadansk Regional Museum	32.0

Except for E.I. Plechev's specimen I did not verify the measurements personally and hence the values are not wholly comparable. Ignoring this deficiency, it may be seen that Okhotsk males do not surpass Chukchi birds in wing length. In particular, in one Anadyr male with an excellent V-shaped patch on the throat the maximum wing length was 33.9 cm. Consequently great length is not at all associated with absence of the patch. On the other hand, among the birds that I collected there were some in which the patch was very faded. For example, in one bird from Uélen the throat patch was very pale and the lateral bands in the anterior apex were not completely joined. In one male from Wrangel Island only pale vestiges of the patch remained. Finally, in Plechev's sample some dark plumelets were to be seen on the white throat as a rudimentary characteristic present in the other species of *S. m. v-nigrum.* A.P. Vas'kovskii reported that two males he had seen were without a black throat patch. This patch is sometimes seen as an irregular phenomenon in male *S. m. borealis* and especially *S. m. dresseri.* The specimen of *S. m. dresseri* that I examined had a small blackish patch on the throat. Hence this character is not a regular feature of other subspecies and it is impossible to prove its regular recurrence from a small number of Okhotsk birds: this conclusion could be disproved by the very next specimen with a patch.

Taking into account the fact that the common eider is characterized by the formation of isolated populations with negligible differences, as noticed above for the Kandalaksha colony (large eggs laid in large numbers), Okhotsk eiders cannot be recognized as a special subspecies on the basis of the available data.

Specimens— 1) Senyavin Strait, July 25, 1900, ♂, Akif'ev; 2 to 7) Providence Bay, July 18, 1912, ♂♀♀♀ and July 20, 1912, ♂♂, Starokadomskii; 8 and 9) same place, July 20, 1912, ♂♀, Arngol'd; 10 and 11) same place, September 24, 1912, ♂♀, juv., Starokadomskii; 12 and 13) Émma Bay, August 2, 1914, ♀♀, Starokadomskii; 14) Providence Bay, August 12, 1914, ♀, Arngol'd; 15) Kolyuchin Bay, August 19, 1914, ♀, Starokadomskii; 16 and 17) Wrangel Island, June 25, 1928, ♂ and without date, pull., 1929, G.A. Ushakov; 18 and 19) Meechken Island, May 13 and June 1, 1931, ♂♂, 2° anno, Belopol'skii; 20) Cape Hawaii, August 2, 1932, pull., Mineev; 21 and 22) southeastern part of Wrangel Island, August 5, 1932, pull., Mineev; 23) Providence Bay, August 26, 1932, ♀, Portenko; 24 to 26) Rodgers Bay, September 27, 1932, ♂♂, 1° anno and October 1, 1932, ♀, 1° anno, Mineev; 27) Cape Schmidt, without date, 1933, ♂, Portenko; 28 and 29) Chaun Bay, June 25 and 29, 1933, ♂♀, Pavlov; 30) Providence Bay, without date, 1933, ♂, Pavlov; 31) Cape Schmidt, without date, pull., Portenko; 32 to 34) Uélen, September 27, 1933, ♂, June I and 7, 1934, ♂♀, Portenko; 35) southeastern part of Wrangel Island, June 8, 1934, ♂, Mineev; 36) same place, without date, ♂, Vakulenko; 37 to 44) Uélen, June 13 and 14, 1934, 3♂♂, June 18, 19 and 26, 1934, ♂, 3♀, and July 29, 1934, ♂, Portenko; 45) Wrangel Island, without date, 1937, ♂, Portenko; 46 to 51) Providence Bay, Plover, November 4, 15, 17, 19 and 30, 1937, 5 ♂♂ and ♀, Butenko; 52 and 53) same place, December 4 and 7, 1937, ♂, ♀, Butenko; 54 to 78) Cape Chaplin, February 6, 7, 9, 13, 14, 15 and 20, 1938, 20 ♂♂ and 6 ♀♀, Butenko; 79) same place, March 28, 1938, 1♀, 2° anno, Butenko; 80 to 83) Providence Bay, May 4, 1938, ♂, and June 24, 1938, ♂♂, ♀, Butenko, 84) same place, July 12, 1938, ♀, Portenko; 85) Ryrkaipiya village, July 18, 1938, ♂, 2° anno, Portenko; 86) Kivak village, July 29, 1938, ○, Butenko; 87) Providence Bay, August 6, 1938, pull., Butenko; 88) Wrangel Island, August 24, 1938, ♀, Druzhinin; 89 and 90) Rodgers Bay, September 15, 1938, ♂, juv. and early October 1938, ♀, Portenko; 91) Wrangel Island, Akatylanva boundary, June 8, 1939, ♂, Portenko; 92) Rodgers Bay, June 12, 1939, ♀, Portenko; 93 and 94) Akatylanva boundary, June 13, 1939, ♂♂, Portenko; 95 and 96) Somnitel'naya Bay, June 14, 1939, ♂, ♀, Portenko; 97 to 105) Amerikanskaya River, Wrangel Island, June 15, 1939, 7 ♂♂ and ♀♀, Portenko; 106) Nasha River, June 29, 1939, ♂, Portenko; 107 and 108) estuary of the Amerikanskaya River, July 15, 1939, ○⊙, Portenko; and 109 and 110) Somnitel'naya Bay, July 15, 1939, ♀♀, Portenko.

Biological collection— 1) clutch of four eggs, Rodgers Bay, July 4, 1932, Mineev; 2) four eggs, Providence Bay, July 6, 1938, Butenko; 3) one egg, Providence Bay, July 12, 1938, Butenko; 4) two eggs from a clutch, Nasha River, June 27, 1939, Portenko; and 5) clutch of five eggs, Rodgers Bay, June 29, 1939, Portenko.

Mergus merganser L.—Merganser

Bones were found in the archaeological excavations on St. Lawrence Island.

According to H. Friedmann (1934a), some bones of this species were discovered in five different 1,000-year-old excavations on the southeastern tip of the island.

The merganser has not been pointed out by anyone for the Chukchi peninsula or for Wrangel Island though it flies over the western part of the Chukchi peninsula especially. It nests on the Kolyma, where J. Koren (Schaanning 1954) collected a young bird on September 25, 1915, and on the upper course of the Anadyr to the east almost to the estuary of the Maine (Portenko 1939b). But it is even fewer in numbers at these extremes of distribution in northeastern Asia.

32. **Mergus serrator** L.—**Red-breasted Merganser**

Local name—Chukchian: Kyrguérgaatl'.

Distribution and status—Nests in the interior of the Chukchi peninsula but in very small numbers. Flies away in the winter. Altogether absent from Wrangel Island.

The references by E.W. Nelson to the nesting of this merganser on the Chukchi coast from Providence Bay to Cape Schmidt were based only on conjecture. In his 1883 work (p. 103) it is stated that though he did not notice it on the Siberian coast of the Arctic Ocean in summer, 1881, its known distribution along adjoining coasts suggested that it should be found there too. In Providence Bay, P.T. Butenko and I noted the red-breasted merganser several times in the summer; there is no doubt about its nesting in the neighborhood of the bay. On July 12, 1938, I put up a lone male at Émma Bay. In the same year, on July 11, Butenko collected a male near Kivak village and later, on August 6, shot two mergansers at Providence Bay. Apart from these finds by Butenko and myself no one has noticed other mergansers there, including I.O. Olenev who wintered in 1931/1932. E.W. Nelson (1887) found the red-breasted merganser nesting on St. Lawrence Island in the summer of 1884. H.B. Collins (Friedmann 1932a) evidently collected a female in September in Gambell. According to an eyewitness account by O.W. Geist (1939) a male was shot in 1932. F.H. Fay and T.J. Cade (1959) regarded this species of duck as rare; only a few residents in Gambell had encountered it there. Between May 25 and June 10 pairs and lone males in breeding dress were noticed. On June 6, 1960, a male and a female flying above Boxer Bay were noticed by E.G.F. Sauer (Sauer and Urban 1964). The tibiotarsus and carpo metacarpus of a red-breasted merganser were found in archaeological excavations (Friedmann 1934a).

É.V. Schmidt once saw two pairs in Mechigmensk Gulf in spring flight and collected two males. On July 27, 1934, a Chukchian hunter at Uélen brought me a male merganser as a rare bird of those parts. The chukchian name "Kyrguérgaatl' " which I have transcribed as spelled by a resident of Markovo was not unknown to the Chukchians in Uélen. I myself never saw a merganser in the immediate neighborhood of Markovo but found them in the interior of the peninsula on the Kol'oam-Véem and Utte-Véem rivers. On the former the merganser was sighted on August 11, 1934, in the middle reaches. On August 15 I found a brood somewhat further up the river, nearer to Lake Kool'ong. Red-breasted mergansers were seen more often on the Utte-Véem River. On July 6, 1934, birds flew over the lower course of the river singly and in pairs. Quite often they were also seen upstream. On July 10, I again noticed a male on my return journey near the lower reaches of the river. A little before, on July 5, I saw three mergansers in gray plumage over the Inchoun lagoon. On July 4, while waiting at Mitkulen because of thick mist, I noticed a flock flying east over the sea. The flock consisted of males and females. Farther to the west along the north coast of the Chukchi peninsula mergansers were not found at all, not even by the *Vega* expedition. In 1956 I found a red-breasted merganser in the interior of the Chukchi peninsula on the Amguema. I repeatedly saw a pair of mergansers or one of them for a whole month at the 91st km and hence am inclined to regard them as nesting birds. É.V. Schmidt never found mergansers at Chaun Bay or even on the lower reaches of the Kolyma. But S.A. Buturlin (1906b, p. 5) found innumerable red-breasted mergansers on the lower reaches of the Kolyma.

Habitat—On the Kol'oam and Utte-Véem rivers and their tributaries red-breasted mergansers stay close to the shoals in the nesting period. I found a brood by the shoal under a low bluff. At Émma Bay, I found a male feeding in the shallows by the rocky shore. Mergansers avoided the sea though they were seen near the shoreline.

Seasonal phenomena—In 1956 a pair of mergansers was seen on June 14 on the Amguema when the ice started to drift over a considerable stretch of the opened river. As late as July 14 I found a flying pair, the male behind the female, quacking away quietly. The brood I found on August 15, 1934, consisted of a female and eight downy chicks which were comparable to teals in size. The adult female was in molting condition, having shed all of her primary flight feathers. When she was shot down the brood huddled close and swam quickly away up the river in spite of very strong current on the shoals. I retrieved her only the next day.

Food—The stomach of a female collected on the Utte-Véem River on July 9, 1934, contained about 20 tiny stones. The stomach of a male from Uélen shot on July 27 contained the vertebrae and other bones of tiny fish, 10 calcified strips of cephalopod molluscs and tiny stones.

A male collected on arrival near Kivak village was very fat.

Economic importance—Though there is nothing to prevent the shooting of mergansers it has no economic significance because of its rarity.

Systematics—Based on the available material I could not detect any differences justifying geographic races of red-breasted mergansers.

Specimens— 1) Middle reaches of Utte-Véem River, July 9, 1934, ♀, Portenko; 2) Uélen, July 27, 1934, ♂, Portenko; 3) upper course of Kol'oam-Véem River, August 15, 1934, ♀, Portenko; 4) Kivak village, June 11, 1938, ♂, Butenko; and 5 and 6) Providence Bay, August 6, 1938, ○○, Butenko.

Order V. FALCONIFORMES—DIURNAL BIRDS OF PREY

33. **Buteo lagopus kamtschatkensis** Dement.—**Rough-legged Buzzard**

Local name—Chukchian: Pòs'yan-pyglyàu at Uélen and Pòchan-pòvlyau at Seishan. In Eskimo: yă-yā-yĭ-kă on St. Lawrence Island.

Distribution and status—Nests in the Chukchi peninsula but only at places and in small numbers. Flies away in the winter. Absent from Wrangel Island.

Not one find has been reported from the south coast of the Chukchi peninsula.

On St. Lawrence Island it nests sporadically and perhaps not every year. O.W. Geist (1939) took a young female on September 20, 1934, at Gambell village and noticed another bird after a few days. According to F.H. Fay and T.J. Cade (1959), on August 6, 1956, a nest with two nestlings was found east of Boxer Bay. Another pair was noticed in the southwestern part of the island. In 1950 a disused nest was found, evidently of a rough-legged buzzard, by a rivulet entering Boxer Bay. According to the information collected, the birds had nested in the preceding year but were not sighted at all in 1950. On June 16, 1954, two paired buzzards were noticed in the same region but a lone bird was noticed on August 8, 1957 flying near Cape Ivunat. On June 12 and 26 E.G.F. Sauer and E.K. Urban (1964) noticed a buzzard 2.5 miles from the valley of the Boxer River.

I saw the rough-legged buzzard singly around Uélen only in spring flight. This bird was seen more often farther to the west in the same spring flight; for example, two or three birds on the same day near Utten village. In the interior of the peninsula, I found the buzzard in the nesting period in the middle reaches of the Utte-Véem River. It was noticed on July 7, 1934. Later I saw a paired buzzard there on July 9. Around Cape Serdtse-Kamen' this raptor was seen several times in the spring of 1934 and an excellent specimen was presented to me. On May 17 I found three or four pairs there. On June 23, 1970, V.V. Leonovich detected a nesting pair near Seishan on the rocks by the shore. Evidently there were nestlings in the nest. On June 26 and July 7, solitary birds were noticed in the neighborhood of Énurmino. On May 16, 1934, traveling toward Cape Dzhenretlen from Kolyuchi Island, I noticed first one and later two buzzards. In the interior of the country I found a buzzard nest around the 87th km on the middle reaches of the Amguema in the summer of 1956. Evidently only one pair lived there. It was the only bird of prey noticed in the entire neighborhood. On June 28, 1970, A.A. Kishchinskii sighted a buzzard 20 km south of the Ukouge lagoon. Later he saw this bird in early June by the rocky knolls near Cape Schmidt. This species was very rare.

The hunter A.G. Ushakov wrote to me from Pevek that rough-legged buzzards were seen every year in large numbers in spring flight around Chaun Bay. Once a female with an egg was collected; a nest with three nestlings was found in 1963; and young birds were quite often found sitting on the elevations on the tundra and on telegraph poles at the end of June.

In a valley 30 miles east of Bol'shoi Baranov Kamen', J. Koren (Thayer and Bangs 1914) saw a nest with nestlings on July 13, 1912. F.B. Chernyavskii examined and photographed a nest with nestlings on the banks of the Levaya Yarak-Véem River on July 10, 1965. In 1916 and 1917, Koren (Schaanning 1954) collected a female with nestlings and also four clutches of eggs in the Kolyma delta.

Habitat—I found a nest near the Amguema in surroundings very typical of this bird: a narrow ravine, on one side of which a rock jutted out abruptly, overhanging the cliff. The adjoining knolls had gentle slopes with terraces covered with rock debris. It was quite easy to find the nest because there was no more suitable place for it in the neighborhood. In search of prey the buzzard quite often flew over the flood plains. In spring flight, in the eastern part of the Chukchi peninsula, I always saw the buzzards near coastal elevations with rock outcrops where they probably nested later. I noticed the tracks of gophers in the snow in the valley of the Dzhenretlen, which might attract the buzzards. But not far away there was a buzzard just flying over the hummocks where there was nothing to prey upon. A pair of ravens chased the buzzards, which were regarded as undesirable competitors in the selection of convenient nesting sites. On May 24, 1934, around Uélen, I saw a buzzard on the edge of the terraces on the nearest knoll, where there were many thawed patches and mouseholes.

Seasonal phenomena—Traveling along the north coast of the Chukchi peninsula in May, 1934, I noticed rough-legged buzzards for the first time on May 16 around Dzhenretlen but was informed in Neshkan that they had been sighted two days before. Until May 20 the buzzards were seen almost every day. Their mass flight was evidently already over. At Uélen I noticed lone buzzards on May 24 and 25, after which they disappeared, presumably returning to the breeding grounds in the interior of the peninsula.

The male collected on May 18 on arrival was emaciated, i.e. devoid of subcutaneous adipose formations. It was an adult with large testes: 10×23 and 9×21 mm.

On June 10, 1956, I found buzzards on the Amguema which were already settled and flying singly, sometimes over the flood plains and sometimes over the mountain valley in search of prey. On July 2, when I examined the rubble-rocky terraces of knolls close to the 87th km, a male buzzard suddenly flew toward me with a scream. It hung around for some time before it flew off in the direction from which it had come. I followed it and soon the buzzard got very agitated. It began to swoop on me from above with folded wings and talons out. The strong wind allowed the bird to hover above me almost in one place, which helped in photographing it. The female was seen right at the nesting site. She was wary, uttered a few cries and soared very high, while the male often came within range of a good shot. From the ravine the chirping of nestlings could be heard. The male was particularly noisy. Its call resembled the scream of the common buzzard but was sharper and drier, i.e. not so ringing, and shrill.

The ravine was very narrow. Opposite the nest there was a tiny ledge where the buzzards could settle. It was sprayed with the white excreta of the birds and a large number of feathers discarded during molting were littered around. Two weeks later, on July 16, I again visited the nesting area. The female, sitting on the favored spot opposite the nest became agitated and flew off on seeing me at a distance. Soon, the male appeared, began to swoop and was shot. I had to go after the bird. When I returned the female was flying around the nest and was also shot. Fearing that it would drop to the bottom of the ravine, I quickly grabbed it in my hands. The bird caught my hand with one claw and pierced the flesh at two places with the talons. From the grip of the talons I could visualize what a strong weapon the buzzard has for holding and killing small animals.

The male was a two-year-old with testes of 7×18 and 6×17 mm. Small layers of subcutaneous fat covered the hind portion of body. The weight was 855 g. Evidently it had incubated for some time since it had a faint brood patch. The female was an adult bird with a 25 mm long ovary. The diameter of the largest follicle was 3 mm. The subcutaneous fat formed a thin layer only on the belly. The weight of the bird was 1,205 g. It had a large brood patch.

The nest was built in a niche under an overhanging stone on which there was a larger, abandoned nest. Both were equally inaccessible because of the overhang of the rocks. The occupied nest was made of brown branches with some bright colored lining. With the binoculars I could see a nestling in grayish dress inside. It was the size of a jackdaw.

J. Koren found a nest on top of a very high peat mound at Bol'shoi Baranov Kamen' on the steep incline of a knoll. On July 13, 1912, four nestlings aged 5 to 10 days were found in it. In the Kolyma delta nests were placed on the ledges of steep cliffs at a height of 40 to 80 ft. F.H. Fay and T.J. Cade found a nest with two yearlings on St. Lawrence Island on August 6, 1956. It was placed on top of an outlier rising above the edge of a hill valley (Fay and Cade 1959, plate 12b). The nest examined by F.B. Chernyavskii was built on a cliff ledge on the left bank of the river and housed three downy nestlings.

Food—The stomach of a female collected was fouled with the red wool of the lemming and that of the male with the wool of some field vole. Judging from the plumpness of the two birds, they did not suffer for want of food in the hills. It is interesting that, not far from their nests, I noticed a scampering adult gopher which evidently was not afraid at all in the neighborhood of nesting buzzards. This is one more example of the apparently strange phenomenon of some species of animals that serve as food for the predator seeking the protection of the predator's nest. Generally gophers are eaten by buzzards. In particular, F.B. Chernyavskii found the remains of this prey in the nest he examined.

Systematics of the subspecies—After renewed study of the rough-legged buzzards and other representatives of the genus *Buteo* that I took as long ago as 1928–1929 (Portenko 1929), I recently revised the material on rough-legged buzzards preserved in the Institute of Zoology, Academy of Sciences of the USSR, to ascertain primarily from the measurements the existence of the Kamchatka forms described by G.P. Dement'ev (1931). I unfortunately have with me only three specimens from Kamchatka. They were very light-colored and their wings were not particularly long, quite contrary to the characters given by G.P. Dement'ev in his description. One must therefore refrain from acknowledging the existence of a Kamchatka subspecies.

In 1955 T.J. Cade (1955) published his revision of rough-legged buzzards based mostly on American material. Though unaware of my work, Cade came to the same conclusions.

It should be nevertheless pointed out that the material from which *B.l. kamtschatkensis* was described, as also the Kamchatka material that was available to Cade and myself, was very inadequate, particularly in view of the appreciable individual variations in buzzards.

According to Cade, buzzards with mixed characteristics of the two subspecies inhabit both shores of the Bering Sea, Asiatic and American. He does not even use the subspecies names. As far as my Chukchi birds are concerned, they do not show signs of transition of *B.l. sancti-johannis*.

I therefore differentiate three subspecies:

1) **Buteo lagopus lagopus** (Pontopp.). The mainground of the upper parts is brown, if some mottles formed by the edges and patches on some feathers are ignored. On this ground only the white patch on the nape and the white basal half of the tail stand out prominently. Some bleaching in the rear part of the shoulder

feather arrangement is noticed. The forehead and the crown are variegated, but with a predominance of brown, the streaks are broad and dark. Some feathers on the back have ocherous patches on the sides, a russet rim is seen at the fringe of the patch and the brown background of feathers. The lower back is dark and uniformly brown. On the underside of the body, on an ocherous-brown breast, much darker chestnut brown patches stand out in the centers of feathers and whitish patches on the sides. The cream color distinguishing the breast from the blackish-brown sides of the body is intensely speckled and is seen only through them. There is a median row of white spots on the abdomen. The breeches are rusty brown with round white spots; the legs of the same color with tiny ocherous barring. Dark streaks are seen on the breast of females and the bands on the tail are less distinct. In this respect, the plumage of the adult female is somewhat similar to the breeding plumage. In young buzzards, in the breeding plumage, the brown streaks on the head, neck and upper back are so broad that they suppress the light ocher-colored fringes or have a roughly similar width. Elsewhere, the main color on the back is brown with a purple or lilac tinge. The underparts are brownish with a distinct ocherous band across the lower part of the breast. The darkest birds come from Scandinavia and the Kola peninsula. Farther to the east light-colored birds are increasingly found.

Distribution—From Scandinavia to the lower Ob and Ob Bay. P.A. Rudakov collected an adult female with nestlings at least on Cape Taran; I later identified the birds as typical *B. l. lagopus.*

2) **Buteo lagopus kamtschatkensis** Dement. This name has come to be used to describe the pale-colored Siberian buzzard. In 1875, N.A. Severtsov (1875, p. 170) included in his list of Turkestan birds *Archibuteo lagopus B.* var. *sibirica* Taczan. as wintering forms but did not describe their features. In 1888, M.A. Menzbier (1888) described *Archibuteo pallidus* as a species, emphasizing that the name *sibirica* was used for some individual variants to which W. Taczanowsky and N.A. Severtsov drew attention. In 1931, G.P. Dement'ev described *Buteo lagopus kamtschatkensis* from Kamchatka and in 1939 E. Stresemann (1938) proved that the name *pallidus* was already used as *B. pallidus* Lesson 1831. Finally, in 1951 G.P. Dement'ev (1951, p. 312) proposed the name *B. lagopus menzbieri* as nomen emendatum for the Siberian subspecies. This name should be retained if the Kamchatka subspecies is recognized. Since, however, recognition will have to be withheld, the much older synonym *B. l. kamtschatkensis* Dement. retains priority according to the rules of nomenclature.

In Siberian rough-legged buzzards the upper side of the body is highly variegated in color because of the presence of white edges on the feathers. Until they are shed, the white color predominates on the head and shoulders and in the caudal base. The brown rod-like patches on the head are narrower and lighter than in *B. l. lagopus.* The large white patches are characteristic of the entire dorsal aspect, probably with the exception of the lower back. The brown color is lighter than in *B. l. lagopus* and has a gray shade. The rufous patches are also lighter. The underparts are very light-colored. The streaks on the throat are narrower. The breast has brown and ocherous brown patches on a cream ground. The commissure between it and the abdomen is broad and devoid of brown patches. Often the whole ventral

Specimens— 1) Cape Serdtse-Kamen', May 18, 1934, ♂, Portenko; and 2 and 3) 87th km near Amguema, July 16, 1956, ♂♀, Portenko.

34. **Aquila chrysaëtos canadensis** (L.)—**Golden Eagle**

Local name—Chukchian: Tíl'metil'. In Eskimo: kă-wăkh'-puk on St. Lawrence Island.

Distribution and status—Very occasionally flies into northwestern and southeastern parts of the Chukchi peninsula, in summer as well as in winter.

According to A.M. Bailey (1926) some species of eagle was sighted in 1921 at Providence Bay. O.J. Murie (1936) reported collection of a golden eagle on St. Lawrence Island near East Cape in the 1934/35 winter. Judging from the description, it was a young bird. It was rumored that two eagles were sighted at that time on the island. As É.V. Schmidt told me, in January, 1934, he saw a golden eagle flying north over the Mechigmensk tundra. The Chukchians expressed great surprise and said the sighting was a very rare occasion for them. I have no doubt that the latter record was indeed a golden eagle since eagles do not winter in the north.

Even J. Billings (Sarychev, 1811, p. 58) points out that eagles were seen during the very short local summer and sea eagles could be seen throughout the summer season. A.I. Argentov (1861a, p. 494) listed the following names among the raptors of the Trans-Lena region: bald eagle, motley-mountain eagle, gray eagle with white undertail, osprey.... The reference to the gray eagle with white undertail is probably to the golden eagle, but the details of distribution are not known. F.B. Chernyavskii found lone eagles in the valley of the Malyi Anyui with poplar, Korean-willow and larch stands. It is highly probable that the golden eagle from the Anyui forests flies into Chaun Bay region.

I did not encounter the golden eagle even once in the interior of the peninsula and could not find a reliable specimen in the territory. H.T.L. Schaanning (1954) identified a young female specimen from the lower Kolyma collected by J. Koren as *Aquila chrysaëtos canadensis* but only on the basis of the known range of the Canadian subspecies (as I too have done in the absence of specimens). According to him, the lower Kolyma specimen differed from the Norwegian golden eagle only in the intense rust-brown color of the nape. In one way or another there was some difference. According to O.J. Murie, the golden eagle caught in a trap on St. Lawrence Island killed and tore two polar foxes in the trap. The bird was so run down from cold and exhaustion that it keeled over and died before the eskimos came.

35. **Haliaeetus albicilla** (L.)—**White-tailed Sea Eagle**

Distribution and status—Very occasionally flies into the southeastern and more often into the northwestern part of the Chukchi peninsula but not in winter.

During his sojourn at Cape Chaplin P.T. Butenko saw the wing of a sea eagle in a Chukchian yaranga. He brought it as material proof. According to the hunter, the eagle was collected in June, 1938. I never encountered this eagle but the older references were totally conjectural. In the travel records of J. Billings (Sarychev,

1811, p. 58) a reference is made to sea eagles encountered in the summer somewhere on the northern slopes of the Anadyr Range but they could have been either golden eagles or sea eagles. On the other hand, A.I. Argentov (1861a, p. 494) mentions the bald eagle among the predatory birds of the Trans-Lena region, i.e. undoubtedly a sea eagle. But the territory he describes is so large that there was no justification in including the sea eagle among the inhabitants of Chukchi land that he covered. In another work, A.I. Argentov (1857a, p. 85) writes that an osprey lived in Chaun parish. Since Chaun parish partly covered the Anyui tributaries it is quite difficult to see what Argentov had in mind: a sea eagle which was called an osprey in Anadyr or an osprey which perhaps entered Anyui as an uncommon visitor. According to V.D. Lebedev and V.R. Filin (1959), a sea eagle was certainly sighted on June 4 and 6, 1958, on the west coast of Aiok Island. On August 9 and 11 it was noticed chasing molting geese near the Tikhaya River in the western part of the Karchyk peninsula, and on August 15 on the west coast of the peninsula.

The white-tailed sea eagle also nests on the Anadyr and Kolyma. J. Koren (Schaanning, 1954) recovered two clutches on the lower Kolyma.

Seasonal phenomena—A.I. Argentov (1861a, p. 495) reported that the eagles he described spent only the summer in the north. This reference once again confirms that Argentov had seen the sea eagle, which was a visitor, while the golden eagle was encountered throughout the winter. According to him the eagle was seen before all other birds in the spring, in mid-March by the old calendar.

The clutches recovered by J. Koren contained two eggs each. In one of them, found on May 7, 1917, the eggs had been incubated for not more than three days. They had been incubated for 18 to 20 days in the other, found on May 23. The former must have been laid around May 3. The nests were built on the tops of larch trees by the lake at a height of 30 to 35 ft.

Systematics—J.E. Thayer and O. Bangs (1914, p. 33) believed that "*Haliaeetus leucocephalus alascanus* Townsend" was encountered on the arctic coast of Siberia, especially on the lower reaches of the Kolyma, though J. Koren could not get at any specimens. The sight record of the sea eagle made by Koren is not convincing: the American sea eagle is very similar to the corresponding Russian species.

Specimen—Cape Chaplin, June 1938, ○, Butenko.

? Thallassoaëtus pelagicus (Pall.)—White-shouldered Eagle

Among the eagles of the Trans-Lena region, A.I. Argentov names a motley mountain eagle. The word "péstryi" (meaning "motley") is pronounced by the local Anadyr and Kolyma residents as "péstryi", which means the same thing. I feel that Argentov knew of the white-shouldered eagle *Thallassoaëtus pelagicus* (Pall.), which in his time must have penetrated Chaun parish of the Trans-Lena region.

36. Hierofalco gyrfalco grebnitzkii Sev.—Gyrfalcon

Local name—In Eskimo: Thlō′-yŭk on St. Lawrence Island.

Distribution and status—Nests in very small numbers in different parts of the

Chukchi peninsula. Found somewhat more often in fall and winter migrations, mainly in the first half of winter. Flies into Wrangel Island very rarely.

In the summer of 1881 E.W. Nelson (1883) saw a gyrfalcon around Providence Bay. According to I.O. Olenev, a pair of gyrfalcons nested on a rock between Émma and Providence bays in summer, 1931, and in the following year, eggs and nestlings were found. Predators other than the gyrfalcon were not noticed at Providence Bay. On my visits to this bay I did not find the gyrfalcon even once. P.T. Butenko, who wintered there, encountered a gyrfalcon once on December 5, 1937.

Gyrfalcons were collected many times on St. Lawrence Island, but outside the breeding season, and nests were not found. According to O.J. Murie (1936), in 1935 a young male was taken on September 21 at Kukuliak village and evidently an adult female on September 27 in Savunga village. T.J. Cade (Fay and Cade, 1959) found the wings of a gyrfalcon killed in Boxer Bay in 1949/50 winter. It was learned that gyrfalcons nested on the cliffs three miles west in earlier years. On May 21,1952, a gyrfalcon was noticed near Gambell and some kind of dark-colored falcon near Cape Sevu on May 1. In January, 1956, a gyrfalcon was found in a trap on the northern slope of Kukulgit hill. These predators remained on the south coast of the island in the winter. According to F.H. Fay (1961) their number on St. Lawrence Island in the winter did not exceed 50. E.G.F. Sauer and E.K. Urban (1964) saw two gyrfalcons which were paired on August 22 and 24, 1960, above Sivokak Mountain.

There are no observations for the east coast of the Chukchi peninsula. On Bol'shoi Diomede Island J. Koren (Thayer and Bangs, 1914) saw a gyrfalcon on December, 15, 1912. In the summer of 1881 E.W. Nelson found a gyrfalcon around Cape Dezhnev. According to my observations, in the fall of 1933 a lone gyrfalcon remained for a long time around Uélen. I saw it for the first time on September 3 and thereafter not until September 27. P.T. Butenko found it there on October 1; later I saw it again on October 19, and for the last time on November 12. In spite of my searching for it in 1934, no gyrfalcon was to be found in the nesting area there. J. Koren saw one at Cape Ikechurun on October 20, 1912. V.V. Leonovich found a nesting pair by the bird colony near Seishan on June 30, 1970, and saw a lone bird at Énurmino on June 24. A member of the *Vega* expedition, Dr. Stuksberg, saw a white falcon on September 27, 1878, when the *Vega* was passing through Kolyuchin Bay, but in size it was closer to the Iceland gyrfalcon. Some kind of falcon was seen while wintering around Pitlekai but the bird was not collected. No gyrfalcon nested in the neighborhood of the Ukouge lagoon which was thoroughly explored by A.A. Kishchinskii in the summer of 1970. A flying white bird was noticed only once, on July 12.

Some references are available for Cape Schmidt. J. Koren noticed a gyrfalcon on September 10, 1912, and A.A. Savich saw some white raptor on February 22, 1915, over the cliffs. V.M. Artobolevskii (1927) quite correctly regarded this observation as of a gyrfalcon. V.Ya. Isaev told me of finding a pair of gyrfalcons by a nest on the upper course of the Ékichun River 20 km west of Cape Schmidt. He also collected adult birds and found nestlings. On September 12, 1911, J. Koren saw a gyrfalcon by Cape Kiber. S.A. Buturlin (Dement'ev, 1936) saw this bird near Cape Enraukun. F.B. Chernyavskii found a very light-colored falcon on June

21, 1965, at the source of the Yarak-Véem River in the eastern part of the north Anyui Range.

A.I. Argentov (1861a) evidently called the gyrfalcon a partridge hawk and placed it among the wintering birds of the Trans-Lena region. J. Koren (Schaanning, 1954) collected a fully feathered nestling in the Kolyma delta on July 11, 1917, and an adult male on the lower Kolyma on August 13, 1917.

On Wrangel Island a gyrfalcon was noticed on three occasions by A.I. Mineev (1936, p. 177), twice in late fall in Rodgers Bay and once by the bird colony. I did not see it there. According to a report of R.I. Newcomb (1888, p. 280), the meteorologist of the *Jeannette* expedition saw a raptor in September, 1879, on Herald Island. Judging from the description it was probably an Iceland falcon.

Habitat—Almost all of the innumerable observations on the gyrfalcon in the Chukchi peninsula and Wrangel Island were made in the proximity of the coastal cliffs, where it hunted the sea birds living in colonies and would fly out to sea to hunt prey on the wing. At Providence Bay I.O. Olenev found a nest on a cliff joined to the rocky massif of the hilly coast by a narrow isthmus. It was very difficult to reach. The advantageous position for nesting justified a repeat nesting by the gyrfalcon at the same place the following year. V.Ya. Isaev found a nest on a mountain precipice located about 20 km from the seacoast.

A gyrfalcon that I noticed in the fall of 1933 around Uélen remained for a long time on the coastal cliffs. It could be seen flying from one cliff to another within the range of a shot though it also soared high over the knolls. On September 3 I noticed it flying over the western edge of the settlement and P.T. Butenko saw it on November 10 over the nearby tundra, to which place it may have been attracted by the ptarmigans wandering at that time. On Wrangel Island A.I. Mineev noticed a gyrfalcon on two occasions in the settlement and once flying past the bird colony.

According to the information gathered, gyrfalcons nested on St. Lawrence Island in the crevices of cliffs where bird colonies were located, three miles west of Boxer Bay.

Seasonal phenomena—In 1932 I.O. Olenev saw a pair of gyrfalcons by a nest around May 15. On June 27–28 two eggs and two nestlings which had just emerged were seen in the nest. The latter was on top of a cliff 25 to 30 m above the water. It had a modest lining. The previous year, in the last few days of August, a nestling which was already feathered but not yet flying was found in it. In the nest found by V.Ya. Isaev, also built on a cliff, two nestlings covered with down were found on March 23, 1935. Their flight and tail feathers had not emerged from the stubs.

The gyrfalcon is sighted in fall migrations more often than at other times of the year. A.A. Savich noticed it on February 22, 1915, but there are no other observations in the second half of winter. At the end of winter the gyrfalcon evidently migrated to the south.

Habits—The gyrfalcon which I tracked at Uélen was an adult, very wary bird. When we came around the cliff, it flew toward us with a characteristic kva-kva-kva-. . . note which I had heard several times before from gyrfalcons and falcons. I refrained from taking a long shot but was later sorry because the bird never came close. On another occasion it flew quite close to me when I was walking in the settlement without a gun.

Food—On September 3, 1933, when I saw the gyrfalcon for the first time, eiders and brent geese were in flight. On September 27 I noticed how gyrfalcons flew from cliff to cliff, evidently attracted by the birds remaining there, i.e. cormorants and buntings. Ravens followed them in fives, which disturbed the gyrfalcon all the time. The eskimos at Providence Bay told A.I. Mineev that the gyrfalcon could kill a murre, alcid, old squaw, black-legged gull or small tundra bird and would attack even an eider. P.T. Bol'shakov presented me with a young gyrfalcon shot on Mednyi Island in the act of catching a pintail on the wing. According to the observations of O.W. Geist (1939), gyrfalcons on St. Lawrence Island killed ducks without difficulty. Only in one case was the predator seen to let go of its quarry. Gyrfalcons were twice seen falling to the ground holding onto a duck. Once a harlequin with talon marks on the back was found on the ice of a lake. It was reported that gyrfalcons hunted mice also. In winter, according to Fay, gyrfalcons fed mainly on eiders and old squaws.

Systematics of the subspecies—Much has been written about the geographic affinity of gyrfalcons but in the absence of any collections from the territory in question detailed classification is not possible. At present, there are two contradictory points of view. According to one, the gyrfalcon is a polymorphic species forming some subspecies. According to the other it does not form even a single subspecies. The first view was long supported by Russian ornithologists. The second was proposed by Ch. Vaurie (1961b). G.P. Dement'ev, who studied gyrfalcons in greater detail than others, quite recently (1960) recognized seven subspecies including *Falco gyrfalco* (?) *altaicus* Menzbier 1891. Most recently, Dement'ev (Dement'ev and Shagdarsurén, 1965) placed the Altai gyrfalcon among falcons. I have already (1951, p. 195, footnote) expressed my views on the taxonomic evaluation of the Altai falcon and am now inclined to regard it as only a subspecies. As far as true gyrfalcons are concerned, as before (1939b, vol. II, pp. 58 to 62) I distinguish three sub-species in northern Eurasia: 1) *Hierofalco gyrfalco gyrfalco* (L.), 2) *H. g. uralensis* Menzb. and Sev., and 3) *H. g. grebnitzkii* Sew. Of these the first two are beyond doubt real subspecies with good characteristic features. The third calls for some comment.

Firstly, gyrfalcons from northeast Asia, called *H. g. grebnitzkii*, are very divergent in color though light-colored and white types predominate. Secondly, the gyrfalcon collections from northeast Asia are still inadequate. Thirdly, no ornithologist is yet in a position to compare a good series of gyrfalcons collected on both sides of the Bering Sea.

The subspecies *H. g. grebnitzkii* cannot as yet be regarded as thoroughly studied. The nature of the transitions to the American subspecies *H. g. obsoletus* (Gm.) and the exact eastern boundaries of distribution are not known for certain.

I would like to state the following in support of my view on the classification of gyrfalcons into subspecies: Russian ornithologists gathered gyrfalcon specimens gradually over many years, this being no mean achievement. The forms of gyrfalcon and their taxonomic significance were examined and reexamined by several specialists several times. Ornithologists of several generations have gathered ideas on their individual forms. For several years Ch. Vaurie reviewed the subspecies of almost all Palearctic birds but had neither time nor resources to examine the individual species at length. His views on the geographic affinity of the birds were therefore of a very generalized nature and overlooked several details that could not be justly ignored. The merging of all of the subspecies is temptingly simple but it would not provide any idea of the affinity of the gyrfalcon and its character.

Because of the absence of bird collections from the Chukchi peninsula and Wrangel Island, I would like to recount all of the known observations on white and dark-colored specimens.

At Providence Bay, P.T. Butenko noticed a gyrfalcon which was generally white.

On St. Lawrence Island, according to O.W. Geist (Murie, 1936), both dark and white gyrfalcons nested and spent the winter. Two of the specimens he collected were identified by H. Friedmann as of the subspecies *Falco rusticolus uralensis*. One of them, shot at Kukuliak on September 21, 1935, was fairly pale in color with narrow bars on the underside of the body. The whitish crown was heavily barred. The blue legs and claws were suggestive of immaturity. The second bird was bigger, much darker and more barred ventrally. The head was uniformly dark on top. On the upper surface of the tail there were hardly any pale bands, in total contrast to the broad pale bands of the previous specimen.

In the collection of Alaska University there are two other specimens: an adult white female collected on December 17, 1928, and a dark young male taken on November 24, 1928, while the Musuem of the Zoology of Vertebrates at Berkeley has a white female in adult plumage but with blue legs (hence, not old) collected on October 30, 1932. T.J. Cade found the wings of a white specimen and reported on the white gyrfalcons he had seen or collected.

The gyrfalcon which I encountered around Uélen had a white torso speckled black, black flight feathers, a subterminal band on the tail and yellow claws. It was very similar to the specimen I collected in Penzhin (Portenko, 1939b, vol. II, pp. 59 and 60, and Plate 12). Stuksberg at Kolyuchin Bay and A.A. Savich at Cape Schmidt saw white birds. According to V.Ya. Isaev the specimens he secured were slightly darker than my Penzhin specimen, which he saw. At Cape Kiber J. Koren noticed an almost completely white gyrfalcon, as S.A. Buturlin did at Cape Enraukun. A.I. Mineev described the gyrfalcons he had seen on Wrangel Island as grayish-white.

In the Chukchi peninsula, on Wrangel Island and St. Lawrence Island, white gyrfalcons predominated. There is no doubt that the dark birds were not always recognized by the observers as gyrfalcons but were simply ignored.

37. **Falco peregrinus harterti** But.—**Peregrine Falcon**

Local name—Chukchian: Ĭetgìtel and ĭettìeĭ; probably the name jejtschietsch found in the records of the *Vega* expedition pertains to the peregrine falcon. In Eskimo: tl'ùyak at Providence Bay.

Distribution and status—Nests in the Chukchi peninsula but in small numbers. As a rule, flies away in the winter though some birds remain on the south coast where wintering eiders and old squaws gather. In search of quarry, flies far out to sea. Was noticed in one case off the southeast coast of Wrangel Island.

Since I found the peregrine falcon commonly in the nesting areas on the shores of Anadyr Bay, the inadequate observational data reveal nothing about this bird's nesting habits on the Chukchi coast from Krest Bay to Providence Bay. In that section of the coast, there were several bird colonies which should have attracted the predator. On August 26 and 28, 1932, P.T. Butenko and I noticed probably the same peregrine falcon on the seacoast east of Providence Bay. Butenko, who wintered there in 1937/38 and stayed almost a year, could count the occasions when he had seen this bird, especially on December 22, 1937, and January 12, 1938. This conclusively proves the wintering of the peregrine falcon at least on the south coast of the Chukchi peninsula.

Only a single record is reported for St. Lawrence Island. According to a report by A.M. Bailey (1956) a young male was collected on September 15, 1950, near Savunga. On September 16, 1948, V.N. Lyubin collected a young peregrine falcon that was perching on a ship in the Bering Sea. In the collection of the Institute of Zoology, Academy of Sciences of the USSR, there is a peregrine falcon secured by I.N. Akif'ev on August 14, 1900, in Mechigmensk Gulf. In summer, 1933, a peregrine falcon nested on the cliffs between Capes Dezhnev and Uélen. On August 30 I noticed a young female near one of the lagoons southwest of Uélen. On September 6, P.T. Butenko saw two peregrine falcons around Cape Dezhnev. On September 11, I again saw a young female in a ravine near Uélen and finally on September 14 a peregrine falcon in flight there by the cliffs. In summer, 1934, I succeeded in finding peregrine falcons in the breeding grounds in the interior of the Chukchi peninsula. On August 11, I saw broods by the nests on the bank of the Kol'oam-Véem River at the transition from the lower to the middle course, and collected an adult male and some young birds. On July 5 I came across a pair of peregrine falcons near the nests on the southwest bank of the Inchoun lagoon and secured a female. During his travels in the interior of the Chukchi peninsula J. Billings (Sarychev, 1811, p. 58) noticed some hawks. It is highly probable that the peregrine falcon was more commonly found than the gyrfalcon. This could have been only at the beginning of Billings' travels, i.e. not far from the place that I visited, because the peregrine falcons flew away in September.

On May 20, 1934, I saw a peregrine falcon flying between Seitun and Utten villages. Judging from the nature of the coasts, this species should be nesting throughout the rocky sea coast from Mitkulen to Cape Serdtse-Kamen', but hardly farther to the west where the coast is depressed. On May 27, 1879, the members of the *Vega* expedition noticed a bird of prey in dark plumage and of the size of a sparrow hawk. It flew to one of the cliffs at Cape Dzhenretlen. The Chukchians called it jejtschietsch. Judging from all of this, it could have been a peregrine falcon. On July 7, 1909, J. Koren (1910) found a nest with a clutch on Kolyuchi Island. On July 19, 1938, I saw a female peregrine falcon flying along the south coast. There is no doubt that the conditions there were very favorable for the nesting of peregrine falcon.

Along the north coast of the Chukchi peninsula, J. Koren (Thayer and Bangs, 1914) encountered peregrine falcons here and there singly and in pairs. A.A. Kishchinskii did not see the peregrine falcon in the nesting areas on the tundra in the neighborhood of the Ukouge lagoon. On June 30, 1970, a freshly shed flight feather was found there. What was observed on July 12 and 13 was a male, judging from its small size. According to É.V. Schmidt, in mid-July, 1939, he happened to come across the breeding area of peregrine falcons on the lower course of the Mlelo-Véem River flowing into Chaun Bay from the east. A.G. Ushakov, the hunter, wrote to me from Pevek that according to his observations in the early 60s, peregrine falcons nested on the steep banks of the Mlelo-Véem River 30 to 40 km from the estuary and 10 km from the estuary of the Ichu-Véem river. They were generally not uncommon along the eastern shore of Chaun Bay.

V.D. Lebedev and V.R. Filin (1959) saw a peregrine falcon on July 8, 1958, on the southwest coast of Aiok Island.

On September 6, 1822, Matyushkin (Wrangel, 1841, vol. II, p. 268), traveling from the source of the Baranikha to Malyi Anyui, noticed a peregrine falcon attacking geese on the wing. On July 10, 1965, F.B. Chernyavskii found a nest on the banks of the Levaya Yarak-Véem River to the east of the north Anyui range. In his diary G.U. Sverdrup (Schaanning, 1928) writes of a peregrine falcon noticed on Chetyrekhstolb Island on May 25, 1925. On the lower reaches of the Kolyma J. Koren (Thayer and Bangs, 1914, and Schaanning, 1954) collected four specimens and found seven clutches in 1912 and 1916/1917.

The peregrine falcon has not yet been collected by anyone on Wrangel Island. On August 23, 1939, Tayan went far out to sea for walrus hunting and saw a gray-colored falcon flying close by. Taking into account the habits of this falcon in chasing its prey far out to sea, I feel that what Tayan saw was indeed a peregrine falcon.

Habitat—In the interior of the Chukchi peninsula the peregrine falcon nests on elevated or prominent sections of the river bank. On the Kol'oam-Véem River a nest was built on a cliff in the form of a gigantic head that could be seen from afar, even from the Inchoun cliff top. The fine rock debris was colored in contrasting ocherous, brown and puce colors. On the opposite, left bank of the river, which was plainer, though high, there was a big ice face. The place was very hospitable and peregrine falcons ruled over it. On the appearance of the party the birds began swooping on them as though the men were trespassing on their nesting territory. In the south of the Inchoun lagoon peregrine falcons loved to nest on a low, rocky section of the bank, still at a commanding height. The nesting area visited by É.V. Schmidt on the Mlelo-Véem River was a scaly scrap rising to a height of 100 m above the water. The nest found by F.B. Chernyavskii on the Yarak-Véem River bank was 150 m from the nest of a buzzard and was inaccessible.

At Providence Bay and around Uélen, I regularly noticed peregrine falcons by the cliffs. On the evening of September 11, 1933, I noticed a young female settled for the night on a cliff half-way along a ravine. The bird, ruffled and pressed to the rock, was almost invisible in the twilight. The point chosen for nesting was very convenient for offense if necessary. On August 30, I encountered a young female sitting in ambush under very different conditions—on a low bank of the lagoon.

A reference has already been made to the sighting of the peregrine falcon far out to sea. I became familiar with this bird's habit of searching for prey far from shore when I studied the birds from a ship. They always came out to the ship when

I returned to Vladivostok in the fall. On October 3, 1934, the ship entered the southern part of the Okhotsk Sea to the west of the Kuril Range. For two or three days, two young peregrine falcons, a male and a female, escorted the ship, sometimes settling on the mast. One of them was nearly killed on being hit by the ropes. From time to time the birds would fly off abeam of the ship and hunt small birds on the wind. In one case I clearly saw how the peregrine falcon would touch the water and skim the surface for some time. Unfortunately it was at a great distance and I was not sure whether the bird had not settled on some floating plank. The observation was so unusual that I asked P.T. Butenko, standing by my side, if the bird was not sitting on the water; he confirmed it[1]. On September 19, 1939, a young peregrine falcon approached a ship crossing Anadyr Bay. On September 26 a young male again approached the ship, crossing to Olyutorka. It settled several times and was shot. On October 3 a young male stayed with the ship in the southeastern part of the Okhotsk Sea but not as far as Laperuz Strait. It finally appeared with a bird in its talons and settled in the rigging where it began to tear at its prey. On being shot in the wing the peregrine falcon fell overboard without letting the prey fall from its talons until the last moment. Crested auklets were swimming around the ship but it was not certain what the bird in the talons was. In other cases, peregrine falcons hunted for phalaropes at sea. I noticed how birds in flight would push the prey forward in their talons and tear it to pieces with the beak. The peregrine falcon undoubtedly is an expert in bird hunting at sea. It can, when need be, consume its prey right there and even rest a while sitting on the water.

Arrival—On Chetyrekhstolb Island, a flying peregrine faclon was noticed on May 25, 1925. West of Utten village, I saw a peregrine falcon on May 20, 1934. Evidently these May dates should be regarded as the arrival time of the peregrine falcon in the Chukchi peninsula.

Breeding—In a nest found by J. Koren on July 7, 1909, on Kolyuchi Island there were three eggs; one of them which had probably been incubated first contained a chick ready to hatch.

I was able to make only brief observations on a nest. On July 5, 1934, my party came to a nest on the southwest bank of the Inchoun lagoon. It turned out to be empty, but the birds were nevertheless very aggressive. One of them, for some reason, rushed at a gull which, being close to its nest, was naturally very restless. The gull dodged the attack by jumping into the water. After this the peregrine falcon left it. When the party came close to the nest the falcons circled above us and the female was shot. It was a plump specimen with subcutaneous adipose formations. The finegrained structure of the ovary did not suggest activity that year but, judging from the brood patch, it had incubated. The fate of the clutch or the brood remained unknown. As soon as the female was killed the male climbed out of range and was not seen there on our way back on July 12.

On August 11, 1924, we came to a nesting area on the Kol'oam-Véem River on the opposite bank. A female began hovering over us and swooped somewhat like a

[1]The article by W. Kost (1967, Wachtel "wassert" im Roten Meer. Vogelwarte, vol. 24, No. 1, pp. 40 and 41) and R. Cook's note to it furnish some instances of the landing of non-swimming birds on water.

tern. Our unsuccessful shots frightened her and she flew off to the nest. After the shooting from a hide, a young bird was seen with partially grown flight feathers and much embryonic down among the feathers (Fig. 40). A second nestling which escaped somewhere into the neighborhood from the slope flew into the river and was later collected under the bank. Finally, the male flew in with a scream. It first made for the female but, noting the unfavorable situation, turned and rushed at me with fierce determination. I shot it without difficulty. It was a moderately plump bird with hardly any perceptible subcutaneous adipose formations. The testes were small: left 3×6 and right 3×5 mm. In mid-July, 1939, É.V. Schmidt was attacked by a peregrine falcon on the Mlelo-Véem River. Half a kilometer from there he came across the other member of the pair but the young were not to be found anywhere.

Migration—In the fall of 1933 I noticed the peregrine falcon for the last time around Uélen on September 14. As pointed out, on the south coast of the Chukchi peninsula the peregrine falcon was noticed twice in the winter. Both times its flight was noticed during a strong wind which caused the movement of swimming birds. On December 22, 1937, a strong south wind broke the ice in Providence Bay and eiders, old squaws, ravens, murres, alcids and along with them the peregrine falcon were seen on the leads formed in the ice. On January 12, 1938, a strong north wind piled a large amount of ice on the surf line north of Cape Chaplin and opened up extensive areas of water on the south side. Innumerable old squaws, a small number of eiders and alcids were seen on them. P.T. Butenko saw a peregrine falcon attack an old squaw but lose the prey because the duck fell in the water. The unlucky predator turned back to the hills.

Food—In addition to what has been said about the diet of the peregrine falcon consisting of different species of birds, the following will also be of some interest. In Providence Bay I noticed a peregrine falcon unsuccessfully attacking puffins flying from the rocks and turning toward the open sea. Around Uélen, I once put up a huge flock of emperor geese along with some lesser snow and brent geese. Following them, I saw a brent goose rolling on the ground under the attack of a peregrine falcon. Both birds, predator and prey, were young. The falcon attacked the goose on the wing. I was separated from them by the rivulet, which I was able to cross only 10 minutes later after finding a convenient ford. By that time, the falcon had succeeded in plucking out the feathers of the neck and breast, and had begun to tear the meat from the goose's breast. It had killed the goose and exposed and slashed the jugular veins. On my approaching the peregrine falcon (it was a large young female) stiffened in a characteristic menacing posture. She paused, kneeling, and stretched her neck out low as giraffes do. The posture showed the falcon to be a voracious bird unwilling to be separated from her quarry. She tried to lift it but could not. After an unsuccessful shot, the falcon returned twice but, realizing that she was a target, ultimately left the place altogether.

The talons of a female shot on the Kol'oam-Véem River on August 11, 1934, held the feathers of a ptarmigan. The stomach of a young bird collected at that time contained the meat and feathers of a small bird and the stomach of another contained the claws, bones, meat and feathers of a sandpiper. Atop the cliff in a niche concealing a nest bones of birds and wings of Baird's sandpiper were found scattered. It undoubtedly was a place where the peregrine falcons could quietly enjoy their food taking advantage of the extensive view of the area. In the stomach of a young male collected on September 26 on the ship at Olyutorka I found the feathers, bones and eyeballs of a tiny bird, and in the crop bits of meat, an eyeball, feathers and a claw of a second bird. From the claws the bird could be identified as a fork-tailed petrel *Oceanodroma furcata* (Gm.), which was probably caught without difficulty under the calm weather conditions.

Economic importance—The damage caused by the peregrine falcon in destroying edible and inedible birds under Chuckchi peninsula conditions is negligible.

Systematics of the subspecies—In spite of the large number of articles concerning the classification of the subspecies of peregrine falcon this question continues to be discussed, as disclosed by Ch. Vaurie (1961a) in his latest review of the genus *Falco*. In his revisions he generally favored a maximum simplification, reducing the number of subspecies, especially in the territory of the USSR, since his collection from there was the smallest. The material available with me on peregrine falcons of the Russian North allows me to study the subspecies in greater detail with greater accuracy.

In the 30s I had occasion to study the specimens of peregrine falcon preserved in the Zoological Museum, Moscow, and undertook a revision of the subspecies following B.K. Shtegman, based on the collection of the Institute of Zoology, Academy of Sciences of the USSR. My review was not published. Later, almost with each new peregrine falcon skin coming my way, I again began comparing them with the series. I made another thorough revision in 1963 based on the completely reliable material available with me for northeast Asia. A discussion follows on these subspecies.

1. **Falco peregrinus leucogenys** Brehm. This is the lightest colored of the known subspecies of peregrine falcon (Fig. 38). Individual variations are quite large. Transverse bands on the inner secondaries and shoulder feathers of males are quite often not to be found. At first glance the color on the upper parts stands out in a light bluish-gray tone. The crown has a grayish bloom. The barrings on the back are blackish-gray. Below, a pure white throat, neck, cheeks, upper breast, and lower breast stand out prominently. The barrings on the flanks and on the thighs are narrow, usually not broader than 2 mm. The spots in the middle of the abdomen are small; sometimes they are altogether absent. The ocherous color of freshly molted feathers is very light.

The females differ from other subspecies in the same light bluish-gray color, very narrow barring and tiny spots (Fig. 39).

The subspecies of young peregrine falcons differ in detail and do not provide a wholly distinct picture.

In its distribution, *F. p. leucogenys* is an arctic and subarctic form, nesting mostly on the tundra from Novaya Zemlya to the Yana River, where it is encountered along with *F. p. harterti*.

This light-colored subspecies forms the most distinct class. Its range in the nesting area is now generally known but there is great confusion in the nomenclature. Recently E. Stresemann and Ch. Vaurie (1961a) tried to restore the oldest of synonyms which, as we will presently see, is untenable. For this lightest-colored of subspecies he again proposed the name *F. p. calidus* Lath. and gave a very inadequate description; the specimen has not been preserved. The bird was described from a migratory specimen from India where several subspecies are found. If Ch. Vaurie believed that the nominal form of peregrine falcon *F. p. peregrinus* Tunst. is spread from the British Isles to the Ussurian region there is no justification in giving the name *calidus* to the pale tundra form. Ch. Vaurie incorrectly assumed that only northern peregrine falcons in flight were encountered in India. In fact, northern peregrine falcons may remain near the nesting areas for wintering and the more southern birds from central Siberia could be flying south.

This synonym *F. p. leucogenys* Brehm. has a significant advantage. The name itself bears a diagnostic feature, i.e. white cheeks. The description includes such characteristic features as the heavily barred upper parts (in the dark subspecies, the barring is less visible), russet patches on the sides of the nape and yellowish-white underparts with speckles which become transverse bars on the thighs. The narrow black lores and white cheeks constitute the chief character. The name *leucogenys* has been widely used in Russian ornithological literature from the time of M.A. Menzbier and if tradition has strictly to be followed it is more in favor of *leucogenys* than *calidus*. Finally, B.K. Shtegman gave an altogether accurate description of the light-colored subspecies and called it *caeruleiceps*. This name could not be upheld since it was antedated by two older synonyms, though it had the advantage of clarity.

2. **Falco peregrinus harterti** But. Old males are darker above while the crown, nape and upper back are considerably more black (Fig. 38). The light background shade of the back is more slate than gray. The white zone on the ears covers a smaller area than in the preceding subspecies. The underparts are not so white, have a yellowish bloom, even in old plumage, and are densely dusted with very tiny gray speckles (like coal dust). The spots are bigger and blacker and the barring broader, up to 3 mm in width.

The females are marked by the same characters but somewhat less prominently. They are dark above and very patchy below (Fig. 39).

This is a very dark form resembling the preceding subspecies in the color on the upper parts, and next subspecies in the color on the ventral aspect.

It nests from the Yana to the Bering Sea: on the lower reaches of the Yana, on the lower course of the Kolyma in the Chukchi peninsula, in the Anadyr Range and Koryatz Zemlya.

3. **Falco peregrinus pleskei** Dement. The adult males and females are very well distinguished by their dark, black upper parts and obvious patchings on the lower side. The patches and bars are not only bigger and coarser but also darker.

The limited but thoroughly processed material on peregrine falcons in northeast Asia that I collected quite clearly and convincingly proves the actual existence of two subspecies: *F. p. harterti* and *F. p. pleskei*. The former in all respects is darker than *F. p. leucogenys* and closer to *F. p. pleskei*, especially in the color of the underside. Some females of *F. p. pleskei* cannot be distinguished from *F. p. harterti* by the patchiness and the color of the underparts, but the former are noticeably darker toward the top.

I regard *F. p. kleinschmidti*, described by G.P. Dement'ev, as a synonym of this form, which is the darkest subspecies inhabiting the USSR except *F. p. pealei* Ridgw., which is very dark-colored.

It nests in central Yakutsk. The northern limit of its distribution is defined by the records in the Lena valley 200 km south of the Bulun and the Yana 70 km below Verkhoyansk. Further, it nests on the Okhotsk coast, at least on the southern part. The southern limit of its range has not yet been established. In the collection of the Institute of Zoology, Academy of Sciences of the USSR, there is a male specimen collected in mid-July (old calendar), 1896, 100 versts south of Yakutsk. It is not so dark as peregrine falcons from around Yakutsk and from the Vilyui basin. Assuming that there is no error in the location of this find, the more southern subspecies (*F. p. peregrinus*?) should be regarded as extending beyond Yakutsk. I feel the southern boundary of the dark-colored Yakutsk subspecies should not extend as far as Japan, as Ch. Vaurie would have it.

If we recognize the two subspecies *F. p. harterti* and *F. p. pleskei*, we should refrain from using the synonym *F. p. japonensis* Gm. This name was given to the bird collected in the sea near Japan where any of the four subspecies of peregrine falcon inhabiting Siberia could be encountered. A male specimen from Yokohama preserved in the collection of the Institute of Zoology, Academy of Sciences of the USSR, for example, is properly identified as *F. p. harterii*.

4. **Falco peregrinus anatum** Bp. Two males from America, from Labrador and Long Island, are similar to my *F. p. harterti* in the color of the upper parts but differ noticeably in the pattern of the underside of the body. The throat, neck and the breast are white without spots as in *F. p. leucogenys* while the barring on the abdomen and sides are perceptibly narrower than in *F. p. harterti*. If the American peregrine falcons in Alaska are the same as in eastern North America, *F. p. anatum* should be regarded as closer to the Russian *F. p. harterti*.

Two females from Labrador and Texas are also closest to females of *F. p. harterti*, but in them as in the males, the bars and spots on the underside of the body are somewhat displaced to the rear and the breast is almost devoid of spots. In one specimen bold streaks are found on the lower breast. In both these specimens the bars are narrower, the spots smaller and the entire pattern not so black as in *F. p. harterti*.

In the photograph accompanying A. Brooks' paper (1926) the differences in the pattern on the underparts of *F. p. anatum* and the Palearctic subspecies of peregrine falcon are clearly visible.

W.C. Hanna (1940b) reports the find of a male peregrine falcon near Cape Prince of Wales, Alaska, on May 25, 1939, so light in color that H. Friedmann identified it as *Falco peregrinus calidus*. In the photograph illustrating Hanna's paper the amount of white in the anterior underparts is very large, as in American peregrine falcons. I am therefore of the view that the find at Cape Prince of Wales should be regarded not as a migratory specimen of *F. p. leucogenys* but as, probably, a very light-colored variant of *F. p. anatum*.

Specimens— 1) Mechigmensk Gulf, August 14, 1900, ⨀, Akif'ev; 2) Inchoun Lagoon, near the estuary of the Utte-Véem River, July 5, 1934, ♀, Portenko; and 3 to 5) Kol'oam-Véem River, August 11, 1934, ♂, sen., ♀, ○ juv., Portenko.

38. **Aesalon columbarius (L.)—Merlin**

Known for certain as a very rare species, entering the Chukchi peninsula occasionally.

According to E.W. Nelson (1883, p. 78), a merlin was collected at Providence Bay. On May 27, 1934, I noticed this tiny falcon between Dezhnev and Uélen in a snowstorm when a north wind was blowing. The appearance of migratory birds under such conditions was entirely natural. Three falcons of the size and color of a kestrel noticed by O. Nordquist (Palmén, 1887) on September 18, 1878, on the Veber cliffs at Cape Schmidt in all probability represented a brood of merlins. On the lower Kolyma the merlin is not a great rarity though its appearance has been established only outside the nesting season. J. Koren (Schaanning, 1954) took four specimens each fall from 1915 through 1918 on the lower Kolyma. E.P. Spangenberg (1960) sighted a female merlin on June 2, 1959, near Cape Green village.

Finally, on August 19, 1939, I was informed that some small gray-colored bird of prey landed on the weathercock of the Polar Station at Rodgers Bay, Wrangel Island. It was in all probability a merlin.

39. **Cerchneis tinnunculus (L.)—Kestrel**

Flies to Chukchi peninsula very rarely.

According to G.P. Dement'ev (Buturlin and Dement'ev, 1936, vol. III, p. 67), in 1933, V.V. Lyapunov collected a kestrel on a ship in the sea north of the Chukchi peninsula between Yakan and Billings capes. According to Dement'ev, who saw it, it was a very pale-colored female. Since I have had no occasion to examine it, I cannot define its subspecific status.

Order VI. GALLIFORMES—GALLINACEOUS BIRDS

40. **Lagopus lagopus lagopus (L.)—Willow Ptarmigan**

Local name—Chukchian: Réumreu; reumrou according to the records of the *Vega* expedition.

Distribution and status—Nests in the Chukchi peninsula but not everywhere and not always in the same numbers. Common in the interior of the peninsula, being more numerous in the western than in the eastern part. Does not nest at all in the mountains or on the seacoast. Wanders fairly extensively in the winter, though not regularly, and could be encountered in places where it does not nest. Absent altogether from Wrangel, Diomede and St. Lawrence islands.

In the summer of 1956, I found this species nesting in the valley of the middle course of the Amguema and nearabouts. In spite of the winter destruction of ptarmigans by hunters near the villages, by the summer others had appeared there in the river valley around the village. Around the settlement at the 91st km, I came across ptarmigans quite frequently. Some eggs were given to me from around the tundra.

In May and July, 1939, E.M. Meller collected some specimens between the upper reaches of the Tadleo and Amguema rivers. Neither I nor Butenko found the willow ptarmigans around Uél'kal' and Notapenmen villages by the entrance to Krest Bay. L.O. Belopol'skii (1934) did not encounter them even on Meechken Island during his prolonged sojourn there. Even N.F. Kallinikov (1912, p. 152) noticed that ptarmigans were few in the southern part of the Chukchi peninsula but quite numerous along the Arctic Ocean coast. I.O. Olenev reported hearing the calls of ptarmigans from time to time at Providence Bay but did not find them in the winter. He saw them in large numbers on the tundra near Kurupka village 40 km northwest of the bay and also at Pinkegnei village north of Cape Chaplin. On January 21, 1938, P.T. Butenko found their tracks near Yanrakynnot village. A specimen of willow ptarmigan was given by I.N. Akif'ev to the Zoological Museum, Academy of Sciences, evidently from around Senyavin Strait but unfortunately without exact dates. E.W. Nelson (1883, p. 80) did not find the willow ptarmigan at all on the Chukchi coast and only states that the bird is found on the Siberian coast. I did not find willow ptarmigans on the Lawrence Bay shore but in the summer of 1957 A.P. Kuzyakin found pairs and heard the call on the tundra between Lawrence Bay and Poutyn village. He was given a clutch from Akkani settlement. He heard the call of ptarmigans at three points south of Poutyn 7 or 8 km along the footpath on the night of June 26/27 but they were not seen at all to the north.

According to my observations and as confirmed by the Chukchians, ptarmigans do not nest at all around Uélen. They are seen in the winter on the nearby knolls but in different numbers in different years. In the 1933/34 winter only once, on October 19, did I find three ptarmigans on a knoll. On December 7 a flock flew along the spit toward Uélen village. In November and December, 1933, the ptarmigans were sometimes seen on the south coast by the large Uélen lagoon.

Inland in the eastern part of the Chukchi peninsula I found the willow ptarmigan in a nesting area on the western shore of Lake Kool'ong; on August 18, 1934, I found broods there. During my journey up the lower and middle course of the Utte-Véem River from July 6 through 10, 1934, I put up solitary ptarmigans on three occasions and in one case a couple. By no means could this bird be called common there. At the same time, P.T. Butenko found willow ptarmigans in large numbers in the winter on a tributary of this river, the Yararmumny, and in the rivulets entering it. On January 15, 1934, he found flocks of 20 to 30 birds, on January 16 a flock of up to 100 birds and almost as big a flock on January 7.

During a spring excursion on May 21 of the same year I found a pair of willow ptarmigans on the seacoast east of Mitkulen rivulet. On May 19 a lone ptarmigan rose from the hummocks east of Cape Unin. The day before, on May 18, I collected a male and heard the calls of innumerable ptarmigans on the slopes of Cape Serdtse-Kamen'. My party had been told about the ptarmigans the day before by the teacher in Neshkan village.

Around Kolyuchin Bay, according to the observations of the members of the *Vega* expedition (Palmén, 1887), the willow ptarmigan was rare on the coast but quite common inland. Near Pitlekai, sometimes even in the village itself, mostly solitary birds were noticed from mid-November, 1878, to mid-February, 1879. But in December and January innumerable tracks of wandering flocks were also seen. In the spring when the ptarmigans began occupying the nesting territories one bird was noticed right at Pitlekai on May 27, 1879. One was taken there on June 18. In general, however, the ptarmigans disappeared from the coast in the spring, having colonized on the tundra inland. O. Nordquist saw two large flocks 10 to 12 miles from Pitlekai on December 14, 1878; there were over 50 birds in one of them. In December and January innumerable tracks were noticed near Irgunnuk and Dzhenretlen. On February 17, 1879, near Irgunnuk, a lone ptarmigan was shot. On May 22, 1879, a reindeer Chukchian brought 10 ptarmigans from the eastern shore of Kolyuchin Bay. On his journey to Kolyuchin Bay E. Almquist came across these birds on June 17. In May, 1934, travelling along the seacoast, P.T. Butenko saw more than 10 ptarmigans beyond Kolyuchin Bay.

The Chukchians told me that the willow ptarmigan flew over Kolyuchi Island from time to time in the winter but was not found there in summer and I did not find it there myself. On April 25 and 26, 1934, I found many ptarmigans and their tracks at Cape Vankarém. There were upward of 30 birds in one flock. According to É.V. Schmidt, willow ptarmigans were many in the valley of the Amguema River. In the summer of 1956 I found them in large numbers in the nesting area near the 91st km. In the summer of 1970 A.A. Kishchinskii explored the coastal tundra from Vankarém to the Amguema estuary but did not find ptarmigans at all in the nesting area. Old excreta was found from time to time in the coastal ravines. On April 29, 1934, I found a sick bird in the Amguema estuary on the coast opposite the Iul'tyn Range. Next day I saw tracks within sight of Métégyn knoll.

According to the data of A.A. Savich (Artobolevskii, 1927), willow ptarmigans were seen in small numbers the year around at Cape Schmidt. In a hunt on March 7, 1915, tracks were found and on June 7 a pair of ptarmigans was brought in by the Chukchians. Unfortunately the skins were not preserved and the species could not be accurately identified. According to V.Ya. Isaev, in the coastal belt of Cape Schmidt willow ptarmigans were encountered even in the winter though relatively rarely. They were quite common around the mountain valleys. There they could be found in the winter every 4 or 5 km. At places they were found in large numbers; they were seen in the spring when calling was at its peak.

According to the observations of É.V. Schmidt, in 1938 ptarmigans for some reason were few in the valleys of the Ékiatap, Kuvét, Pegtymel' and Palya-Véem rivers, but comparatively numerous on the Chaun River. A.I. Argentov (1857b) included ptarmigans among the birds constantly present on Aiok Island. But according to the observations of V.D. Lebedev and V.R. Filin (1959), in the summer of 1958 the willow ptarmigans was less numerous there. According to the local residents these birds were found in large numbers in the fall but disappeared in the spring. On July 23 a male was found on the western shore of Chaun Bay. The willow ptarmigan was encountered more often on the forest tundra in the Karchyk peninsula. Two broods were found there on the Tikhaya River on August 10.

According to the expert hunter K.N. Yakovlev, willow ptarmigans were somewhat fewer in the Chaun region than on the east tundra, i.e. in the Ostrov region. The J. Billings expedition (Sarychev, 1811, pp. 54, 58, 61 and map), which crossed the interior of the Chukchi peninsula from Mechigmensk Gulf mostly via the northern slopes of the Anadyr Range up to Anyuev, noticed ptarmigans in summer and winter. They were noted particularly on February 14, 1792, on the Gek rivulet entering the Sukhoi Anyui south of Chaun Bay. According to F.P. Wrangel (1841, vol. II, p. 222) the ptarmigans bred in large numbers in the valley of the Pogynden River, especially in August. However, a hunter who was specially sent out on August 22, 1822, brought back only one bird which was the last bird noticed by the Wrangel expedition right up to the Anyui coast. F.B. Chernyavskii found broods and single birds in small numbers in the summer of 1965 in the east of the north Anyui Range and in 1966 in the southwestern parts; in 1966 they were also found in the neighborhood of Bilibino settlement, in the basin of the Malyi Anyui, and finally south of Cape Schmidt, in the basin of the Kuvét, Kuékvuń and other rivers.

É.V. Schmidt told me that willow ptarmigans were very numerous on Bol'shaya Baranikha but were fewer on the tundra east of the Kolyma than west of it. From the latter zone, mass flights took place to the willow zones in the lower Kolyma flood plains. From 1914 through 1917 J. Koren (Schaanning, 1954) gathered 19 specimens of willow ptarmigan and a clutch on the lower Kolyma.

Habitat—The nesting areas of willow ptarmigans are associated with the willow shrubs beside rivulets or lakelets. In early July, 1934, in the nesting time on the Utte-Véem River, I put up ptarmigans on the fringe of shrubbery rising to a man's height. A month later I encountered broods at the foot of the steep bank of Lake Kool'ong in willows rising to a height of a meter or more scattered on hummocky tundra. On May 21 I encountered a calling male with a female on a pebbled spit by the Mitkulen rivulet. The coastal spit was densely overgrown with *Elymus mollis* grass and creeping willow. On May 18, in the immediate vicinity of Cape Serdtse-Kamen', calling males were seen on thawed patches on the slopes of knolls by the beds of tiny osiers. In the summer of 1956 I found many willow ptarmigans nesting in the flood plains of the Amguema. They were mostly confined to the willow plantations by the rivers but were occasionally seen on the hummocky tundra nearby. They were altogether absent far from the flood plains, even in willow plantations along the rivulets, which were free of the ice cover very late.

E.M. Meller collected a breeding female near Pereval'naya on hummocky tundra with tiny shrubs. A.P. Kuzyakin put up two pairs near Yandagai on wet, depressed, rocky low-sedge tundra on July 9/10, 1957. According to É.V. Schmidt, the number of willow ptarmigans occupying the river valleys that he visited east of Chaun Bay depended wholly on the presence of shrubbery growth.

Willow ptarmigans were seen even in the winter in tall shrubs until they were buried by snow. According to I.O. Olenev, at Providence Bay the ptarmigans were not seen in the winter because of thick, continuous snow cover but they wintered in large numbers in Pinkegnei, where the willow grew tall. On the Yararmumny River P.T. Butenko found flocks of ptarmigans in the valleys of rivulets where shrubs grew to a height of 1.25 m above the snow. In mid-January, 1934, large flocks were seen there, the conditions for their residence then being obviously very favorable. Near Cape Schmidt V.Ya. Isaev found ptarmigans in the winter in the mountain valleys covered with shrubs. Where the shrubs were spread over large areas the birds were found in huge numbers. In the western parts of the Chukchi peninsula, in the river valleys, much taller willows grow and at places innumerable ptarmigans gathered on them. On the Anadyr and Kolyma the flood plain willow plantations served as the main winter refuge for the mass flights of ptarmigans.

As the shrubs begin to be covered more and more with snow, the birds are compelled to migrate either to very tall shrubs or to windswept places where even the ground shrubs remain uncovered. The birds find such places along the slopes of mountains and on the seacoast. On September 29, 1878, the members of the *Vega* expedition were struck by the disappearance of ptarmigans from around Pitlekai. The Chukchians explained that the birds had migrated south into the windswept mountains. On October 19, 1933, I found willow ptarmigans on a knoll very near Uélen in an environment more suitable for rock ptarmigans. The knolls had long been covered by snow and had a wintry appearance but at places there were dark spots with the soil and shrubs exposed by the strong wind. The birds sheltered at the edge of rock debris in pits dug deep in the snow. According to I.O. Olenev willow ptarmigans remained in large numbers at Kurupka village near Providence Bay, where strong winds cleared the snow.

The seacoast is an altogether special winter habitat of willow ptarmigans. In November and December, 1933, the birds sometimes came to the southern bank of the Uélen lagoon, where they were confined to a tundra terrace with peaty mounds and curtains of procumbent willows. On December 9, I encountered some ptarmigans running about and churning up the snow; some fell in it. Judging from the tracks, these places were also visited by hares and foxes.

In the course of the 1878/79 winter solitary ptarmigans were encountered at Pitlekai, mostly in the sandy hills on the coast where the grass showed above the snow and the birds, after feeding, would shelter among the hummocks. On April 25 and 26, 1934, I came across innumerable tracks of ptarmigans on the low Cape Vankarém. There were also thawed patches and areas of snow churned up by the birds themselves, as also much excrement. A flock settled on the hummocks, which under coastal conditions served as a general refuge for the ptarmigans to rest and hide from predators. I was particularly surprised at an incident involving an encounter with a bird on May 19, 1934, southeast of Cape Unin 2 km from a high rocky shoreline. I was making my way with difficulty across the hummocks among thawed pools when I scared a lone ptarmigan in an altogether uncharacteristic environment: water, ice and melting snow. It is possible that the bird was hiding there to escape the attack of some predator.

On April 29, traveling west of the Amguema estuary, I found a sick bird again among hummocks and encountered their tracks farther along the coast. According to V.Ya. Isaev, in the coastal zone by Cape Schmidt ptarmigans were rarely seen on the wind-swept hill slopes covered with weeds.

Spring migrations and return to the breeding grounds—Periodic migrations, evidently over considerable distances, are made by willow ptarmigans in the Chukchi peninsula. Their return to the breeding area has been noticed by various observers. In the spring of 1879, on the seacoast by the wintering post of the *Vega*, willow ptarmigans were seen in May in larger numbers than in winter. But they later disappeared altogether, preferring the shrubs inland.

On April 26, 1934, at Cape Vankarém, I encountered very wary willow ptarmigans. The flock took off as soon as the watching male gave a shriek. Evidently they were wandering birds. In 1956 hunters told me about the arrival of these

PLATE V

Sandhill crane *Grus canadensis* (L.) with fledgeling in the valley of Utte-Véem river. July 8, 1934. Pic. by L.A. Portenko.

birds. In the course of the winter, in the immediate vicinity of the settlement by the 91st km, these birds were entirely destroyed but others were seen late in the spring. I myself saw them in the flood plains of the Amguema only from June 11 when the calling was at its peak. On June 14 the males flew over the flood plains, perhaps in search of females. On the evening of June 15, a pair of ptarmigans flew past my window. At that time the paired birds had already built their nests.

According to É.V. Schmidt, in the willow growths along the Kolyma the population of ptarmigans decreased from the beginning of May. In the Chukchi peninsula the wintering ptarmigans were confined to the willows up to mid-May. Residents on Aiok Island told V.D. Lebedev and V.R. Filin that the ptarmigans there disappeared in the spring.

Spring molt—According to Schaanning (1954), among the males gathered by J. Koren on the Kolyma, brown feathers were already seen on the neck of two collected on February 25 and April 22, 1916. Of the 10 birds given to the members of the *Vega* expedition on May 22, 1879, the necks of eight were more or less brown. In one male only two white feathers remained on the occiput, the cheeks were nearly brown and the brown feathers on the throat and crown were speckled. In a specimen taken on May 23 some brown feathers showed through on the head and neck. White patches were seen even in June in these areas. The Chukchians said the head and neck of willow ptarmigans turned dark in April-May (they called this period "imleradlin").

In 1934, on May 17, I was told in Neshkan that the necks of ptarmigans turned black (they appeared so in the bright light of the arctic day). On May 18, in Nettekenishken, a male shot had russet feathers on the neck and a prominent reddish superalium, but its head remained white. On the evening of the same day, at Cape Serdtse-Kamen', I collected a solitary male whose crown and dorsal portion of the neck were white. Only tiny chestnut-colored feathers were seen while the ventral aspect of the head and neck was almost completely bare.

On June 11, 1956, on the Amguema, I encountered males which were already in complete breeding plumage. On June 13, I noticed many dark feathers on one of them even on the back. On June 16 the entire back of another male was dark. The back of another bird collected on June 25 showed several colored feathers but even on July 12 I found a male whose overall color was still quite white. On June 9, 1958, V.D. Lebedev and V.R. Filin noticed a male in breeding plumage on Aiok Island. On June 4 and 7, 1916, J. Koren collected two males in this plumage on the Kolyma.

The females acquire summer plumage late. On May 21, 1934, east of Mitkulen, I saw a dirty-white female along with a male in breeding plumage.

On May 31, 1939, E.M. Meller collected a female on which colored feathers had grown patchily on the back, head and neck, as also among the white wing coverts. On June 11, 1956, I found a female with motley feathers on the back on the Amguema. In another female, taken on June 18, such feathers were still few. On June 22, 1916, J. Koren collected a specimen which was in full summer plumage on the Kolyma.

Mating call—On May 18, 1934, at Cape Serdtse-Kamen', I collected a male with enlarged testes of 8×10 and 7×9 mm. It did not have subcutaneous adipose formations. In the neighborhood at that time, several males were making the mating call in the typical atmosphere of a spring evening on the Chukchi coast. On May 21 I encountered a pair on a spit east of Mitkulen. The male was in a highly excited condition and when the female was shot it flew around for a long time, finally settling on the hummocks.

According to the observations of V.Ya. Isaev, at Cape Schmidt, in 1935, willow ptarmigans began calling at the end of April; until the first half of May the calling was at its peak. Some males were still calling at the end of May even after the females had become inconspicuous.

On June 11, 1956, on the Amguema I found males that were still calling. They were basking on the dry mounds, flying from time to time, but low, and giving out a characteristic kokh-kokh-kokh—kebav-kek-kek-kekh-kekh-kekh.... On rising, the birds described an arc and then continued their flight in the direction opposite to that in which they took off. They usually sat deep inside the bushes or on an elevation and followed my movements from there. On June 16 the calling was still heard sometimes but was noticeably fainter. The call at times sounded like kokh-kokh-kékékéké-kekh-kekh... , i.e. the line was shortened. One male in full breeding dress sat in the open on a grassy spit in a snowfield but most of them were concealed. Later ptarmigans could be put up only from bushes or high mounds.

The shrieks of males could be heard sometimes until the end of June but only at night. I was always reminded of the usual crow of the domestic cock. On the night of June 26/27, 1957, A.P. Kuzyakin heard the call of ptarmigans near Poutyn. Frightened birds screamed even in July but evidently due to a different type of excitation. In July the males were in full summer plumage (Fig. 41).

Breeding—The biggest follicle in the ovary of a female collected near Pereval'naya Station on May 31, 1939, was of the size of a cherry. At the end of June 1956, at Amguema, I was given two eggs from a clutch containing 10 eggs. One of them turned out to be fresh while the other was slightly incubated. A clutch of 10 eggs was given to A.P. Kuzyakin on June 24, 1957, in Akkani village. The eggs were slightly incubated, their average weight being roughly 22 g. J. Koren's collection from Kolyma has a clutch (found on June 17, 1916) of six eggs incubated for two days but he found four three-day-old downy chicks on June 22, 1917.

On August 18, 1934, I encountered a brood on the knolls on the western side of Lake Kool'ong. On being chased, the male deserted the chicks and flew at least 200 m away. The young stuck to the edge of the shrubs and were found partly in the shrubs and partly between the mounds. They were already three-fourths the size of adults. Ovaries could be distinguished in the specimen found. Subcutaneous adipose formations were absent. On August 10, 1958, V.D. Lebedev and V.R. Filin found two broods containing six or seven birds each on the banks of the Tikhaya River (Karchyk peninsula).

Fall molt—The Chukchians confirmed (Palmén, 1887) that willow ptarmigans sported the winter dress in September-October (they call this period "kutschkau"). The young male from Kolyma in J. Koren's collection shot on September 29, 1916, was dark on top and white below. The female taken on October 25, 1914, was already pure white. It is interesting that the winter females shot on December 18, 1914, and January 3, 1916, had some dark feathers on the nape.

Fall and winter migrations—Near the winter anchorage of the *Vega* in the fall of 1878 willow ptarmigans were seen only from November 16 through 18. Later they were seen from time to time, more often singly, right up to the middle of February; one bird was collected on March 3. In the fall of 1933, around Uélen, I encountered the first winter ptarmigans on October 19. After this they were sometimes seen in November and December. Their tracks were noticed on November 10. On November 12 P.T. Butenko put up four ptarmigans; they were very wary, flew away 50 paces, and hid for a long time. On November 17 he again found four ptarmigans there. On December 7 a flock flew into Uélen; we found some at another point nearby on December 9. Butenko came across flocks on the Utte-Véem River on January 15 and 17.

It is interesting that the ptarmigans killed around Uélen in October and November had appreciable adipose formations under the skin; the December birds were plump but those collected on the Utte-Véem River in January were either emaciated or had negligible adipose layers. The testes of males were 3×4 and 2×3 mm in size and the ovaries of females showed a fine-grained structure.

According to É.V. Schmidt mass flights of ptarmigans into the Kolyma willow plantations occurred in January and February.

Food—According to research by the members of the *Vega* expedition, tiny willow branches, together with willow leaves and red bilberries, two blades of grass and gall-like formations were found in the crop of a willow ptarmigan caught on February 17, 1879. Some of the willow shoots were 3 mm in diameter and the longest of them was 30 to 55 mm. The crop of a bird found on May 23 was also full of willow branches, mostly with buds, and also leaves and shoots of red bilberry and *Empetrum nigrum*, with two blades of grass and some quartz grains. The bird was emaciated.

The following were found in the crops and stomachs of specimens that I collected:

1) Uélen, December 9, 1933. About 800 shoots, more than 100 flower buds and one dry willow leaf in the crop. 2) Uélen, December 9, 1933. The stomach showed much digested remains of stalks and buds of willow; there were also tiny stones. 3) Uélen, December 13, 1933. The crop contained about 1,000 bits of stalk and up to 100 large buds of willow. In the stomach were the digested remains of stalks and many tiny stones. 4) Yararmumny river, January 16, 1934. The stomach contained much digested remains of stalks and many tiny stones. 5) Utte-Véem River, January 16, 1934. In the crop there were about 100 bits of downy willow shoots and 30 to 40 tiny flower buds. 6) Utte-Véem River, January 26, 1934. The crop contained about 800 bits of willow shoots and over 100 flower buds. 7) Utte-Véem River, January 26, 1934. About 700 bits of shoots and about 60 flower buds of willow were found in the crop.

The crops and stomachs of three ptarmigans obtained in May, 1939, near Pereval'naya by E.M. Meller showed buds, tiny leaves and shoot tips of willow, year-old berries and tiny stones.

Economic importance—Because of its small population the willow ptarmigan is nowhere found in the Chukchi peninsula on a commerical scale and is a rather rare hunter's prize. According to the hunter, K.N. Yakovlev, on the tundra between Chaun Bay and the Kolyma, where the ptarmigan is found in larger numbers than in the eastern parts of the Chukchi peninsula, it is not dressed. They are caught sometimes in large numbers but for personal consumption. On the lower Kolyma, according to É.V. Schmidt, the local people catch the ptarmigans in snares by the hundreds, taking upward of 1,000 in a winter.

Systematics of the subspecies—I have undertaken revision of the subspecies of willow ptarmigans based on the material of the Institute of Zoology, Academy of Sciences of the USSR, quite a number of times, beginning in 1930. In the course of the past 35 years, the collections have gradually been supplemented and now I have come to new conclusions compared to what was published in my Ural work (1937a).

The subspecies of willow ptarmigans are best differentiated by the color of the male plumage in the more complete summer dress which they wear in August and September.

I differentiate the following subspecies within the USSR:

1. **Lagopus lagopus lagopus** (L.) (Synonyms: *L. l. koreni* Thayer and Bangs, *L. l. kapustini* Serebr., and *L. l. septentrionalis* But.). Even in my Ural work 30 years ago, I felt that the northern subspecies under the various synonyms were difficult to differentiate. All the apparently divergent geographic races in the North are explained by the fact that the birds were not gathered at different points in the same condition of summer plumage. Moreover, it was found that the Swedish specimens were particularly small. The Swedish material in the collection of the Institute of Zoology, Academy of Sciences of the USSR, was generally unsatisfactory either qualitatively or quantitatively. One old stuffed specimen is in summer dress with an abnormally light color but the label gives the date as December, 1829. Another specimen is marked as a male when in fact it is an adult female. Three reliable males from Sweden did not have as short a wing as was expected after the female was mistaken for a male with a wing length of only 190 mm. Neither in color nor in size do the males of willow ptarmigans from Sweden differ from Kola and far-eastern birds. The lone male from Alaska (from Norton Sound) is an old museum specimen obtained by I.G. Voznesenskii on August 23, 1843. In plumage pattern it is indistinguishable from the males of northern Eurasia though it has yellowed over the years. With the series of 54 well-prepared late summer males available to me I must conclude that all the ptarmigans from Scandinavia to Alaska belong to the same subspecies. This view is, however, nothing new: J.L. Peters came to the same conclusion (Peters, 1934b, vol. II, p. 30).

The wingspan varies fairly widely. I measured it using a metal tape (Table 32).

The color is identical: nor do the wing measurements provide any basis for classifying the geographic races though short-winged populations are noticed in the far western and eastern parts of the range. In the east, especially among the ptarmigans of the Koryatz foothills, birds with more massive, blunt or bulging beaks are encountered more often but such birds stray into the other parts of the range too.

Distribution—Tundra and forest tundra from Scandinavia at least to Alaska. The southern boundary in the northern forest zone is not clear. Along the Ural Range the nominal form is encountered down to 62° north. It inhabits the basins of the Podkamennaya Tunguska and Vilyui, the middle reaches of the Aldan, the Anadyr

Table 32. Wing length of summer males of *L. l. lagopus* (L.), mm

Locality	Wing length
Sweden	208, 206, 205
Kola peninsula	218, 215, 212, 210, 208, 208, 206
Mezen'—Northern Urals	223, 213, 211, 210, 208, 207, 206, 205, 204
Yamal—lower reaches of the Yenisei	218, 218, 216, 215, 212, 211, 209, 205
Taimir—Lena	219, 218, 211, 210, 210, 205
Yana—Chukchi peninsula	213, 209, 200, 197
Koryatz foothills	211, 208, 207, 206, 205, 205, 204, 204, 203, 203, 203, 200, 200, 200, 199
Norton Sound	204

Range and the Koryatz foothills to Tilichikov.

2. **Lagopus lagopus birulai** Serebr. A lone male is known in full summer plumage resembling in color the nominal form. The wing length is 215 mm but specimens in other plumages possess the maximum wing length.

Distribution—Novosibirsk Island.

? **Lagopus lagopus kamtschatkensis** Mom. None of the ornithologists who studied the subspecies of willow ptarmigans had a good collection of summer males from Kamchatka. Two males in transitory post-breeding dress and two summer females from Kamchatka which were with me revealed individual characteristics that led me to exclude them from the nominal form. The question of the actual form of *L. l. okadai* Mom. from Sakhalin also remains undetermined.

3. **Lagopus lagopus sserebrowsky** Doman. The summer males are characterized by a dark color and a cold reddish-brown shade. The best character is the short wing.

Distribution—Southern part of eastern Siberia from Baikal Range to Bureinsk.

4. **Lagopus lagopus brevirostris** Hesse represents an intermediary form between *L. l. sserebrowsky* and *L. l. maior* Lor. The summer males from Chulyshmak (terra typica) in P.P. Sushkin's collection are of the same type and resemble *L. l. sserebrowsky* in the dark reddish color but differ in their long wing. The feathers on the upper side of the body have large, distinct dark patches in the center. Along the western periphery of the range are found specimens which very much resemble *L. l. maior* in color.

Distribution—Altai and West Sayan.

5. **Lagopus lagopus kozlowae** Port. The summer males show a very characteristic pattern on the upper side of the body: instead of patches there is a transverse arrangement of parallel streaks. The head, neck and breast have a characteristic clayey shade. Grayish-brown fields, specks and stars are seen on the white flight feathers. These are not seen in any of the other subspecies that I have collected. Compared to *L. l. brevirostris*, the upper portion has a more reddish shade.

Distribution—Changai Range, Tannu-Ola, and Munkhu-Sardyk as also, evidently, the Chental hills.

6. **Lagopus lagopus maior** Lor. The summer males are characterized by very light and yellowish coloration. The reddish brown or rusty tones are replaced by yellowish-brown tones in this subspecies. Central black patches are well developed on the feathers on the back. Large size is characteristic of this subspecies.

Distribution—From Orenburg and Mias to Tomsk, to the north to Tyukalinsk and in the south covering the northern Kazakhstan steppes.

7. **Lagopus lagopus pallasi,** nomen emendatum pro *rossica* Serebr. The color of the summer males is impregnated with a very bright rust red whereby the subspecies is easily distinguished from others. The head, neck and breast are of a reddish-chestnut color. A yellow banding is well developed on the back.

Distribution—From the Leningrad region to the Northern Urals including southern Karelia, Novgorod region, Kalininsk, Moscow and north to Sol'vychegodsk.

P.S. Pallas (1811, vol. II, pp. 64 and 70) did not distinguish tundra from willow ptarmigans but was acquainted with some subspecies of these two species. In listing the forms of undetermined taxonomic importance, celled *Varietas*, he twice included the name *rossica* in italics. But he did not describe how *rossica* was to be distinguished from *sarmatica* and other forms. The name *rossica* (Pall.) is a "nomen nudum". Nevertheless, it covers the name *rossicus* Serebr. Hence the central Russian willow ptarmigans should be given a new name.

I measured the wing length of different subspecies of willow ptarmigans (Table 33), both summer and winter birds with a metal tape. The wear of the flight feather tips in the course of a year was relatively slight. The wing length averaged 211 mm in 55 winter males of *L. lagopus lagopus* (L.) and 210 mm in 94 males in the breeding plumage. This value in 66 summer birds was 209 mm. The wing of females was on an average 10 to 12 mm shorter than that of males.

Specimens— 1) Cape Dezhnev, October 19, 1933, ♀, Portenko; 2) Uélen, November 17, 1933, ♀, Portenko; 3) same place, December 9, 1933, ♂, Portenko; 4) same place, December 13, 1933, ♀, Portenko; 5) Yararmumny River, January 16, 1934, ♂, Portenko; 6 and 7) Utte-Véem River, January 26, 1934, ○○, Portenko; 8) Énurmino village, May 19, 1934, ♂, Portenko; 9) middle reaches of Utte-Véem River, July 7, 1934, ♂, Portenko; 10) Lake Kool'ong, August 19, 1934, ♀, juv., Portenko; 11) Pereval'naya, May 8, 1939, ♀, Meller; and 12 and 13) same place, May 31, 1939, ♀♀, Meller.

Biological material—Two eggs, middle reaches of the Amguema River, end of June, 1956, Portenko.

41. **Lagopus mutus pleskei** Serebr. —**Rock Ptarmigan**

Local name—In Eskimo: Àqăr-yā'-ĭk on St. Lawrence Island.

Distribution and status—Common in the nesting areas in the mountains of the Chukchi peninsula but few in number in the eastern part. During winter migrations approaches the seacoast and penetrates Diomede and Kolyuchi Islands. Altogether absent from Wrangel Island.

É.V. Schmidt noticed the rock ptarmigan in the mountains between Cape Bering and the apex of Mechigmensk Gulf but in much smaller numbers than in the western part of the Chukchi peninsula. On the knolls around Providence Bay neither

Table 33. Wing length in subspecies *Lagopus lagopus* (L.), mm (colored and white plumage)

No.	Subspecies	Color	Males				Females			
			Max.	Min.	Mean	No. of samples	Max.	Min.	Mean	No. of samples
1.	*L. l. lagopus*	Colored	226	192	210	160	211	182	197	72
		White	225	193	211	55	213	180	198	74
2.	*L. l. birulai*	Colored	226	215	222	3	216	205	211	4
		White	225	225	225	1	—	—	—	—
?	*L. l. kamatschatkensis* (Kamchatka)	Colored	211	198	203	5	196	188	192	2
		White	219	200	212	3	201	195	198	2
	L. l. okadai (Sakhalin)	Colored	214	204	208	3	—	—	—	—
		White	—	—	—	—	—	—	—	—
3.	*L. l. sserebrowsky*	Colored	202	190	197	11	188	175	182	7
		White	191	191	191	1	203	191	196	3
4.	*L. l. brevirostris*	Colored	213	197	205	14	203	184	192	7
		White	227	218	222	2	200	200	200	1
5.	*L. l. kozlowae*	Colored	216	196	205	15	195	184	192	4
		White	220	220	220	1	201	189	194	8
6.	*L. l. maior*	Colored	230	208	216	10	217	200	207	8
		White	223	200	216	6	212	204	208	2
7.	*L. l. pallasi*	Colored	223	197	207	24	208	181	193	26
		White	218	203	212	6	200	188	196	6
8.	*L. l. alexandrae*	Colored	208	199	203	2	—	—	—	—
		White	202	202	202	1	—	—	—	—
9.	*L. l. alleni*	Colored	205	200	203	3	198	198	198	1
		White	206	206	206	1	—	—	—	—

I nor P.T. Butenko found it at all. Based on information supplied by the eskimos, O.W. Geist (Murie 1936) and F.H. Fay and T.J. Cade (1959) wrote that some type of ptarmigan was encountered every year in small numbers in the winter in the mountains of St. Lawrence Island but no one had seen them in the summer. Both the species of ptarmigans—*Lagopus lagopus* and *L. mutus*—could fly there and until specimens were obtained it could only be conjectured which of them it was, if not both. In the latter half of August, 1855, Lieutenant Brooks secured some ptarmigans in the mountains overlooking Senyavin Strait. In the work on J. Rodgers' expedition (Heine, 1859, p. 170), they are called "ptarmigans" and most probably they were rock ptarmigans.

On the knolls around Uélen, I did not encounter this species but according to W.S. Brooks (1915) two male rock ptarmigans were obtained on June 16, 1913, near Cape Dezhnev. In June, 1970, V.V. Leonovich noticed the presence of rock ptarmigans around Énurmino. In the summer of 1956, I encountered a lone pair on the knolls on the middle reaches of the Amguema around the 91st km. In the mountains running south from Cape Schmidt to Chaun Bay É.V. Schmidt saw rock ptarmigans on the upper reaches of the Telekai-Véem, Chantal'veegyrgyn, Ékiatap, Kuékvyn', Kuvét, Pegtymel', Palya-Véem and Chaun rivers. These birds were common there, though not numerous. Three specimens were noticed by Schmidt on Aiok Island. In the mountains on Baranikha rock ptarmigans were seen quite often.

In general, however, this species was encountered by Schmidt in almost all the mountains in the Chaun region and farther west to the Kolyma. C.H. Merck, a member of J. Billings' expedition who traveled with a reindeer caravan along the northern slopes of the Anadyr Range in the fall of 1791, brought back for P.S. Pallas (1811, vol. II, p. 68) a ptarmigan which from its small size and grayish-yellow color could easily be identified as *Lagopus mutus*. In 1965, F.B. Chernyavskii found this species in the eastern part of the north Anyui Range. In 1966 he found it in the southwestern part and, what is more, in the mountains to the south of Cape Schmidt. Everywhere it was less common than the willow ptarmigan. In 1905, S.A. Buturlin (1906b) found a rock ptarmigan in the Kolyma delta. As could be expected, it was less numerous than the willow ptarmigan. In the Kolyma estuary J. Koren collected one on June 29, 1912, in Troyanov Bay south of Cape Medvezhii (Thayer and Bangs, 1914). He also saw a rock ptarmigan in Sukharnoe village on June 24.

In the winter the rock ptarmigans wander and are encountered at places where they are not seen in the nesting period. On January 15, 1938, P.T. Butenko obtained a male and a female around Rirakyanot village. According to É.V. Schmidt, in the 1935 winter, when there was much snow, some birds were collected in February in Lawrence Bay where they were not seen in other years. J. Koren noticed this species on Bol'shoi Diomede Island. On the knolls closest to Uélen, I found old droppings, evidently of rock ptarmigans. On November 14, 1933, P.T. Butenko encountered four rock ptarmigans on the south bank of the Uélen lagoon though willow ptarmigans were quite often found there. The *Vega* expedition did not find this species on Kolyuchin Bay but I saw fairly recent droppings on Kolyuchi Island which, judging from the small amount, were of the rock ptarmigan.

Habitat—In the Chukchi peninsula the rock ptarmigan is strictly confined to the mountains. Along the Amguema, I found its droppings on the peaks and in the foothills of the knolls. I found a male once on a mossy wet terrace on top of a knoll. A pair was confined to the rubble at the base. According to É.V. Schmidt, in the mountains south of Chaun Bay rock ptarmigans were seen 300 m above sea level.

Spring molt—The males taken at Cape Dezhnev on June 16, 1913, had summer feathers on the crown, occiput and sides of the head. The male that I saw on June 20, 1956, on the Amguema was still completely white though the plumage was very soiled. In the variegated dress of the female, white feathers predominated.

Breeding—On June 20, 1956, I encountered what was probably a nesting pair. The male headed me off because a female was hiding around there. Taking off, the female followed the male. Both the birds settled not far away, then decided to approach me again; the female again hid herself but I could not find the nest.

A young male collected near Uélen on November 14, 1933, had small testes of

2×3 mm and faint subcutaneous adipose formations. The male taken at Yanrakynnot on January 15, 1938, had bigger testes: 2×6 and 2×5 mm. In the female shot together with this male, the ovary was 12 mm long and of fine-grained structure. Both the specimens lacked adipose formations.

Economic importance—The rock ptarmigans live in uninhabited hilly places and hence are secured by hunters very rarely, mostly when the birds are migrating.

Systematics of the subspecies—I recorded the results of my revision of the subspecies of rock ptarmigans in my Ural and Anadyr works (Portenko, 1937a, 1939b, vol. II). I called the Siberian subspecies *Lagopus mutus pleskei* Serebr. F. Salomonsen (1939), who processed a lot of material on the Eurasian and American rock ptarmigans, including some of the specimens from the collection of the Institute of Zoology, Academy of Sciences of the USSR, combined the Siberian and American birds into a single subspecies. I do not have much material from America and for the time being retain the name *L. m. pleskei* Serebr., given for the north Siberian subspecies.

Specimens— 1) Uélen, November 14, 1933, ♂, Portenko; and 2 and 3) Yanrakynnot village, January 15, 1938, ♂♀, Butenko.

Order VII. GRUIFORMES—CRANES

42. **Grus canadensis canadensis** (L.)—**Sandhill Crane**

Local name—Chukchian: Kéitchànyr, keitchàn, and khesànyr; ketschanger according to the *Vega* records. In Eskimo: satỳl'gak in Providence Bay and să-tĭl'-lŭ-ghŭk on St. Lawrence Island.

Distribution and status—Nests in the Chukchi peninsula and flies away in the winter. Common and, at places, numerous. Lone birds and flocks seen on Wrangel Island from time to time.

Nidification—N.P. Sokol'nikov recorded in his manuscript that the crane lived around Krest Bay. On July 24, 1931, near Uél'kal' village, on the western shore of the bay, L.O. Belopol'skii (1934) chased a pair of cranes several times in the day, from which it could be concluded that they nested there. In June, 1961, V.É. Yakobi came across them there several times.

Eskimos in Notapenmen village told me that the cranes nested on the eastern shore of Krest Bay; at least they had heard their calls there.

According to W.S. Brooks (1915), in June, 1913, two pairs of sandhill cranes nested on the western side of Providence Bay. I.O. Olenev, who wintered at Émma Bay in 1931/32, told me that a pair nested there. Moreover, the cranes were constantly seen far up Providence Bay. Belopol'skii had with him the skin of a crane from there. In May, 1938, P.T. Butenko repeatedly hunted cranes in flight on the tundra near Cape Stoletiya. On July 12, 1938, on the depressed part of this tundra and also on the slopes of neighboring knolls, I found some pairs nesting not far from one another. One pair had a chick. On June 12 and 14, 1957, A.P. Kuzyakin noticed three cranes on the eastern side of Providence Bay.

Sandhill cranes nested on St. Lawrence Island in small numbers. O. Nordquist (Palmén, 1887) heard their call from July 31 through August 2, 1879, when the

Vega expedition landed there. E.W. Nelson (1883, p. 92) erred when he referred to this observation as pertaining to Lawrence Bay. He himself visited the island at the end of May and early June, 1881, and recorded a small number of sandhill cranes.

In 1913 W.S. Brooks noticed two pairs on the southeastern tip of the island; on June 27, a pair with a chick was collected. H.B. Collins (Friedmann, 1932a) reported the presence of this bird on the island in the summer of 1930. O.W. Geist (Murie, 1936) took at least three specimens on June 25, 1936. F.H. Fay and T.J. Cade (1959) did not find nests but the reindeer shepherds reported that they occasionally saw the nests inland. On August 31, 1957, a young crane was noticed at the western end of the Kuzata lagoon. Fay and Cade quite often encountered flocks of three to six cranes each in the course of a summer in the riverine valleys. They were evidently solitary birds. According to E.G.F. Sauer and E.K. Urban (1964), in 1960 stray pairs occupied sections on the plateau and wet pastures in the valleys of the Boxer and Vanmaii rivers. Observations were made near one nest. Finally, H. Friedmann (1934a) identified the bone fragments of cranes and a whole metatarsus in archaeological excavations on St. Lawrence Island.

In the second half of August, 1855, the members of Capt. J. Rodgers' expedition (Heine, 1859, p. 170) noticed some cranes on the coast of Senyavin Strait. A. Th. Middendorff (1877) incorrectly classified these data as pertaining to St. Lawrence Island. Innumerable breeding cranes were noticed there by Senyavin Strait from June 28 through 30, 1879, on the southeastern shore of Konyam Bay, during the *Vega's* halt. In his manuscript N.P. Sokol'nikov also mentions that numerous cranes inhabited Senyavin Strait. As É.V. Schmidt told me, the sandhill crane was not a rarity on the Mechigmensk tundra and around Lawrence Bay.

In 1957, A.P. Kuzyakin found the cranes very common in the breeding areas on the tundra adjoining Lawrence Bay to the south. The nesting density there was one pair per sq km. He found two or three pairs on Akkani and five or six pairs on the slope by the bay, 500 to 700 m from the settlement. On June 22/23 and July 5 he noticed a pair between Chulkhyn settlement and Yandagai, and finally came across a calling pair near Poutyn.

The cranes did not nest on the Diomede Islands. I did not find them in the nesting areas even on the Dezhnev knolls or in the immediate neighborhood of Uélen but found innumerable birds farther inland along the banks of the Kol'oam and Utte-Véem rivers. Some idea of the population may be had from the following excerpts from my dairy: on August 10, 1934, my party entered the estuary of the Kol'oam River. We found broods of cranes in the middle reaches by midday. On the 11th we did not find them, but all day on the 12th we quite often heard calls coming from the tundra and again encountered broods; in the evening, we noticed three flying cranes. On August 13 pairs were seen at places and on the 14th calls were heard; on the 15th pairs were found here and there along the banks. Moreover, two flocks were sighted. On August 16 we again saw cranes but no observations were made on the 17th. On the following day, August 18, cranes were sometimes found flying around Lake Kool'ong. The birds had changed their feeding ground.

In the valley of the Utte-Véem River the party was a month ahead. On July 6, on the lower reaches of this river, I saw some cranes and heard their calls incessantly. On the sandy bank of the rivulet I saw many tracks. On July 7 the cranes were not to be found at all for some reason, but the search for broods on the 8th was successful. On July 12, on the tundra at the southwestern corner of the Inchoun lagoon, I saw three cranes and one of them was collected. On July 21, on my way from Inchoun to Uélen, I heard the calls and disturbed a solitary bird on the tundra.

In the summer of 1970 V.V. Leonovich noted sandhill cranes in small numbers around Énurmino. The calls of three pairs were heard simultaneously from the same place.

The members of the *Vega* expedition (Palmén, 1887) found cranes common in the interior of the Chukchi peninsula. From June 14 through 16, 1879, E. Almquist encountered flocks of five or six birds each on the high banks of the rivers entering Kolyuchin Bay. The Chukchians told him that the cranes nested far inland. E.K. Brusevits saw cranes on July 8. On July 25, 1909, J. Koren (1910) found a pair and attempted to locate the nest on the tundra from the western side of Kolyuchin Bay. In the summer of 1970 A.A. Kishchinskii found cranes common in the nesting area in the marine tundra between Vankarém and the Amguema estuary. He traced nests and broods.

In June and July, 1956, I saw lone cranes and heard their calls on the Amguema by the 91st km, but they nested only on the left bank. V.Ya. Isaev noticed a flock in the spring of 1935 in the valley of one of the tributaries of the Amguema on the lower reaches. He found them also around Cape Schmidt. A.A. Savich collected a sandhill crane there on June 4, 1915 (Artobolevskii, 1927). On August 11, 1966, F.B. Chernyavskii found a flock of five birds in the valley of the Pil'gyn River west of Cape Schmidt. A.I. Argentov (1857a) wrote that, apart from storks, cranes also inhabited Chaun parish. According to É.V. Schmidt, cranes were innumerable in the Chaun depression and would fly far into the mountains up the river valleys. In mid-June, 1959, E.P. Spangenberg (1960) found sandhill cranes in large numbers around Pevek and inland, where it turned out to be quite a common bird.

In É.V. Schmidt's opinion this crane is not rare on Aiok Island. V.D. Lebedev and V.R. Filin (1959) found it in large numbers on Aiok Island and also in the Karchyk peninsula. On June 6, 1958, they counted up to 40 pairs and found a nest over a 6 km stretch along the west coast of Aiok Island. They found two more nests on June 22. On July 10 they came across a brood with a chick in the Karchyk peninsula. Sandhill cranes were innumerable in the fall flight also.

K.N. Yakovlev told me that the crane was found in small numbers in the Chaun and East Tundra regions. J. Koren (Thayer and Bangs, 1914) noticed cranes on July 18, 1912, 40 miles east of Cape Bol'shoi Baranov and at Balagan on July 19. A party from Wrangel's expedition (1841, vol. II, p. 213) came across two cranes 22 versts from Balagan and four versts from the bank of the Bol'shaya Baranikha. According to Wrangel this bird was so rare there that only a few of the local residents had seen it. Most recently, É.V. Schmidt noticed cranes on the Baranikha in fairly large numbers.

P.S. Pallas (1811, vol. II, p. 106) had reported seeing cranes on the Kolyma. Calling it *Grus vulgaris*, he wrote that cranes were present on the Kolyma and Anadyr in quite large numbers. According to E.P. Spangenberg (1960) the sandhill crane now occurs sporadically on the lower reaches of the Kolyma and does not nest in the river valley. On the right bank it was seen from Krai Lesov village to Ambarchik village. A pair was seen every 3 to 5 km. On the left bank it was encountered on Kamennyi and Darovatyi capes. According to K.A. Vorob'ev (1963), this is a common breeding bird on the tundra along the lower course of the Chukoch'ya River. It was apparently found in the nesting area to the west up to the lower reaches of the Alazei. It is surprising that S.A. Buturlin, who studied the avifauna of the lower Kolyma in 1905 in such detail, did not find the sandhill crane at all. Nor did J. Koren find it on the Kolyma 10 to 20 years later. It is impossible to miss such a prominent and noisy bird even by chance. There is therefore reason to believe that the western limit of distribution of this species varies from year to year and the new sightings in recent years do not prove that the sandhill crane spread up to the Kolyma or Alazei in the past.

W. Taczanowski (1873, p. 112) reported the occurrence of the sandhill crane north of Yakutsk. Since this species was mentioned along with two American birds, *Turdus aliciae* Baird and *Macroramphus griseus* (Gm.), it is quite possible that Taczanowski had with him G. Maydell's specimens from the Anadyr region. Even P.S. Pallas (1811, p. 106, on the common crane) writes that the crane was said to have been noticed around Olyutorka. On the lower reaches of the Apuka, I found sandhill cranes in the summer of 1959 and 1960 but nidification could not be accurately ascertained.

The sandhill crane does not nest on Wrangel Island but flies past it in summer. It was collected in the summer of 1927 near Cape Blossom (Mineev, 1936, p. 177). At the end of July or early August, 1933, Mineev noticed cranes west of Rodgers Bay. This bird was once seen by G.A. Ushakov (Bannikov, 1941). In July, 1939, I twice encountered the same flock on the tundra between Rodgers and Somnitel'naya bays. Probably it was a year-old brood which, as happens in the case of geese, had not yet dispersed. In mid-June, 1960, S.M. Uspenskii and his colleagues (Uspenskii, Bëme and Velizhanin, 1963) found a group of four cranes near Cape Hawaii and somewhat later noticed two lone birds in Tundra Akademii. According to A.G. Velizhanin (1965), in July two birds were noticed in the estuary of the Nasha River. The crane does not fly into Wrangel Island every year.

Flight courses and population of flying flocks—The available observational data suggest that the bulk of the sandhill cranes cross Bering Strait at the narrowest part of it, coming in the spring from Alaska past the Diomede Islands to Cape Dezhnev and going back by the same route in the fall. Evidently only a certain number of them cross the Bering Sea in the south. Having reached Cape Dezhnev, the cranes fly on in one of two directions: 1) northwest to Cape Serdtse-Kamen' and farther along the coast of the Chukchi Sea; and 2) southwest to the south coast of the Chukchi peninsula and on to the Anadyr and Koryatz foothills.

The existence of two flight courses joining up at Cape Dezhnev is seen quite distinctly in the fall. In 1933, I observed the flight from the heights of the Uélen knolls, from which Cape Serdtse-Kamen' in the west and Alaska in the east can be seen in clear weather. On August 28, I sighted a flock flying from the southwest from the direction of Lawrence Bay. In it, I counted 31 cranes. In all other cases, flocks were seen flying along the north coast of the Chukchi peninsula. At times, it could be confirmed with the binoculars that they covered the course straight from Cape Serdtse-Kamen'. On August 20 I noticed a flock of 11 birds, on August 28 a flock of 15, on the 29th a flock of seven, and on September 11 a flock of nine. Finally on September 14, I saw 10 flocks in which with the help of the binoculars I successively counted 39, 13, 6, 70, 70, 20 and 160 birds.

T.H. Bean (1883, p. 166) noticed the flight above Bering Strait on the American side on August 18, 1880, when he saw sandhill cranes flying near the Diomede Islands.

According to A.M. Bailey (1925, p. 232) in the spring of 1922 many flocks of cranes crossing Bering Strait were noticed by Capt. J. Bernard, who wintered in a schooner in the ice roughly 30 miles from Cape Dezhnev. In 1928 F.L. Jaques (1929) also traced the fall flight over the narrowest part of Bering Strait. In the flocks he counted about 20 birds on August 27 and 12 and 20 birds on August 30. All the cranes flew in a southeastern direction to Cape Prince of Wales. One eskimo from Malyi Diomede reported that the cranes in flight did not stop on the Diomede Islands. In 1953, on Malyi Diomede Island, J.W. Brooks noticed the flight from Alaska to the Chukchi peninsula (Kenyon and Brooks, 1960). Flocks of cranes crossed from the northern as well as the southern side of the island. On May 17 four flocks were seen; on May 18, a flock of 27 and another of 24 birds; and other flocks were noticed by the eskimos. On May 20 a flock of 62 cranes and three cranes along with four lesser snow geese were noticed.

I noticed the mass movement of cranes in spring flight in 1934 near Inchoun; on May 21, I counted flocks of 13, about 30, 80, 28 and 30 birds successively. In addition I saw one more flock and two lone cranes.

In 1956, at Amguema, I noticed that many birds settled separately along the upper course of the river right from the time of arrival. I noticed the sandhill cranes arriving on June 13 from the same direction.

On St. Lawrence Island, according to F.H. Fay and T.J. Cade, the cranes were seen flying every year but in small numbers, more often in pairs or flocks of three to six birds. There were evidently no mass flights there.

N.F. Kallinikov points out (1912, p. 151) that flying cranes gathered sometimes in very large flocks in the Chukchi peninsula. In the spring of 1938 P.T. Butenko noticed flocks of cranes in flight over Providence Bay. On May 30 he counted 20 birds in a flock at Cape Stoletiya. According to the observations of L.O. Belopol'skii, sandhill cranes in spring flight followed the coast at Krest Bay and later crossed the bay. In his paper in the Russian the direction was shown as east to west while in the German translation it was given as west to east. In Notapenmen, the eskimos told me that the cranes came in the spring from the southwest. I think this is possible since a small number of sandhill cranes come from America via the central part of the Bering Sea. In the spring different flocks could well converge at Krest Bay. In the fall, as V.É. Yakobi told me, the movement of cranes in a northeasterly direction was recorded. O.I. Belogurov noticed their flight almost every day beginning from August 22. They were large flocks of 40 to 70 birds invariably flying northeast. On September 1 there was a mass flight of 10 flocks of 50 to 100 cranes each. After September 1 the size of the flocks and their numbers decreased. At that time other migratory species of bird were flying south.

The existence of a flight course (or in any case a flight direction) over the southern part of the Bering Sea is confirmed by instances of sandhill crane flights over Bering Island. L. Stejneger (1885, p. 317) indirectly refers to them. On May 18 and 20, 1914, a pair of cranes was collected there by N.P. Sokol'nikov. According to G.Kh. Ioganseen (1934) a pair was noticed in the spring of 1929. P.S. Pallas 1811, p. 106) reports migratory cranes in Kamchatka.

Habitat—In the nesting period the sandhill crane is confined to the dry tundra regions intersected by rivulets, lakelets or shrubs. N.F. Kallinikov (1912, p. 151) writes that cranes prefer the same places as geese and swans, i.e. plane tundra. However, I quite often came across cranes in hilly areas and even in the mountains.

In Providence Bay, near Cape Stoletiya, I found some nesting pairs in low-lying regions as also on the slopes of the nearby knolls. I happened to come across a downy chick concealed in the rock debris at a height of roughly 400 m above sea level. I found three cranes evidently with chicks in very hilly terrain west of the Inchoun lagoon. On being chased they withdrew far up the slopes but when I found them they were in the valley with meadow grass and lakelets. When my party moved along the middle reaches of the Utte-Véem River we saw rocks in the background on the right bank. The rocks appeared white due to the growth of *Eriophorum vaginatum*. They recalled fields of buckwheat in bloom. The calls of cranes could be heard from there. On July 21, 1934, I put up a solitary crane on the second knoll on my way from Inchoun to Uélen. Around the tundra the calls of the birds were heard. On August 12 I encountered a brood flying over a hill by the banks of the Kol'oam River in its middle reaches. On August 19 I saw cranes resting on the slopes of a knoll on the western shore of Lake Kool'ong. The bird selected a patch of tundra above the shrubs.

In the nesting period A.P. Kuzyakin encountered sandhill cranes in the grassy glens and on the gentle slopes of hills with a low-sedge cover. At the end of June, 1957, sizable areas of the slopes were still covered with snow, interspersed with pools of cold meltwater. The entire locality presented the appearance of very early spring. According to the observations of E.P. Spangenberg, around Pevek the sandhill crane was the most common of birds on hills and mountains. In the lower course of the Kolyma it occupied the hilly tundra and was absent from the river valley in the nesting period.

Based on his observations on the Chukoch'ya River, K.A. Vorob'ev (1958) came to the conclusion that hilly relief was a necessary condition for the nidification of this species. The information that I gathered did not confirm that the sandhill crane is strictly confined to the rocks although this bird may well prefer such a habitat. According to Vorob'ev, the sandhill crane colonized the arctic grassy tundra in northeastern Yakutsk above 70° north, where shrubs were altogether absent.

During the spring flight I put up a crane on a knoll by Cape Serdtse-Kamen'. On June 10 I scared a lone injured bird near Uélen at the top of the knoll at a height of above 300 m. In the spring V.Ya. Isaev found a flock in the hills in the Amguema basin. According to É.V. Schmidt the cranes penetrated to the mountains south of the Chaun lowlands. Although this bird prefers a rocky terrain it climbs only to the height of dry grassy tundras in the hills.

The close proximity of a river is a prerequisite for the habitation of this bird. I became convinced of this during my expeditions along the Kol'oam and Utte-Véem rivers and near Cape Stoletiya. The river sometimes comes to the rescue of birds being persecuted. On August 10, 1934, two nonflying birds walking away from me resorted to swimming.

I noticed that cranes in search of food frequented large areas with meadow vegetation, avoiding extensive water holes and marshy tundra. The food resources are somehow distributed between neighboring nesting pairs. When the resources are exhausted the cranes migrate locally. Even on the Anadyr I noticed that the cranes visited the sandy river spits. On the Utte-Véem River I happened to come across a tiny narrow valley with a sand dune surrounded by dense shrubs. From the tracks in the sand it was evident that the area was visited by cranes and hares.

On Wrangel Island I encountered a crane in patches of dry grassy tundra. A.G. Velizhanin once saw a crane among the hummocks 50 paces from the shore.

Spring flight and arrival—The sandhill crane arrives in the Chukchi peninsula in mid-May. Capt. J. Bernard noticed many flocks crossing Bering Strait in early May, 1922. According to A.M. Bailey, in the spring of the same year, 1922, the first cranes coming from Cape Prince of Wales to Siberia were noticed on May 10. According to the observations of J.W. Brooks, in 1953 the flight was continuous from May 17 through 20 on Malyi Diomede Island.

In spring, 1934, flying flocks were seen over the Dezhnev knolls on May 17. During my trek along the northern Chukchi coast, I also noticed the first crane on that day, on a knoll at Cape Serdtse-Kamen'. Frightened, it flew off with a cry in a northwesterly direction. On May 21 I saw a mass flight over the Inchoun mountains. The calls were audible from a great distance. Finally I saw a solitary crane rising from the mountainside while another soared close by. Later, flocks were to be seen spread out in angular formations. They all flew inland from the coast at Uélen to the Inchoun mountains, where they would gain height, re-group with much noise and proceed without resting. When I went along the coastal ice on May 25 and turned at Cape Dezhnev I saw a small group of cranes flying up from the south over Bering Strait. A lone bird flew toward me when I was climbing a knoll. Possibly it was the same bird that I saw on June 10 when I was climbing a high knoll by the Vtoraya rivulet.

On St. Lawrence Island, according to Fay and Cade, the flight occurred in May. The local population spending the summer on the island arrived in the middle two weeks of May.

According to the observations of P.T. Butenko, in the spring of 1938, in Providence Bay, the first two flocks of cranes arrived on May 17. Evidently he noticed the nonbreeding cranes on his way to Sireniki on May 25. The cranes remained in flocks even on May 30 at Cape Stoletiya. L.O. Belopol'skii noticed the spring flight over Krest Bay from May 16 through June 1, 1931. According to V.É. Yakobi, in 1961 the first three cranes in Uél'kal' were noticed on June 7. In 1956, deep in the Chukchi peninsula on the Amguema, I sighted the first crane on June 13. It flew with a scream from the west bank of river. In 1958 V.D. Lebedev and V.R. Filin noticed the first pairs of cranes 25 km north of Pevek on May 28. Next day from the plane they saw two pairs on Aiok Island, where there was still much snow. Some sections of tundra were already exposed and the river had opened up.

Breeding—According to these observers the cranes had already formed pairs by the end of May and early June. On June 26, 1957, A.P. Kuzyakin saw cranes dancing and uttering cries near Poutyn. Their feathers were scattered about and many tracks were found on the bare soil. On St. Lawrence Island F.H. Fay and T.J. Cade witnessed the courtship ceremonies of a pair in June, 1950. According to the observations of E.G.F. Sauer and E.K. Urban, in 1960 pairs were seen moving about and feeding in early June. On June 7 a nest was found in the grassy undergrowth on the lakelet. It was 1 m across and an egg 97 mm long lay on a grass bed (see photograph with Sauer and Urban's article). On June 11, when the female got off the nest, the male began its courtship dance. On the approach of a man the incubating female pressed herself close to the bottom of the nest. Later she stole away undetected but after 100 m began to cry and struggle as though her wings were damaged. The male then joined the female. While one of the birds incubated the other usually kept watch close by. Once a crane frightened from the nest settled on the ground near the nest of an arctic jaeger and was fiercely attacked. The crane succeeded in withdrawing, protected itself by flapping its wings, but could not take off under the attack. The chick had not emerged from the egg even on June 30 and the nest was later found empty.

A.A. Kishchinskii knew of two nests around the Ukouge lagoon. There were two eggs in one of them on June 21, 1970, but it was empty on June 29. On June 30 N.I. Makurin found two very tiny chicks 2 km from the nest, behind a knoll where cranes had not been seen before. Possibly the chicks had traveled that far by themselves. On June 28 Makurin found another nest with two pecked-out eggs. They were gone on June 30. Evidently the chicks emerged and hid themselves, since the adult cranes were no less energetic on July 4 than on June 27. In early July, N.F. Kovriga found two downy chicks among adults. On July 13 Kishchinskii found a pair of cranes with chicks. The feather stubs on the back and wings were emerging through the down.

On June 6, 1958, V.D. Lebedev and V.R. Filin saw a nest with two unincubated eggs on the west coast of Aiok Island. On the south coast of the island, on June 22, two nests were found with two eggs in each. The chicks inside were fully formed and ready to hatch out. The nests were built on mounds on marshy tundra. They took the form of a pit without any lining. On July 10, in the Karchyk peninsula, a downy chick was encountered along with two adults, which were leading.

According to É.V. Schmidt, not more than two eggs were present at any time in the nests that he found. Nor did he find more than two chicks in the broods: more often there was only one fledgeling.

I had no occasion to listen to the spring call. But in 1956, on the Amguema, I often heard the calls of cranes in the second half of June and in the first 10 days of July. On June 30, in the afternoon heat, a crane soared to a great height, spiraling upward and flapping its wings from time to time.

I came across broods many times. On sighting people the adults usually left the chicks which, if they were still very small, would hide in the grass or other topographic features. On July 8, 1934, my party heard the cries of cranes on the middle reaches of the Utte-Véem River. P.T. Butenko set off with his Winchester for

PLATE VI

Eggs of sandpipers: *1*, *2*, *3*—American stint; *4*, *7*—little stint; *5*, *8*, *9*—eastern little stint; *6*, *10*—Temminck's stint; *11*, *12*, *13*—pectoral sandpiper.
Pic. by V.S. Rozhdestvenskaya.

hunting. When he collected a male the female remained at the same place, remaining 200 or 300 paces away. Finally Butenko noticed a chick in the grass and chased it. It was a pretty bird of the size of a common whimbrel, covered with rusty-yellow down (Fig. 42). Growth traces of contour feathers were not yet to be seen and there were no subcutaneous adipose formations. The tiny testes measured 1 × 2 mm and were easily recognizable.

On July 12, on the tundra near the southwestern bank of the Inchoun lagoon, I noticed three adult cranes which came very close and behaved as though they were with young. But I could not find the brood. The female sometimes moved farther away from me and sometimes came close, but not within 150 paces. I sat in ambush in high grass and was not noticed by the male, which flew away but later returned and suddenly landed quite close. It suspected something unusual and gradually approached out of curiosity. I shot it at a distance of only 80 paces. It was a plump well-fed specimen with large testes 6 × 18 and 5 × 16 mm in size. In comparison, a male taken from a brood on July 8 was marked by very small testes 6 × 12 and 4 × 8 mm in size; it was devoid of subcutaneous adipose formations. Both the cranes collected at broods turned out to be males. As in some predators and sandpipers, they exhibited greater spunk and came closer to danger than the females.

On August 10 I encountered a brood on the lower course of the Kol'oam River. The behavior of the adult birds by then differed noticeably. This was due to the fact that the chicks were already quite big and were ready to take off. The cranes slowly moved away from them, later began to settle and lie in hiding in the grass. When I climbed onto a meadow terrace one of them was lying 80 to 100 paces from me. But when I tried to come closer it flew off very swiftly out of range of a shotgun. Just then another crane took off. Later the chicks, especially one of them, probably a male, showed great restlessness. They flew around with cries, not closer than 200 paces. Sometimes a crane would fly low over the water, raising its neck incongruously. Sometimes it would settle on the bank, hobble and drag its wing along the ground. The chicks gradually dispersed and it was quite difficult to chase them on the tundra. An adult crane flew over to one of them and began chasing the one in front. Another chick plunged into the water, first hid among the aquatic growth and later even swam. I could never have imagined that I would have an opportunity to shoot a swimming crane. The first chick also set off to swim across a narrow pool in the river and continued to move away, chased by both of the adult birds. If I had not combined collecting with observations, which to me were very interesting, the collecting would have been even more fruitful. But it can be seen from this encounter with a brood that a family of cranes, even when caught unawares, is far from being helpless. The chick collected was of the size of a demoiselle crane (wing length 38.1, beak from the nostril 4.23 and tarsus 18.33 cm) and had well-developed testes 3 × 21 and 2 × 20 mm in size. It was a lean bird almost wholly covered with growing feathers. The primary flight feathers had emerged from the stubs only to 13 or 14 cm, so the chicks could not yet fly. The embryonic down covered the eyes, occiput, parts of the back, the inside of the secondary flight feathers, the lower part of the back in a very large quantity and above and below the tail. True down could be seen under the lesser wing coverts, along the fringe and especially on the abdomen. The emerging gray feathers were very beautiful because of the silvery sheen on a silken surface. The legs were of a dark horn color but the beak retained a light brownish-flesh color with whitish-pink at the end. A young crane obtained on Sheneberg on August 30, 1926, had the same color in the unfeathered portions but was in full juvenile plumage.

On August 12, 1934, along the middle reaches of the Kol'oam River, I encountered a brood in which the chick was already able to fly. It utilized this ability as soon as the collecting party approached. The adult birds followed it, calling loudly as usual. They returned later without the chick but remained far off.

During my excursion to Cape Stoletiya on July 12, 1938, I encountered two or three pairs not far from each other. On seeing men approaching the cranes at first followed them carefully, later took off and cried for a long time out of fear. On a knoll I encountered a chick which was still covered with down but already of the size of a demoiselle crane. It ran so fast that I could not catch it. I circled the knoll so as not to come upon it directly from above; I lost the chick. It evidently hid in the rubble and, being tired from running, stayed there. I found the adult crane at least half a km from the chick. Frightened by my shot, it took an unusual course, flying very low over the ground, and settled at the base of the knoll. There it began searching for food as if nothing had happened. It did not return to the place where the chick was found.

In 1957, to the south of Lawrence Bay, A.P. Kuzyakin scoured the tundra for a nest. By June 20 through 22 the clutches of the cranes were no doubt complete but the birds easily deserted the nesting areas and did not return for hours. On July 12 a special search was made lasting the whole day. One pair took off with a cry from the rocky debris. The place was thoroughly searched but nothing could be detected. Later the call of cranes was heard at another place which Kuzyakin had already covered. Evidently the birds had been silent and concealed at that time. Later they kept circling two earth mounds and finally a tiny chick was noticed through the binoculars near each of them. On being approached the adult cranes took off suddenly with a cry while the chicks hid. One of them leaped five steps and tried to run off with a chirp. The body length of the chicks caught was 20 and 21 cm and weight 91 and 108 g. The egg teeth were not shed in either of them.

The old birds did not fly away when the chicks were caught. They fell to the ground, fluttered their wings and hobbled and came within 100 to 120 paces. The male was shot. Even five hours later the female was silently, restlessly, searching for the chicks. When A.P. Kuzyakin opened the bag containing the chicks, the female heard their chirping, and flew low overhead at a height of not more than 30 or 40 m. The chicks in the rucksack chirped continuously and when it was opened they began a squabble to get out.

Through the binoculars A.P. Kuzyakin noticed a large chick near another pair but it was so hidden that it could not be clearly seen.

According to W.S. Brooks (1915), on June 27, 1913, on St. Lawrence Island, a pair of cranes was collected with a chick aged about one week.

Like other large birds, the crane does not nest every year. The summer quarters of nonbreeding birds are not known in detail. The following observations on Wrangel Island led me to believe that lone cranes did spend the summer there. During the day on July 2, 1939, I heard the call of cranes and around evening saw a set of five on the tundra on my way to Atternon. The birds were flying in formation over the grass in search of food. They came not closer than 200 paces and then flew away again. Judging from the fact that two of the birds were larger and more rufous while three were somewhat smaller and grayish, it was a year-old brood consisting of two adult and three young birds. During the day on July 14, I again came across five cranes but more to the west, between the hunter's hut and Somnitel'naya Bay, closer to the hills. They were far away and were flying toward the sea. On the morning of July 15 I again heard them calling in the estuary of the Amerikanskaya rivulet. It is quite clear that the brood was on Wrangel Island for two weeks, having found favorable conditions there. The nonbreeding cranes spent the summer on St. Lawrence Island.

In his paper on the birds of the Trans-Lena region A.I. Argentov (1861a, p. 488) places the cranes among birds in which all of the flight feathers are cast together during molting. I could not check this phenomenon myself in the Chukchi peninsula but believe that the migration of flocks to Wrangel Island may be an attempt at isolating themselves for molting. The plumage of July males that I collected in the Chukchi peninsula was very disheveled. The adult cranes left Russian territory in that rufous plumage.

Migration—As soon as the young birds are able to rise on their wings the cranes begin to prepare for migration. At the end of the summer of 1934 I made the following observations on the Kol'oam River. On August 12 three cranes flew in the evening. Pairs were noticed on the 13th and a call was heard on the 14th. On August 15 pairs were sighted here and there along the coast. Two flocks were calling and wheeling before they settled on the tundra. There is no doubt that that day should be regarded as the beginning of flock formation prior to migration. On August 18 the cranes wandered in the neighborhood of Lake Kool'ong, and next day I noticed an arriving young bird. On August 20, when the party was descending the Kol'oam River, the cranes behaved altogether differently. The broods or small flocks noticed the party from a very great distance and gradually flew away. On August 21 I encountered only two or three pairs but some pairs were seen as late as the 23rd. On the following day I heard the call of a crane in a river estuary for the last time.

In the previous fall (1933), according to my observations near Uélen, the migration proceeded as follows: On August 20 a flock of 11 birds was noticed moving along the north coast from the northwest toward Uélen. There they formed two groups: six birds went round Cape Dezhnev from the north while the rest crossed over the knoll. It enabled me to determine the height of their initial flight as 500 m or so. Approaching the knoll three-fourths of the way up it, the cranes soared steeply. Flocks were noticed on August 28 and 29 and small flocks on September 11. There was a mass migration on September 14. Only 10 flocks were seen in all. The weather was gentle and quiet with a slight south breeze and the sun was often seen. Some cranes flew high above the sea and three flocks were seen very far away; others were moving nearer to Uélen. While I was on the nearest knoll, some cranes flew toward me. I concealed myself but the wary birds were alerted and turned sharply aside with a cry at least 200 paces from me. In the evening the cranes also came from the south side of Cape Dezhnev. Their calls were heard throughout the latter half of the day. Having flown over the Chukchi peninsula and reached the sea at Bering Strait, the cranes were quite often confused. They either turned aside uttering cries, sometimes even going back for some distance, or changed their altitude. But ultimately they took the direct route to Alaska. T.H. Bean (1883) saw cranes crossing Bering Strait on August 18, 1880. F.L. Jaques (1929) noticed them on August 27, 1928, on a clear day but with a cold northwest wind after a snowstorm on the Siberian coast. Two flocks were noticed on August 30 in a south wind. In the interval between these observations Cape Dezhnev was again covered with snow. In 1931, L.O. Belopol'skii collected a crane in Providence Bay on September 26. In my opinion this was a very late date. On September 5, 1961, according to the observations of O.I. Belogurov, the last flocks passed over Uél'kal'.

As in the case of the common crane, flocks of this species exhibit small angular formations. More often, however, I found that the formations were shorter on one limb. While changing formation the flocks sometimes looked like clouds.

Food—A study of the stomach contents of cranes confirmed that the sandhill crane under the conditions of the Chukchi peninsula is essentially dependent on vegetation, though it consumes insects as well.

1) Middle course of the Utte-Véem River, July 8, 1934, ♂. A large proportion of grass remains: shoots, stalks, and rootlets. Many tiny stones. 2) Same place, pullus. Remnants of grass: shoots, stalks, and rootlets. Many tiny stones. 3) Southwest corner of Inchoun lagoon, July 12, 1934, ♂. Judging from the tiny fragments, chitin of several dozen *Carabidae*. A large amount of grass remains: shoots, stalks and rootlets. Many tiny stones.

In my observations of the cranes on Wrangel Island using the binoculars I saw how the birds sometimes moved in formations, foraging in meadows.

Economic importance—Hunting sandhill cranes is very difficult. It is secured only by chance. Its economic importance is therefore negligible. The meat of an adult male cooked under field conditions was tough and not particularly tasty.

Systematics of the subspecies—The sandhill cranes form four subspecies.

1) **Grus canadensis canadensis** (L.) of relatively small size with a short beak and not very long legs. Siberian specimens are indistinguishable from American birds. *G. niediecki* described by A. Reichenow (1906) based on a specimen from Anadyr Bay should be regarded as a synonym. Judging from the absence of rust coloration, it was a two-year-old bird; its wing length was 43 cm and tarsus 16.5 cm.

It nests in northeastern Siberia from the Alazei to the Bering Sea, in Alaska and Canada, in the north up to Banks Island and Baffin Land, in the south to the southern parts of Mackenzie and Keewatin and also on Southampton Island.

2) **Grus canadensis tabida** (Peters) are bigger birds. Occur from British Columbia to Michigan and south to Oregon and Colorado.

3) **Grus canadensis pratensis** Meyer are of very large size and a much lighter bluish color. Breeding grounds extend from Alabama, south Mississippi and south Georgia to Florida.

4) **Grus canadensis nesiotes** Bangs and Zappey are a small form with a large beak. The color of the upper parts is very dark. They occur on Pines Island and in the western part of Cuba.

The color of the sandhill crane is very interesting. The ocherous-rufous down of the chicks is replaced by the juvenile plumage growing underneath which is generally light ash gray in color with a bluish shade on the head and neck and a brownish shade on the back and shoulders. This is apart from the blackish-horn color of the flight feathers and bright ocherous-rufous coloration of parts of the plumage on the crown, upper side of the neck and back. The feathers on the crown and nape are of the same color and very bright. In a specimen collected by Sheneberg, the ocherous color on the dorsal side of the neck is less prominent than in the chick available with me, though in other respects the coloration is very similar. The entire upper back is of ocherous color, dark with a rufous tinge. The broad tips of feathers on the shoulders and the wing and tail coverts are of dark ocherous color. The tips of lateral feathers are very narrow and pale. The young cranes migrate in August from the Chukchi peninsula to America in this gray plumage with an ocherous-rufous on the upper part of the body. Around Markovo on May 28, 1932, P.T. Butenko collected a young wintered female in a uniform grayish-blue plumage.

It would appear that even the adult cranes after the winter molt arrive in Russia in fresh gray plumage but I noticed many rufous birds in the spring flight of 1932. As far as the summer birds are concerned, I was surprised that even in Anadyr sandhill cranes were in a rusty shade dorsally. In the Chukchi peninsula and on Wrangel Island I did not see one pure gray bird. Two specimens that I collected on the Utte-Véem River differed sharply in their rust red color from all the other birds (about 20 bird skins of Anadyr and American cranes) that passed through my hands. The male that I collected on June 8 was particularly rust red. The lower part of the neck, shoulders, back and inner secondaries, the crop and the sides of the breast were rust red, the color of thick fresh rust on iron. All the feathers, irrespective of the extent of rust coloration at their tips, preserved the gray coloration at the basal region and were covered by overlying feathers. The impression is created that the bird has a very striking coloration toward the top. Rust-colored feather edges, large or small, are characteristic of most of the wing coverts. It was less developed in feathers of the lower part of the neck, breast and rump. The three extreme inner secondaries in the sample were albinic and symmetrical, i.e. almost identical on the right and left wings. The white color had also acquired a rust-cream shade. Instances of partial albinism on the wings of the sandhill crane have been reported in the literature before, notably by E.W. Nelson (1887, p. 96). Evidently it is not a very rare phenomenon. The rest of the bird is normally colored though the gray on the head and neck is very dark because of the worn-out condition of the plumage. The white on the chin and throat also has rust speckles. This rust contamination is not seen on the primary flight and tail feathers. The bare portions on the forehead and crown are saturated with the red color. The legs are black.

In a specimen that I collected on July 12 the rust color is very dull and brownish. Its extent is small, the back, shoulder feathers and crop being more intensely rust-colored. All the other sandhill cranes whose skins I studied had appreciably less rust coloration. I have the impression that the males are invariably more rufous than the females. A.I. Mineev described the cranes on Wrangel Island as smoky-rust colored birds. V.M. Artobolevskii wrote about a specimen collected near Cape Schmidt as having a bright rufous coloration in its plumage, particularly on the upper portions of the tail and wing coverts. Even on the occiput and the rear portion of the neck there were quite a number of bright rufous feathers. The adult crane in worn-out plumage taken by G. Maydell on the Anadyr, judging from the description by W. Taczanowski (1891), was very similar to my specimen of July 8, 1934, from the Utte-Véem River. The intense brownish-rust bloom on its back and secondaries merge to form an almost uniform color field. The feathers at the base of the neck, back, shoulders, breast and sides have broad rust brown fringes while the feathers on the wings are of a more intense rust shade. Taczanowski quite correctly emphasized that the rust coloration covered only the feather surfaces as in swans, geese and ducks.

The rust coloration of sandhill cranes was the subject of a special study by P.A. Taverner (1929). He was the first to draw attention to the fact that the freshly growing feathers in an adult crane were not red. Chemical analysis showed that the rust coloration disappeared from the feathers on boiling them in a weak hydrochloric acid solution. It could be ferric oxide.

The ocherous color of feathers in young cranes depends on the pigment. Consequently it is common for all of the original feathers and if there is any change it is only because of decoloration. In the worn-out condition such feathers appear almost cream in color, while the worn-out feathers in the adult crane are dull and brownish.

The rust color of sandhill cranes covers only the upper side of the body or the sides. It extends to below the body, neck and parts of the head in aquatic birds. This difference is explained by differences in behavior. The aquatic birds acquire a passive coloration while swimming in rust-colored water or submerging the head and neck in it. The sandhill crane evidently is actively colored, although apparently until now no one has stated this for certain. It has long been known that the incubating common crane covers itself with marshy silt. Without going into historical details, attention is drawn to references in Burma, E. Gomera and Cimera, given in the new edition of Naumann (1897).

If the crane in fact does coat itself with silt the question arises as to how common cranes remain gray while the sandhill crane is rust red. Evidently the factor responsible is the chemical properties of the oil gland secretions. In any case, there is much that is not known for certain and the rufous color of the sandhill crane requires more detailed study.

Specimens— 1) Uélen village, August 30, 1926, ○, Sheneberg; 2 and 3) middle reaches of Utte-Véem River, July 8, 1934, ♂, sen., ♂, pull., Portenko; 4) estuary of Utte-Véem River, July 12, 1934, ♂, Portenko; and 5) lower course of Kol'oam-Véem River, August 10, 1934, ♂, juv., Portenko.

43. **Antigone leucogeranus** (Pall.)—**Siberian Crane**

Distribution and status—Very rarely, by chance, flies into the western outskirts of the Chukchi peninsula, near Chaun Bay.

In the description of Chaun parish covering the territory from Cape Yakan to the lower Kolyma, A.I. Argentov (1857a, p. 85) reports that the Siberian crane is seen among the birds from time to time. According to É.V. Schmidt, the crane was noticed on the lower reaches of the Chaun River roughly from 1925 through 1927. This crane even nested on the tundra west of the Kolyma. It was sighted in flight over Kolyma settlement but quite rarely. In the spring Schmidt saw not more than two or three flocks counting 4 to 12 birds. On the right bank of the Kolyma, it was seen only once in many years.

Systematics—The Siberian crane differs considerably from sandhill and common cranes. It should be placed in the genus *Antigone* Reichb. which also contains *A. rubicunda* (Perry), *A. antigone* (L.), and *A. vipio* (Pall.). All these are large birds with large unfeathered sections on the head continuing downward from the eyes, with elongated but not crescentiform secondaries which are not curly, and with red or reddish legs, etc.

Note—Ch. Vaurie (1965, p. 360), reporting the summer records of coots *Fulica atra atra* L. in the far North, mentions the Chukchi peninsula. He considers possible the occurrence there of the American coot *F. americana* Gm. It is not known how Vaurie got confused. Coots have not been sighted by anyone nor collected in the Chukchi peninsula. In my Anadyr work (Portenko, 1935b, vol. II, p. 34), I wrote that in the collection of the Institute of Zoology, Academy of Sciences of the USSR, two specimens were preserved with labels, which were not original, reading quite erroneously "T. Tschuktschensis, Maydell". In the Anadyr region where G. Maydell traveled, coots were not found either.

Order VIII. CHARADRIIFORMES—SHORE BIRDS, GULLS AND ALLIES

Family CHARADRIIDAE—PLOVERS, SANDPIPERS, SNIPES

44. **Pluvialis squatarola** (L.)—**Gray Plover**

Local name—In Eskimo: Sagỳl'ma and turìk in Providence and Krest bays.

Distribution and status—Nests sporadically in the Chukchi peninsula, rarely on south coast, and more commonly, though still in small numbers, on the north coast west of Kolyuchin Bay. On Wrangel Island, breeds in large numbers, being one of the most noticeable of shorebirds. Flies away in the winter.

Factual information about the nidification of the gray plover in the Chukchi peninsula is very modest. L.O. Belopol'skii (1934) collected a July specimen near Uél'kal' at Krest Bay and regarded the gray plover there as a rare breeding bird. On August 6, 1932, I noticed a solitary adult bird on the east shore of the bay opposite. Farther to the east, on the south coast of the Chukchi peninsula, the gray plover is absent because of the hilly terrain. At Providence Bay, T.H. Bean (1883) happened to encounter young gray plovers in flight. He secured a male on September 12, 1880, and a female on September 13. This plover is absent from St. Lawrence Island and has not been found on the east coast of the Chukchi peninsula. In Uélen, I saw three young gray plovers on the wing only once, on September 18, 1933. They were probably of the same brood. Even E.W. Nelson (1883, p. 84) points out that the gray plover is less numerous on the Chukchi coast. On July 24, 1909, J. Koren (1910) encountered a brood on the west side of the entrance to Kolyuchin Bay. According to his much later data, the gray plover was seen along the entire arctic coast. On July 23, 1912, he (Thayer and Bangs, 1914) found some pairs on Aiok Island. On July 19 he saw many nesting birds around Balagan. É.V. Schmidt noticed the gray plover once in the spring in the Karchyk peninsula opposite Aiok, while it nested around Pevek. In 1958 V.D. Lebedev and V.R. Filin (1959) found a few gray plovers in these places. On June 9, on the south coast of Aiok Island a male was collected from a pair. A pair was again noticed on June 22. A male was encountered on July 9 from a flock of four or five birds in the Karchyk peninsula. In 1965 and 1966 F.G. Chernyavskii reportedly found gray plovers in the breeding season on the upper reaches of the Yarak-Véem River in the eastern part of the north Anyui Range and almost everywhere southwest of Cape Schmidt. Unfortunately specimens were not collected and the identification of the species is doubtful. Plovers could certainly be expected in these areas.

The gray plover is altogether absent from the interior of the Chukchi peninsula.

On Wrangel Island this is an abundantly nesting species which together with the turnstone and the robin sandpiper constitutes the main population of waders on the island. Though much fewer in numbers than the above two species, it is more noticeable. Even the expedition by J. Rodgers in early September, 1881, collected a gray plover, among other birds (Gilder, 1883, p. 93). A. Crawford (Snyder, 1926) took three adult specimens. According to the observations of V.F. Vlasova and A.I. Mineev, the gray plover on Wrangel Island was common in the breeding area and was even more numerous than the turnstone. I came across it in the breeding area in the Tundra Akademii south of Bruch spit and near the estuary of the Krasnyi Flag River. In the latter area the gray plovers were more numerous and more uniformly distributed. Pairs nested at a distance of roughly 1 to 2 km from each other. On the south coast of Wrangel I found innumerable plovers in the nesting sites on all my visits, extending from the middle course of the Mamontovaya River to the lower course of the Nasha River. S.M. Uspenskii, R.L. Bëme and A.G. Velizhanin (1963) regarded the gray plover as a common breeding bird on Wrangel Island, being numerous in the dry plains of the island, especially in the central hilly section. Broods were encountered there. Moreover, A.G. Velizhanin (1965) called it abundant on the south coast.

Habitat—In the Chukchi peninsula the habitat of the gray plover is confined to the coastal plain. In Krest Bay, I found it on the flat banks of a lagoon. A flying brood was seen at Uélen on a rubble spit. T.H. Bean collected specimens on a spit in Providence Bay. J. Koren found nesting pairs on Aiok Island where sand dunes penetrating far inland adjoin mossy areas.

On Wrangel Island the nesting areas of the gray plover are at a different height. It prefers a patchy tundra, typical of arctic deserts adjoining water. In Tundra Akademii, gray plovers were confined to dry sections bordering marshy lowlands in the breeding season. The first wandering brood was seen on the clayey flat banks of the estuary of the Krasnyi Flag River. I encountered another brood in the rivulet valley covered with marsh. Along the south coast of Wrangel Island gray plovers nested in large numbers on the flat tundra between the knolls and the sea.

They not only did not avoid the knolls but climbed the terraces and nested on the flat apical parts of knolls. I came across a nesting pair on the rubble plateau of one of the knolls by the Mamontovaya River at a height of about 250 m. The birds had selected a moist patch there. Later I found them high in the meadows on the knolls by Atternon and along the valley of the Nasha River. The bulk of gray plovers nevertheless nested by the foothills and on the flat parts of tundra, with the exception of the pebbled spit on the shore.

According to A.G. Velizhanin, gray plovers nested on the tundra at elevations and also along the banks of rivers and on the seashore.

Arrival, nidification and migration—According to the observations of V.F. Vlasova and A.I. Mineev gray plovers come to Wrangel Island in the last 10 days of May. In spring, 1939, the first whistling gray plover was heard on May 27. I noticed the arriving flocks on June 2 in Akatylanva. By the end of that day mating calls were heard and on June 3, I noticed a pair in coitus. The male was on top of the female, which remained standing. Later I found a dug-out pit which was exactly circular in form. Gray plovers evidently began to breed immediately upon arrival. On the following days the call notes and whistles of these birds were heard more often. On June 5, I noticed that the gray plover, which had been very wary until then, began coming closer; it began to stick to the nesting sites. On June 8, it struck me that the females were rarely seen; evidently they had begun laying. On June 11, on a knoll by the Mamontovaya River, I found a pair and shot the male at a distance of not more than 30 paces. After the shot the female rose quietly from the nest and began to fly around in the immediate vicinity.

Right from the time of arrival the size of testes in males began gradually increasing. With the commencement of hatching, it began to decrease again (Tables 34 and 35). The arriving birds were characterized by appreciable subcutaneous adipose formations. At the end of June the gray plovers were emaciated but in early August the adipose formations formed afresh.

Table 34. Testis sizes in gray plovers collected in 1939 summer, mm

Date	Left	Right
June 5	10 × 6	7 × 5
June 8	14 × 8	9 × 5
June 11	14 × 7	7 × 5
June 26 through July 2	9–8 × 6–5	7–5 × 6–3
July 13 through Aug. 2	8–5 × 5–3	6–4 × 5–2
Aug. 16, 1938 and 1939	6–4 × 4–2	4–3 × 3–2

Table 35. Ovary size and follicle sizes in gray plovers collected in 1939 summer, mm

Date	Length of ovary	Diameter of biggest follicle
June 4	12	5
June 12	18	15
July 29	15	4
Aug. 2	10	3

On June 22, 1931, V.F. Vlasova found a clutch of three eggs, and two full clutches with incubated eggs on June 28, 1932. In one of them, the limbs were already formed in the embryos; another was developed very unevenly: only the rudimentary circulatory system was seen in one egg while the other showed a well-developed network of blood vessels. In another the head was formed in the embryo.

According to my observations, in 1939 around Rodgers Bay gray plovers with eggs could be found until the end of June although they were highly developed. In the first 10 days of July the birds stayed very close because they were with chicks. On July 14 and 15, at Somnitel'naya Bay, I saw many broods with nonflying chicks; the adult birds among them were quite restless. They ran, slid on the belly and cried in anguish, especially the females. As late as August 2 I collected a nonflying chick which was only half feathered (Fig. 43). Unlike other waders, the chicks of gray plovers did not hide but ran so fast that I could hardly catch them. The adult birds, though restless, remained aloof.

According to the observations of A.G. Velizhanin, in 1960, chicks hatched in mid-July on Wrangel Island.

On July 24, 1909, J. Koren encountered a brood on the grassy-meadow tundra on the western shore of Kolyuchin Bay. Fairly big chicks quickly ran and hid in the grass and moss. Their speed could be judged from their chirping; as soon as Koren turned toward the source of the chirping the chick would fall silent and scamper off with the speed of a rat. Since the chirping was heard from different directions the searches proved futile.

On Wrangel Island, when approached at the end of July, 1939, the gray plovers were less restless. At that time they were the most active and noticeable of all the birds on the tundra. On sighting a man the gray plovers would fly out toward him, circle and whistle loudly, but remain at a good distance. On August 16, I saw a male with two young. The nape of one had a white downy patch which was still noticeable. The male rushed up and was collected.

On August 16, 1938, in Tundra Akademii, I found a brood of three young birds just beginning to fly. Next day I came across another brood of four young. On August 19 a young gray plover along with an adult circled me. It even cried, though not much, and rather quietly. Around August 20 the gray plovers flew away from Wrangel Island. According to the observations of A.G. Velizhanin, in 1960 they began to gather for migration to the south coast on July 25. The migration took place in the first half of August. On September 18, 1933, I found a brood of three young birds in Uélen.

Habits—The call of the gray plover in the breeding season resembles the whistle of a sea pie in flight. It may be transcribed by the syllables ky-iii...and sometimes as kiu-liii. The song line is simple in the young birds and complex in the old ones.

The adults leave the nests or chicks in different ways. Some are very wary and remain aloof while others creep on the belly, dragging the ends of their tail feathers on the ground, but not coming close. According to the observations of F.B. Chernyavskii (1967), on seeing a polar fox the gray plovers get off the nest well in advance and attack the predator individually or in pairs.

Food—The stomachs of gray plovers collected on Wrangel Island showed the following contents:

1) August 16, 1938. Sixty *Lepidoptera* caterpillars and five tiny (3 to 8 mm) stones. 2) June 4, 1939. Remains of three species of beetles, totaling four, four caddis worms, 20 small crawfish, and 1.5 g gravel. 3) June 8, 1939. Thirty-one large and two small caterpillars, 15 beetles of the type *Poecilus* (tribe *Platysmatini*) and remains of six other beetles. 4) June 11, 1939. Three caterpillars, 20 larvae of other insects (beetles), three tiny grass blades, four moss shoots and a tiny pebble. 5) June 26, 1939. Twenty-six caterpillars, 12 *Chrysomela* beetles and 0.25 g coarse-grained sand. 6) June 26, 1939. About 50 *Chrysomela* beetles and 10 pebbles weighing 3 g. 7) June 29, 1939. Five caterpillars, remains of 10 *Diptera*, 2 *Chrysomela* beetles and many remains of tiny beetles. 8) July 2, 1939. Eighteen caterpillars, 20 *Diptera*, about 20 *Amphipoda* and remains of tiny insects. 9) July 2, 1939. Digested mass of tiny insects and 16 tiny stones 5 to 8 mm in diameter. 10) July 13, 1939. Ground-up remains of tiny insects, filling one-half of stomach, two caddis worms, three shoots and seeds and 3 g pebbles. 11) July 22, 1939. About 20 *Chrysomela* beetles, remains of eight caterpillars and 4 g pebbles. 12) July 26, 1939. Forty *Trichoptera* larvae, 18 tiny (5 to 10 mm) stones. 13) July 29, 1939. Digested remains of beetles filling 80 per cent of stomach and 1 g coarse quartz sand. 14) July 29, 1939. Two caterpillars, mass of beetle remains and 1.5 g tiny pebbles. 15) July 29, 1939. Remains of two caterpillars, *Chrysomela* beetles and other tiny insects and 2 g tiny quartz pebbles. 16) July 29, 1939. Ground remains of *Chrysomela* beetles and 2 g tiny pebbles. 17) July 29, 1939. Much digested remains of caddis worms, and 0.1 g sand. 18) August 2, 1939. Caddis worms, remains of tiny insects and six grains of coarse quartz sand. 19) August 2, 1939. Eighteen *Chrysomela* beetles, 14 caterpillars and 2 g quartz pebbles. 20) August 2, 1939. Caterpillar, innumerable remains of *Chrysomela* beetles and 1 g coarse-grained sand. 21) August 2, 1939. Six larvae of *Trichoptera*, remains of *Chrysomela* beetles and fine pebbles. 22) August 16, 1939. Six *Trichoptera*, caterpillar, tiny beetles in ground-up condition and 1.5 g tiny quartz pebbles. 23) August 16, 1939. Remains of tiny beetles, 14 caddis worms, and 0.5 g tiny pebbles.

Economic importance—The economic importance of this bird is negligible. It is difficult to catch it outside the breeding season, when hunting is not permitted. Nor does it rate a special hunt. There is no doubt that the eggs and chicks often fall prey to the polar fox but even in this respect it is not prominent among other birds. I noticed how the gray plovers chased jaegers which posed a threat to the young of various birds.

Systematics—There are different opinions about the taxonomic status of the genus to which the gray plover belongs. The point at issue is whether it should be classified in a special genus *Squatarola* Cuv. or can be combined with the golden plovers in the genus *Pluvialis* Briss. For a very long time the separation of the genus *Squatarola* depended on such characteristics as the presence of a hind toe in the gray plover. P.R. Lowe (1922) drew attention to several other anatomic features that distinguished the gray plover from the dotterels: 1) presence of two and not three free ribs as in *Pluvialis* and 2) eight distinct characters in the structure of the skull and the presence of a white collar in the downy chicks. While arguing for separation of the genus *Squatarola*, P.R. Lowe nevertheless conceded that the anatomic characters he had singled out pertained to the proportions of certain parts.

In the search for similarity with other dotterels and in grouping them, he proceeded in a very formal manner. Lowe, for example, saw more similarity between the dotterel and ringed plover than between the dotterel and the gray plover. He gave exceptional weightage to the anatomic characters which by themselves cannot always establish the systematic position of birds. Recently, W.J. Bock (1958) reexamined the key differences between the gray plover and the dotterel, also in terms of anatomic material, and furnished a very convincing evaluation. He explained the differences in the skull of the gray plover as due to the development in this bird of supraoptical glands as a consequence of its life style associated with brackish basins. In fact, in its distribution the gray plover is mostly a marine bird, occupying arctic islands and coasts, while the dotterels with rare exceptions are associated with the mainland tundras and marshes. The skull characters of the gray plover carry more juvenile features and the bird itself has a more primitive form than the dotterel. Lowe called it a living fossil.

Although I have not conducted comparative studies of the skeletons of gray plover and dotterels, I have had occasion to handle a large number of processed specimens. I have made several observations on these two birds in nature and familiarized myself with the details of their nest life, habits, voice, etc. The gray plover and the dotterel are so close and similar that, as far as I am concerned, it is impossible to place them in different genera. The close affinity between the gray plover and the dotterel embraces not only their similar body proportions, color of plumage and eggs and way of life, but also their ranges, which adjoin one another as in the case of preeminent subspecies. Obviously one may suggest that these birds formed subspecies in the historic past and that the gray plover was a high-altitude arctic dotterel. Under the influence of various (dissimilar) ecological factors the two species moved away from each other in evolution but traces of neighborly distribution are to be seen even now. This suggestion is confirmed by instances of similar relations in the distribution of other northern birds, as for example in the case of swans or finches.

The gray plover does not form a subspecies although rudiments of some geographic variations are noticed. In the 30s many works were devoted to the subspecies of gray plovers: 1) G.C. Low (1938), 2) G.P. Dement'ev (1930), 3) L.A. Portenko (1939b, vol. I), and 4) J.L. Peters (1934a). All these workers more or less came to the conclusion that the classification of the species *P. squatarola* (L.) was beset with difficulties.

In 1964 I again measured the gray plovers available in the collection of the Institute of Zoology, Academy of Sciences of the USSR, numbering 107 specimens (Table 36) and came to the conclusion that the gray plovers of Wrangel Island, males as well as females, differed in general only in a much longer wing.

The greater wing length is a characteristic, among others, of other Wrangel birds, for example, *Cepphus mandti tajani* and *Plectrophenax nivalis vlasowae*.

If the Wrangel gray plovers are acknowledged as 'natio', they cannot be assigned any one of the available synonyms since Pallas' *hypomelus*, *hypomelanus* and *Pardela* refer in general to Siberia: there is not a single reference to the wing length among the characters he ascribes. For exactly the same reason, the name *australis* Reichenbach is not appropriate since the picture by Gul'd (to which it pertains)

Table 36. Length of bill and wing of gray plovers in adult plumage, cm

Locality	Males				Females			
	Max.	Min.	Mean	No. of samples	Max.	Min.	Mean	No. of samples
Bill length								
Europe, West Siberia up to Gydan tundra	3.21	2.60	2.87	9	3.09	2.62	2.91	15
Central Siberia: Yenisei, Taimir and Khatanga	3.21	2.60	2.87	14	2.94	2.65	2.82	6
Lyakhov Island, Lena River and Yakutia	3.16	2.77	2.95	11	3.04	2.84	2.92	4
Wrangel Island	3.18	2.67	2.94	21	3.12	2.65	2.85	7
Anadyr and Far East	3.22	2.83	2.96	8	3.45	2.87	3.06	7
America	3.10	2.95	3.01	5	—	—	—	—
Wing length								
Europe, West Siberia up to Gydan tundra	20.14	18.89	19.44	9	20.32	18.83	19.52	15
Central Siberia: Yenisei, Taimir and Khatanga	20.68	19.16	19.73	14	19.99	19.55	19.77	6
Lyakhov Island, Yakutia: lower reaches of the Lena, etc.	20.24	18.23	19.34	11	19.61	19.33	19.48	4
Wrangel Island	20.95	19.05	19.87	21	20.87	19.49	20.31	7
Anadyr and Far East	20.62	18.05	19.51	8	20.41	19.12	19.69	7
America	20.05	18.69	19.39	5	—	—	—	—

drawn on the basis of winter Australian specimens shows nothing in common with Wrangel gray plovers.

I have with me only five gray plovers from North America, which generally have very short wings. This character is reflected in the name *cynosurae* of Thayer and Bangs, which was not completely accepted.

I cannot take upon myself the responsibility of assigning a special name to Wrangel gray plovers.

Specimens— 1) Rodgers Bay, June 7, 1931, ♀, Vlasova; 2) Uél'kal' village, July 24, 1931, ♂, Belopol'skii; 3 to 5) Rodgers Bay, June 29, July 12, and August 23, 1932, ♀♂♂, Vlasova; 6) Wrangel Island, without date, ♀, Vlasova; 7) Uélen, September 18, 1933, ♂, Portenko; 8 and 9) Krasnyi Flag River estuary, August 16, 1938, ♂♂, Portenko; 10 to 14) Akatylanva area, June 4, 5, 8, 11 and 12, 1939, ♀ ♂♂ ♂♀, Portenko; 15 and 16) Nasha River, June 26, 1939, ♂♂, Portenko; 17) same place, June 29, 1939, ♂, Portenko; 18 and 19) Atternon area, July 2, 1939, ♂♂, Portenko; 20) Nasha River, July 13, 1939, ♂, Portenko; 21) Rodgers Bay, July 22, 1939, ♂, Portenko; 22 to 27) Atternon area, July 24, 26 and 29, 1939, 5 ♂♂ and ♀, Portenko; 28 and 29) same place, August 2, 1939, ♂, and pull., Portenko; and 30) Rodgers Bay, August 16, 1939, ♂, Portenko.

Biological material— 1) Clutch of three eggs, southeastern Wrangel Island, June 22, 1931, Vlasova; 2) three eggs of four in a clutch around Rodgers Bay, June 28, 1932, Mineev; and 3) clutch of four eggs from around Rodgers Bay, June 28, 1932, Mineev.

45. **Pluvialis dominica fulva** (Gm.)—**Siberian Plover**

Local name—Chukchian: Totl'ékel'khyn and tudljekidlin in the records of the *Vega* expedition. In Eskimo: dū-rēk' (durick) on St. Lawrence Island.

Distribution and status—Nests in the Chukchi peninsula but not everywhere. Common in the tundras adjoining the north coast and in the interior of the peninsula. Sometimes numerous in wanderings and flights. Flies away in winter. Not reported for certain on Wrangel Island.

E.M. Meller collected Siberian plovers on August 7 and 11, 1939, in the immediate vicinity of Pereval'naya Station northwest of Krest Bay. Near Uel'kal' village, P.T. Butenko saw flying plovers in the fall of 1932 and I.O. Belogurov saw them in the fall of 1961. A specimen acquired by Capt. Moore in the summer of 1849, probably from Providence Bay, was identified by J.E. Harting (1871) as *Charadrius longipes* Temminck. In 1911 a young flying bird was collected on September 27 at Providence Bay by hunters of the freighter *Vaigach.* P.T. Butenko shot a female on the wings in the spring of 1938 near Cape Stoletiya.

E.W. Nelson (1887, p. 125) gives the distribution of the Siberian plover as the east up to St. Lawrence Island, but no specimens were available from there in order to establish the subspecies accurately. H.B. Collins (Friedmann, 1932a) obtained five September birds in Gambell village. According to the observations of O.J. Murie (1936), the Siberian plover was noticed there in relatively small numbers in fall flight. In Kukuliak village he secured eight specimens. According to F.H. Fay and T.J. Cade (1959) the number of these birds varies noticeably from year to year. In 1950 the Siberian plover was one of the most common plovers on the island and three nests were found. From 1952 through 1954 it did not breed at all, but in 1956 some breeding pairs and a brood of three young birds were found at Boxer Bay. There and on the Kuzata lagoon in 1957 adult and young birds were encountered in larger numbers than in any other year. In 1960 E.G.F. Sauer and E.K. Urban (1964) found seven nests around Boxer Bay and noticed one pair near Kangi by the western end of the Kuzata lagoon. Two plovers were also noticed near Gambell.

On August 19, 1932, I came across flocks of young plovers wandering on the south shore of Lawrence Bay. In that part of the Chukchi peninsula the Siberian plover was found by A.P. Kuzyakin as a characteristic though less numerous bird. Even in favorable places there was less than one pair per km^2. Despite his best efforts Kuzyakin found only one nest with chicks. W.S. Brooks (1915) collected a pair of plovers at Cape Dezhnev on July 14, 1913, i.e. in the breeding season. According to my observations, in 1934, in the vicinity of Uélen, Siberian plovers nested but in small numbers. In the early summer I came across calling birds there and even saw some flying toward me. In spring flight I saw flocks and pairs but not once in significant numbers. In the preceding fall (1933) the plovers were quite common during migrations and flight around Uélen. They flew in flocks but they could never be called particularly numerous. During my expedition up the Kol'oam-Véem River I found solitary birds on three occasions: in the middle, upper and lower reaches of the river. They were undoubtedly nesting birds since they became very restless on seeing us. Sometimes the whistling of the plover could be heard around the tundra. On July 21, 1934, I traveled from Inchoun to Uélen and along the road across the tundra encountered many whistling plovers with their broods. During the journey up the Utte-Véem River plovers were not seen at all near the banks. What I found were undoubtedly local birds in the estuary of the river and in the hilly tundra to the southeast of Mitkulen. I saw the plover only once in the estuary, whereas they were common on the hilly tundra.

W.S. Brooks collected a female on July 17, 1913, at Cape Serdtse-Kamen'. In mid-July, 1909, J. Koren (1910) found a lone brood on the west side of the entrance to Kolyuchin Bay. According to my observations, in the interior of the Chukchi peninsula, on the Amguema River by the 91st km, plovers were very common in the breeding area and were often sighted though not numerous. Within walking range I might find two or three nesting pairs. At Cape Schmidt, in early August, 1938, I heard the call of plovers in the neighborhood. According to V.M. Artobolevskii (1927) this species was represented in A.A. Savich's collections and hence could have originated from around Cape Schmidt. V.D. Lebedev and V.R. Filin (1959) collected what was evidently a female on June 17, 1958, on Aiok Island, where this bird was few in numbers.

A.I. Argentov (1861a) referred to a short-legged gray plover with green and yellow spots, undoubtedly a plover, in the trans-Lena region. J. Koren (Thayer and Bangs, 1916) noticed large flocks of young birds at Cape Shelagskii before migration and scared eight specimens of adult and young plovers on their way from that cape to the lower Kolyma from May 30 through August 27, 1912. He believed the Siberian plover was common in the breeding grounds all along the arctic coast of the Chukchi peninsula. He found two clutches at Cape Bol'shoi Baranov. S.A. Buturlin (1906b) found this species very numerous in the nesting area on the lower Kolyma.

Habitat—The favorite breeding haunts of the Siberian plover are the sections of dry tundra on or near hillocks. On an excursion southeast from Cape Mitkulen I noticed that the plovers preferred very high hillocks and particularly areas overgrown with grass *Eriophorum vaginatum*. The plovers nesting on depressed tundra also selected patches with that grass and in its absence selected the highest hummocky tundra. Individual, very large mounds served as common observation points from which the plovers could watch for approaching danger. On the river bank I found plovers only in places where dry patches of tundra bordered the river. In the estuary of the Utte-Véem River I came across this bird on a dry grassy bank where the vegetation lost its usual tundra appearance because of the exceptionally good drainage. On the Amguema the plovers nested on large hillocks among hummocky tundra and around hills but did not ascend the high knolls.

According to J. Koren this bird invariably nests on hilly tundra with a variegated cover of white lichens. A.P. Kuzyakin found plovers near rock debris but not actually in it in areas covered with lichen and tiny stones.

According to the observations of E.G.F. Sauer (1962), on St. Lawrence Island plovers nested in dry, elevated areas, invariably on soil covered with gravel and lichen. The type of soil was more important to them than the composition of the vegetation or the degree of protection from the cold, often gale-force winds. The nesting area quite often intersected valleys, hillocks or terraces but bereft of large rocks or cliffs so as to leave a good view of the neighborhood. There were tiny islands of moist tundra, rivulets or tiny lakes. The plovers sometimes fed in the same territory and sometimes flew away off the low-lying tundra or the high hillocks; after raising the young they resettled there or, later, close to the seacoast.

Around Uélen, in the spring of 1934, I noticed a few plovers flying over the sea. They settled at places that resembled their nesting sites. Similarly, in fall flight I usually saw the plovers on dry patches of tundra close to the slopes of knolls and never on the seacoast, but then I found young flying gray plovers there. As an exception I saw flying flocks in the estuary of the Kol'oam River on its shallow sandbeds.

Arrival—Siberian plovers arrive in the last few days of May and early June. In the spring of 1934 around Uélen I collected the first, lone plover on May 31. That day the weather, which had been bad from the evening of May 26, began to improve. Though the storm receded the general atmosphere was wintry. The plover was found on the Uélen spit where it was never found at other times. The bird was attracted by the first thawed patches. On June 1, I heard the call of a plover on the wing and on June 3 saw a few birds flying over the sea. On May 30, 1938, P.T. Butenko collected a female flying over Providence Bay. In 1960, according to the observations of E.G.F. Sauer, three pairs were seen on St. Lawrence Island on June 8; from June 10 through 18, the plovers arrived or were in flight. They totaled 11 pairs, six single birds and three plovers together. They appeared in the west or south and flew at a height of 40 to 60 m. At that time, large areas of the tundra were still covered with snow and ice; the weather was cold and west winds prevailed.

According to the observations of J. Koren, in 1912, the first plover was seen on the lower Kolyma on May 30.

Nidification—On June 4, 1934, around Uélen, I noticed flocks and pairs which landed on the thawed tundra. There still were many snow patches and meltwater pools on it but the sun was seen through the clouds from time to time, which caused much animation among the birds. On June 7 the weather turned exceptionally fine, bumble bees flew about in large numbers and the awakened caterpillars were nibbling at the buds. The plovers were running and flying, calling all the time. Two of them flew toward me, circled high above me and cried incessantly: kyu-kyui, kyu-kyui.... In general, however, the call of this bird took diverse forms. Thus began the plovers' breeding season.

On arrival, the testes of males were 7 × 11 and 6 × 10 mm in size and the ovaries of females were characterized by a coarse-grained structure. The size of the biggest follicle was 5 mm in a female obtained on May 31. All of them were plump, well-fed birds but the ovary of a female taken on July 11, and probably already with chicks, had a fine-grained structure. The subcutaneous adipose formations were reduced to a filmy condition.

On June 10, 1956, in the Amguema basin by the 91st km, I found plovers in an environment where winter was still everywhere. From the morning it was cloudy and cold. Later it became stormy and finally a real storm broke. The plovers were confined to hummocky tundra singly and in pairs, still in small numbers. Their dull calls were heard from time to time. The birds huddled together due to cold with the head tucked in the wing. On June 11, I encountered a lone male on the edge of the bank. When I sat down to rest the bird came within 30 to 40 paces of me. The plovers would often come very close to a seated or, especially, a recumbent man though they were generally very wary birds. On June 13 and 14, I found pairs at the same place. Evidently they had arrived at nesting sites of their choice.

On June 16, I heard vigorous mating calls. Two plovers flew at a great height. Sometimes they beat their wings so slowly that they called to mind the flight of terns. The tips of the wings nearly met on the up beat as well as the down beat. The call "chyui" was heard. The calling continued on June 18 and 20 and the calling male would soar over the neighboring knolls, i.e. at least 400 m up. I found another male in excellent nuptial plumage on an elevated section of the tundra and got very close to him. On June 24, on one of the high, dry knolls, I lay down to rest and two plovers came to within 40 paces of me (Fig. 44). Later, they ran off, flew away and then returned, crying all the time. I set out to search for their nest but without success. I was convinced that it was impossible to find the nest from the behavior of these birds. On June 28 there was another pair in the foothills. All the time the birds were dolefully crying "kiiip" and "tidli" or "tudli". Another pair flew in on hearing the cries. I observed a similar phenomenon on June 30 and July 2 but the plovers quieted down later and I heard their call only once on July 16.

On July 5, 1912, J. Koren gathered two clutches of four eggs each by Bol'shoi Baranov Kamen'. Chicks were about to hatch out.

On St. Lawrence Island in 1960, E.G.F. Sauer heard the calling in flight only twice. On June 10 the male of a pair flying at a height of 40 m rose one meter above the female and, spreading its wings wide, beat them slowly and deeply, a song accompanying the flight. Later the two birds did a 180° turn and settled. In one case another male joined a flying pair. It began to call in the same way, probably desirous of winning over the female, but left unsuccessful.

By June 18 pairs had occupied the nesting territories and protected them from intrusion by other plovers and especially turnstones nesting under similar conditions. They raised an alarm at the sight of men, polar foxes, jaegers and gulls, and chased away even buntings and longspurs. Somehow they were reconciled to the presence of dunlins. The male and female were constantly in mutual contact, visually or aurally. Until incubation they were more alert than any other plovers.

The nesting territories covered an area of 0.25 to 0.5 km in length and were at least 3.8 km inland from the sea. The seven nests found were on gravel with lichen and the clutches or the incubating eggs were quite unnoticeable against the variegated background. The nests consisted of several lichens, mostly *Thamnolia vermicularis* numbering 250 to 260 pieces. The color of the eggs was very variable: some had patches of coarse and prominent design which were small in others; they were sometimes gathered at the blunt end of the egg, and sometimes covered it fairly uniformly. The male incubated by day and the female at night. The chicks emerged from July 7 through 28.

On July 12, 1934, to the southeast of Mitkulen, I came across restless pairs. When I entered an area where tiny chicks were evidently hiding the male and the female would run away from me, then come close again, settle on the hummock and stand there for a long time, fly away, and so on. They gave out a loud whistle suggesting profound anguish. They behaved similarly on August 14, 16, 20 and 22, when they were found not in pairs but singly.

It was a very difficult task to locate the nest of this bird. In the eastern part of the Chukchi peninsula A.P. Kuzyakin made five attempts to find one and sat in wait for two hours for this purpose. On July 9, 1956, he finally detected a nest with downy chicks after watching for 1.5 hours.

The female started up with a cry and came close. Later she gradually withdrew and disappeared. When Kuzyakin changed places the female returned and ran at him. She was incessantly chirping, foraging and feeding. Ultimately, she flew off to a distance of more than half a kilometer. The male, which had been sitting aloof started up and flew at Kuzyakin with a cry while the female stealthily ran to take the male's place. Downy chicks were found there. The nest was found not less than 1 km from the place where the female first flew at the intruder.

Migration on the north coast of the Chukchi peninsula begins toward the end of August. In 1912, at Cape Shelagskii J. Koren noticed large flocks of young birds on August 27 before migration.

In the fall of 1933, on arriving at Uélen, I made my first excursion into the tundra on August 27 and encountered flocks of young plovers already wandering. Broods, three or four young birds together, were encountered more often. The adult had evidently already migrated. These plovers remained on the tundra to no apparent purpose; probably they were just practicing flying. Their whistling was heard quite often. Wanderings continued during the first 10 days of September but on the last day, flocks in flight were also seen. On September 10 I found broods of three very young plovers. The feathers on the crown, beak base and tail still had the embryonic down. In the twilight I literally stumbled on them, so confident were the birds. Other broods did not permit such a close approach. They were to be the last plovers I saw in 1933. The young birds caught in the fall varied very widely in plumpness: there were emaciated birds with filmy subcutaneous adipose formations and later there were others with patches of subcutaneous fat on the back and neck. The plovers turned out to be plump in the later stages. In the young males the testis sizes varied from 1 to 2 mm; granular structure could not be seen in the female ovaries.

In 1932, at Lawrence Bay, I saw flocks of young plovers even on August 19. On St. Lawrence Island, according to the observations of O.J. Murie, the first flying plovers were seen even in August. They were encountered throughout September and left the island in October. F.H. Fay and T.J. Cade mentioned some other timings: flocks of plovers in fall plumage were often seen after August 10 and the bulk of their population left the island after mid-September. According to the observations of E.G.F. Sauer, toward the end of July, 1960, the plovers left the dry tundra with their chicks and settled on the moist tundra and in the valley: the old birds singly and the young ones in groups were often encountered along the shoreline in mid-August. He saw the last two plovers at Boxer Bay on August 21 and one in Gambell on August 28. According to the eskimos, the plovers arrived gradually in ever increasing numbers at Southwest Cape in the latter half of September. They gathered in 20s or more and circled high in the air. Often they were attacked by gyrfalcons and then the flocks would climb almost out of sight. These flights would be repeated with intervals on the ground but ultimately the plovers flew away across the sea.

In Providence Bay a young plover was caught by the collectors on the cargo freighter *Vaigach* on September 27, 1911. P.T. Butenko encountered plovers at Uél'kal' on September 2, 1932. O.I. Belogurov found some on August 28 and 29, 1961. Flights of large flocks were noticed at the end of September.

Weight—The female collected on May 30, 1938, weighed 130 g.

Economic importance—This plover, though not so small a sandpiper, does not catch the eye of the northern hunter, who has an abundance of much larger fowl to choose from.

Systematics—According to the widely held, established view the plovers form two species: one with white and the other with brown auxiliaries.

Having studied more than 200 skins of adult plovers and being well acquainted with these birds in nature, I am inclined to accept this division into species but not without some reservation.

In outer appearance and especially in the color pattern the two species are very similar, the differences being mainly in the quantitative indexes. In behavior, tone and life style there are no significant differences. It is customarily believed that the ranges of the species *Pluvialis apricaria* (L.) and *P. dominica* (Müll.) overlap for a very long stretch from Bol'shezemel'sk tundra to Taimir. However, this view is not based on nests found but on summer specimens which remain single and are not confined to the breeding areas. Specimens with transitional characteristics are known.

P. apricaria (L.) and *P. dominica* (Müll.) perhaps form preeminent subspecies which are developed enough to be regarded as species, but in my view they cannot be recognized as good species.

In the following review of plover forms, the discussion is confined to adult birds. The wing length is given jointly for the males and females.

1) **Pluvialis apricaria** (L.)—The feathers on the back along the peripheries have large yellow patches numbering up to three pairs. Therefore the back is markedly variegated and appears yellowish and light-colored. The auxiliaries are white. The large white patches along the sides of the breast extend into the white zones along the flanks. In well-prepared bird skins the black area on the underside of the body covers only the central portion, though it is fairly broad. On the undertail coverts white predominates. The overall size is large. The wing length is 172 to 188 mm, the average of 58 birds being 181 mm.

Distribution—From Iceland to Taimir. Known to occur from far eastern points: ♀, July 10, 1843, Taimir River, hence nesting period; ♂, June 8, 1905, Lake Essei and ♂, August 9, 1934, Kotui River in the premigration period. The mass distribution eastward evidently ceases at Yamal and on the lower course of the Yenesei. Along the Urals the plover is found down to Oshe-nër (61°38′ north) and in Western Europe to Sweden, the Baltic states, the British Isles, Holland and the Federal Republic of Germany (Ems). It does not nest in Novaya Zemlya or Greenland.

Nothing can be said about the separation of the subspecies *P. a. altifrons* (Brehm.) for want of adequate material. Western European ornithologists differentiate this subspecies.

2) **Pluvialis dominica fulva** (Gm.)—The yellow patches along the edges of the feathers on the back are not very big and there are not more than two pairs of them: as a result the upper parts appear more black than in *P. apricaria.* The auxiliaries are brownish-gray. The white patches along the sides of the breast are smaller. Along the flanks there is a white band which is narrow and interrupted by black patches. In general the black color has a much greater spread than in the preceding species. The overall size is relatively very small. The wing length is 150 to 171, the average of 121 measurements being 161 mm.

Distribution—From Bol'shezemel'sk tundra to the western parts of Alaska. H. Seebohm collected this plover in Kue, on the lower Pechora, but the extensive distribution of this species begins only on the Gydan tundra. In arctic Alaska it reaches Cape Barrow and evidently is a common bird up to Wainwright. Nidification on the hilly tundra of the Siberian ranges south of the northern forest limit has not been confirmed by nests. At present it nests in the Anadyr basin and in the Chukchi peninsula and represents a lone species of plover there. Birds with a maximum wing length (171 mm) are encountered in different parts of the range.

3) **Pluvialis dominica dominica** (Müll.)—This is similar in color to *P. d. fulva* and in size to *P. apricaria.* The black sides of the body are without white commissures. In some birds there is almost no white coloration on the black undertail coverts. In wing length it is only slightly bigger than *P. apricaria*: 178 to 189 mm, the average of 17 measurements being 182 mm. The wing length of my Wrangel male was short but the color on the sides was completely black. Hence I have no doubt as to its belonging to the subspecies *P. d. dominica.*

At the end of the last and beginning of the present century this subspecies was a common breeding bird on the Anadyr and in the Chukchi peninsula, west at least to Kolyuchin Bay. I have now proved its nidification on Wrangel Island. In Alaska it is common only from Wainwright. Its numbers have greatly decreased recently but it is still not rare in North America from the central part of Alaska to Baffin Land.

Specimens— 1) Providence Bay, September 27, 1911, ♂, 1° anno, Arngol'd; 2 to 5) Lawrence Bay, August 19, 1932, ♂♀♀♀, 1° anno, Portenko; 6 and 7) Uélen, August 29, 1933, ♂, ○, 1° anno, Portenko; 8) same place, September 9, 1933, ♀, 1° anno, Portenko; 9 to 11) Cape Dezhnev, September 10, 1933, ♂♂♀, Portenko; 12) Uélen, May 31, 1932, ♀, Portenko; 13) same place, June 4, 1934, ♂, Portenko; 14) estuary of the Utte-Véem River, July 11, 1934, ♀, Portenko; 15) Cape Stoletiya, May 30, 1938, ♀, Butenko; and 16 and 17) Pereval'naya, August 7 and 11, 1939, ♂♀, Meller.

46. Pluvialis dominica dominica (Müll.)—American Plover

Distribution and status—Undoubtedly nested even at the end of the last century in the Chukchi peninsula but was evidently not common. Now found in the breeding area on Wrangel Island as a great rarity.

E.W. Nelson (1883, p. 84) writes about the distribution of the American plover in the Chukchi peninsula in very vague terms. According to him it was a large plover flying north and northwest up to the Arctic Ocean shore and from there all along the Alaskan shore of the Bering Sea, sometimes reaching the adjoining Siberian coast and the islands in this sea, from where specimens had been obtained. In this part of its range, including the islands of the Bering Sea and the northern Alaskan coast, its habitat alternated with a similar tiny Asiatic form which also came to these northern latitudes in the summer to breed.

On its visit to Lawrence Bay the *Vega* expedition acquired a bird and a clutch of three eggs in Nunyamo village. Unfortunately the specimen was lost and hence its exact identification remains doubtful. After wintering in Kolyuchin Bay, on June 3, 1879, a female American plover was brought to the expedition from Maingatir and on June 14 and 15, during a journey inland toward Kolyuchin Bay. E. Almquist shot three specimens of which one male was of this subspecies. No one has found it in the Chukchi peninsula.

During the visit of the *Vega* expedition to the northwestern tip of St. Lawrence Island from July 31 through August 2, 1879, some kind of plover was seen but specimens were not obtained and hence the species could not be confirmed. Similarly, during the visit of the *Corwin* expedition to that island in the summer of 1884 a plover was noticed which according to E.W. Nelson (1887, p. 124) bred there. However, no specimens were collected in this case either. Hence it is not quite clear on what basis Nelson placed the St. Lawrence Island plover among the golden plovers *Charadrius dominicus* (Müll.). H. Friedmann (1932a), noting that Nelson gave both "races" for St. Lawrence Island, ruled out their coexistence and arrived at a compromise, altogether erroneous verdict that the plovers on the island represented a form intermediary between the two subspecies. Recently this question was resolved to some extent when O.J. Murie (1936) collected from St. Lawrence Island a series of migratory September plovers belonging beyond doubt to the subspecies *P. d. fulva* (Gm.). Finally, E.G.F. Sauer (Sauer and Urban, 1964), who raised in captivity 10 chicks brought from the neighborhood of Boxer Bay, accurately determined their subspecies as *P. d. fulva.*

Since I collected a specimen of the American plover on Wrangel Island I list here all the records on that island, though quite tentatively because of the impossibility of distinguishing the American from the Asiatic subspecies from a distance. In the course of his brief landing on Wrangel Island near the estuary of the Kler River, on August 12, 1881, E.W. Nelson noticed a solitary plover in breeding plumage. He classified this report (Nelson, 1883, p. 84) under the name *Charadrius dominicus fulvus* (Gm.). A.I. Mineev did not find the plover on Wrangel Island. On May 28, 1939, I managed to secure a male on the territory of the Polar Station at Rodgers Bay. On July 22 I encountered what was evidently a nesting pair near the estuary of the Nasha River. In any case, the female behaved as though chicks were close by. Not far from there, in the nearest pass, I encountered two young plovers on August 23. Thus the fact of nidification of plovers on Wrangel, however rare it may be, was accurately established. Further, the nidification of the American plover on this island should not be thought strange considering that many birds of

American origin are encountered there. The lone specimen that I collected does not exclude the possibility of finding the Siberian subspecies on the island too.

Habitat—A nesting pair under my observation inhabited an elevated tundra plateau. Even the young birds raised by this pair were encountered in the fall somewhat west in the pass between the valley of the Nasha River and Rodgers Bay. The male arriving in the spring, was confined to the thawing pebbled spit not far from the Station building.

Seasonal phenomena—The arrival of a lone male on Wrangel Island on May 28, 1939, is somewhat ahead of the arrival of Siberian plovers in the Chukchi peninsula. I noticed the bird after midday and it had certainly only just arrived. It was a well-fed bird with subcutaneous fat in the form of patches and with large testes of size 5 × 12 and 5 × 10 mm.

On July 22 I encountered these along with other plovers near the estuary of Nasha River. The disturbed birds whistled and approached me but the American plover was very wary. The male was seen only for a brief period. The female, too, flew off somewhere but returned. One of the other plovers chased this female and later the roles were reversed; in a word, the situation left no doubt that the American plover had chicks somewhere close by. The calls of the American and other plovers could be closely compared in this situation. The whistle of the American plover was considerably gentler and fainter than that of the others; nevertheless the two were very similar.

From 50 to 60 follicles were counted in the ovary of a female collected by the *Vega* expedition at Kolyuchin Bay on June 3, 1879. The biggest was 12 mm in diameter, the next five or six being 5 to 6 mm in diameter. The eggs procured in Nunyamo, according to the description by V. Meves, were 33.5 × 47.5 and 33.3 × 48 mm in size. The dominant color of two of them was grayish-white with dull bluish-black surface patches. Large and small blackish-blue patches bunched at the blunt end of the egg and greenish-liquorice brown patches were scattered here and there. The color of the third one was more yellowish-gray and brown patches predominated: black patches were almost unnoticeable.

Food—The stomach of a female from Maingatir contained the remains of a beetle (*Chrysomela* ?). The male collected around Kolyuchin Bay was emaciated. In its stomach were found larvae and shards of beetles, bits of leaf of *Ledum palustre* (?) and some root hairs.

Specimen—Rodgers Bay, May 28, 1939, ♂, Portenko.

47. **Eudromias morinellus** (L.)—**Dotterel**

Local name—Chukchian: Pekongadlj in the records of the *Vega* expedition.

Distribution and status—Breeds in the Chukchi peninsula but sporadically and rarely. A single stray flight known for Wrangel Island.

According to W.S. Brooks (1915), a specimen of the dotterel was collected on June 14, 1913, by J. Dixon at Émma Bay, and a pair was taken on June 17; two eggs were collected in the apical part of Providence Bay. A.P. Kuzyakin on June 14, 1957, saw three dotterels around the bay and later noticed a nesting pair by the nest with a clutch.

According to H. Friedmann (1932a) two specimens were obtained in May and June, 1931, near Gambell village in northwestern St. Lawrence Island. On June 7, 1960, E.G.F. Sauer (Sauer and Urban, 1964) noticed two dotterels on a knoll northwest of Boxer Bay.

A.P. Kuzyakin noticed three dotterels by Chulkhyn on the south shore of Lawrence Bay in the summer of 1957. V.V. Leonovich found a clutch and caught a chick between Seishan and Enurmino in 1970. During his excursion inland toward Kolyuchin Bay E. Almquist (Palmén, 1887) collected a female on June 14, 1879, and came to the conclusion that the dotterel was quite common in that area. The Chukchians have their own name for it so it cannot be a rarity. On June 8 and 10, 1970, A.A. Kishchinskii found a pair on the dry elevated tundra in the neighborhood of the Ukouge lagoon, but in all probability they were migratory birds since they were not seen again despite a special watch.

In the later half of June, 1956, I found dotterels on the knolls near the 91st km by the Amguema. This was quite clearly their breeding area. They were present only on two adjacent knolls, behaved as though they were beside their nests and were calling. Once I saw six dotterels together. Hence no fewer than three pairs nested there. According to V.D. Lebedev and V.R. Filin (1959) the dotterel is a rare bird on Aiok Island and in the Karchyk peninsula. On August 4, 1958, a male was collected on the west coast of the peninsula and on June 5 a pair was seen on the south coast of Aiok Island. On June 11, 1965, F.B. Chernyavskii found a nest with a clutch on the upper reaches of the Yarak-Véem River in the eastern part of the north Anyui Range and a male was obtained on June 23, 1966, beside the nest in the valley of the Énmen-Véem River, a tributary of the Bol'shoi Keper-Véem River entering Malyi Anyui.

S.A. Buturlin (1960b) only once encountered this bird in the estuary of the Kolyma in fall flight. J. Koren (Schaanning, 1954) collected two specimens on the lower Kolyma: ♀ on June 1, 1917, and ♀ juv. on August 14, 1918.

On June 9, 1939, I noticed a dotterel on Wrangel Island on the right bank of the lower course of the Mamontovaya River. With the binoculars I could see that the bird was a female but it was too alert to be taken. I also heard its call.

The dotterel flies into Alaska where up to 10 specimens have been recorded (Gabrielson and Lincoln, 1959). At Cape Barrow the female of a pair with a complete egg in the oviduct was collected. In spite of these exceptional cases the dotterel should be regarded as a real Palearctic bird.

Habitat—On the knolls by the Amguema dotterels inhabited the upper terrace in an Alpine environment where even rock pipits and horned larks nested. The terrace was a flat section of hilly tundra with a vegetative cover of lichen, moss and grass interspersed with fine rocky debris. The dotterels could run about there freely. At the foot of the knoll they remained on dry hummocky tundra.

At Providence Bay, A.P. Kuzyakin found dotterels on the slopes of the knolls; E.G.F. Sauer found them at Boxer Bay atop a rocky terrace on a western slope. The nests found by F.B. Chernyavskii were situated on a dry terrace and on a dry gentle slope.

On Wrangel Island I noticed a dotterel in the pass between the Mamontovaya

River, where it flows east-west, and the coast west of Somnitel'naya Bay. Snow still lay in isolated patches and zones of the rubble tundra.

Nidification—In the second half of June, 1956, on the knolls by the Amguema, I noticed dotterels which had ceased calling. The following observation convinced me that the dotterels nested there:

On June 16, following the deserted terrace more than four-fifths up the knoll, I suddenly heard the call "chët', chët', chët' ", resembling more the call of some birds of the sparrow group. The dotterels were calling each other in two places, the sound of their call being sometimes gentle and sometimes piercing. The birds were already on the run when I noticed a beautifully colored female only 150 paces away. She disappeared in a few moments.

On June 20, on the same knoll, I again heard the call of a dotterel but saw it only when I descended to the foot of the knoll on the marshy hummocky slope. One dotterel hid between the hummocks. Later it climbed up the mound and began to run around in all directions. For a long time it preened itself, fluffed its feathers, stretched itself, and finally flew onto another mound. This is how several waders behave when a man is sighted by their nest. I set out to search for it but without success. Another dotterel flew toward it and a scuffle arose between them. It was late and, being far from my tent, I had to abandon these chancy observations.

On June 24, on the top terrace, I found a female and two males together. The female stood out well in full, dark coloration and also by her large size. She was aggressive and quite active.

Judging from their behavior, the males were in a subordinate position. They seemed to stretch their necks up and looked leaner. On my approach the dotterels took off but soon returned. I lay down and the female several times approached me, on the last occasion within 40 paces. The birds were calling each other and later flew low. I followed them and saw six dotterels on a low terrace among patchy tundra. They were crying and flustered, the females attacking the males. The whole environment resembled an area where mating calls could be heard. Three birds took off. Some lone dotterels were flying fairly high with a cry sounding sometimes like "chët' " and sometimes like "ch'yu", not like the call of other plovers.

On June 28, I heard the call there but on July 2 I did not find a single dotterel. It is quite probable that the females migrated while the males were engaged in incubation.

At Providence Bay on June 17, 1913, J. Dixon gathered two incubated eggs. On June 14, 1956, A.P. Kuzyakin found three slightly incubated eggs. In form they were similar to the eggs collected in Khibinakh but differed in their light bluish-gray color without the olive background. On June 29, 1970, V.V. Leonovich found a clutch with three considerably incubated eggs between Seishan and Enurmino and on July 9 a downy chick whose flight feathers were poking through. The nest found by F.B. Chernyavskii by the Yarak-Véem River was in the form of a shallow pit lightly lined with Iceland moss. It contained four eggs of a light cream color with rather vague reddish-brown patches (Fig. 45). Both the birds were around the nest. The nest found on the Énmen-Véem River was also in the form of a pit but was lined with moss, lichen and dry willow leaves. One of the three eggs lying in the pit was 27×41 mm in size. The male was incubating and attempted to withdraw. The female was absent.

Specimen—Énmen-Véem River, Malyi Anyui basin, June 23, 1966, ♂, Chernyavskii.

48. **Charadrius hiaticula tundrae** (Lowe)—**Ringed Plover**

Local name—Chukchian: *Argitodljakidlin* in the records of the *Vega* expedition.

Distribution and status—Breeds throughout the Chukchi peninsula and is quite common, but not numerous. Altogether absent from Wrangel Island.

E.M. Meller collected a male in flight on June 5, 1939, in the watershed of the Amguema and Tadleo rivers. According to the observations of V.É. Yakobi, in June, 1961, the ringed plover was very common around Uél'kal' where it was collected many times. In the summer of 1931 L.O. Belopol'skii noticed this bird breeding on Meechken Island. E.W. Nelson (1887, p. 126; under the dubious name *Aegialitis semipalmatus* Bonap.) records the ringed plover as quite common at Providence Bay. On June 4, 1913, W.S. Brooks (1915) noticed two there and collected a male. From Émma Bay I.O. Olenev brought me a specimen shot in the latter half of July, 1932. P.T. Butenko obtained three ringed plovers from different places at Providence Bay, notably near Cape Stoletiya, and also near Kivak village in the summer of 1938. On July 12 of the same year, 1938, I encountered a solitary plover on the bank of a rivulet north of Cape Stoletiya. On June 19, 1957, A.P. Kuzyakin found a nest at Providence Bay with a clutch. P.T. Butenko collected a positively migratory bird on August 20, 1938, at Cape Chaplin.

On St. Lawrence Island the ringed plover is evidently very rare. In bygone days it was mentioned by E.W. Nelson (1887). According to F.H. Fay and T.J. Cade (1959) a female bird was collected on May 28, 1956. E.G.F. Sauer (Sauer and Urban, 1964) noticed the ringed plover (*Charadrius semipalamatus*) on June 8, 1960, at Boxer Bay and two birds on June 14 in Kangi.

On the east coast of the Chukchi peninsula I chanced to catch two young ringed plovers at Lawrence Bay. According to a report by A.P. Kuzyakin this species was generally rare there. By Akkani village, in Lawrence Bay and in Poutyn only stray pairs were seen. In Poutyn he found a nest with a clutch.

On July 15, 1913, W.S. Brooks shot two males on the northern side of Cape Dezhnev. According to an eyewitness account by A.M. Bailey (1926), two ringed plovers were noticed on July 11, 1921, at Uélen; I am convinced the specimen collected was wrongly identified as *Ch. semipalmatus*. In early summer of 1934 near Uélen I noticed males calling right from their arrival and shot two pairs on June 13 in the estuary of the Pervaya rivulet. But the plovers did not remain in the nesting area and were seen later on the lagoons much farther off. Along the Kol'oam-Véem River I found the ringed plover only once, on August 12, in the middle reaches of the river. It was a nesting bird since it started up close to me. I came across some plovers during my excursion up the Utte-Véem River. Finally, on July 3, I found a nesting pair around Mitkulen.

W.S. Brooks collected a male and a female on July 17, 1913, at Cape Serdtse-Kamen'. The members of the *Vega* expedition noticed lone and paired plovers on July 17, 1879, not far from Pitlekai. On June 20 and 25 two specimens were secured by Dzhenretlen. In 1881 E.W. Nelson found the plover quite common by Kolyuchin Bay.

According to my observations on the Amguema in 1956, ringed plovers were common in the breeding area in the interior of the Chukchi peninsula. Not less than four pairs nested within range of my walking trips from the 91st km. From July 27 through 29, 1909, J. Koren (1910) found some ringed plovers in the neighborhood of Vankarém and incorrectly called them *Ch. semipalmatus*. According to the observations of A.A. Kishchinskii, in the summer of 1970 ringed plovers were quite common on the marine pebbled spits along the coast from Vankarém to the estuary of the Amguema. In early August, 1938, according to my observations, plovers were quite common on the pebbled spits east of Cape Schmidt rnd around Ryrkaipiya village. In the summer of 1958 V.D. Lebedev and V.R. Filin (1959) found the ringed plover quite numerous along the coasts of Aiok Island and at Chaun Bay. On June 20 they collected a male on Aiok Island and on July 24 a young bird.

Among the various names of plovers listed by A.I. Argentov (1861a) for the Trans-Lena region there are two or three that could apply to the ringed plover. E.W. Nelson (1883, p. 84) writes that in the summer of 1881 he found *Aegialitis semipalmatus* almost wherever he happened to land on the coast of the Chukchi peninsula. Though the bird was not numerous he saw a pair at almost every halt. J. Koren (Thayer and Bangs, 1914) often noticed ringed plovers on his halts at different points on the arctic coast of the Chukchi peninsula but could not find nests or chicks.

Flying from Cape Schmidt to Wrangel Island, I immediately noticed the absence from Wrangel of birds that were so common on the similar pebbled beach at Cape Schmidt.

Habitat—The ringed plover settles down for breeding on seacoasts, lagoons and rivers, selecting mostly spits of all kinds whether they are pebbled, sandy or even silty-muddy. It avoids zones right on the surf line on the seacoast but colonizes close by on broad pebbled beaches or on the rubble tundra. E.W. Nelson found this plover on the sandy and pebbled shores of lakes not far from the sea. According to the observations of L.O. Belopol'skii, the plover often nested on Meechken Island on marine spits near a colony of terns. At Pitlekai the ringed plovers were encountered on sand dunes. According to my observations, at Cape Schmidt plovers favored broad flats separated from the sea by surf breakers. Along the Utte-Véem and Kol'oam-Véem rivers they were encountered on sandy as well as pebbled spits; on the Amguema, they nested on the pebbled spits which were flooded at high water, but in two cases I came across nesting ringed plovers far from the river, in the broad, dry, warmed-up sandy-rubble fields.

Plovers often lived close to villages, being attracted by the presence of insects. On June 10, 1956, at 91st km, a large number of recently arrived plovers were feeding at the rubbish heaps right by the houses along with turnstones, longspurs and pied wagtails. That day there was a snowstorm and the birds found themselves under adverse atmospheric conditions. Two days passed this way and then they assembled on the nearest thawed patches. Plovers remained near Ryrkaipiya village in summer too. Right from their arrival they fed in the outskirts of Uélen. E.M. Meller noticed the ringed plover feeding near the Polar Station.

Arrival—As a bird living largely on insects, the ringed plover arrives late. In the spring of 1934 I noticed it for the first time around Uélen on June 5. Later, on June 7, I found a lone male on the south bank of the Uélen lagoon. The bird, evidently in anticipation of pairing, had occupied the spit and was calling vigorously. By June 13, I found two pairs in the estuary of the Pervaya rivulet and a lone plover near Uélen. The males were calling and chasing small waders. Another day I found one more lone plover calling in the estuary of the Pervaya lagoon but did not see it at all on the 15th, when all of the plovers had migrated for some reason.

In 1938 P.T. Butenko collected the first plover at Providence Bay on June 6. E.M. Meller shot a male on the Pereval'naya on June 5, 1939. On June 10, 1956, on the Amguema, I noted ringed plovers still arriving. It was wintry weather and a snowstorm was blowing. The huddled plovers with their heads tucked in their wings presented a very pathetic sight. Sometimes a bird would scamper a meter or so and stop because of the bad weather. V.D. Lebedev and V.R. Filin noticed the first of the arriving flocks on the south coast of Aiok Island on June 6, 1958.

Nidification—Under favorable weather conditions the ringed plovers begin calling right from their arrival. On June 7, 1934, I encountered a plover around Uélen occupying a small spit on the lagoon. The bird flew around flapping its wings slowly and deliberately, calling to mind the flight of a butterfly or a bat. Its note could be heard for at least 1 km.

The testes of arriving males were already enlarged (Table 37).

In the females collected on June 13, 1934, the biggest follicle in the ovary was 6 mm in size; subcutaneous adipose formations were negligible. The female shot by P.T. Butenko near Cape Stoletiya on July 12, 1938, had an ovary of almost imperceptible granular structure; it was 9 mm long and the bird was emaciated.

On the Amguema in 1956, according to my observations ringed plovers began occupying the nesting sites on June 13. I heard their loud calling on June 16 for the first time. On the evening of June 20 mutual calling was heard. On June 20, 22 and 24, when I visited the nesting area, the plovers exhibited great restlessness. Some came within 30 paces (Fig. 46). On June 9, 1961, V.É. Yakobi found a ringed plover in the nesting area near Uél'kal'. From June 26, 1956, the plovers on the Amguema began to be very restless on my appearance. They would run within 10 paces

Table 37. Testis size (mm) and subcutaneous adipose formations in ringed plovers

Date	Left	Right	Adipose formations
June 6, 1938	6×3	5×3	Significant
June, 7 1934	8×5	7×4	—do—
June 13, 1934	9×4	8×3	Filmy
July 9, 1934	4×2	3×2	—do—

and then quickly draw to one side (Fig. 47). One female crept into a depression and began to quiver and chirp. I could not find the nest though I examined the exposed area most thoroughly and studied the bird's behavior. Only on July 4, after repeated visits to the spit, did I finally find the nest, near which the ringed plover was most active. It ran a few steps, later turned its back on me and sat down.

Before my eyes the bird suddenly vanished: I saw only the white triangle of the underneath of the tail. It could have been taken for a pebble and certainly not for a bird (Fig. 48). In this strange posture the plover watched the intruder askance. Sometimes the ringed plover would stagger to its feet, drag its tail on the ground and gradually move away as though wanting the intruder to follow. But all this unusual behavior ceased when I withdrew 100 to 150 paces. The cry of the ringed plover could be written as "k'yuvi" and "tyuvik". Sometimes the second member of the pair would come and then a lilting trill like "otverni-ka, otverni-ka, otverni-ka" was heard. The birds met each other with the cry "kyuv, kui". Once there were three restless plovers by this nest. I found three birds beside another nest on another occasion. In the first instance the ringed plovers could have come from adjacent territory 200 to 250 m away but in the second case there were no nesting sites close by.

Whenever I came to the nest I did not find the incubating bird but when I sat by it for a while at a convenient distance and angle for photographing, the female would often settle on the eggs at a distance of only 6 to 8 m. Sometimes I sat near the plovers for 3 hours but they did not leave.

The nest was in the form of a pit dug in the dark soil of the spit, which was in the flood zone and not on the clean pebbles, contrary to my expectation. Nevertheless, the clutch merged surprisingly with the surrounding background and I could not locate it immediately on a second visit. The clutch consisted of four eggs (Fig. 49). On July 14 the clutch was still there in the nest but on July 17 neither the eggs nor the shells were to be seen. The parent birds were also absent. Probably the chicks had emerged on July 15.

On June 19, 1956, A.P. Kuzyakin found a nest with a clutch of four almost completely incubated eggs at Providence Bay. It was located by the edge of the landing strip at the airport and was only 10 m from the tail of an LI-2 aircraft. The ringed plover was initially scared by the blast from the propeller but soon returned and sat in the nest in spite of the fact that mail was being loaded and people were crowding around to emplane. On June 26 A.P. Kuzyakin found a second nest on the pebbled spit of the lagoon in Poutyn. It contained four much incubated eggs. On July 17, 1913, W.S. Brooks collected a male along with a downy chick at Cape Serdtse-Kamen'.

Fig. 48. View of camouflaged ringed plover *Charadrius hiaticola* L.

On July 3, 1934, near Mitkulen, a pair of plovers got very agitated on the approach of men and began flying about uttering a doleful, plaintive whistle. But even much later, on August 12 on the Kol'oam River, a lone plover flew near me; it was probably of a late brood. On July 24, 1961, V.D. Lebedev and V.R. Filin caught a young ringed plover from among four birds in a brood on the western shore of Chaun Bay.

Migration—On August 19, 1932, I encountered two fully grown young ringed plovers at Lawrence Bay. There were traces of subcutaneous adipose formations in one of them while the other turned out to be altogether emaciated. On August 20, 1938, P.T. Butenko collected a young male, also emaciated at Cape Chaplin. Evidently the ringed plover flew away in the latter half of August.

Food—The following contents were found in the stomachs examined:

1) Uélen, June 7, 1934. Heads of five *Carabidae*, 18 larvae of dipterans, eight tiny spiders and some pebbles. 2) Uélen, June 13, 1934. Tiny bits of beetle chitins, 5 to 10 tiny larvae of dipterans and pebbles. 3) Uélen, June 13, 1934, two *Carabidae* (one almost whole), two *Staphilinidae* (one whole), one beetle larva (*Carabidae* ?), about 10 deformed larvae of dipterans and some pebbles. 4) Estuary of the Utte-Véem River, July 9, 1934. Head, throat and shard of beetle, heads of two hymenopterans, 100 to 150 tiny larvae of dipterans, one caterpillar and pebbles.

E.M. Meller found caterpillars, larvae of dipterans, and pebbles in the stomach of a specimen taken at Pereval'naya on June 5, 1939.

Weight—A June male from Plover weighed 52 g.

Systematics of the subspecies—In the territory of the USSR, I differentiate as before (Portenko, 1939b, vol. I, pp. 158 and 159) two subspecies of ringed plover.

1) **Charadrius hiaticula hiaticula** L. The color of the upper parts is lighter and the overall size greater. Specimens from Western Europe, Vistula, the Baltic Sea and Scandinavia were studied. This subspecies is also found in the Kola peninsula, and I collected a light-colored male at Belush'aya Bay on Novaya Zemlya on July 19, 1930.

2) **Charadrius hiaticula tundrae** (Lowe). The color on the upper parts is darker and the size somewhat smaller. It is found from Novaya Zemlya to Bering Strait.

Charadrius hiaticula semipalmatus—Br., in my opinion, is a good subspecies distributed from Alaska to Baffin Land and northern Labrador. It is characterized by its very small size, dark color and, what is more, well-developed webs between the bases of the three anterior toes. Between the middle and the outer toes the web reaches the distal end of the second joint of the outer toe.

All of the specimens obtained in the Chukchi peninsula listed below belong to the subspecies *Ch. h. tundrae* with absolute certainty and I have no doubt that E.W. Nelson, J. Koren (1910), A.M. Bailey (1926) and others who called Chukchi ringed plovers by the name *Ch. semipalmatus* erred for want of specimens and critical identification. This American tendency to identify Chukchi with Alaskan birds has been a characteristic event of full-scale lists, for example of A.C. Bent (1929) and in *Check List of North American Birds* (1957, p. 167).

Specimens— 1) Émma Bay, latter half of July, 1932, ♂, Olenev; 2 and 3) Lawrence Bay, August 19, ○○, 1° anno, Portenko; 4) Uélen, June 7, 1934, ♂, Portenko; 5 and 6) same place, June 13, 1934, ♂♀, Portenko; 7) middle reaches of the Utte-

Véem River, July 9, 1934, ♂, Portenko; 8) Providence Bay, Plover, June 6, 1938, ♂, Butenko; 9) Cape Stoletiya, July 12, 1934, ♀, Butenko; 10) Kivak village, June 22, 1938, ○, Butenko; 11) Cape Chaplin, August 20, 1938, ♂, Butenko; and 12) Pereval'naya Station, June 5, 1939, ♂, Meller.

49. Charadrius mongolus stegmanni Port.—Mongolian Plover

Distribution and status—Nests in small numbers on south and east coasts of the Chukchi peninsula.

I came across the Mongolian plover in the Chukchi peninsula only once. On June 5, 1956, I was passing along the north shore of Krest Bay and saw two bright-colored males on the rocky tundra. They were fairly confident and flew off to the foot of knolls only after some time. A very dull-colored bird, evidently a female, joined them.

If we are to believe J. Dixon (1918) that Capt. Moore's collection came from Plover, then evidently two specimens of Mongolian plover in summer dress were taken at Providence Bay even in 1849. On July 20, 1912, L.M. Starokadomskii collected three Mongolian plovers at Émma Bay. Of them a male and a female were preserved in the collection of the Institute of Zoology, Academy of Sciences of the USSR, in the form of bird skins, the third specimen was preserved in alcohol. In the same bay Copley Amory, Jr. (Riley, 1918) collected a female on July 22, 1914. P.T. Butenko shot a male on Plover spit, Providence Bay, on June 6, 1938. In V.N. Lyubin's collections there was an adult bird with two tiny downy chicks found on Érdman Island in that bay. Finally, A.P. Kuzyakin encountered this plover on June 15, 1957, by the lake south of the airport. At the end of the first 10 days of August, 1909, J. Koren (1910) collected a young bird at Cape Chaplin (Indian Point).

According to H. Friedmann (1936) the Mongolian plover was collected at Gambell village on St. Lawrence Island.

In 1957, A.P. Kuzyakin found two nesting areas at Lawrence Bay. On June 19 he found three plovers of this species by the lake in the outskirts of the settlement. He traced the nest with eggs on June 21. On July 7 he collected a male with two downy chicks on Bennet islet in the same bay.

The Mongolian plover has not been reported on the north coast of the Chukchi peninsula or on Wrangel Island.

In the collection of I.N. Gabrielson and F.C. Lincoln (1959) several instances are cited of flight into Alaska in June and September. H. Friedmann (1934b) reported that on June 10, 1933, three eggs and a male were collected at Goodnews Bay.

Habitat—I encountered newly arrived Mongolian plovers around the knolls on a debris cone. They flew off toward the foothills. Somewhat later, around the knolls, I came across a pair of mountain finches. The snow still lay on the hills but below it was rapidly thawing under the bright sun.

At Providence Bay A.P. Kuzyakin noticed a plover in the breeding season on the gentle slope of a knoll. He found a nest at Lawrence Bay on level shingle, 30 m from a partly built house. Such a habitat is quite unusual for the Mongolian plover which is a hill, even Alpine bird.

Arrival—The plovers that I noticed on June 5, 1956, had evidently arrived quite recently. On June 6, 1938, P.T. Butenko collected an arriving male which was distinguished by significant subcutaneous adipose tissue. It weighed 57.5 g and had fairly large testes 3 × 8 and 3 × 7 mm in size.

Nidification—On June 19, 1957, A.P. Kuzyakin noticed a calling male. He found a nest on June 21 on the pebbled spit with grass beds and low willow growth. It was at the center of a small flowering willow creeper shrub and contained only two eggs, which were slightly incubated. It was probably a second, induced clutch, since the number of eggs did not increase over the next three days. There were no more large follicles in the ovary of the female, which was collected. The color of the eggs was greenish-olive with dark brown, almost black patches which were more prominent and denser at the blunt end. The sizes were 26.6 × 37.9 and 26.8 × 37.3 mm and weights 13.05 and 13.07 g. The weight of the female was 63.5 g.

On July 7, 1957, on Bennet islet, after 10 to 12 minutes of tracking A.P. Kuzyakin noticed how the Mongolian plover male sat on the nest and was covering two one- or two-day chicks. The nest was in the form of a small pit among short, thin shoots of flowering willow pressed to the ground. It was 8.5 cm across. The soft lining at the bottom consisted of dry, dark brown leaflets of a creeper and short blades of dry grass. The sides of the pit were lined with fresh moss.

Systematics of the subspecies—I could do no better than repeat what I have already written (1939b, vol. I, p. 160).

Two subspecies should be differentiated in eastern Siberia.

1) **Charadrius mongolus mongolus** Pall. Lighter in color toward the top and the breast is more yellowish. It nests in the Alpine belt of the Stanov Range, especially by Lake Okonon and probably on Sikhote-Aline.

2) **Charadrius mongolus stegmanni** Port. Darker in color toward the top. The breast is of a reddish-brick red shade. Nests in Kamchatka, on the Commander Islands, in the Koryatz foothills and in the Chukchi peninsula.

Prof. E. Stresemann (1940) assigned the name *stegmanni* a year later.

Specimens— 1 to 3) Émma Bay, July 20, 1912, ♂, ♀, ○, Starokadomskii; and 4) Providence Bay, June 6, 1938, ♂, Butenko.

50. **Arenaria interpres oahuensis** (Bloxh.)—**Common Turnstone**

Local name—Chukchian: Yenatkuatschelten according to the records of the *Vega* expedition. In Eskimo: Tratrek in Providence Bay and sagyl'ma according to Mineev's records; sŭ-ghūl'-muk on St. Lawrence Island.

Distribution and status—In the Chukchi peninsula, nests only on the seacoast and is seen inland only in flight. Distributed sporadically depending on the coastal features. Numerous at Krest Bay but breeds in small numbers elsewhere all along the coast. Very common and numerous shorebird on Wrangel Island.

E.M. Meller collected a migratory female in the watershed of the Amguema and Tadleo rivers on June 8, 1939.

On the seacoast by the entrance to Krest Bay, I found turnstones in large numbers. On September 2, 1932, I noticed them in the outskirts of Uél'kal' village and on August 6 found broods and flocks near Notapenmen village. Around these same villages a year earlier, small breeding colonies of turnstones were found by L.O. Belopol'skii (1934). Eighty kilometers farther east, in the Syautokama River estuary, he found some seven birds in spring flight. On a long stretch of the south coast of the Chukchi peninsula where the rocky cliffs are washed by the sea turnstones were rare. This is partly true of Providence Bay also in spite of the fact that some finds have been recorded there. T.H. Bean (1883) obtained a male at the end of Plover spit on August 14, 1880. In the summer of the following year, 1881, these birds were noticed there by E.W. Nelson (1883). I found two young turnstones on August 26, 1932, near Plover spit. P.T. Butenko bagged a male on the wing there on June 6, 1938. In mid-July, 1938, I did not see the turnstone at all at Providence Bay but a July specimen came into A.N. Druzhinin's possession: he gave it to Moscow Zoological Museum. Butenko collected a turnstone at Kivak village on July 22 and at Cape Chaplin on August 18.

The first find on St. Lawrence Island was made by another compatriot, I.G. Voznesenskii, who collected a male on July 2, 1843. Later, according to E.W. Nelson, the *Corwin* expedition found numerous turnstones there in the nesting area; in particular, mating and pairs by the nests were noticed at the end of June, 1881. As for Nelson's references to the additional record of *Arenaria melanocephala* (Vig.) in moderate numbers on St. Lawrence Island and in a small number of instances on the Asiatic coast of the mainland, I would simply place them as young common turnstones. According to A.M. Bailey (1926) some turnstones were noticed near Gambell village in June, 1921; a downy chick was also found. O.J. Murie (1936) had with him two females taken in Kukuliak village on August 27, 1935. According to F.H. Fay and T.J. Cade (1959), in the summer of 1950 the turnstone was somewhat less common than the dotterel on St. Lawrence Island. In June he counted five nesting pairs and a nest with a clutch by Lake Trautman. In the neighborhood of Boxer Bay turnstones were quite common at the foot of knolls on outcrop rocks. From 1952 through 1957 it was the most common of shore birds on the island. Large flocks were seen in fall flight. From July 10 through 14, 1953, four males were collected around Gambell village. E.G.F. Sauer and E.K. Urban (1964) found three nests in 1960 around Boxer Bay and regarded the turnstone as common. After nesting, late summer wanderings were noticed.

Finds of I.G. Veznesenskii are known on the east coast of the Chukchi peninsula. He secured a young female on August 11, 1843, in Mechigmensk Gulf. I noticed two young birds on August 19, 1932, at Lawrence Bay. A.P. Kuzyakin found a colony of turnstones on the southern shore of Lawrence Bay around Chulkhyn; they were quite common there. Farther west he found lone pairs. In June, 1970, V.V. Leonovich found them in a limited number around Lawrence Bay and gathered a nest with a clutch.

E.W. Nelson (1887, p. 129) mentions rather vaguely that turnstones were noticed on the northwestern side of Cape Dezhnev (East Cape). I collected a female by Dezhnev settlement on August 16, 1932. Around Uélen, on June 7, 1934, I heard males calling right from their arrival and noticed a turnstone even on July 14. But I found this shorebird in a nesting area only farther west—a pair around Mitkulen. I did not notice one turnstone in the breeding season in the interior of the peninsula along the Kol'oam-Véem and Utte-Véem Rivers.

On June 28, 1970, V.V. Leonovich encountered a lone bird near Énurmino.

A few finds were made by the *Vega* expedition too. On June 12, 1879, a female was collected on the coast near the winter anchorage. E. Almquist brought back a male and a female shot on June 14 from a trip into Kolyuchin Bay. Later a male was obtained on June 15 by Dzhenretlen and one on June 19 by Pitlekai.

On the Amguema I observed turnstones only on the wing. They were quite common on June 10 and 11, 1956, at the 91st km. A flock of six birds remained near the house. Copley Amory, Jr. (Riley, 1918) collected three young turnstones on August 12, 1914, from Cape Vankarém. In 1966, in the post-nesting period, this shorebird was seen many times by F.B. Chernyavskii in the hilly country southwest of Cape Schmidt. On July 15, 1912, J. Koren (Thayer and Bangs, 1914) noticed a flock of about 20 birds at Chaun Bay. He called them *Morinella melanocephala* (Vigors) but I am convinced that they were young common turnstones. On July 23 I found the common turnstone on Aiok Island where it nested along with other plovers. According to V.D. Lebedev and V.R. Filin (1959) the turnstone was not numerous there. One bird was seen on June 22, 1958, and two on June 29 on the south coast of Aiok Island. On July 19, 1912, J. Koren (Thayer and Bangs, 1914) noticed the turnstone at Balagan. S.A. Buturlin (1906b) saw it only once in the spring on the lower reaches of the Kolyma.

On Wrangel Island turnstones were among the first visitors. In early August, 1881, when the *Corwin* repeatedly attempted to approach the coast, which had not been explored, small flocks of turnstones flew toward the ship and circled it, according to E.W. Nelson, as though they wanted to know what the ship was doing there. Once or twice they were noticed near Herald Island. However, no one who landed on the shores of Wrangel Island saw a single specimen there. E.W. Nelson (1883, p. 83) cited all the above references erroneously as of *Strepsilas melanocephala* Vig. In the 20s three turnstones were obtained on Wrangel Island by A. Crawford (Snyder, 1926). As reported by G.A. Ushakov (Bannikov, 1941), the turnstone nested regularly on the tundra and was fairly common. According to the observations of A.I. Mineev this bird was quite common on the island though not numerous. However, from my own observations I have the impression that the turnstone exceeded in numbers all the other plovers there: it was common, even plentiful. I found turnstones quite common even near the estuary of the Krasnyi Flag River, on the northern tip of the island. I found broods on the tundra by Bruch spit. From the southern shore of Predatel'skaya Bay up to Rodgers Bay I saw turnstones in very large numbers, as also in the valley of the Mamontovaya River in its lower reaches. After arrival they were particularly noticeable by their animation and mobility. In my diary for June 7, 1939, I wrote that the tundra was full of singing turnstones. In numbers they undoubtedly exceeded other plovers and American knots. In mid-July they began to be less noticeable but I saw a hurrying flock of several dozen birds over the lake at Somnitel'naya on July 15. Around July 20 the turnstones became very rare at some place but continued to be often seen at other places. According to S.M. Uspenskii, R.L. Bёme, and A.G. Velizhanin (1963) the turnstone was one of the common birds on the island and more numerous than other waders; it was encountered more often on the coastal plains. According to A.G. Velizhanin (1965) it was even more numerous in Tundra

Akademii, where it also nested.

Habitat—On Wrangel Island turnstones nested particularly often on patchy sections of tundra where rivulets of meltwater flowed or where water was generally available. Turnstones were altogether absent from the rubble-patchy tundra in the high watershed south of the lower course of the Mamontovaya River. But they were found in large numbers on both slopes of the hill range nearest to the seacoast. They do not require flat plateaus and they are no strangers to hilly topography. As I noticed not only on Wrangel but earlier even on Novaya Zemlya, turnstones avidly occupied the patchy tundra characteristic of the arctic desert landscape. It made no difference whether the bare sections of the patches were rubbled or pebbly. When the sun warmed them up, such places with lowly vegetation had many insects to attract the turnstones. In overcast, cold weather the birds migrated to the surf line or remained on the shores of lakes. In the latter half of the year, which was colder than usual, the turnstones, and especially the young, remained on the lakelets or on lagoon spits, for the same reason: few insects remained in the nesting areas and the birds switched to other food. Extensive pebbled spits almost devoid of vegetation did not attract the turnstones except on the first few warm summer days when there was a very large amount of thawing snow in the tundra. On June 8 I wrote in my diary that in the warm part of the day the turnstones gathered insects on the warmed-up spit. But near the water line the waders preferred the pebbled sections of the shore. A.I. Mineev wrote that the turnstone chose dry, pebbled areas on Wrangel Island.

V.D. Lebedev and V.R. Filin noticed turnstones on the dry marine tundra on Aiok Island.

According to the observations of A.A. Kishchinskii, along the coast from Vankarém to the Amguema the turnstones inhabited the spits separating the lagoons from the sea. On the banks of the lagoon the pebble beach gave way to wet, grassy tundra with lakes, rare patches of lichen-covered rubble and driftwood. The turnstones foraged in such places. They were agitated at the sight of man; a downy chick was caught there. They were hardly seen in dry pebbled areas. Around Mitkulen I found them on patchy tundra along the knolls. According to the observations of A.P. Kuzyakin, around Chulkhyn nesting pairs lived on the rocky low-sedge tundra quite far inland. E.G.F. Sauer and E.K. Urban found turnstones in the same habitats where dotterels nested, but the turnstones were also found somewhat farther away in very dry, rocky areas. Flocks appearing in mid-summer at first fed on the dry tundra. But at the end of July they moved into the depressed, moist tundra and later toward the shore line.

Right from their arrival the turnstones were found at quite unusual places. On the Amguema by the 91st km they fed for a few days at waste dumps by the side of the house along with plovers, longspurs and pied wagtails. Turnstones were encountered more often than others in the thawed patches close by but one flock for some reason chose a snow bank beside the house. On Wrangel Island I saw an arriving turnstone running along the snow bank. Another was bathing in a pool of meltwater on the ice. It appeared as though the birds needed to cool themselves.

In fall flight turnstones were most often encountered on the pebbled beaches. I found them in large numbers together with dunlins on the shores of the bay at

Notapenmen village. They were swarming among heaps of sea-kale gathered by the waves. According to A.G. Velizhanin the turnstones quite often assembled before migration near the settlements on Wrangel Island, where they dug in the rubbish along with buntings. At Providence Bay, I saw turnstones on the pebble beach. A.M. Bailey found them on St. Lawrence Island on the gravelly beach.

Arrival—In 1931 L.O. Belopol'skii noticed the first flock of turnstones in the estuary of the Syautokama River on May 24. It was the earliest known arrival date. At Providence Bay P.T. Butenko collected the first turnstone on June 6, 1938. It was a male with large testes 4 × 10 and 3 × 8 mm in size, and emaciated. Judging from the large testis size, the bird was not a recently arrived one. In the spring of 1934 at Uélen, I also noticed on June 6 the first turnstone. It was already occupying the nesting territory. It flew at me calling, like a plover. I next noticed a turnstone on June 14, so that the exact arrival date around Uélen could not be determined. In spring, 1879, near the winter anchorage of the *Vega*, the first turnstone was collected on June 12. A migratory female was shot on June 8, 1939, in the watershed of the Amguema and Tadleo. On the Amguema, at the 91st km, I noticed migratory turnstones on June 10 and 11, 1956.

In the spring of 1939, on Wrangel Island, the first turnstones were seen very early. On May 28, although the weather had turned worse and a north wind was blowing, I noticed a small flock flying to the north of the Station and had a good look at the male, which was very close.

Nidification—Having reached Akatylanva on June 2, I found the arriving turnstones which were calling persistently. Next day I found they were coming close, evidently gathering in order to nest. On June 5 their cry was heard incessantly. Often three birds were seen together. Evidently the males were in the majority, two males to one female. On June 7 they were vigorously chasing each other. On June 11, crossing the tundra, I found pairs everywhere. The birds sat on heaps or mounds and were calling. None of them tried to lead me aside. Since the male and the female were observed together in the open the female had evidently not yet begun incubating the eggs. On June 12 the turnstones called less and allowed a closer approach. I could not find the nest at that time but I came across hollowed-out round pits.

The left testis of a male collected at Rodgers Bay on May 31, 1939, was 5 × 6 mm in size and there was appreciable adipose tissue under the skin. In all June males the adipose formations were smaller. The testis sizes were as follows: in a male taken on June 3—6 × 10 and 5 × 6 mm; in a male taken on June 7—left testis 5 × 8 mm; and in a bird collected on June 9—5 × 10 and 3 × 6 mm; but the testes of a bird obtained on June 12 were smaller—5 × 7 and 3 × 5 mm.

On June 29 a nest with four eggs was found near Rodgers Bay. On July 1 it was found destroyed, evidently by a jaeger. The developed embryo form was found inside the shell. Jaegers no doubt inflicted much destruction on the turnstones. As soon as one appeared the turnstones would run to hide. The eskimos gathered the turnstone eggs for their own consumption; these eggs with embryos were available until the end of June. A.I. Mineev found a nest with three eggs in the southeastern part of Wrangel on June 26, 1931. V.V. Leonovich collected a clutch with four highly incubated eggs on June 14, 1970, around Lawrence Bay. According to T.J.

Cade, on St. Lawrence Island a nest with four eggs was found on June 25, 1950. In the neighborhood of Boxer Bay E.G.F. Sauer found the first full clutch of four eggs on June 15, 1960, a second one on the 18th and a third one on June 19. The nests were located on sections of dry gravel among lichen-filled, mossy tundra. The nesting material consisted of year-old leaves, grasses and lichen, especially *Thamnolia vermicularis*. On the approach of a man the turnstones would often rush at him with a cry. If the incubating bird were alone it would usually begin to withdraw, pretending to be sick and helpless. Turnstones would chase polar foxes, clawing the head and back. According to F.B. Chernyavskii (1967), on Wrangel Island the turnstones attacked the polar foxes singly or in pairs, swooping from the nest well in advance.

According to the observations of A.P. Kuzyakin, at Lawrence Bay some male turnstones were still calling on June 22 and 23, 1957. On July 9 he found three downy juveniles. On St. Lawrence Island, according to A.M. Bailey, a downy chick was caught on June 29, 1921. The bird had left the nest. A.A. Kishchinskii found a downy chick on July 17, 1970, near the Ukouge lagoon.

On July 12, 1934, near Mitkulen, I encountered a pair of turnstones which tried to lead me aside. The testis size of the male collected did not exceed 6 mm but the bird was not emaciated, judging from the subcutaneous adipose formations. On Wrangel Island, in the first half of July, 1939, the call of the turnstone was increasingly rare and the birds were less visible. On July 11 some flew very close to me but the chicks could not be traced.

S.M. Uspenskii and R.L. Bëme encountered broods with nonflying chicks on Wrangel Island on rubbled tundra from July 17 through 22, 1960. From July 20 the yearlings began to be seen.

On July 22, 1939, at the end of Rodgers lagoon, I collected a chick. Nearby an American knot had settled for some reason. The head and belly of the chick were still downy and the back was hardly covered with wing coverts. A week later I found many young birds there. In early August broods were seen everywhere along the pebbled beach. From August 2 through 7 old birds were still agitated on sighting me. In the preceding year, 1938, near the Ozero lagoon, I found young turnstones on August 11. On August 14 I came across broods by Bruch spit on the north side of Wrangel Island. Initially an agitated female and later a male flew at me. Finally, the whole of the brood including three young birds began circling me, crying all the time. The female shot turned out to be a plump bird with ovaries having a granular structure in relief. On August 16, in the estuary of the Krasnyi Flag River, not all of the adult birds were disturbed by my presence. The young ones permitted a close approach. On August 17 I noticed the last of the male turnstones flying and calling.

Wandering and migration—On Wrangel Island the turnstones began to flock as early as July; they were lone birds or ones whose nests had been destroyed. On July 1, 1939, I noticed a flock flying high. On July 15 I counted some dozens of birds in a flock though lone birds were also encountered along the spits. The number of turnstones that had left their offspring to their own devices gradually increased but they became quite rare on the tundra in the last 10 days of July.

On the outskirts of Boxer Bay, from June 27 and throughout July, 1960, E.G.F.

Sauer noticed flocks counting up to six birds. Since the nesting turnstones were with clutches even on June 19 the flocks evidently consisted of nonpaired birds.

In mid-August, 1939, on Wrangel Island, I saw broods which were still united. They usually consisted of four birds; adult birds were not found among them. At least, most of them at that time had already deserted the island. The separation of the weaned broods from the adults in mid-August was so distinct that it is quite easy to understand the error committed by E.W. Nelson and others, pointed out above, in regarding the young and old turnstones as two species. On August 13, 1939, I noticed for the first time two large flocks above the banks of the lagoon. I did not see a single turnstone on the tundra on the 16th where they had been plentiful only recently. On the morning of August 23 I saw a flock flying high.

In 1938 I noticed some of the last of the young turnstones at Rodgers Bay on August 24. According to the observations of A.G. Velizhanin, in 1960 turnstones flew away from the south coast of Wrangel Island after the first snowfall. Even on September 9 they remained in Somnitel'naya settlement along with buntings. On August, 6, 1932, I encountered broods and flocks of turnstones near Notapenmen. The testes of a male collected were down to 2×4 and 2×2 mm. The female ovary exhibited a fine grained structure. Both birds were plump. On August 15, 1912, at Chaun Bay, J. Koren saw a flock of nearly 20 young birds which he mistook for black turnstones. On August 19, 1932, I encountered two young birds at Lawrence Bay and on the 26th at Providence Bay. The latter date was certainly close to migration time. In the young female that I secured near Dezhnev settlement on August 16, 1932, the tiny ovary was still hardly distinguishable and the subcutaneous adipose formations were absent. A young female taken by P.T. Butenko at Cape Chaplin on August 18, 1938, had a filmy ovary and was very plump. The young male shot at the same time was emaciated. The testis size was 2×3 and 2×2 mm.

Voice—The call of the turnstone is very diverse. Over a long distance I found a resemblance to the mutual calling of finches, but close by it reminded me of the cry of an agitated redshank. Still closer, the mating call was a clear and sharp chirp like "kigi-kigi-kigi...ki-ki-ki" or "chigi-chigi-chigi...kikikiki...". In other cases I found a similarity with the call of terns because of the admixture of the chirping sounds "kr" and "rrr".

Food—The stomachs of turnstones that I collected showed the following items: 1) Dezhnev settlement, August 16, 1932. Fragments of shards of a tiny beetle, heads and other remnants of nine hymenopterans, heads and wings of four butterflies, heads, wings and other remnants of 10 dipterans and about 50 tiny stones. 2) Mitkulen village, July 12, 1934. Head of one *Carabidae*, head of one hymenopteran, head of one *Tripulidae*, heads and fragments of the bodies of about 30 caterpillars and many tiny stones. 3) Wrangel Island, August 14, 1938. Remnants of nearly 30 caterpillars and small beetles and 0.5 g small gravel. 4) Same place, June 7, 1939. Ground remnants of tiny insects, occupying three-fourths of the stomach; coarse sand. 5) Same place, June 9, 1939. Three much-digested larvae of insects, 1 g coarse sand 1 to 3 mm in size. 6) Same place, June 12, 1939. Beetle *Chrysomela*, three beetles of the type *Poecilus* (tribe *Platysmatini*), remnants of caterpillars, seeds and ground-up plant remnants and 0.5 g coarse sand.

E.M. Meller found insects, some fibers and sand in the stomach of a turnstone. The stomach of a female shot near the winter anchorage of the *Vega* on June 12, 1879, showed the larvae of driftwood beetles. Insect larvae were also found in the stomachs of other specimens.

The weight of a male collected at Plover on June 6, 1938, was 73 g.

Economic importance—Because of its small size the turnstone is not hunted but on Wrangel Island, where it is abundant, the children and womenfolk of visiting eskimos gather the eggs of turnstones more often than of other shorebirds.

Systematics of the subspecies—The turnstone forms three clearly distinguished subspecies: *Arenaria interpres interpres* (L.), *A. i. oahuensis* (Bloxh.), and *A. i. morinella* (L.)

Their distinctive characteristics and distribution were taken from my original collections (Portenko, 1939b, vol. I, p. 162). The synonym *pacificus* Nelson (1883, p. 83) for *oahuensis* (Bloxh.) should be mentioned.

Specimens— 1) St. Lawrence Island, July 2, 1843, ♂, Voznesenskii; 2) Mechigmensk Gulf, August 11, 1843, ♀, 1° anno, Voznesenskii; 3) Wrangel Island, June 14, 1928, ♀, Ushakov; 4 and 5) southeastern Wrangel Island, June 11, 1931, ♂ ♀, Mineev; 6) Rodgers Bay, June 20, 1931, ♂, Zvantsev; 7 and 8) Notapenmen village, August 6, 1932, ♂ ♀, Portenko; 9) Dezhnev settlement, August 16, 1932, ♀, 1° anno, Portenko; 10) Mitkulen village, July 12, 1934, ♂, Portenko; 11) Providence Bay, Plover, June 6, 1938, ♂, Butenko; 12) Kivak village, July 22, 1938, ○, Butenko; 13) Providence Bay, end of July, 1938, ○, Druzhinin; 14) Bruch spit, August 14, 1938, ♀, Portenko; 15) Wrangel Island, August 16, 1938, ○, Druzhinin; 16 and 17) Cape Chaplin, August 18, 1938, ♂, ♀, Butenko; 18) Rodgers Bay, May 31, 1939, ♂, Portenko; 19) Akatylanva, June 3, 1939, ♂, Portenko; 20) Mamontovaya River, June 7, 1939, ♂, Portenko; 21) Pereval'naya Station, June 8, 1939, ♀, Meller; 22) Mamontovaya River, June 9, 1939, ♂, Portenko; and 23) Akatylanva, June 12, 1939, ♂, Portenko.

Biological material—Clutch of three eggs, southeastern Wrangel Island, June 26, 1931, Mineev.

Arenaria melanocephala (Vigors)—**Black Turnstone**

Its occurrence in the Chukchi peninsula is not certain. E.W. Nelson's reference (1887) to the occurrence of this species on St. Lawrence Island in 1881 should be disregarded since he listed it for the Chukchi peninsula as well.

According to F.H. Fay and T.J. Cade (1959) the black turnstone has been sighted twice in the recent past. On August 3, 1942, one was sighted near Southwest Cape and two on July 13, 1955, in Savunga; the female was collected and is preserved in the museum in Washington.

51. **Totanus erythropus** (Pall.)—**Spotted Redshank**

On May 21, 1879, O. Nordquist (Palmén, 1887) found the first of the shorebirds for that year on the heights of Dzhenretlen. It flew in from the sea inland to the southeast. The bird was brown with a fairly long beak and short neck. Once it gave out the note "tschiuli". The Chukchians called it enatotschidlin and said that it was common far inland in the summer but not by the sea. I.A. Palmén relates this observation in a footnote to the text when discussing dowitchers. I am inclined to believe that the bird noticed was a spotted redshank. In the transcription of the note, I find syllables resembling "chu-vik", with which the residents of the North refer to the spotted redshank. It closely parallels the call note of this sandpiper. From this, the call of the spotted redshank could be recognized among different call notes even without seeing the bird, for example, at night. The listed characters, i.e. brown color, fairly long beak and short neck, are also characteristic of the spotted redshank in flight. The flight of this species nesting on the Anadyr and even its nidification are entirely probable in the interior of the Chukchi peninsula. V.D. Lebedev and V.R. Filin (1959) found wandering redshanks in the Karchyk peninsula. Two young males were collected on the upper reaches of the Tikhaya River on August 10, 1958, and a flying flock consisting of six birds was noticed on August 11; later, two more redshanks were seen. A flock, evidently of spotted redshanks, was noticed on June 6 on the southwest coast of Aiok Island.

52. **Glottis nebularia** (Gunn.)—**Greenshank**

A single instance of spring flight known on the south coast of the Chukchi peninsula.

P.T. Butenko encountered the greenshank together with the tiny wood sandpiper in the neighborhood of Sireniki village not far from Providence Bay during spring flight on May 26, 1938.

The male collected had enlarged testes 4 × 8 and 3 × 6 mm in size. Subcutaneous adipose formations were absent.

The weight of the bird was 138 g.

Specimen—Sireniki village, May 26, 1938, ♂, Butenko.

53. **Rhyacophilus glareola** (L.)—**Tiny Wood Sandpiper**

A lone instance of flight known for the south coast of the Chukchi peninsula during spring flight.

On the evening of May 26, 1938, P.T. Butenko found and collected the wood sandpiper together with a greenshank in the neighborhood of Sireniki village not far from Providence Bay. A.A. Savich's collection, as confirmed by V.M. Artobolevskii (1927), contained a specimen of wood sandpiper with no indication of the exact location of the find. It is not unlikely that it originated at Cape Schmidt. Among the waders whose names are listed by A.I. Argentov (1861a) for the Trans-Lena region the wood sandpiper must certainly figure but it is difficult to determine under what name it has been listed: "black plover with a white breast" or "forest song plover".

The male collected had enlarged testes 4 × 8 and 3 × 7 mm in size and was devoid of subcutaneous adipose formations. Its weight was 58.5 g.

Specimen—Sireniki village, May 26, 1938, ♂, Butenko.

54. **Heteroscelus incanus brevipes** (Vieill.)—**Siberian Tattler**

Distribution and status—Flies from time to time into the Chukchi peninsula. Found for certain on the south coast.

P.T. Butenko collected a female on June 9, 1938, on Plover spit at Providence Bay. According to H. Friedmann (1933) a specimen of this subspecies was taken in July, 1932, on St. Lawrence Island. Among the waders gathered by A.A. Savich, as reported by V.M. Artobolevskii (1927), there was a specimen probably originating at Cape Schmidt. On June 3, 1970, A.A. Kishchinskii encountered a migrating tattler near this cape on the pebbles by the lagoon.

In 1965 F.B. Chernyavskii repeatedly encountered tattlers in the eastern parts of the north Anyui Range by the western boundary of the Chukchi peninsula.

Habitat—Tattlers were found by Chernyavskii on the banks of hill streams and broods were found on a pebbled spit with low willow shrubs.

Nidification—On June 11, 1965, F.B. Chernyavskii found a pair with downy chicks on the upper reaches of the Yarak-Véem River. The old birds tried to distract him.

The ovary of the female taken at Providence Bay on June 9, 1938, had a coarse-grained structure. There were some isolated subcutaneous adipose formations. The weight of the bird was 99 g.

Specimen—Providence Bay, June 9, 1938, ♀, Butenko.

55. **Heteroscelus incanus incanus** (Gm.)—**American Tattler**

Local name—In Eskimo: Qŭl-mŭs'-sŭk-ŭ-kă-wŏk' on St. Lawrence Island.

Distribution and status—Nests in small numbers in the eastern part of the Chukchi peninsula.

An instance is known of flight into Wrangel Island.

On June 8, 1956, approaching Égvekinot, I saw on the shores of Krest Bay a tattler which had probably flown in very recently. According to L.O. Belopol'skii, he found this sandpiper several times at Krest Bay in the nesting period and also in flight. He collected a specimen on Meechken Island in the migratory period. I happened to examine this specimen and can confirm that it was a genuine *H. i. incanus*. At Providence Bay, though its occurrence was reported several times, the tattler cannot be regarded as common. Even T.H. Bean (1883, p. 165) came across the tattler at Plover Bay on the eastern rim of Hawaii in fall flight and collected two specimens but did not see more of them. Probably based exclusively on Bean's reference, E.W. Nelson (1883, p. 90) writes in very general terms that this bird was common on the shores of the Bering Sea on the Siberian side as also in Alaska but was not known north of Bering Strait. In the records of the Zoological Museum, Academy of Sciences of the USSR, a female specimen of this species taken by E.E. Arngol'd on July 25, 1913, at Providence Bay was entered in 1914 and later discarded because of bad preservation. However, the identification of the species cannot be relied upon since in another case V.L. Bianki identified a young American knot in I.N. Akif'ev's collection as *Heteractitis incanus*. On August 11, 1932, I came across some birds on the shores of Émma Bay but did not find this sandpiper there in 1938. P.T. Butenko collected a specimen at Providence Bay, on Plover spit,

Fig. 51. Dowitcher *Limnodromus griseus* (Gm.). Ukouge lagoon.
July 12, 1970. Photo by A. A. Kishchinskii.

Fig. 52. Nest with clutch of American knot *Calidris canutus* (L.). Rodgers
Bay. End of June, 1934. Photo by A. I. Mineev.

Fig. 55. Dunlin *Pelidna alpina* (L.) by nest. Around Amguema by 91st km. July 11, 1956.

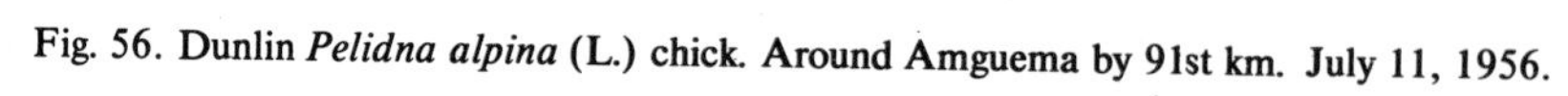

Fig. 56. Dunlin *Pelidna alpina* (L.) chick. Around Amguema by 91st km. July 11, 1956.

Fig. 57. Nest with clutch of eastern little stint *Pisobia ruficollis* (Pall.). Around Amguema by 91st km. June 30, 1956.

Fig. 58. Female of gray phalarope *Phalaropus fulicarius* (L.). Ukouge lagoon. June 22, 1970. Photo by A. A. Kishchinskii.

Fig. 61. Temminck's stint *Limonites temminckii* (Leisl.) by nest. Around Amguema by 91st km. July 5, 1956.

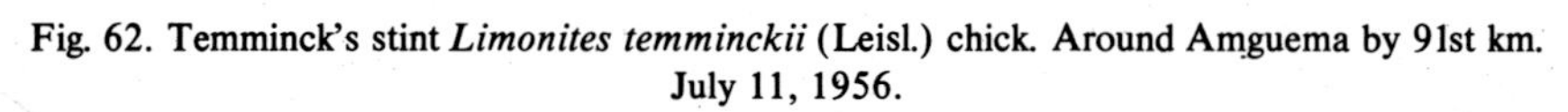

Fig. 62. Temminck's stint *Limonites temminckii* (Leisl.) chick. Around Amguema by 91st km. July 11, 1956.

Fig. 63. Female pectoral sandpiper *Heteropygia melanotos* (Vieill.). Ukouge lagoon. July 15, 1970. Photo by A. A. Kishchinskii.

Fig. 64. Female pectoral sandpiper *Heteropygia melanotos* (Vieill.) sitting on nest. Around Amguema by 91st km. July 5, 1956.

Fig. 65. Nest with clutch of pectoral sandpiper *Heteropygia melanotos* (Vieill.). Around Amguema by 91st km. June 30, 1956.

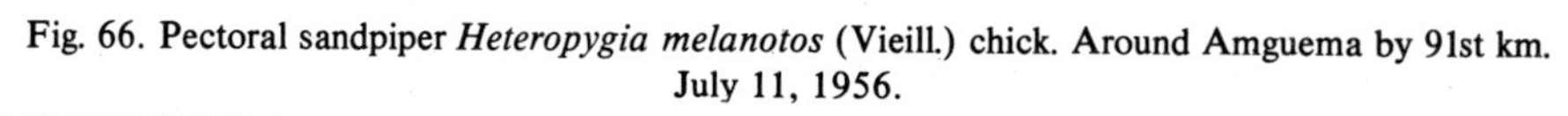

Fig. 66. Pectoral sandpiper *Heteropygia melanotos* (Vieill.) chick. Around Amguema by 91st km. July 11, 1956.

Fig. 67. Male northern phalarope *Phalaropus lobatus* (L.). Amguema River by 91st km. June 22, 1956.

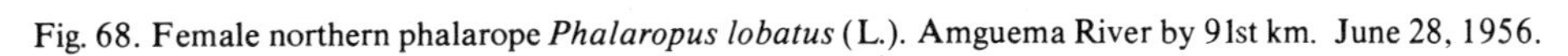

Fig. 68. Female northern phalarope *Phalaropus lobatus* (L.). Amguema River by 91st km. June 28, 1956.

Fig. 69. Nest with clutch of northern phalarope *Phalaropus lobatus* (L.). Grass covering slightly drawn apart. Amguema River by 91st km. June 28, 1956.

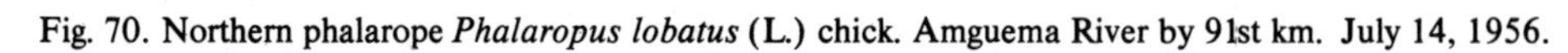

Fig. 70. Northern phalarope *Phalaropus lobatus* (L.) chick. Amguema River by 91st km. July 14, 1956.

during spring flight and another near Sireniki village in the fall.

According to F.H. Fay and T.J. Cade (1959) probably this subspecies of tattler was noticed on St. Lawrence Island in July and August in 1950, 1953 and 1957. A lone female was collected on July 16, 1955, and another on August 8, 1957. The eskimos believed that the tattler nested there in the high hills. H. Friedmann (1934a) thought that a sandpiper bone about 1,000 years old, found in one of the main excavations on the southeastern tip of the island, belonged to this subspecies.

During my expedition up the Kol'oam-Véem River, in the interior of the Chukchi peninsula, I twice came across American tattlers, on August 13 and 20, 1934, in the upper reaches of the river. Finally, at Kolyuchin Bay, E. Almquist (Palmén, 1887) collected a specimen on June 1, 1879, near the *Vega*, i.e. near Pitlekai.

On July 11, 1932, a migrating specimen of American tattler was killed on the ice in Rodgers Bay.

Habitat—I found it on the Kol'oam River, probably not far from the nesting area. In one case the sandpiper was hidden under an old snow bank overhanging a pebbled bank. In another it flew away from the rocky bank onto a pebbled islet. The sandpipers that I noticed at Émma Bay were also hidden under a thawing shield of snow which overhung a narrow pebbled bank flattened with rock debris. T.H. Bean found these sandpipers on rocks. The specimens brought back by the *Vega* expedition was taken near the ship. On Wrangel Island a flying sandpiper was shot on the ice in Rodgers Bay.

Arrival—The tattler arrives in the very last days of May or early in June. The records are as follows: June 1, 1879, around Pitlekai; June 8, 1931, on Meechken; and May 30, 1938, at Providence Bay. In the last case, a male was collected with testes 7 × 14 and 6 × 12 mm in size and appreciable adipose formations. For purposes of comparison it may be pointed out that the testis size of males collected on August 4, 1938, and August 11, 1932, were identical at 2 × 4 and 2 × 3 mm; the former was emaciated while the latter had filmy adipose formations.

On June 8, 1956, near Égvekinot, I came across a tattler on the shores of the bay, i.e. not yet in the nesting grounds.

Nidification—Evidently the adult birds leave their chicks very early because a female was collected at Providence Bay far from the mountains as early as July 25, 1913. The female find on Wrangel Island on July 11, 1932, should not be regarded as anything more than a case of inflight.

Migration—Most of the records after the nesting period were made in August. The female collected on August 20, 1934, was very plump and had ovaries with a fine-grained structure. T.H. Bean found these sandpipers at Providence Bay as late as September 14, 1880.

Habits—The tattler is a very wary bird. It does not fly away from a man on sighting him at a distance but hides itself. Unlike other sandpipers, it is not very vociferous. On the Kol'oam River a bird flying away from me on the opposite bank gave a low whistle.

Food—The stomach of a specimen collected on August 20, 1934, revealed the bones of a tiny fish and very small fragments of insect chitins.

Systematics—I described the differences between American and Siberian tattlers in my *Fauna of the Anadyr Region* (Portenko, 1939b, part I, pp. 179 and 180). In less detail but with the addition of beak sketches the differences were later described by D.L. Serventy (1944). Based on the additional material gathered, in particular, in the Koryatz upland, I have changed my views and now regard the two forms of tattler as subspecies and not species, with of course distinct characteristic differences.

Specimens— 1) Meechken Island, June 8, 1931, ♂, Belopol'skii; 2) Rodgers Bay, July 12, 1932, ♂, Mineev; 3) Émma Bay, August 11, 1932, ♂, Portenko; 4) Kol'oam-Véem River, August 20, 1934, ♀, Portenko; 5) Providence Bay, May 30, 1938, ♂, Butenko; and 6) Sireniki village, August 4, 1938, ♂, Butenko.

56. **Numenius borealis borealis** (Forst.)—**Eskimo Curlew**

Evidently nested as late as the 80s of the last century on the north coast of the Chukchi peninsula, but now extinct.

There is only one reference to a record of this species in the Chukchi peninsula. E.W. Nelson (1883, p. 90) writes that four migratory specimens were noticed in Vankarém, on the north coast of Siberia, on August 6, 1881. They were lone curlews seen on the Siberian coast in the course of frequent visits. I.A. Palmén (1887) disagrees with this reference. It should not, however, be forgotten that in the 80s of the last century the eskimo curlew was not rare. Two specimens were collected on the Anadyr and I think it is highly probable that Nelson did not err: he knew this species well from observations in Alaska.

It should be assumed that this bird, which is still not totally extinct in America, no longer inhabits the Chukchi peninsula. Evidently it used to breed there, judging from the fact that four specimens, i.e. a brood, were seen.

57. **Numenius phaeopus variegatus** (Scop.)—**Whimbrel**

Local name—Chukchian: Iĭnatvàasylgyn. In Eskimo: Sukhtū'-vuk on St. Lawrence Island. According to Argentov, "cloudberry plover" in the Trans-Lena region.

Distribution and status—Not a single reliable record known for the Chukchi peninsula though possibility remains of nidification in the interior. A case of inflight is known for Wrangel Island.

Calling the whimbrel by the American name of the subspecies *Numenius hudsonicus* Lath., E.W. Nelson writes (1883, p. 90) that it is not known for the Bering Sea islands and the adjoining islands of northeastern Siberia but beyond a doubt visits St. Lawrence Island as also the Siberian coast in the summer. Under the same name, *Numenius hudsonicus*, O.J. Murie (1936) reported some finds on St. Lawrence Island: three specimens were collected at Gambell village on August 11, 1933, and July 1935, and a female on August 3, 1935. Another female was shot on the coast at Kukuliak village on August 5, 1935, and yet another one mile southeast on August 2, 1935. Some small flocks were noticed flying high over this village. I.N. Gabrielson (Gabrielson and Lincoln, 1959) reported the whimbrel for St. Lawrence Island. According to F.H. Fay and T.J. Cade (1959) these sandpipers were noticed in May on the west coast. One bird was noticed on May 25, 1956, and three on

May 29. Probably three whimbrels of this species were encountered in the summer too, in early August.

A.I. Argentov (1861a, p. 494) mentions a "cloudberry plover" for the Trans-Lena region. As I came to learn from the residents of Markovo and Penzhin villages, this name referred to the whimbrel. I learned the name for the whimbrel from Chukchian hunters at Uélen but could not ascertain from them where this bird occurred. For the Chukchi peninsula there are no concrete references to the find of a whimbrel though cases of inflight and even nidification are quite probable.

F.B. Chernyavskii noticed *Numenius phaeopus* time and again on the southwestern slopes of the north Anyui Range. On June 23, 1966, a nest was found with a clutch in the valley of the Énmen-Véem River (Fig. 50).

The whimbrel is not rare in the Anadyr basin but, according to S.A. Buturlin (1906b), was common on the lower reaches of the Kolyma. I may add that, according to É.V. Schmidt, a fairly large number of whimbrels were noticed on the Panteleikha River. J. Koren (Schaanning, 1954) caught a male on the lower Kolyma on June 25, 1917.

A lone whimbrel flying over the tundra was collected on June 27, 1932, in southeastern Wrangel. No one sighted it either before or after this instance.

Habitat—On Panteleikha, É.V. Schmidt encountered whimbrels on the hill slopes, on the rocks and in the marsh overgrown here and there with tiny rose willow. On the slopes of the north Anyui range, according to F.B. Chernyavskii, they were confined to the hilly tundra. They were to be found in much larger numbers among thin deciduous forests.

Nidification—The nest found was located on a forest slope among shrubs of dryad tundra with small waterholes. It was in the form of a shallow pit lined with fragments of lichen trampled down with dry stalks of ledum, willow and blueberry. It contained four eggs of greenish-olive color with indistinct longitudinal light brown smears alternating with dark brown dots. The size of one of them was 38 × 56 mm. The birds behaved most watchfully beside the nest, got down at a distance and did not start up until they were within 25 to 30 m of the nest.

Systematics of the subspecies—I have discussed the subspecies in a special paper (Portenko, 1937b).

Specimen—Southeastern Wrangel Island, June 27, 1932, ♂, Mineev.

Numenius tahitiensis (Gm.)—**Bristle-thighed Curlew**

According to F.H. Fay and T.J. Cade (1959) a young male was collected on August 24, 1957, on St. Lawrence Island at the western end of the Kuzata lagoon.

58. Limosa lapponica menzbieri Port.

59. Limosa lapponica baueri Naum.—**Bar-tailed Godwit**

Distribution and status—Encountered many times in the Chukchi peninsula in the migratory period, more often in flocks. Quite rare otherwise. Not found as yet for certain in the breeding grounds. Not even once seen on Wrangel Island.

On June 20 and 21, 1913, W.S. Brooks (1915) noticed a flock of nearly 20 godwits in the western part of Providence Bay and collected eight birds, all of them males. They were undoubtedly single birds.

On St. Lawrence Island according to H. Friedmann (1932a), two young males were collected on August 1 and 23, 1930. O.J. Murie (1936) reported a male shot on August 31, 1935, at Kukuliak village. Finally, F.H. Fay and T.J. Cade (1959) reported a find, probably of this godwit on July 7, 1954, at Gambell village.

On August 19, 1932, I collected a young male at Lawrence Bay and shot lone females on June 3 and 4, 1934, near Uélen.

There is no information about this wader farther away for the north coast of the Chukchi peninsula right up to Aiok Island, where it was found in small numbers by V.D. Lebedev and V.R. Filin (1959). On June 21, 1958, two females were collected from a flock of about 15 birds. Later two males from a flock comprising six to eight birds were shot on the Kozmina River in the western part of the Karchyk peninsula. Lone godwits and flocks of them were noticed there.

J. Koren (Thayer and Bangs, 1914) noticed a bar-tailed godwit on July 18, 1912, 40 miles east of Bol'shoi Baranov Kamen'. Copley Amory Jr. (Riley, 1918) collected a male on August 9, 1915, at that cape. J. Koren further noticed bar-tailed godwits in Balaganchik on July 19, 1912, in Sukharnoe on June 23 and on the lower Kolyma on May 30.

The bar-tailed godwit evidently was not rare in the nesting areas in the Kolyma delta. At present, judging from the finds there, this could represent the eastern boundary of its range in Asia. S.A. Buturlin (1934, vol. I, p. 74) found some nesting colonies in 1905 in the Kolyma delta and collected downy chicks. J. Koren (Schaanning, 1954) shot an adult on July 19, 1916, and collected a godwit and a clutch on June 19, 1917.

Habitat—W.S. Brooks noticed the godwits on an extensive marsh on the western side of Providence Bay. At Lawrence Bay, I encountered this sandpiper on a lakelet on a big spit by the exit to the sea. It was wading in water up to the belly and was apparently looking for tiny molluscs at the edge of the shore grass. At Uélen, I saw a solitary female which flew in from the sea to the tundra on the southern bank of the lagoon. Another day I managed to locate it there. It was confined to a section of low tundra with tiny pools of meltwater and patches of unthawed snow. On the lower Kolyma S.A. Buturlin (1906b) found the bar-tailed godwit very common in the nesting area, mostly on the low tundra.

Seasonal phenomena—In the spring of 1934, at Uélen, I noticed godwits on June 3. Being uncommon in these places the bird is at once noticed. The godwit found was a female in the plumage of a two-year bird with a well-developed ovary in which the biggest follicle was 5 mm. There is no doubt that it would have been laid in the forthcoming summer. Subcutaneous adipose formations were dispersed.

The gathering of males at Providence Bay noticed by W.S. Brooks on June 20 and 21, 1913, may be explained only as the summer flocking of nonpaired birds. The young male that I collected at Lawrence Bay on August 13, 1932, had fairly prominent testes 2 × 4 and 2 × 3 mm in size with subcutaneous adipose formations in whole patches.

August 31, 1935 was the very last date of sighting of a young godwit on St. Lawrence Island.

Habits—W.S. Brooks reported that a flock he noticed consisted of very confident birds. It was not just by chance that he bagged eight of them. In fact, the bar-tailed godwit permits the close approach of man, which is unusual for such a large bird. I am convinced of this especially after hunting the bird.

Food—The following items were found in the stomach: 1) Lawrence Bay, August 19, 1932. Heads of three caterpillars, 66 tiny molluscs and many tiny stones. 2) Uélen, June 4, 1934. Heads, breast and shards of a *Carabidae*, head, breast and shards of four *Scarabeidae*, two beetle larvae, seven larvae of dipterans, about 10 larvae of some unknown insects, four large seeds, shoots of moss and other plants, tiny rootlets and some small stones.

Economic importance—Being very rare, even such large waders as godwits and curlews, under the conditions of the Chukchi peninsula, must be excluded from the list of birds having any importance as food.

Systematics of the subspecies—I devoted a separate article (Portenko, 1936, pp. 194 to 197) to the subspecies *Limosa lapponica* (L.) and gave an outline in *Fauna of the Anadyr Region* (Portenko, 1939b, vol. I, p. 172). Since then there has been no criticism of the division of Russian bar-tailed godwits into three subspecies but objections were advanced against the new name. Nevertheless, there was no proof whatever that any of the old names was for certain a synonym of the form *L. lapponica menzbieri* that I had marked out. Therefore I consider myself justified in maintaining the division and the names suggested in my paper.

The bar-tailed godwits that I collected at Uélen and Lawrence Bay undoubtedly belong by color to the subspecies *L. lapponica baueri* Naum. H. Friedmann also placed the specimens from St. Lawrence Island among the subspecies *L. l. baueri* Naum. Though Friedmann was not then aware of *L. l. menzbieri* as I described it he pointed out that the specimens from St. Lawrence Island had a less whitish rump than a bird of the same age from Bol'shoi Baranov Kamen' available with him. I think it is most probable that this last specimen belonged to the subspecies *L. l. menzbieri*. Judging from the migratory birds collected in the Anadyr basin, *L. l. menzbieri* is found in the western part of the Chukchi peninsula.

Specimens— 1) Lawrence Bay, August 19, 1932, ♂, Portenko and 2) Uélen, June 4, 1934, ♀, Portenko.

Limosa limosa melanuroides Gould—**Black-tailed Godwit**

F.H. Fay and T.J. Cade (1959) cited a lone find of a blacktailed godwit for St. Lawrence Island. They had a good look at it with the binoculars on August 5, 1957, in the Boxer River valley.

60. **Limnodromus griseus scolopaceus** (Say)—**Dowitcher**

Distribution and status—Nests in the Chukchi peninsula but is distributed sporadically. At some places not so rare. Pairs evidently assembled for nesting found on Wrangel Island.

According to V.É. Yakobi, in 1961 the dowitcher was very common around

Uél'kal'. Four specimens were collected there. In the fall large flocks of young birds were seen. P.T. Butenko shot this wader on May 30, 1938, near Cape Stoletiya, Providence Bay.

On St. Lawrence Island the dowitcher is evidently not very rare in the breeding grounds. In 1937, according to H. Friedmann (1938), this sandpiper was collected for the first time, but F.H. Fay and T.J. Cade (1959) cite some very recent finds. An adult male was collected on May 30, 1953. A solitary bird and three separate pairs were noticed on June 22 and 23, 1954, on the Kuzata River. The dowitchers became very agitated when people searched for their nests. A brood was collected on August 14, 1957, at the western tip of the Kuzata lagoon; it comprised two adult birds and three young females. Pairs and small flocks were noticed there.

I saw some transitory birds on August 11, 1932, at Lawrence Bay around the cultural center. P.T. Butenko encountered three and shot two on the same day near the exit to the sea. V.V. Leonovich encountered this sandpiper there in June, 1970. On June 29, 1957, A.P. Kuzyakin put up three dowitchers on three occasions around Uélen (3 km to the south) and noticed a lone bird on the night of July 1/2. But I did not come across this sandpiper in 1932 or 1933 either at Uélen or in the interior of the peninsula along the Kol'oam- and Utte-Véem rivers. V.V. Leonovich noticed the dowitcher four times around Énurmino and even with a brood on July 5, 1970.

In 1879 the members of the *Vega* expedition collected two specimens near Kolyuchin Bay: a male on June 20 around Dzhenretlen and a female on June 23 around Pitlekai.

On the Amguema in 1956, in the vicinity of the 91st km, I found a dowitcher at three places where it no doubt nested. E.W. Nelson (1883, p. 85) writes that this sandpiper was found quite commonly at Cape Vankarém on August 6, 1881. In the summer of 1970 A.A. Kishchinskii found it common on the tundra from Vankarém to the estuary of the Amguema (Fig. 51). According to V.D. Lebedev and V.R. Filin (1959), the dowitcher was a fairly common breeding bird on the south coast of Aiok Island and on the western shore of Chaun Bay. It is particularly plentiful in the southeastern part of the island, where two males were obtained on June 10, 1958, and a downy chick on June 28. A male was shot on July 25 on the shores of Chaun Bay. Large flocks were noticed in the feeding areas at the exit of Malyi Chaun Strait, Chaun Bay.

On July 3, 1966, F.B. Chernyavskii found some pairs in the neighborhood of Bilibino, on the southwestern slopes of the north Anyui Range.

It is significant that toward the east, on the lower reaches of the Kolyma, this bird was not recorded either by S.A. Buturlin in 1905 or later by J. Koren. But in 1959, E.P. Spangenberg (1960) encountered nesting pairs north of Krai Lesov village down to the seacoast. Around Mikhalkino village, three to six nesting pairs were seen every kilometer or so. Clutches were gathered. In northeastern Yakutsk, according to K.A. Vorob'ev (1963), the dowitcher was common in the breeding grounds in the west up to the lower Yana. V.S. Zaletaev collected a solitary female on July 15 on the Anabar River in the neighborhood of Uryung-Khaya village.

Toward the south this bird is now found down to Koryatz Zemlya, where I saw it on the shore of Korf Bay.

On June 5, 1939, on Wrangel Island, somewhat east of Predatel'skaya Bay near Akatylanva, I encountered a pair of dowitchers of which the male was collected. The birds behaved as though they had been settled in the nesting territory right from arrival. In June, 1938, L.I. Leonov collected a female on Henrietta Island. Whether these cases represent migration or the vanguard of the species, gradually extending the limits of its range, or whether they are fairly constant in lesser known regions, is difficult to determine. It will not be without interest to add that on September 6, 1956, S.M. Uspenskii collected a young female from a brood on Bennet Island.

Habitat—At Lawrence Bay I came across dowitchers on the sandy bank of one of the innumerable lakelets. On Wrangel Island a pair of these sandpipers were enjoying a wet patch on the hummocky tundra, by a chain of lakelets separating the extensive spit from the mainland. Because of the snow thawing streams and rivulets were flowing through the hilly area, which was dotted with little puddles. The place was in many respects typical of the habitat of dowitchers in the general arctic environment.

Along the Amguema, in 1956, I came across a pair on a shallow lakelet overgrown with annual grass. In another case I saw a male on the wet, grassy marsh on the shore of a large lake. In yet another case I found the dowitcher on wet, marshy land with green grass. In a fourth case a sandpiper was attempting to settle on wet, marshy land with mud.

Near Uél'kal', V.É. Yakobi came across these dowitchers in dense grassy vegetation by a rivulet. A.P. Kuzyakin put them up around Uélen on marshy low-sedge tundra. On Aiok Island, V.D. Lebedev and V.R. Filin particularly noticed large numbers of dowitchers along the shores of shallow lakes. A downy chick was caught on the lake shore among flooded vegetation. Most of the flocks were feeding on the shoals along the western shore of Chaun Bay.

In the north Anyui Range F.B. Chernyavskii noticed pairs at the thin deciduous forest line on the tundra-like flat tops of hills. On the Kolyma, E.P. Spangenberg correctly pointed out that these sandpipers chose extensive depressed sections of the tundra abounding in shallow lakelets, while they needed for their nests relatively high dry grass on mounds out of the water.

Arrival—The dowitcher arrives in the last few days of May or early June, judging from the recorded dates: May 30, 1938, at Providence Bay; June 4, 1939, around Predatel'skaya Bay; May 30, 1953, on St. Lawrence Island; and May 19, 1957, on the lower Kolyma (Sudilovskaya, 1964).

Nidification—On the morning of June 4, 1939, on Wrangel Island I was still in my tent when I heard a bird call which was very similar to the chirping of the warbler-cricket. These notes reminded me of gurgling, which one could imitate with saliva bubbles behind the teeth. Children do such things and I at first thought, quite seriously, that it was the work of the eskimo children accompanying me. I hastily left the tent, gun in hand and saw a dowitcher slowly walking between the mounds, very much resembling the snipe in general behavior. Later I saw the second sandpiper. After some time one of them began flying behind the other without exhibiting any special urgency. The impression was that the breeding season had just begun for them. They fed at a distance from each other and their behavior was sluggish and monotonous. The left testis of the male collected was 8 × 6 mm in size. The right one was damaged by the shot. Subcutaneous fat was seen at some places. The testes of the male collected at Providence Bay on May 30 were 4 × 11 and 3 × 9 mm in size. The bird was devoid of adipose formations.

On June 18, 1956, on the Amguema, I collected a pair, probably in the nesting territory. The birds came so close that I could photograph them. Disturbed, they gave out a gentle "dzhzh" sound. On July 7, in another place, I came across what was evidently a male. It also permitted a close approach, within 25 paces. Later it began to run, finally took off with a loud cry and rose very high. Another day, in a third place, crossing a marsh that was the nesting habitat of the pectoral sandpiper, I came upon a solitary dowitcher. The bird gave out an anxious call and allowed me to photograph it from closer than 20 paces. Later, with the same call, it started up and flew away. In all three cases the behavior of these sandpipers showed a standard pattern but they did not reveal their nests.

In the north Anyui Range, on July 3, 1966, according to the observations of F.B. Chernyavskii, the dowitchers were flying restlessly and uttering loud trills as though they were raising young.

Migration—The dowitchers that I collected, evidently still in migration on August 19, 1932, were young females with filmy ovaries and insignificant subcutaneous adipose formations.

On August 17, 1961, O.I. Belogurov noticed large flocks of young dowitchers on the shores of Krest Bay, north of Uél'kal'. On August 14, 1957, on St. Lawrence Island, a brood not yet disbanded was collected.

Food—The following items were found in the stomachs of young birds from Lawrence Bay: 1) Six larvae of insects, fibers and threads of plant matter and amorphous mass, three seeds and many tiny stones. 2) Jaws and pieces of chitins of an unknown insect, many fibers and threads of plant matter, two tiny seeds and many small stones.

The Wrangel specimen showed nine caterpillars, a beetle of type *Poecilus* (tribe *Platysmatini*), twigs and shoots of moss and 0.25 g sand.

The weight of the male from Providence Bay was 94.5 g (sic).

Systematics—Specimens from northeast Asia belong to the subspecies *Limnodromus griseus scolopaceus* (Say), which differ distinctly from the nominal form *L. g. griseus* (Gm.) in the very dark color of the upper parts, especially in juveniles, and the large number of tiny speckles toward the bottom and along the sides of the body and finally in the much broader black bands on the rump. *L. g. scolopaceus* is also distributed in north Alaska and on the Mackenzie. American ornithologists are inclined to regard it even as a separate species, which I think is an exaggeration.

I was long interested in the genetic relations of dowitchers with true godwits and snipes. Some field observations in this respect are of interest. But for the color the dowitcher is very similar to the snipe in its general habits and behavior. It walks hunched and the beak is held downward, almost scraping the ground. It is also similar in flight; in particular, it descends headlong to the ground from a great height almost in a straight line. I was astonished at the similarity in the coloration of the chicks of dowitchers and snipes.

On Wrangel Island an inexperienced observer could at first mistake the dowitcher for the American knot abundant there. In adult plumage these two sandpipers somewhat resemble each other in color but the dowitcher is darker toward the top, more yellow toward the bottom, and in flight flashes a white patch on the back. The American knot is of heavier build, the feet thicker and the beak short (Fig. 53). Toward the back it is a much lighter gray; there is an orange shade ventrally. In flight, the back appears dark. The voices of these sandpipers are altogether different.

Fig. 53. Silhouettes of shorebirds similar in color: left—dowitcher *Limnodromus griseus* (Gm.) and right—American knot *Calidris canutus* (L.).

Specimens— 1 and 2) Lawrence Bay, August 19, 1932, ♀♀, 1° anno, Portenko; 3) Cape Stoletiya, Providence Bay, May 30, 1938, ♂, Butenko; and 4) Predatel'skaya Bay, June 4, 1939, ♂, Portenko.

61. **Gallinago gallinago gallinago** (L.)—**Common Snipe**

Distribution and status—Commonly nests in the interior of the Chukchi peninsula. Not found on Wrangel Island.

E.M. Meller collected a male in the watershed of the Amguema and Tadleo rivers on June 21, 1939. V.É. Yakobi came across a snipe on June 30, 1961, in the neighborhood of Uél'kal'. The bird flew away, but not far off, and later returned to its original place. Others, too, noticed it several times, so evidently it colonized there. V.V. Leonovich heard the calling of the snipe on June 4, 1970, around Lawrence Bay.

In the interior of the Chukchi peninsula the snipe is not rare. On July 6, 1934, I came across some on the lower reaches of the Utte-Véem River. In the summer of 1956, according to my observations, there were a fairly large number of them in the nesting area along the Amguema by the 91st km. Evidently this species was noticed by V.D. Lebedev and V.R. Filin (1959) on June 6 and 14, 1958, on the southwest coast of Aiok Island. J. Koren did not find snipes on the north coast of the Chukchi peninsula but gathered three clutches on the lower Kolyma (Schaanning, 1954).

Habitat—On the lower reaches of the Utte-Véem River, I came across snipes in the wet meadow tundra, on sizable marshy areas beside the water and on the network of lakes and cut-off meanders. On the Amguema, snipes were confined to the flood plains, islets and wet tundra far from the river, selecting places where there was plenty of grass and water. Around the marsh the birds would often sit on different elevations and dry sections. Several times I roused snipes on the road where the track was filled with water. Under the conditions of the spacious tundra they often remained altogether in the open, neither hiding nor blending into the background.

Nidification—Many snipes nested along the Amguema. They led a very active life, being even more noticeable than other waders. Their cry "chakí, chakí, chakí" or "kuchí, kuchí, kuchí" was often heard, especially in cloudy weather.

The morning of June 10, 1956, was cold, like the end of winter but not the beginning of spring. Toward evening a storm broke. When clouds appeared the snipes began flying and the cry "chakí" was heard. On June 11, walking along the bank of the Amguema, I heard an incessant trill: "chi-chi-chi-chi". A snipe started up from the marshy ground. It spread its wings in a characteristic way and appeared to be sometimes limping, at other times injured. Later a second snipe started up with the cry "kuchí-kuchí" but because it was blowing hard it immediately settled again. This pair could hardly have had a nest but the birds exhibited a clear affinity to the nesting area.

On June 13 the weather was sunny and mild. At 10 a.m. it was +8°C, rising to +10.5°C by midday; in a meltwater pool the water warmed up to +13.5°C. The snipes cried little but later many were calling, sometimes with a kind of bleat. Rising to a great height, a bird would hover for an instant, spread its tail and quickly flap its wings, which generated a trembling sound resembling a bleat.

The testes of a male collected on June 14 were enlarged: 5 × 13 and 6 × 10 mm. The subcutaneous fat was seen as filmy formations. The call of only one snipe was heard because of the high wind.

On June 18 the cloud cover varied and it was windy at midday. The temperature rose to +17°C. Later there was a slight drizzle. The snipes were calling the whole day, most often at a very great height. Many were flying without the "bleat". Some "lay" on one wing, i.e. banked sideways, slowing down and changing direction, sometimes with a "bleat".

June 24 was a sunny, slightly windy day; the day temperature was +16°C. A calling snipe was noticed; the female on the ground beneath was rapidly calling "chak-chak-chak-chak".

There was a warm south wind on June 28. During the day the temperature was +21°C and in the evening +12.5°C. There were clouds, it became breezy, and the first mosquitoes appeared. The snipes were sometimes calling and flying but I did not hear the "bleat". The female was crying.

July 4 was cloudy, with a good wind which had dropped by evening, and the mosquitoes appeared. Real summer weather had set in. The tundra turned green; the leaves quickly came out after the rain. The calls of snipes were heard only from time to time.

On July 5 there was a north wind. The afternoon temperature was only +13°C. In the evening two snipes were flying over the island at a great height, making the "bleat".

On July 6, after a storm with rain and thunder, a snipe was crying "chiki-chiki-chiki" . . . on the marsh.

On July 7, I encountered a snipe in the mud on the road. It was loudly crying "k'ekh, k'ekh, k'ekh" . . . or "chakh, chakh, chakh". Snipes were flying every now and then, within sight, or remained concealed in the grass and shrubs or between the mounds. This strange behavior was probably due to the presence of chicks.

On July 8, not far from the nest of a pectoral sandpiper, I heard the cry of a snipe. When I drew close the bird flew close by, turning from side to side and raising its wings high. I remained for 10 more days on the Amguema but heard no more the call of the snipe.

On July 6, 1934, on the lower reaches of the Utte-Véem River, snipes were much excited by the appearance of my party: they cried often but were very wary.

Food—The stomach of a specimen collected by E.M. Meller showed some leaflets of birch and tiny stones.

Systematics of the subspecies—The specimen from Pereval'naya belongs to the light type of coloration that prompted S.A. Buturlin to isolate the subspecies *Gallinago gallinago raddei*. The auxiliary feathers have dark, narrow bars which widen into broad feather tips (Fig. 54). The ocherous zones on the upper side of the body are very light-colored. Since the light-colored specimens are also encountered in the European USSR, I find it difficult to recognize the form *raddei* as a subspecies. In the color of the upper parts the specimen from the 91st km is very similar to the preceding specimen but the auxiliary feathers have fairly broad uninterrupted bars.

Neither specimen has the smallest resemblance to the American subspecies *G. g. delicata* (Ord.), which is distinguished by the broad, black transverse bars on the auxiliary feathers (Fig. 54), sharper barring on the under parts, and some other color details.

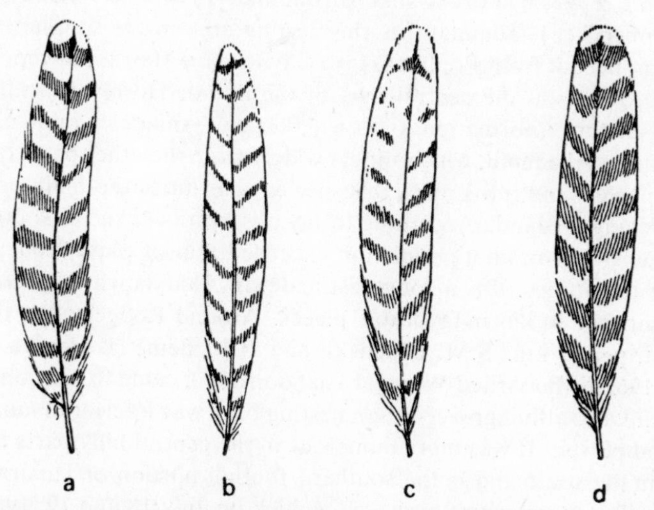

Fig. 54. Auxiliaries in subspecies of common snipes *Gallinago gallinago gallinago* (L.): a—from Kuibyshev region; b—from Pereval'naya; c—from 91st km and d—*G. g. delicata* (Ord.) from America.

The American snipe is therefore not encountered in the USSR. It forms a good subspecies, but nothing more.

Specimens— 1) Pereval'naya, June 21, 1939, ♂, Meller and 2) Amguema River, 91st km, June 14, 1956, ♂, Portenko.

62. **Calidris canutus rogersi** (Mathews)—**American Knot**

Distribution and status—Very rare in flight in the Chukchi peninsula. Numerous in the breeding area on Wrangel Island, being one of the common birds on the island.

Some records are known from the Chukchi coast but only of young birds in fall flight. On August 6, 1932, I noticed two young birds in the neighborhood of Notapenmen village, on the shores of Krest Bay. In the collection of the Institute of Zoology, Academy of Sciences of the USSR, there is a young preserved bird collected somewhere in the Chukchi peninsula by I.N. Akif'ev. Judging from the other, better-dated specimens in its collections, it may be assumed that it was collected at Cape Chaplin, Providence Bay or Lawrence Bay. In an article by B. Conovre (1943) it may be seen that specimens from Cape Chaplin were available in American museums. I.G. Voznesenskii collected three migratory specimens in Mechigmensk Gulf. I did not encounter a single bird near Uélen; nor did the *Vega* expedition find any around Kolyuchin Bay. Copley Amory (Riley, 1918) acquired a young female on August 17, 1914, at Chaun Bay.

While processing the material gathered by V.F. Vlasova and A.I. Mineev (Portenko, 1937b) I confirmed the nidification of the American knot in large numbers on Wrangel Island. Based on my own observations, I can now say that this shorebird is one of the common, characteristic elements of the island's fauna. According to a report by G.A. Ushakov (Bannikov, 1941) it is found on the island in large numbers. It is abundant in the nesting area in the southern half of the island and I noticed it from Predatel'skaya Bay to Cape Hawaii; as reported by A.I. Mineev, it also nests in the central part of the island. However, no hunter could provide satisfactory information as to whether the American knot nested in the north, in Tundra Akademii, which differs widely from the other parts of the island. Along with plovers and turnstones, this species constitutes the main population of waders on Wrangel Island. According to my observations, in the southern part of the island the American knot population exceeded that of plovers but was smaller than that of turnstones. On a rough estimate, in Akatylanva the nesting density was a few pairs per sq km in favorable places. Around Rodgers Bay there was at least one pair per sq km. S.M. Uspenskii and R.L. Bëme (Uspenskii, Bëme, and Velizhanin, 1962), who visited Wrangel Island in 1960, came to the conclusion that the American knot, although a common nesting bird, was inferior in numbers to the turnstone and plover. It was more numerous in the central hilly parts of the island and less so in the south and in the southern foothill portion of Tundra Akademii. R.L. Bëme collected two adult birds and a chick on July 18 and 19, 1960 (Sudilovskaya, 1964) in the valley of the Mamontovaya River. A.G. Velizhanin (1965) arrived at a somewhat different assessment. According to him the American knot was particularly abundant on the south coast, from Rodgers Bay to Somnitel'naya Bay.

Habitat—The American knot selects nesting sites on the patchy rubbled tundra so characteristic of the topography of the arctic wastelands of Wrangel Island. It prefers dry, rubbled, grassy or hummocky areas. I found a nest once on the rubbled upper zone of the watershed ridge separating the Mamontovaya River from the coastal belt of the tundra about 200 m above sea level. I found another nest on the flank of Cape Proletarskii (near Wolfson's grave) on flat rubbled areas 30 to 40 m from the coastal cliffs. I also found broods on rubbled sections of the tundra intersected by streams or ridges overgrown with grass. Right from their arrival the American knots settled on large thawed patches. In early June I noticed how recently arrived waders gathered in the warmest part of the day on the pebbled spit warmed up by the sun and caught insects. At other times, they foraged in the valleys of rivulets. I never saw them on the seashore on Wrangel but encountered migratory young birds near Notapenmen on the shores of Krest Bay.

Arrival—G.A. Ushakov noticed the arrival on May 27, 1928, and May 30, 1929. According to the observations of V.F. Vlasova, this sandpiper arrived on Wrangel Island in the last 10 days of May. In the spring of 1939 I made daily observations of arriving birds and noticed the first American knots only on June 2 at Akatylanva. From morning they began to be seen in flocks which toward the end of the day were already breaking up into pairs. On June 8 I saw four flying knots. Probably they were the last birds arriving.

Nidification—Calling began immediately on arrival on a mass scale and was very typical. The male would rise from the ground along an inclined path, fluttering the wings and resembling very much the calling snipe. Later it would soar on its wings and begin to utter "ku-u-géee . . . ku-uuu-géee . . . " Finally it would slowly descend holding its wings like a bow and emitting a different call—"k'u-yu" or "k'u-gu". The calls varied from bird to bird; for example, I often heard some calling "ku-u-géee" and others calling "k'u-u". The notes are very pleasant to the ear and gentle; they can be heard from a distance. The calls represent the most beautiful phenomenon in the life of the Wrangel tundra and the notes of the multitude of birds are an important element in the overall picture of the arctic summer.

In the first half of June the calling was accompanied by different degrees of activity, depending on the weather and the onset of the laying season. In foggy weather, on June 5, it was very intense but noticeably quieted down toward June 11 and 12. Right from their arrival the American knots were very wary and flew far off on my approaching. Later they began occupying the nesting territories. With the snow thawing in the interior of the island many birds flew away far from the coast. Even on the second day the knots would permit a closer approach and would return to the place where they had been disturbed. But in general they were very mobile, flew from place to place and very often chased one another. On June 5, I noticed a lone knot sitting on a heap; evidently the other member of the pair was already busy at the nest. Freshly scraped pits for the nests were found in considerable numbers. The birds would hollow out many pits before they occupied any.

Special searches for nests were unsuccessful. On June 11 I came upon a nest by chance. The sitting bird fluttered out a few paces in front of me. It ran bent to the ground, ruffled and disheveled its feathers and scraped the rubble with its tail like the *Calidris tenuirostris* that I saw in the Anadyr region. It ran on ahead of me like that without turning for about 200 m and I cannot say how far it would have led me away if I had not turned aside. The nest was in the form of a circular pit in moss and rubble. In it there were three eggs of a greenish color with smeared brownish patches.

F.B. Chernyavskii (1967) also observed that the American knot did not attack an enemy approaching the nest but sat it out fairly firmly, finally trying to lead the intruder away. On June 12 I witnessed copulation. The male held the female standing on her legs. In a female which was fatally wounded a large mass of yolk appeared in the cloaca during the death throes. At that time the clutches of knots were still incomplete.

The knots caught at the time of arrival were distinguished by plumpness and appreciable subcutaneous adipose formations. As an exception, one female was very emaciated, but another was compactly covered with adipose formations. At the end of June and especially in early July, I began noticing a deterioration in the conditions of birds and a diminution in the adipose layers.

The testes began to shrink following mating. The diameters of left testes varied in the range 10–13 × 5–9 mm. They were already reduced on June 8 to 7–9 × 4–7 mm; the diameters of right testes varied in the range 6–10 × 4–7 mm and fell to 6–7 × 3–4 mm. In one male collected on June 5 the diameters of the testes were 8 × 18 mm (left) and 7 × 8 mm (right). In a male collected on July 22 they were only 3 × 4 and 2 × 2 mm.

The ovary length in the female before laying reached 15 to 17 mm and the diameter of the biggest follicle 3 to 6 mm. In the females collected on June 5 the ovary length was 25 mm and the diameter of the biggest follicle 24 mm. This specimen differed from the others in having a continuous layer of subcutaneous fat. As could be seen from the condition of the gonads in the females collected, they had already laid eggs on June 11 and 12. In the females collected on July 2 the ovary length was only 8 to 11 mm and the diamater of the biggest follicle 2 to 3 mm. These measurements were taken in 25 birds.

A.I. Mineev found a nest with a full clutch at Rodgers Bay at the end of June, 1934 (Fig. 52). A nest detected on the coastal tundra in southeastern Wrangel Island on June 26, 1931, contained only two eggs, possibly of a second clutch. The bird killed at the nest was a male. Add to this the fact that A.A. Byalynitskii-Birulya killed males in all three of the nests he found in Novosibirsk and it can be concluded that the eggs are incubated and the chicks reared mainly by the males in *C. canutus*. But G.A. Ushakov was certain that both males and females incubated the eggs.

According to Ushakov the American knot chicks emerged by July 10. Chicks foraging independently were collected on July 16, 1927. Toward the end of June, 1939, I found American knots on Wrangel quite rarely, which is explained by the onset of the incubation period. Up to July 10 the cry "kuu-geee" could be heard sometimes. When I was walking across the tundra knots sometimes flew at me. On July 9 I came across a nest with four tiny downy chicks. The parent bird took off from the nest and crept on its belly right under my eyes. Ruffling up its feathers, it chirped and flew away. The following day it was leading the chicks. On July 11 I came across two broods in the nesting areas. I could not find the chicks. In one case a lone adult and in another two adults were very agitated, flew low over the ground as though they were under fire, ran, bent down, cried "kvi-kvi" and even tried to produce the mating call. On July 14 and 15, on an automobile trip from Rodgers Bay to Somnitel'naya Bay, I saw quite a number of broods. The downy chicks in some of them had reached one-half the size of the adults. Their flight feathers were already growing. On July 22 I saw only a few American knots. Some were still uneasy as when they were with broods: flying close, later fleeing and crying "kvi-kvi". I saw only two of them on July 24. For the last time, I saw a flying flock of six broods on August 2. They were flying in a flock following some plovers which were flying in circles overhead. They cried "kvi-kvi". The flight feathers were not completely grown in the young migrating bird that I shot. The downy cover remained around the beak and especially on the forehead. On settling the brood remained in the company of the plovers.

S.M. Uspenskii and his colleagues noticed broods of nonflying chicks from July 17 through 22, 1960, together with two old birds.

Migration—The American knot leaves Wrangel Island very early, at the end of July and not later than the first few days of August. In 1939 it flew away after only a two-month stay on the island. In 1938, I did not come across a single knot for the simple reason that I arrived on Wrangel Island very late, on August 8. According to the observations of A.G. Velizhanin, in 1960 the migration concluded in the first half of August. A.I. Mineev pointed out quite correctly that American knots did not form flocks before migration and dispersed imperceptibly. But he rather erroneously thought that these knots migrated after the geese.

At Chaun Bay a juvenile female was shot on August 17, 1914. In Mechigmensk Gulf I.G. Voznesenskii collected young birds on August 8 and 11, 1843. In Notapenmen I noticed them on August 6, 1932. The adults evidently isolated themselves from the juveniles and flew away a few days ahead.

Food—An examination of the stomachs of Wrangel specimens revealed very similar contents.

1) June 3, 1939. Caterpillar, ground-up plant remains, and 3 g coarse sand. 2) June 4, 1939. Remains of *Trichoptera* larvae, ground-up plant parts, 0.75 g coarse sand and three feathers, probably its own. 3) June 4, 1939. Much digested remains of insects and 2 g coarse sand. 4) June 6, 1939. Five larvae of *Trichoptera* and 1 g quartz sand. 5) June 5, 1939. Much digested remains of caddis worm and 1 g coarse sand. 6) June 8, 1939. Twenty-two *Diptera* (*Nemotocera*) larvae, *Chrysomela* beetle and 10 other tiny beetles. 7) June 11, 1939. Twenty-four caterpillars, 20 shells of *Cumacea* and 3 g coarse sand. 8) June 11, 1939. Gruel of indeterminate mass and 1 g sand. 9) April 12, 1939. Ground-up remains and 4 g coarse-grained sand. 10) June 12, 1939. Seven larvae of *Chrysomela* beetles, 10 caddis worms and 3 g coarse sand. 11) June 12, 1939. Ground-up remains of tiny insects, belly of *Staphylinidae* and 3 g coarse sand. 12) June 26, 1939. Two *Chrysomela* beetles with a mass of eggs ready for laying, remnants of tiny insects, 10 branchlets and shoots, 2 g coarse-grained sand. 13) July 2, 1939. *Chrysomela* beetle, unidentifiable insect mass, plant shoots and 2 g coarse-grained sand. 14) July 2, 1939. Remains of tiny

Tipulidae, caterpillar, plant shoots and 1 g coarse sand. 15) July 2, 1939. Intensely ground mass of tiny insects and 1.5 g coarse sand. 16) July 2, 1939. Remains of a large number of *Diptera* (*Dolychopodidae*) and about 30 grains of coarse (3 to 5 mm) sand. 17) July 2, 1939. Ground-up remains of tiny insects and plants and 2 g coarse sand. 18) July 22, 1939. About 15 much digested larvae of insects and 2 g coarse sand. 19) August 2, 1939. Much digested remains of *Chrysomela* beetles and caterpillars and 3 g coarse sand.

Economic importance—As a medium-sized wader, the American knot could be of interest to hunters but under Wrangel conditions hunting should be prohibited in order to conserve the fauna. Along with other waders they and especially their young are quite often food for the polar fox. This aspect need not be seriously taken note of if the fox population is controlled.

Systematics of the subspecies—A good series of American knots that I gathered on Wrangel Island allows me to enlarge slightly on the notes on systematics to be found in my *Fauna of the Anadyr Region* (Portenko, 1939b, vol. I, pp. 202 and 203).

In the revision of the subspecies of American knot in his paper B. Conover (1943) described the form *C. c. rogersi* as untenable. He had no specimens from Wrangel, let alone a good series, and it is entirely natural that he could not determine the characteristics of the endemic Wrangel race. The subspecies given below differ clearly but some birds were identified only after recognizing the form in a series. Individual variation is quite appreciable. In summer dress it is manifest in different intensities of the rust shade toward the bottom, the belly and the undertail coverts. Toward the top the development of ocherous patches varies widely. They are altogether absent in some cases while in others the spread of ocherous patches leads to the predominance of a yellow coloration on the upper parts. In females, more often than in males, there are some white feathers with brown edges or color mixtures toward the bottom. Quite often the belly and the undertail coverts are more variegated. The females are somewhat bigger than the males. Evidently the upper wing coverts are darker in older birds.

The American knot is an arctic, high latitude species with nearly circumpolar distribution. Three distinctly discernible subspecies could be classified into two groups: the more rufous *C. c. canutus* and the much lighter *C. c. rogersi* and *C. c. rufa*, which are more grayish-white dorsally. On Wrangel Island there is a form similar to the American form representing the endemic population of Wrangel Island. In some respects it exhibits transition features to the typical form.

1) **Calidris canutus canutus** (L.)—In the typical American knot the dark coloration is more toward the top due to the very narrow fringes of and patches on the feathers. A slightly greenish shade is characteristic of the black color. The fringes and patches are rusty-ocherous and fade into a pale ocher. The rusty shade extends far down the back from the bottom and sides. The underparts are more intensely colored. The differences are best seen in a series: the growth of the black and rust shades on the upper part of the body. Their size is smaller than that of others (Table 38).

Distribution within the USSR—Taimir and Novosibirsk Island; seen in flight sporadically and more or less rarely along all the Baltic Sea coast to Okhotsk. I had no occasion to examine specimens from Greenland and Spitsbergen. According

Table 38. Length of beaks and wings of American knot subspecies, cm

Subspecies	Bill length along cord				Wing length with Vernier callipers			
	Max.	Min.	Mean	No. of samples	Max.	Min.	Mean	No. of samples
				Males				
C. c. canutus (L.)	3.56	2.92	3.18	16	16.42	15.05	15.86	16
C. c. rogersi (Mathews)	3.98	3.11	3.51	20	17.09	16.06	16.58	20
C. c. rufa (Wilson)	—	—	3.62	1	—	—	15.22	1
				Females				
C. c. canutus (L.)	3.32	3.31	3.31	2	16.25	15.75	16.00	2
C. c. rogersi (Mathews)	3.84	3.13	3.54	13	17.59	16.24	16.85	15
C. c. rufa (Wilson)	—	—	3.87	1	—	—	17.14	1

to B. Conover the range of this subspecies begins in the west from northwestern Greenland.

2) **Calidris canutus rogersi** (Mathews)—In summer plumage, the upper parts appear more variegated, whitish-gray with black and ocherous-patches, fading to a pure white. These patches are quite often big and round. The fringes and color mixtures are broader. The underside is a lighter yellow-brick red color. In the series the subspecies is very well distinguished by more grayish and white tones on the upper parts. The size is greater. It nests on Wrangel Island; going by the specimens examined, this form is seen in flight over the Chukchi and Anadyr coasts, on the coasts of the Okhotsk Sea and in Shanghai. B. Conover classified the specimens from Alaska, especially from Cape Barrow, not among *C. c. rufa,* but among *C. c. canutus,* regarding them as transitory between the Siberian and American races. Therefore the possibility is not excluded of the inclusion of arctic Alaska in the range of *C. c. rogersi.*

3) **Calidris canutus rufa** (Wilson). Even paler toward the top, the black and ocherous coloration being less, and paler toward the bottom, than the others. The juveniles are also light-colored. It belongs to arctic America and only to arctic Canada according to B. Conover.

Specimens— 1) Mechigmensk Gulf, August 8, 1843, ♀, 1° anno, Voznesenskii; 2 and 3) same place, August 11, 1843, ♂♀, 1° anno, Voznesenskii; 4) Chukchi peninsula without date, ○, 1° anno, Akif'ev; 5) southeastern Wrangel Island, June 3, 1931, ♀, Vlasova; 6) Rodgers Bay, June 11, 1931, ♀, Vlasova; 7) same place, July 19, 1931, ♂, Vlasova; 8 to 25) Akatylanva, June 2, 3, 4, 5, 8, 11 and 12, 1939, 12 ♂♂ and 8 ♀♀, Portenko; 26) Rodgers Bay, June 26, 1939, ♂, Portenko; 27 to 31) neighborhood of Rodgers Bay, July 2, 1939, ♂♂ and 3 ♀♀, Portenko; 32) same place, July 22, 1939, ♂, Portenko; and 39) neighborhood of Atternon hills, August 2, 1939, juv., Portenko.

Biological collection—Clutch of two eggs, southeastern Wrangel Island, June 26, 1931, Vlasova.

63. **Calidris tenuirostris** (Horsf.)—**Eastern Knot**

Very rare, evidently nests in the Alpine Zone of hills in the western part of the Chukchi peninsula.

Only one observation is known. On June 20, 1956, I saw a pair of big waders above the knolls north of the Amguema at the 91st km. They were flying high with faint whistling calls. Though I saw them clearly with the binoculars I was somewhat doubtful. In the years following I became acquainted with this bird in greater detail under the conditions of the Koryatz uplands and my doubts were dispelled.

64. **Erolia ferruginea** (Pontopp.)—**Curlew-Sandpiper**

Local name—For the birds of the Trans-Lena region A.I. Argentov (1861a) gave the name "red-breasted sandpiper" and in Chukchian imchinvychan. But he had no direct reference to show that the name pertained to the curlew-sandpiper or that it inhabited the Trans-Lena region that we are concerned with.

Distribution and status—Found in the nesting area in the western section of the north coast of the Chukchi peninsula.

I never came across the curlew-sandpiper. T.A. Bostrem, the hunter[1], collected the male of a pair near Dzhenretlen on June 10, 1879. It was the only record made by the *Vega* expedition for Kolyuchin Bay (Palmén, 1887). According to V.M. Artobolevskii (1927, p. 43, second note) A.A. Savich's collections contained a specimen of the curlew-sandpiper whose locality could not be ascertained. The bird was collected somewhere on the coast at Cape Schmidt or in the Kolyma estuary. V.D. Lebedev and V.R. Filin (1959) noticed innumerable pairs on southwestern Aiok Island on June 6, 1958. Two males were obtained on June 6 and 20. To the west of Chaun Bay reliable records were made by J. Koren (Thayer and Bangs, 1914). From July 16 through 18, 1912, he came across some nesting curlew-sandpipers 40 miles east of Bol'shoi Baranov Kamen'. On July 12 he found a brood in the valley 30 miles east of the same cape. On the lower Kolyma, according to S.A Buturlin (1906b), the curlew-sandpiper was very common in spring flight in 1905. In 1912 J. Koren also daily noticed many curlew-sandpipers in spring flight on the lower Kolyma. He collected a series of eight males and two females in 1918 (Schaanning, 1954).

The curlew-sandpiper is not found on Wrangel Island.

The eastern limit of the distribution of the curlew-sandpiper is no longer enigmatic. In 1962 nidification was established by R.T. Holmes and F.A. Pitelka (1964) at Cape Barrow, northern Alaska, where two nests with clutches were found.

Habitat—J. Koren found the curlew-sandpiper east of Baranov Kamen', in one case in a valley and in another on rocky tundra.

Arrival—The observations on June 10, 1879, at Dzhenretlen and on June 6, 1958, on Aiok Island pertained to the migratory period. In 1905, S.A. Buturlin saw the spring flight of the curlew-sandpiper from May 28 through June 2 on the lower

[1]In the monograph by E.V. Kozlova (1962, p. 95) the record by Bostrem was erroneously ascribed to S.A. Buturlin.

Kolyma. J. Koren witnessed their migration on the lower Kolyma in 1912 from May 29 until the opening up of the river. In 1918 he acquired a series of migrating specimens on May 30.

Nidification—On July 12, 1912, J. Koren came across two downy chicks aged six days accompanied by females. One-fourth of a mile away he sighted a pomarine jaeger which had probably caused some damage to the brood. As a result the curlew-sandpiper kept rushing at the marauder and flying around squawking. From July 16 through 18 Koren again found nesting curlew-sandpipers 10 miles to the east but did not see chicks, which were probably grown up enough to hide in the grass.

Food—According to O. Nordquist the male obtained at Dzhenretlen was a plump bird whose stomach contained the larvae of driftwood beetles.

Systematics—Thirty years ago J.E. Thayer and O. Bangs came to the conclusion that the European curlew-sandpipers were indistinguishable from the Asiatic; they compared not only birds in summer plumage but also young ones and ones in winter dress. I made a similar comparison in 1936 and 1945 and came to the same conclusion.

65. **Pelidna alpina sakhalina** (Vieill.)

66. **Pelidna alpina pacifica** (Coues)—**Dunlin**

Local name—Chukchian: Taràsel'khyn, saráasyn and bèkasyl'gyn (from the Russian) for all small waders; tscharykodlin for all waders according to the records of the *Vega* expedition. In Eskimo: Dră-drā'-yŭk on St. Lawrence Island.

Distribution and status—Breeds in the Chukchi peninsula more or less everywhere and represents the most common species of breeding waders; however, not plentiful in any one place. Breeds on Wrangel Island but in small numbers.

The dunlin is common on the shores of Krest Bay. On June 8, 1956, I came across a calling male near Égvekinot. According to the observations of V.É. Yakobi, in 1961 this species was the most plentiful wader around Uél'kal'. A nest was found and mass flight was noticed in the fall.

L.O. Belopol'skii (1933 and 1934) saw the dunlin many times on the tundra near Krest Bay. On August 6, 1932, I found these birds common in the neighborhood of Notapenmen village.

The dunlin has been collected many times in Providence Bay. A specimen joined Capt. Moore's small collection (Harting, 1871) made in the summer of 1849, if not at Providence Bay, somewhere farther along the seacoast toward Lawrence Bay. T.H. Bean (1883, p. 165) collected four specimens on August 13, 1880, at Plover Bay. É.E. Arngol'd shot two adult dunlins, a male and a female, on July 16, 1912, at Providence Bay but, according to the accession register of the Zoological Museum of the Academy of Sciences of the USSR, for 1913, under No. 488, the specimens were destroyed because of poor preservation. In June, 1913, W.S. Brooks (1915) found this species rare at Providence Bay. According to I.O. Olenev dunlins nested at Providence Bay in small numbers. In 1932 he found clutches and chicks. On July 12, 1938, I came across a nesting pair north of Cape Stoletiya. In the same year P.T. Butenko collected a good series in spring and fall flights. In 1957 A.P. Kuzyakin toured the Providence Bay shoreline from June 9 through 18 but did not find the dunlin even once.

On August 18 and 20, 1938, P.T. Butenko obtained some specimens at Cape Chaplin.

On St. Lawrence Island the dunlin was common in the breeding grounds and specimens were collected many times. It was found common even by E.W. Nelson (1883, p. 88). E.G. Harriman's expedition (Friedmann, 1932a) got there three specimens on July 13, 1899. In the last few days of June, 1913, W.S. Brooks saw dunlins on the island but no specimens were taken. Finally, in the first week of July, 1921, A.M. Bailey (1926) noticed some pairs. The dunlins no doubt nested since the gonads in the dissected specimens turned out to be well-developed. O.J. Murie (1936) collected a male on August 17, 1935, at Savunga village and three more males and two females on August 27 of the same year at Kukuliak village. In the years 1950 through 1957 during F.H. Fay and T.J. Cade's fieldwork (1959) the dunlin was the most common wader on the island. In June, 1950, about a dozen pairs were based at Lake Trautman; there were more of them than dotterels or turnstones. At Cape Chibukak six nests were located in an area of about one-half of a square mile. This species was also common at Boxer Bay. On the south coast flocks of 75 to 100 birds gathered in fall flight at the end of August. According to the observations of E.G.F. Sauer and E.K. Urban (1964), in the neighborhood of Boxer Bay the dunlin was perhaps the most common of all the waders in 1960. They found seven nests with clutches. During migrations beginning in mid-July and August on the shores of bays, flocks comprising 20 to 30 birds each were commonly seen.

J. Cassin (1863, p. 322) writes about the specimens taken in August, 1855, in Senyavin Strait. In the collection of the Institute of Zoology, Academy of Sciences of the USSR, there is a specimen collected by I.G. Voznesenskii on August 10, 1843, in Mechigmensk Gulf. On August 19, 1932, I found this shorebird in large numbers on the south shore of Lawrence Bay. Two specimens from there obtained on July 29 and 30, 1948, were given to the Moscow Zoological Museum by V.N. Lyubin. In 1970 V.V. Leonovich also found them quite common there.

According to the observations of A.P. Kuzyakin, in 1957 the dunlin was found everywhere from Akkani to Uélen and was uniformly distributed in distinct pairs. On any 2 to 3 km long stretch of grassy tundra at least one pair could be found. Nevertheless, it was somewhat inferior in numbers to the purple sandpiper. A nest was found between Lawrence village and Yandagai.

On August 13, 1932, I found a brood near Dezhnev settlement. In June, 1913, according to W.S. Brooks, dunlins were very common on the low tundra near East Cape, i.e. evidently near Uélen; specimens were also collected. I studied this part of the Chukchi peninsula better than others but did not find the dunlins particularly numerous anywhere. On August 15, 1932, I found them in large numbers while crossing the tundra from Dezhnev settlement to Uélen and back. In the summer of 1934, according to my observations, dunlins nested in small numbers in the immediate vicinity of Uélen. They were seen more often in flight but I did not see in the Chukchi peninsula the huge gathering of thousands of flocks that I saw at

Zhilovaya Koshka in the Anadyr estuary. According to the observations of A.P. Kuzyakin, in 1957, between the knolls and the lagoon south of Uélen, the dunlin was so common that at least two or three pairs nested per sq km.

On Bol'shoi Diomede Island the dunlin did not breed because of the absence of suitable nesting sites. On Malyi Diomede, K.W. Kenyon (Kenyon and Brooks, 1960) noticed stray birds in spring flight; on May 20, 1958, one landed on the drift ice two miles east of the island. Another was noticed on May 30, also on the ice by the coastal cliffs on the south coast. Finally, on June 1 a male feeding by the water among rocks and snow was collected.

On the Kol'oam-Véem River, I happened to come across broods and flocks even in the post-breeding period. Dunlins were not uncommon along the Utte-Véem River in the breeding areas. From July 6 through 12, 1934, I saw only three birds which may be explained by the fact that dunlins avoid nesting in riverine areas. On July 21, on my way from Inchoun to Uélen, I came across them in smaller numbers than the purple sandpipers, running over the grassy elevated tundra.

At Cape Serdtse-Kamen' J. Koren (Thayer and Bangs, 1914) collected two young birds on August 23, 1911. He came to the conclusion that the dunlin was positively a rare bird found only at certain places on the arctic coast of the Chukchi Peninsula. But according to F.S. Hersey (1916), who visited the Chukchi coast at Lawrence Bay, Cape Dezhnev and Cape Serdtse-Kamen' in the summer of 1914, dunlins were abundant. W.S. Brooks found this species very common at Cape Serdtse-Kamen' in mid-July, 1913. According to the observations of V.V. Leonovich, in the summer of 1970 this wader was common in Énurmino. At Kolyuchin Bay, near the winter halt of the *Vega* (Palmén, 1887), dunlins were seen in fairly large flocks from June 12 through 21, 1879. On June 12 T.A. Bostrem shot nine birds from a flock consisting of 13 dunlins and one turnstone at Dzhenretlen. During E. Almquist's journey to Kolyuchin Bay from June 13 through 17 it was explained that this wader along with the Lapland longspur was the commonest of birds. However, near the winter halt of the *Vega*, toward the end of June and during July, the dunlin was no longer observed. In the interior of the Chukchi peninsula on the Amguema, according to my observations, dunlins were very common in the breeding grounds in 1956. While they were calling from June 10 through 16 they were numerous and exceeded other waders in numbers. But as soon as the clutches were laid the dunlins became less noticeable. On June 30 I encountered some. I recorded in my diary that this bird was common but not numerous. On July 7 I noticed that they were few and relatively rare. On July 10 and 11 chicks began emerging and the dunlins again began to be seen as a common species.

According to E.W. Nelson, wherever the *Corwin* expedition landed on the Chukchi coast in the summer of 1881 the dunlin was found to be numerous; on August 7 specimens were collected at Cape Vankarém. In the summer of 1970 A.A. Kishchinskii found this shorebird common in the breeding grounds everywhere from Vankarém to the Amguema estuary. Clutches and broods were found. According to V.D. Lebedev and V.R. Filin (1959), the dunlin was rare on Aiok Island. A female was collected on June 20, 1958, and a male on June 23.

For the Trans-Lena region, A.I. Argentov (1861a) cited a "black-cropped sandpiper with a white neck". S.A. Buturlin (1906b, p. 7) found a few dunlins on the lower reaches of the Kolyma in spring flight but did not find them at all in the breeding ground even in the fall. On June 8, 1912, J. Koren collected three males and a female on the lower Kolyma on May 30, 1918 (Schaanning, 1954).

Before my journey to Wrangel Island the dunlin had not been mentioned by any one for that island. Based exclusively on the material gathered by A.I. Mineev and V.F. Vlasova, I at first assumed (Portenko, 1937b) that the absence of the dunlin from the breeding grounds was a zoogeographic feature of Wrangel Island. Later I found it in the breeding area, where it was not very rare though not plentiful. In the last 10 days of July, 1939, I came across adult molting birds. The dunlins became common at the end of July and in early August. I therefore feel that some of them arrived on Wrangel to molt. I did not see migratory flocks in the fall but often heard the characteristic trill in the air in the latter half of August. It is difficult to decide who was responsible for the trill: flying birds or the local ones, which performed aerial acrobatics before migration, calling on the others to flock and pointing out the course.

S.M. Uspenskii, R.L. Bëme and A.G. Velizhanin (1963) thought that the dunlin probably nested on Wrangel Island in small numbers. They encountered a pair and a lone bird at Somnitel'naya Bay on July 17, 1960, and a lone dunlin in Tundra Akademii on July 19. An adult specimen was shot on August 9 near Somnitel'naya Bay from flocks consisting of four birds. A young dunlin was also collected. A.G. Velizhanin (1965) even assumed that this shorebird nested from time to time in Tundra Akademii.

Habitat—The occurrence of the dunlin in an area in the breeding season is determined by a combination of two factors: the presence of a good grassy growth, mostly with hummocks, but the latter are not essential, and the proximity at least of lakelets on the coast or of some other freshwater reservoir. The sojourn of the dunlin is associated with the coast no more than in the case of other sandpipers.

At Providence Bay I found the nesting territories of the dunlin in the proximity of the spoonbill; the former selected a moister section of the grassy tundra. When agitated by my presence the male and the female would remain on the marshy land. Around Uélen, dunlins nested on the grassy, wet tundra and along the valley of the Utte-Véem River, but only on the tundra, in particular in the immediate proximity of the pectoral sandpiper, without descending into the flood plains of the valley. On the Amguema, at the 91st km, dunlins nested as a rule on the grassy or hummocky, marshy tundra. But they also settled on wet marshes with peaty mounds and heaps along the edges, and quite often in the places where pectoral sandpipers or even phalaropes nested. The dunlins fed on the grassy, marshy banks of freshwater lakelets.

According to V.É. Yakobi, elevated parts of the tundra with large mounds were the characteristic habitat of dunlins near Uél'kal'. A.P. Kuzyakin found these waders everywhere on the low-sedge tundra from Lake Lawrence to Uélen.

According to the observations of E.G.F. Sauer, right from their arrival dunlins remained on the wet tundra or on dry, rocky elevations on St. Lawrence Island. Of the seven nests detected, only one was on the moist sedge tundra: the remaining ones were on dry sections, among stones densely covered with lichen, or among *Ericacea* on dry ground. During violent storms in August the dunlins gathered at the western corner of Boxer Bay, where the cliffs protected them from strong winds.

On the south side of Wrangel Island these sandpipers loved the marshy banks of the lower course of rivulets. Flowing from the hills, small streams crisscrossed the flat, narrow plateau and, before falling into a gorge, washed through the plateau outcrops, making a marsh of tiny patches of rubbled tundra. Hummocky marshes and fresh green grass were found there. Walking along the edge, I would keep my eyes on the grassy bank of a rivulet and saw dunlins several times. On July 17, 1960, S.M. Uspenskii and his companions found dunlins on the dry, patchy tundra. This has given rise to the question whether they nested there or not.

In spring flight near Uélen I only once saw a dunlin feeding on the silty muddy banks of streams entering a lagoon. On the Amguema, from the time of arrival, the dunlins wandered about, even on the snow, while they protected themselves from the cold northeasterly wind in the depressions between snow-covered mounds, behind strips of ice and in other such uncomfortable corners. On Wrangel Island, in the spring of 1939, I saw them in places where they possibly nested later: on sections of grassy and hummocky tundra west of Somnitel'naya Bay.

T.H. Bean wrote that dunlins foraged along the shore, in the pools left at low tide and in freshwater lakelets. Similar observations were made toward the post-breeding period. On July 10, 1934, I encountered the dunlin feeding on the silty bank of a subsiding old river bed covered with stagnant pools on the Utte-Véem River. The sandpiper had probably deserted the brood. In August, on the Kol'-oam River, flying broods were seen on sandy islets and silty-sandy spits, especially on the shoals in the estuary, but also, though rarely, on the pebbled banks in the middle reaches of the river. Around Uél'kal', V.É. Yakobi noticed dunlins feeding either between the mounds in dense grass along a stream or on the shoals of lagoons and large lakes. On Wrangel Island broods and flocks were seen in mid-August, 1939, on dry sections of tundra where, before, the juveniles and molting adults could be found only in the grassy waterholes.

Arrival—In the spring of 1938, at Providence Bay, P.T. Butenko collected the first of the dunlins on May 30. They were males with enlarged testes.

On St. Lawrence Island, according to F.H. Fay and T.J. Cade, dunlins were seen every year near Gambell on May 19 or so and small flocks of them were noticed within a few days on almost every large thawed patch, often together with pectoral and purple sandpipers in small numbers.

In the spring of 1934, near Uélen, I recorded the arrival only on June 4, when the first flock was noticed together with dotterels. On June 7 the dunlins were still in small groups having not yet occupied the nesting territories.

In 1958, according to the observations of K.W. Kenyon, the first of the birds were noticed on the ice around Malyi Diomede Island on May 20 and 30. At Koly-uchin Bay in 1879, flocks of arriving dunlins were noticed only on June 12. E.K. Brusevits shot some, June 19 through 24. T.A. Bostrem collected some on the 20th; this species was quite common at least up to the 21st. It was always confined to fairly large flocks, not mixing with other sandpipers.

On the Amguema, on June 11, 1956, I found local dunlins formed into pairs and calling, but noticed migratory flocks of four to six birds in each. J. Koren collected a female on the lower Kolyma. It had evidently just arrived, on May 30, 1918. Finally, I came across the first pair of dunlins on June 3 on Wrangel Island, west of Somnitel'naya Bay, in the spring of 1939.

Nidification—Judging from the enlarged size of the gonads, the dunlins arrived ready for breeding. In three of the males taken near Cape Stoletiya on May 30, 1938, the testes were 4×12 and 4×10, 3×9 and 3×8, and 3×9 and 3×8 mm in size. The male from Uélen obtained on July 7, 1934, possessed large testes 6×10 and 5×8 mm in size. In all the remaining specimens obtained on Wrangel Island and in the Chukchi peninsula during the two and one-half months from July 24 through October 3, the size of the testes fell to levels recorded in the period outside breeding: it varied in the range 2–3×2–1 and 2–1×2–1 mm. In the female collected on Wrangel on June 12, 1939, the ovary length was 12 mm and the diameter of the biggest follicle 9 mm. The same day, another female was killed and, judging from the condition of the ovary, it had been laying. In the five Wrangel females shot from July 22 through August 2, the ovaries were 8 to 10 mm long. The size of the follicles decreased to 1 mm or less. The female shot at Cape Chaplin on August 20, 1938, had evidently remained single since it had very worn-out breeding dress and had not yet begun to molt. Among the velvety-black feathers on the belly I found no trace of brood patches. The ovaries, 8 mm long, had no perceptible granular structure. The ovary surface in the old female from Uélen collected on August 29, 1933, showed a structure in relief but fine-grained.

In the dressed dunlins, subcutaneous adipose formations were invariably found. They were less developed in the spring and more in the fall. In all 14 Wrangel specimens the subcutaneous adipose formations were in the form of small isolated patches. In a series obtained in the Chukchi peninsula only two specimens were emaciated; a young female from around Dezhnev taken on August 13, 1932 and a male arriving from Providence Bay on May 30, 1938. In two other males shot at the same time films and isolated patches of fat formation were noticed.

At Uél'kal', V.É. Yakobi even found pairs on June 4, 1961. Around Uélen, in the spring of 1934, I heard the calling of dunlins on June 13. From mid-June they began to be seen more rarely, evidently spending the time on the nests. In Égvekinot I heard the calling of a male on June 8, 1956. Its powerful, endless trill was heard from a long distance. The sandpiper rose into the air with a trill and hovered for quite a long time. From June 9 I began field observations on the Amguema, when the dunlins were partly paired and had occupied the nesting sites. From June 12 through 18 their calling was at its peak.

The most characteristic link in the call of the dunlin is its trill "trr'r'r'..." or "fr'r'r'...". It is heard in different pitches, high and low. Its tempo also changes, sometimes becoming slow and sometimes fast. It terminates in a roulade as though dissolving. The short trill in the form of a peremptory cry can be heard from a frightened or restless dunlin. It serves as the first warning of impending danger. Following that there is usually the sound "dzhvi-dzhvi-dzhvi-dzhvi" or "gvi-gvi-gvi". Later (July 14), I heard the call "dzhigí-dzhigí-dzhigí".

The full-throated calling trill was heard even in the last 10 days of June, especially at night, but the shortened trill began to be heard often from mid-June on. The "tr'r'r' " of the dunlin was heard in early July only when a man approached their nest.

The behavior of these sandpipers near the nest is very typical. On July 12, 1938, at Providence Bay, I came across a nesting spoonbill and, circumventing its nest, saw male and female dunlins nesting in the immediate vicinity. While the spoonbill was flying about the dunlins only parried my approach. Sometimes they would stop and stare at me for a long time. On the Amguema, in 1956, I noticed a similar phenomenon. More often the dunlin was found sitting in the open on a mound. Sensing my intent gaze, the bird would walk away into the grass, sometimes disappearing from the field of vision. On July 4 I came across a dunlin which was agitated, probably even before my arrival. On seeing me it cried for a long time, standing at one place. Later it flew down, rapidly flapping the wings. On another day I came across a dunlin which warned its mate with the alarm note "tr'r'r'". Then it descended from the nest and withdrew out of sight. I put up a dunlin from grass at a distance of 40 paces but could not find the nest in spite of a thorough search.

On July 8 the dunlins allowed me to come close but displayed more intense restlessness. Often I found both the birds in the nesting area. On being approached the birds limply flew low over the ground, sometimes fluttering their wings as when calling. On June 26, 1939, in the valley of a brook flowing into Rodgers Bay, I disturbed a dunlin which took off making the typical trill. It later landed, began walking away, and hid so effectively that I could not locate it again. On July 14 I scared a lone dunlin from the lake beside the hunter's cabin. It took flight with a trill but did not return.

According to a report by V.É. Yakobi, a nest with four eggs was found around Uél'kal' on June 20, 1961. It was located only 100 m from the coastal cliffs on hummocky tundra. The incubating bird flew down to within 1.5 m of the men and began leading them away, feigning injury. Usually, however, dunlins do not parry.

In 1932, at Providence Bay, I.O. Olenev found a clutch on July 2 and 3. Later he saw the chicks, from July 8 through 10.

T.J. Cade was given four nests with full clutches on June 25, 1950. They were located in a dense growth of willow and grass on dry soil. On June 27 six nests were found at Cape Chibukak at an elevation of about 100 ft among the same type of vegetation. There were four eggs in each. In 1960 E.G.F. Sauer and E.K. Urban found seven nests: the first on June 11 and the last on June 23. The female descended from the first nest and walked away, pressing the wings close and spreading the tail. Later she began flying around with a trill at a distance of 50 m. On June 30 the nest was found empty. Two nests were located at 60 and 100 m from the nest of a dotterel. The two species sometimes fed in the same territory, but if the dunlins came too close the dotterels met them with hostility.

On June 22, 1957, A.P. Kuzyakin found a nest with four poorly incubated eggs between Lawrence and Yandagai settlements. The nest was placed on the gentle slope of a hillock and was in the form of a pit lined with dry grass stalks, lichen and year-old leaves of low willow. The pit was 5.5 cm deep and 9 cm across. The weight of the eggs collected was: 10.47, 10.52, 11.16 and 11.26 g.

On July 11, 1956, I found a nest at the 91st km on the Amguema. At that time the male flew unusually close to me, within 20 or 30 paces (Fig. 55). The female remained 100 to 150 paces away. When I began to approach the first bird it alighted, raised its wings and then began to fly to and fro. This meant that its nesting territory measured roughly 40 × 40 paces. Even in such a tiny area it was quite a difficult task to search out its nest on the hummocky tundra. I noticed it only from the prominent light-colored egg among dark-colored chicks. I had to leave to look at the nest of a pectoral sandpiper and left my beret by the nest as an identification mark. Returning, I was exasperated for a while when I could not locate the nest a few paces from the beret.

This nest was on a high, flat mound. It took the form of a circular pit lined, as in the other nests of sandpipers, with lichen and old leaves. The chicks lay stretched inside, filling the pit to the brim. The egg was pecked at the top. It was a light yellowish-green in color with brown patches and the shade was much warmer than the eggs of the pectoral sandpiper.

Both the dunlins were giving out anxious trills all the time. One of them extended it as when calling, sometimes quickening the tempo and raising the pitch, at other times slowing it down, dropping the pitch.

I took all three chicks and next day the fourth, which had emerged from the egg (Fig. 56). It is strange that the bits of shell were not to be seen nearby. These days there was a mass emergence of the chicks not only of dunlins but also of pectoral sandpipers and phalaropes.

On June 27, 1970, in the neighborhood of Énurmino, V.V. Leonovich found three downy chicks. There were adult birds around.

On August 6, 1932, on the eastern shore of Krest Bay, I found some more young birds which were flying weakly. They were mostly confined to the tundra beside a lake, unlike the adults which had migrated to the seacoast. According to T.J. Cade, downy chicks were common on St. Lawrence Island toward the end of July.

On Wrangel Island, on July 14, 1939, I saw a dunlin already with a chick. On July 21, on a knoll along the Nasha River, a very wary sandpiper flew toward me. The wariness was probably because of the presence of chicks. On July 24 I sighted an adult female and two first-year birds with the tail feathers just beginning to grow. The crown was still covered with down. In body size they differed little from adults and already had subcutaneous adipose formations. In the last few days of July and in early August the dunlins began to be encountered more often because the young ones were also to be seen. The old birds were mostly molted. On July 21, 1939, in the estuary of the Nasha River on a marshy spot by the lagoon, there was even a small flock of molting dunlins.

Broods, evidently very late, were also found. Even on August 7, 1939, I noticed a dunlin standing on a green mound, evidently representing its nesting territory, and following my movements. The trill of the agitated birds was heard right up to their migration.

Wandering and migration—On Wrangel Island, in 1939, I noticed broods and flocks of young birds for the first time on August 16. They soon flew away because I could hear their call from sky, for the last time on August 24. On the north coast of the island, in 1938, also on August 16, I saw some young birds only once, near the estuary of the Krasnyi Flag River. In 1960, at Somnitel'naya Bay A.G. Velizhanin noticed a lone young bird on August 3 and a brood on August 9. They were the last of the dunlins.

In 1933, around Uélen, the bulk of the dunlins had left by the end of August. A few were left behind, taking advantage of rare favorable feeding conditions. On August 28, on the tundra, I sighted a dunlin sitting on a mound as though it was still occupying the nesting territory. On October 1 I saw a pair on the bank of a lagoon. Together with phalaropes, the dunlins here and there lived on a coast slushy with ice. Finally, on October 3, I collected a solitary sandpiper on the bank of an already frozen lane; it was a plump adult male, almost totally in winter plumage. In summer, 1934, as early as August 9, I encountered flying young birds beginning to wander in the estuary of the Kol'oam-Véem River. Throughout my excursion I saw only one dunlin on the river itself on August 21. It was mixed up with a flock of young purple sandpipers. Later, returning to the estuary on August 23 and 24 I again found flocks; they found the exposed silt-sand shoals very favorable. On St. Lawrence Island, according to T.J. Cade, dunlins began to flock in the last week of July, and a large group was noticed on the south coast at the end of August. At Boxer Bay, in 1960, according to E.G.F. Sauer, these sandpipers were already wandering over the tundra in flocks of up to six birds from June 27. They gathered along the shores of the bay in flocks exceeding 30 birds in mid-July and August.

According to the observations of O.I. Belogurov, the large-scale migration of dunlins occurred in Uél'kal' as early as August 28–29 in 1961.

Food—The stomachs of dunlins collected at Uélen revealed the following items: 1) August 29, 1933. Tiny fragments of the chitin of a *Carabidae*, ticks and tiny stones. 2) October 3, 1933. Much deformed remains of dozens of tiny crustaceans and tiny stones. 3) June 7, 1934. Jaws and other remains of two *Carabidae*, about 10 larvae of dipterans, pieces of about five unknown insect larvae, bits of skin and the mouth parts of caterpillars and tiny stones.

It would appear that the very late, plump adult male fed on crustaceans. At other times the dunlins fed on insects and their larvae.

The following items were found in the birds collected on Wrangel Island: 4) June 4, 1939. Three *Coleoptera* larvae and about 0.25 g sand. 5) June 12, 1939. Remains of tiny insects, two fragments of mollusc shells, and 0.25 g sand. 6) June 12, 1939. Remains of tiny insects, three caterpillars, a spider, some seeds, and 1 g fine sand. 7) July 22, 1939. Remains of caterpillars and 0.25 g sand. 8) July 24, 1939. Remains of *Chrysomela* beetles and 1 g sand. 9) July 24, 1939. Remains of tiny beetles, filling three-fourths of the stomach capacity, and 0.25 g sand. 10) July 27, 1939. Ground-up remains of tiny insects and 0.5 g sand. 11) July 29, 1939. Remains of tiny insects. 0.25 g quartz sand. 12) July 29, 1939. Six caterpillars and 0.75 g sand. 13) July 30, 1939. Unidentifiable digested mass and 1 g sand. 14) August 2, 1939. Four much digested caterpillars and 1 g sand. 15) August 2, 1939, 1.5 g sand. 16) August 10, 1939. One gram coarse sand. 17) August 16, 1939, 0.25 g much digested gruel and 0.25 g sand.

A study of the stomachs of the Wrangel series of birds showed that the dunlins went around hungry in August. In this case underfeeding stands out as the prime reason for migration.

On June 10 and 11, 1956, even in the winter Amguema environment, I noticed that dunlins pecked out moss stalks from the soil of thawed patches. I could not ascertain for certain whether the birds got at some fresh shoots or even insect larvae but the birds pulled out a fair number of tiny stalks. In one case a longspur was making use of the remains of the meal of a sandpiper.

According to E.G.F. Sauer, in August the dunlins fed on crustaceans and other tiny invertebrates brought in by the surf on the shores of Boxer Bay. At low tide they frequented the washed-up brown algae on which hundreds of thousands of fly larvae, mainly marine *Chironomidae*, thrived.

Weight—Three flying males from Providence Bay taken on May 30, 1938, weighed 61.5, 54.8 and 44.0 g. The differences in weight corresponded to the differences in the amount of subcutaneous adipose formations. The heaviest bird was plumper than the others; slight formations were found in the second one and the lightest was emaciated.

Systematics of the subspecies—After the revision of the dunlin subspecies published in *Fauna of the Anadyr Region* (Portenko, 1939b, vol. I, pp. 200 and 201), additional material became available from the Chukchi peninsula and Wrangel Island in the form of about 20 specimens. I therefore undertook a second revision and introduced the following refinements:

1) **Pelidna alpina schinzi** Brehm.—Distinguished from others in the scanty black patch on the belly, dark coloration with large spots, and very small size (Table 39). Specimens were examined from the Baltic coast and Norway, i.e. migratory birds from Western Europe.

Table 39. Bill and wing length of breeding dunlins, cm

Subspecies	Bill				Wing			
	Max.	Min.	Mean	No. of samples	Max.	Min.	Mean	No. of samples
				Males				
P. a. schinzi Brehm.	2.85	2.75	2.80	2	10.75	10.69	10.72	2
P. a. alpina (L.)	3.27	2.87	3.07	12	11.25	10.40	10.98	12
P. a. centralis (But.)	3.36	2.97	3.13	11	11.52	10.77	11.14	11
P. a. sakhalina (Vieill.)	3.47	3.05	3.21	15	12.48	11.78	12.03	9
P. a. pacifica (Coues)	4.06	3.50	3.80	5	12.37	11.60	11.89	5
				Females				
P. a. schinzi Brehm.	3.06	3.06	3.06	1	11.11	11.11	11.11	1
P. a. alpina (L.)	3.82	2.91	3.43	3	11.73	11.38	11.51	3
P. a. centralis (But.)	3.80	3.02	3.53	9	11.72	11.40	11.52	9
P. a. sakhalina (Vieill.)	3.97	3.37	3.63	14	12.49	11.55	12.06	6
P. a. pacifica (Coues)	4.15	3.89	4.01	3	12.37	12.11	12.24	2

2) **Pelidna alpina alpina** (L.) (=**pusilla** (Falk.))—White ridge on the outer web of the inner primary feathers is narrow; not being broader than the white shaft, the tiny triangular wing speculum is not formed. In the spring plumage the outer side of the body has an intense rufous coloration. The neck and breast have dark, sharp,

broad streaks. In size, it is bigger than *P. a. schinzi*.

It nests on the tundra from the Kola peninsula in the east to the Gydan tundra, and also on Novaya Zemlya.

3) **Pelidna alpina centralis** (But.). Very similar in color and size to the preceding but differs primarily in that the neck and breast have very pale, thin streaks. With a good series it was possible to establish that the white bands in most of these birds in the inner flight feathers extend beyond the coverts; the rusty coloration on top has a yellowish tinge and the size often exceeds that of the nominal form.

It breeds from Turukhansk region to the estuary of the Kolyma. Seen in flight along the Pacific Ocean coast of Asia in appreciable numbers. The nonbreeding birds summer in Kamchatka and Sakhalin in numbers hardly exceeding those of *P. a. sakhalina*. They remain at least until the end of June.

4) **Pelidna alpina sakhalina** (Vieill.)—Differs from all the preceding subspecies in the very broad white bands on the outer web of the inner primary feathers, forming on the composite wing a small triangular white speculum. Individual specimens can be identified by this character. In a series of well-prepared skins the rust color on the upper side differed by its light yellow tone. The neck and breast have thin streaks; between them and the black patch on the belly, there is a white transverse band with a very small number of spots. The wing length is noticeably longer than in *P. a. centralis*.

Breeds in the Chukchi peninsula, on Wrangel Island and in coastal Anadyr.

5) **Pelidna alpina pacifica** (Coues)—This differs from all of the Palearctic subspecies in its long beak. It is similar to the preceding species in color. In some birds the rufous coloration on the upper parts is darker. The white breast band separating the shaded breast from the black patch on the abdomen stands out prominently in a series, and appears broader and cleaner.

Nests in Alaska and farther east on the tundra of North America. The specimen collected by I.G. Voznesenskii on July 29, 1843, at Shishmarev Bay was of *P. a. pacifica*. The following two specimens from Wrangel Island and the Chukchi peninsula should be placed in the subspecies *P. a. pacifica* as they have very long beaks: 1) Cape Chaplin, August 20, 1938, ♀, bill length 4.15 cm and 2) neighborhood of Atternon hill, July 29, 1939, ♀, bill length 4.02 cm.

Specimens— 1) Mechigmensk Gulf, August 10, 1843, ♀, Voznesenskii; 2) Dezhnev settlement, August 13, 1932, ♀, 1° anno, Portenko; 3) Uélen village, August 29, 1933, ♀, Portenko; 4) same place, October 3, 1933, ♂, Portenko; 5) same place, June 7, 1934, ♂, Portenko; 6) lower reaches of Kol'oam-Véem River, August 9, 1934, ○, 1° anno, Portenko; 7 to 10) same place, August 24, 1934, ♂ ○○, 1° anno, Portenko; 11 to 13) Providence Bay, Cape Stoletiya, May 30, 1938, ♂♂, Butenko; 14) Cape Chaplin, August 18, 1938, ♂, Butenko; 15 to 17) same place, August 20, 1938, ♀, sen., ♂ ♀, 1° anno, Butenko; 18 and 19) Wrangel Island, Akatylanva, June 12, 1939, ♀♀, Portenko; 20) Rodgers Bay, July 22, 1939, ♀, Portenko; 21 to 23) neighborhood of Atternon hill, July 24, 1939, ♂♂, juv., Portenko; 24 to 26) same place, July 29, 1939, ♂♀♀, Portenko; 27) Rodgers Bay, July 30, 1939, ♂, Portenko; 28 and 29) neighborhood of Atternon hill, August 2, 1939, ♀♀, Portenko; 30 and 31) Rodgers Bay, August 16, 1939, ○○, 1° anno, Portenko; and 32 to 35) Amguema River, 91st km, July 11 and 12, 1956, pull., Portenko.

67. **Pelidna maritima tschuktschorum** Port.

68. **Pelidna maritima ptilocnemis** (Coues)—**Purple Sandpiper**

Local name—Chukchian: Taràsel'gyn, saràasyn, also bekàsyl'gyn, evidently from the Russian; these are applied to all species of small-sized waders. In Eskimo: Dră-dră'-yŭk on St. Lawrence Island.

Distribution and status—Nests all along the coastal cliffs of the Chukchi peninsula from Providence Bay to Kolyuchin Bay, being one of the commonest sandpipers there. Flies away in the winter. Absent from Wrangel, Kolyuchi and the Bol'shoi Diomede Islands.

The purple sandpiper is not found for certain on the western shore of Anadyr Bay. Neither Butenko and I nor L.O. Belopol'skii (1934) nor V.É. Yakobi found the purple sandpiper at the entrance to Krest Bay. Farther east reliable information is available only from Providence Bay. In Capt. Moore's 1849 summer collections (Harting, 1871) there were one or two specimens from Providence Bay or some other part of the coast up to Lawrence Bay. The collection locality of these specimens should be determined with great caution. According to V.G. Dall (Dall and Bannister, 1869, p. 291), F. Bishoff obtained this species at Plover Bay in 1865 and 1866.

In 1912 É.E. Arngol'd acquired specimens at Providence Bay which were later given to the Zoological Museum of the Academy of Sciences of the USSR. In June, 1913, W.S. Brooks (1915) also collected specimens there. In the course of the first week of July, 1921, A.M. Bailey (1925) found these sandpipers unusually numerous in the breeding area at Émma Bay, where some pairs were noticed on different parts of the tundra, and two nests were taken. In 1932, I came across this species in small numbers on the shores of Émma Bay on August 11 and some specimens on Plover spit on August 25 and 26. It is not without interest that on my last visit to Providence Bay I did not see purple sandpipers; nor were they found by I.O. Olenev, who wintered there. In 1938, P.T. Butenko collected some arriving birds at Cape Stoletiya and at Plover. He also noticed them in Sireniki village and took breeding specimens near Kivak village.

On St. Lawrence Island the purple sandpiper is more or less common though its population is subject to variations. Two subspecies are encountered on this island: *Pelidna maritima tschuktschorum* Port. and *P. m. ptilocnemis* (Coues). On June 24, 1881, E.W. Nelson (1883) found a lone pair nesting on the south coast of the island. According to H. Friedmann (1932a) two females were collected on July 13, 1899. W.S. Brooks found a few purple sandpipers in June, 1913, on the southeastern tip of the island and secured some specimens. F.S. Hersey (1916) came across a small flock and collected four specimens on July 24, 1914, on the northern side of the island. A.M. Bailey noticed some sandpipers of this species on St. Lawrence Island in the first week of July, 1921. H.B. Collins (Friedmann, 1932a) acquired a male at Gambell in September, 1960. O.W. Geist (Murie, 1936) found a dead bird on the tundra and saw a live one with an old bird on July 30, 1935; later O.J. Murie collected a series of fall birds: ♀ on September 24, 1934, ♂ juv. on August 28, 1935, ♀♀ on August 29, 1935, and 4 ♂♂ and 4 ♀♀ on September 6, 1935. According to F.H. Fay and T.J. Cade (1959), the purple sandpiper was a common nesting bird on St. Lawrence Island, nearly as abundant as the dunlin, but its population varied from year to year. In 1950 it was rare on the west coast of the island but was almost as common as the dunlin from 1953 through 1956 and was twice as numerous in 1957. According to the observations of E.G.F. Sauer and E.K. Urban (1964), purple sandpipers were not common at Boxer Bay in 1960; one was noticed on June 20, another on August 10 and some 10 birds on August 18.

On July 21, 1879, the *Vega* expedition acquired a clutch in north Nunyamo village north of the entrance to Lawrence Bay. On August 19, 1932, I found purple sandpipers singly and in pairs and broods on the southern shore. In 1970 V.V. Leonovich found them so common at Lawrence Bay that he saw 10 of them during a six-hour walk. He succeeded in locating a nest. He did not see them at all that year near Énurmino. On July 9, 1957, A.P. Kuzyakin traced downy chicks between the settlement at Lawrence Bay and Chulkhyn. According to him, from Akkani to Uélen it was a common species: one or two pairs nested every sq km. He found three nests south of the Uélen lagoon.

I am personally convinced that purple sandpipers do not nest on Bol'shoi Diomede Island. At East Cape W.S. Brooks found these sandpipers in small numbers in mid-July, 1913; specimens were also obtained. According to his observations the purple sandpiper is the most common of sandpipers breeding in the neighborhood of Uélen. Most often, I found it in the valleys of brooks flowing from the Dezknev knolls and crossing the road from Uélen to Dezhnev settlement.

In the course of my expedition on foot up the Kol'oam-Véem River in August, 1934, I happened upon lone young birds and broods which no doubt had been raised there. I found purple sandpipers to be common on July 21 of the same year on my way back from Inchoun to Uélen. On July 12 I found a restless pair by the nest on the knolls roughly 15 km southeast of Mitkulen. But I did not see them at all in the valley of the Utte-Véem River.

In June, 1879 the members of the *Vega* expedition found that the purple sandpipers, together with dunlins and spoonbills, were the most common of sandpipers in Kolyuchin Bay. Near Dzhenretlen they were collected from June 10 through 29. Later they disappeared either because of intense persecution or because they migrated to the breeding grounds deep into the tundra. On June 5 a solitary bird was noticed at Pitlekai. Some specimens were shot on June 19 and one on June 20 around the ship. On June 3 a Chukchian brought a male purple sandpiper into Pitlekai. Copley Amory Jr. (Riley, 1918) collected a juvenile female at Kolyuchin Bay on August 10, 1914. Farther west, the purple sandpiper did not breed at all. A.A. Kishchinskii thoroughly explored the tundra from Vankarém to the Amguema but did not find this sandpiper once.

For want of specimens one must reject A.A. Bunge's reference for the Lena estuary (Pleske, 1928, p. 260) as also the observations recorded in G.U. Sverdrup's diary (Schaanning, 1928, pp. 15 and 16) for the ice cover from the Novosibirsk Islands to Chetyrekhstolb Island. A.A. Birulya (1907, p. 69) noticed a lone purple sandpiper on June 8, 1902, on Novaya Siberia Island but no specimen was secured in this case either.

The purple sandpiper is certainly not found on Wrangel Island. On the Alaskan shore of Bering Strait it hardly goes up to the Arctic Circle. A.M. Bailey found it in the nesting area at Cape Prince of Wales.

Habitat—There is a noticeable difference in the habitats of the purple sandpiper as between the first half of the breeding season and after the raising of chicks. From its arrival this sandpiper frequents and later nests on the grassy tundra near brooks with rocky beds coming down from the uplands. The juveniles, however, remain on the pebbled banks. The short legs and thick toes with rough claws are suited to walking on gravel and fine stones.

In the spring of 1934, near Uélen, I saw a newly arrived purple sandpiper on the pebbled bed of the Vtoraya brook. But these sandpipers remained mostly on nearby grassy, thawed patches. Later they were encountered on the large, well-warmed thawed patches on the first terrace of the uplands near Uélen. I also noticed them on the flat grassy tundra during the period of calling. On my way from Inchoun to Uélen I encountered broods on the elevated tundra, which was grassy and rather wet at places. Sometimes they were found in places with succulent grass and shrubs, where they could not be chased. Initially, I mistook them for dunlins, which are the main inhabitants of the grassy tundra. Nevertheless, from my observations around Uélen, I have the impression that for their summer sojourn the purple sandpipers were mostly confined to the valleys of streams and brooks flowing from the uplands, having pebble or rubble beds.

According to A.P. Kuzyakin the purple sandpiper was confined to the damp parts of low-sedge tundra in the nesting period, especially in the valleys of brooks along the coast from Lawrence Bay to Uélen; it did not fly to the seacoast even to feed.

On St. Lawrence Island E.W. Nelson found a pair nesting on the windy, exposed top of a knoll where the vegetation consisted of tiny lichens and low arctic plants. At Émma Bay A.M. Bailey found some pairs nesting along the banks of small brooks. The nest he found was built on gravel on the shore of the bay.

On August 28, 1933, I encountered juvenile sandpipers of this species on the Vtoraya rivulet (Téeyu-Véem), a mountain brook cascading over a bed paved with gravel and stones between low, steep banks. The sandpipers behaved like gray wagtails: they wandered among the rocks and ran across the little shoals. One of them sat on a rock, pressed to it like a ball and outwardly resembling a tiny, dark-colored rock. On the Kol'oam-Véem River the juveniles remained on the rocky parts of the banks covered with rubble and pebbles. On August 19, 1932, I found juvenile purple sandpipers by a small brook flowing from the high southern shore of Lawrence Bay to the spit through a network of lakes. They ran along the rocks overhanging the stream and on being chased flew away up the brook. At Émma Bay, in the post-breeding period, I noticed purple sandpipers on the pebbly and rocky banks as also on the rubble banks of lakelets on the spit south of Plover. On St. Lawrence Island F.S. Hersey encountered a flock in the post-breeding period on a lagoon with a rocky bank by a small watershed.

In fall flight, in September, 1933, I sighted this sandpiper on the pebbled spit on which Uélen village is situated. The birds were confined to the surf line, especially among sea-kale cast up by the waves. On Novaya Zemlya I most often found purple sandpipers, among other birds in this kind of setting.

In the estuary of the Kol'oam-Véem River I noticed a juvenile purple sandpiper intruding into a flock of migratory pectoral sandpipers. Along with them, it alighted on a sandy islet in a huge shoal.

This sandpiper, not being a hill bird, is almost always confined to elevated coasts where its habitats are associated with the disintegration products of hill rocks.

Arrival—The purple sandpiper arrives earlier than other sandpipers and flies away later. On the south coast of the Chukchi peninsula, at Providence Bay, P.T. Butenko collected the first arriving bird on May 22, 1938; it was a male. Near Uélen, in the spring of 1934, I noticed the arrival even earlier. On May 21 I saw two sandpipers of this species on the eastern slopes of the Inchoun knolls. They flew past me crying "trrryu". On May 27 I noticed a few purple sandpipers on my way from Dezhnev settlement to Uélen. The sandpipers were flying close by which showed that they were already busy in their nesting territories. It is interesting that all of the seven birds caught that day turned out to be males. I therefore feel that the males arrived somewhat earlier than the females and soon got busy in the nesting territories. On June 2 I noticed two birds separately on thawed elevations where the purple sandpipers did not nest eventually. Judging from the small number, they too were males. On June 4 I came across these birds singly and in pairs.

In the spring of 1879, too, the males were the first to be collected at Kolyuchin Bay.

Nidification—The testis sizes in the arriving birds collected at Plover on May 22 and June 9 were 3 × 10 and 3 × 9, and 4 × 10 and 4 × 9 mm. The testis in males of a series that I secured on the Vtoraya rivulet on May 27 measured 8 × 12 and 7 × 10, 7 × 12 and 6 × 10, 7 × 10 and 6 × 9, 7 × 10 and 6 × 9, and 6 × 10 and 6 × 9 mm. The male from Uélen taken on June 7 had testes of the same size in spite of the commencement of sexual activity: 7 × 11 and 6 × 9 mm. Large or small subcutaneous adipose formations were noticed in all arriving purple sandpipers with the exception of an emaciated specimen from Plover collected on June 9. One of the two males collected on June 10, 1879, near Dzhenretlen was plump and the other emaciated.

On June 4, 1934, I collected a female at Uélen. The oviduct contained an egg in soft shell. The biggest follicles in the ovary were 8 and 15 mm across. That day the purple sandpipers were calling vigorously over the tundra. They were flying, fluttering their wings or noisily trilling "r'r'r'r'r'...". Some pairs permitted a close approach. Sometimes the head of a sandpiper hiding behind a mound would appear right in front of one and later the call "chigí-chigí", resembling that of a dunlin, would be heard. On June 7 the purple sandpipers were calling with no particular excitement. As before, they permitted a very close approach and did not fly away when one came near, but only ran away. It could be seen that the sandpipers were confined to the nests. On June 13 the calling continued and I heard the trill even on the 15th. More often, however, the restless call "chigí-chigí" could be heard. On being approached the sandpipers did not even run but walked away slowly. Some would try to hide behind a mound while others would raise a wing on my coming too close. In June, 1881, on St. Lawrence Island, E.W. Nelson encountered a male which took off 10 to 15 paces away from him and began calling, rapidly fluttering its wings. It also gave out a trill, pure, quite musical, and gentle, combined with a hard, whistling sound. On concluding its brief song the bird would swoop to the ground with wings outspread, either picking up something to eat or silently standing for some time on some projecting rock or mound.

On June 29, 1934, I found three unincubated eggs. It was certainly a second clutch. The eggs had the characteristic pear-shaped form and excellent variegated coloration. In two of them the background was a pale greenish-gray. It was a warmer shade due to the admixture of yellow in the third. There were large patches like smears at the blunt end while the background at the sharp end was free of them. The deeper patches were brownish-violet while the surface ones were sepia, almost black. The sizes of the eggs were: 2.74 × 3.85, 2.73 × 3.74 and 2.72 × 3.70 cm. According to the observations of V.V. Leonovich the males were calling vigorously at Lawrence Bay on June 15 and 16, 1970. Many pairs apparently had not yet nested. Nevertheless, on June 18, a nest was found with a full clutch of highly incubated eggs. It was completely exposed on low-sedge-moss tundra. It was 10.2 cm across and 6.1 cm deep. The eggs measured 2.68 × 3.84, 2.63 × 3.82, 2.70 × 3.79, and 2.64 × 3.73 cm. The sandpipers fluttered out of the nest right under their feet. While Leonovich was packing the egg the bird literally landed on his hand. The eggs brought by the *Vega* expedition from Nunyamo were of comparable size: 2.58 × 3.9, 2.65 × 3.75, and 2.6 × 3.75 cm. According to a description by I.A. Palmén (1887), the ground color was yellowish-gray. The patches, some of a faded gray and others of a fairly dark, baked color, were concentrated in a ring at the broad end. There were also tiny greenish-brown speckles distributed at random.

On July 3, 1921, A.M. Bailey found a nest containing three recently hatched chicks and an egg at Émma Bay (see photograph, Bailey, 1925). The parent birds were much agitated; by returning to the nest they betrayed its location. A second nest had been located by another worker, who left an identification mark. Bailey did not see the female incubating in that nest. She got down from the nest and walked unsteadily to and fro, feigning injury as if her legs and wings had been cut. The eggs were four-fifths incubated.

On June 29, 1957, A.P. Kuzyakin found three nests south of Uélen with clutches of four eggs each. They were so highly incubated that only one of the clutches could be processed for the collection. All of these nests were placed on low, flat mounds. They were 9 or 10 cm across and the trough 3.2 to 5 cm deep. The color of the eggs was a light grayish-olive. Prominent brownish patches were concentrated at the blunt end of the eggs; they were smaller and rarer at the sharp end. There were also a few grayish patches. The sandpipers allowed them to approach within two or three steps but betrayed the nest when they started up abruptly.

On July 9, 1957, A.P. Kuzyakin traced small downy chicks, three on the same mound, at Lawrence Bay.

On St. Lawrence Island O.W. Geist found a dead chick on July 30, 1935. Its head and neck were still covered with down. Alongside was a live chick with the parent bird.

On August 12, 1934, southeast of Mitkulen and on July 21 on my way from Inchoun to Uélen, I found adults which ran from me and became restless, evidently because they were with their broods. From August 13 I came across lone birds and broods along the banks of the Kol'oam-Véem River. On the 21st I noticed a flock of juveniles though groups of four birds, beyond doubt broods, were seen as before. On August 23 and 24 the purple sandpipers were still seen with broods but in small numbers.

Among the 10 young birds available in my series I found only one specimen, taken at Uélen on September 27, 1933, that had appreciable adipose formations. All the others were devoid of them. The ovaries were in the form of films while the male testes varied in size from 1 to 2 mm. In behavior they closely resembled the adults. On the approach of a man the juvenile sandpipers would freeze in a stiff posture for some time and then move away leisurely.

In two of the adult females collected on August 11, 1932, at Émma Bay, only a fine-grained surface could be seen in the ovaries. Both of the birds were emaciated.

Molting—These adult females were in a state of intense molt. One of them was left with the three front pairs of flight feathers and another had only two. The birds could hardly fly. Most of the tail feathers were still not adequately formed. New feathers of the winter plumage had formed on the crown, in part on the back and shoulders and on the underside.

Migration—In the fall of 1933 I studied the migration of juvenile purple sandpipers thoroughly around Uélen. In September they were found only from time to time. On the 23rd I noticed them at two points in twos and threes and collected a bird for the last time on the 27th.

Food—The following items were found in the stomachs: 1) Lawrence Bay, August 19, 1932. Heads of three *Carabidae*, heads and other parts of 28 hymenopterans, 14 tiny midges, two lower insects, 29 black eggs of insects, three tiny molluscs and 28 tiny stones. 2) Same time. Head of one *Carabidae*, fragments of head and shards of an unknown beetle, heads of six hymenopterans, three black eggs of insects and many tiny stones. 3) Same time. Four tiny crustaceans, many tiny stones and coarse sand. 4) Uélen, August 29, 1933. Head of a beetle, ground remains of dozens of tiny dipterans, and stones. 5) Same time. Fragments of the head of one *Carabidae*, head of a hymenopteran, pieces of insect larvae and the remains of dozens of tiny dipterans. 6) Uélen, May 27, 1934. Tiny pieces of the chitin of a large *Carabidae*, jaw of a caterpillar, some dozens of tiny gemmae or buds and tiny stones. 8) Same time. Fragments of heads and shards of three *Carabidae*, jaws of caterpillars, some dozens of tiny gemmae or buds, moss shoots and tiny stones. 9) Same time. Heads of five *Carabidae*, two larvae of dipterans, moss shoots, dozens of tiny gemmae or buds and tiny stones. 10) Same time. Small pieces of the chitin of two to four *Carabidae*, pieces of insect larvae, moss shoots, about 10 tiny gemmae or buds and tiny stones. 11) Same time. Heads, jaws and bits of the skin of four caterpillars, moss shoots and other plant remains and tiny stones. 12) Same time. Tiny pieces of the chitin of a *Carabidae*, shoots of moss and other plants, gemmae, tiny leaves and other plant remains and tiny stones. 13) Uélen, June 7, 1934. Fragments of heads of 13 *Carabidae*, jaw and skin of a caterpillar, four larvae of dipterans and tiny stones. 14) Same time. Small remnants and jaws of eight *Carabidae*,jaws of two caterpillars, two fly larvae, insect cocoon, teeth and vertebra of lemming or vole and many tiny stones.

The stomach of a specimen collected around Dzhenretlen on June 10, 1879, was filled with the larvae of driftwood beetles. The stomach of another bird shot at that time showed the same larvae and coarse sand. Finally, the specimens taken on

June 18 had the larvae and elytrae probably of *Harpalus*, as also coarse sand.

Weight—The male collected on June 9, 1938, at Plover weighed 70.8 g.

Economic importance—Being a small creature, the purple sandpiper cannot be regarded as a game bird which is specially hunted. But because it permits a close approach it quite often becomes the target of Chukchian youngsters. I myself saw a young sandpiper killed by a youngster at Uélen and was told that such kills were usually made for want of something more useful to do. The youngsters simply threw stones at the birds.

Systematics of the subspecies—I have studied the division of purple sandpipers into subspecies in detail on the basis of a good series of birds that I collected in the Chukchi peninsula, comparing them with the collections in the Institute of Zoology, Academy of Sciences of the USSR. Some results of my revision were published in a special article (Portenko, 1937d, pp. 225 and 226). The question whether the Atlantic and Pacific purple sandpipers should be regarded as species or subspecies depends on one's point of view. I feel there is little justification for regarding them as species because, even among Pacific birds, there is as sharp a difference of form as in *P. m. ptilocnemis*. I confine myself in this review to the Pacific subspecies.

Only recently was I able to lay hands on the revision of Pacific purple sandpipers made by B. Conover (1944). Conover had with him incomparably more material from America but even then recognized the same subspecies as I do. The sole point of disagreement is in the specific evaluation of Atlantic and Pacific purple sandpipers.

I have drawn up the following descriptions based on my own material:

1) **Pelidna maritima ptilocnemis** (Coues) is distinguished by its very long wing (Table 40) and very light coloration. In the breeding plumage the rusty fringes of the feathers on the upper side are very broad and of light color, almost yellowish. In the winter plumage the upper parts are a pale bluish-gray. There is much white on the underparts in all plumages. In connection with this white no analogy is to be drawn with the bunting subspecies *Plectrophenax nivalis hyperboreus*, also inhabiting St. Mathew Island.

Table 40. Wing length of the subspecies of purple sandpipers, cm

Subspecies	Males				Females			
	Max.	Min.	Mean	No. of samples	Max.	Min.	Mean	No. of samples
P. m. ptilocnemis	12.89	12.54	12.71	2	13.16	13.02	13.09	2
P. m. couesi	12.15	12.15	12.15	1	12.36	12.36	12.36	1
P. m. quarta	12.19	11.55	11.75	6	12.27	11.79	12.03	2
P. m. tschuktschorum	12.63	11.90	12.22	10	12.95	12.13	12.68	3

Distribution—Pribylov, St. Mathew and Hall Islands. I also have with me specimens from St. Paul's Island.

2) **Pelidna maritima couesi** Ridgw.—I have only two specimens in the breeding plumage. They are of a noticeably more intense coloration, darker with a large number of spots on the underside, and with a much shorter wing length than in the

preceding subspecies.

Distribution—Aleutian and Shumagin islands (type description from Atta Island).

3) **Pelidna maritima quarta** Hart.—In summer dress this is very similar to *P. m. couesi* but the rusty fringes of the feathers on the upper parts are broader. As a result, the bird appears uniformly rufous dorsally. The lateral patches are crude with indistinct edges. The sides are speckled more densely in females than in males. I was able to establish these differences by a comparison with two genuine *P. m. couesi* from the Aleutian Islands.

Distribution—Commander Islands.

4) **Pelidna maritima tschuktschorum** Port.—A series of 15 properly prepared skins of the purple sandpiper from the Chukchi peninsula (Providence Bay, Uélen) differs distinctly from two properly prepared specimens of genuine *P. m. couesi* from the Aleutian Islands, as also from the series of *P. m. quarta*, whose features were listed above. Leaving the latter, which are very obvious, let us examine the divergence from *P. m. couesi*. These are mainly in the breeding plumage both of the male and of the female. The upper parts in *P. m. tschuktschorum* as I described it for the Chukchi peninsula are generally very light-colored and variegated because of the large number of white feather tips on the back. The rusty color is brighter. The upper side of the neck is whiter. The supercilium, sides of the head, chin and throat are of purer white: there are no variegated patches on the whitish background. The abdomen and the flanks are in the form of triangular spots much smaller in size and number than in *P. m. couesi*, in which the flanks are spotted more densely and crudely. Between the brown upper breast and the black lower breast there is a white band. The black patch does not have a regular form but is so sharp that it creates some resemblance between this subspecies of purple sandpiper and the dunlin, especially when the birds are seen on the tundra.

As far as the wing length is concerned, it is somewhat longer on the average in *P. m. tschuktschorum.* But this cannot be used as a diagnostic feature because the difference is only a general one. From my point of view it nevertheless confirms the existence of this subspecies alongside the others.

Ten males were differentiated from a single male *P. m. couesi* by the characters I have listed but these features were found clearly reproduced when comparing some females which also contained only one of *P. m. couesi*. The type for my description was a male from Uélen collected on May 27, 1934. The paratype was a female obtained there on June 4, 1934. I collected both of them.

Distribution—Chukchi coast from Providence Bay to Kolyuchin Bay.

According to B. Conover, *P. m. tschuktschorum* is an Alaskan purple sandpiper. On the Alaskan peninsula some specimens approached *P. m. couesi* in their characters. Twelve specimens taken on St. Lawrence Island showed transition to *P. m. ptilocnemis*. From the Chukchi peninsula, Conover gathered 20 genuine specimens of *P. m. tschuktschorum*.

5) **Pelidna maritima kurilensis** Yamashina—Two specimens in the collection of the Institute of Zoology, Academy of Sciences of the USSR, collected from Urup Island on April 19, 1845, were in winter plumage. They also have a short wing length as in *P. m. quarta* and, what is more, a very short beak. This material is un-

fortunately inadequate for thorough confirmation of the existence of this subspecies.

According to B. Conover the name *arquatella* Pall. could be applied to this subspecies.

It should be emphasized that the purple sandpiper is a bird that is far from settled, but it winters in many cases near the place where it was hatched. It flies away from the Chukchi coast and, as may be judged from more than 10 specimens gathered by I.G. Voznesenskii on the Aleutian and Kodiak islands, the southern subspecies winters along with the northern subspecies.

Specimens— 1 and 2) Providence Bay, July 16, 1912, ♂♀, Arngol'd; 3) same place, September 24, 1912, ♀, 1° anno, Arngol'd; 4 and 5) Émma Bay, August 11, 1932, ♀♀, Portenko; 6 to 8) Lawrence Bay, August 19, 1932, ♂♂♀, Portenko; 9) Providence Bay, August 25, 1932, ♂, Portenko; 10 and 11) Uélen, August 29, 1933, ♀♀, 1° anno, Portenko; 12 to 14) same place, September 23, 1933, ♂♀♀, 1° anno, Portenko; 15) same place, September 27, 1933, ♀, 1° anno, Portenko; 16 to 22) Téeyu-Véem River, May 27, 1934, ♂♂, Portenko; 23) Uélen, July 4, 1934, ♀, Portenko; 24) same place, June 7, 1934, ♂, Portenko; 25) Providence Bay, Plover, May 22, 1938, ♂, Butenko; 26) same place, June 9, 1938, ♂, Butenko; and 27 to 29) Kivak village, July 22, 1938, ○○, Butenko.

Biological material—Three eggs, Uélen, June 29, 1934.

69. **Pisobia ruficollis ruficollis** (Pall.)—**Eastern Little Stint**

Local name—Chukchian: Békasyl'gyn at Uélen in relation to all tiny waders; this name is no doubt borrowed from the Russian language. Argentov's "red-breasted sandpiper" used for one of the sandpipers of the Trans-Lena region probably refers to the eastern little stint.

Distribution and status—Nests in the Chukchi peninsula but is distributed sporadically. Common at places. Not found on marine tundras from Cape Schmidt to the Kolyma, and absent from Wrangel Island.

The eastern little stint nests on the shores of Krest Bay. According to the observations of V.É. Yakobi, it was relatively few in numbers in 1961 in the neighborhood of Uél'kal'. In the fall two or three of these stints were found there on the bank of the lagoon but their number increased at times because of migratory flocks. On 9, 1956, I came across lone birds and pairs, already occupying the nesting places, on the northern shore of the bay east of Égvekinot. On August 6, 1932, I noticed a small number of juvenile stints in the neighborhood of Notapenmen and collected a chick. At Krest Bay, L.O. Belopol'skii (1934) also found this species in the nesting area.

At Providence Bay this is a regularly breeding species but no one has seen it in large numbers. On August 13, 1880, T.H. Bean (1888, p. 164) collected a juvenile male at Plover Bay which he identified as *Actodromas minutilla* (Vieill.) Br.[1] On

[1]I.A. Palmén (1887) was apparently the first to notice the error but he landed in another by assuming that what was obtained was a Temminck's stint. L. Stejneger (1888, p. 308) quite correctly pointed out that the specimen collected by Bean and preserved in the National Museum in Washington under No. 81413 was a young *Pisobia ruficollis* and not *P. minutilla*. In the Russian

July 16, 1912, É.E. Arngol'd collected an adult specimen at Providence Bay which is preserved in alcohol in the Institute of Zoology, Academy of Sciences of the USSR. W.S. Brooks (1915) found some nesting pairs at the apex of Providence Bay and gathered two clutches on June 11, 1913. The following year, 1914, a young male was taken on July 31 at Providence Bay and another on August 1 at Émma Bay by the members of the Hydrographic Expedition on the freighters *Vaigach* and *Taimyr*. A male and a female were collected by Copley Amory, Jr. (Riley, 1918) on August 4 at Émma Bay. In 1921, A.M. Bailey became acquainted with the eastern little stint there (1926). In his view they nested, but eggs were not found. In 1932, I.O. Olenev, who wintered in Providence Bay, found a nest with eggs in summer, noticed chicks, and gave me adult specimens that he collected. On August 11, 1932, at Émma Bay, I collected a young female. Finally, in 1938, P.T. Butenko shot some specimens in the migratory and breeding periods around Providence Bay. According to the observations of A.P. Kuzyakin, in 1957, at Providence Bay, the eastern little stint was common in the first half of June and a few pairs were found every sq km. But after June 15 most of them migrated and these tiny sandpipers became rare. Nevertheless, three nests were found.

No one has reported the eastern little stint for St. Lawrence Island.

The east coast of the Chukchi peninsula is poorly studied but some finds are known from there. In August, 1855, W. Stimpson, a member of J. Rodgers' expedition (Heine, 1859), shot a shorebird in Senyavin Strait. This bird was identified by J. Cassin (1863, p. 322) as *Tringa minuta* Leisler. It should be remembered that it was a young eastern little stint. In Senyavin Strait on July 24, 1900, I.N. Akif'ev collected an adult specimen which joined the collection of the Institute of Zoology of the Academy of Sciences of the USSR. A juvenile specimen obtained by I.G. Voznesenskii on August 9, 1843, in Mechigmensk Gulf is also preserved there. I.A. Palmén erroneously gave the date of this find as June 28, 1843: Voznesenskii did not always write June and July legibly, and also used the old calendar. On August 19, 1932, I found a small number of eastern little stints on the southern shore of Lawrence Bay and collected a juvenile. V.N. Lyubin gave two specimens shot there on July 29, 1948, to the Moscow Zoological Museum. According to a report by A.P. Kuzyakin, stray pairs nested in 1957 by the lagoon near Poutyn and along the southern shore of Lawrence Bay. Five kilometers west of the settlement he found a nest with a clutch. At Lawrence Bay V.V. Leonovich found the stint but in smaller numbers than around Énurmino and Seishan. On June 18, 1970, he gathered a nest with four very slightly incubated eggs. The nest was 8 cm across and 5.7 cm deep. The bottom was lined with willow leaves. The bird took off from under his feet. The eggs were not covered at all. Their sizes were: 2.22 × 3.18, 2.19 × 3.14, 2.23 × 3.12 and 2.21 × 3.1 cm. Their weights were respectively: 7.68, 7.79, 7.42 and 7.44 g. Because of local conditions, the eastern little stint does not breed on the Diomede Islands.

literature, S.A. Buturlin writes of this error (1905, vol. II, p. 128, note 2) that Dr. Ch. Richmond kindly reported to him that the lone specimen from Plover Bay preserved until then in Washington museum and regarded by Bean as *Tr. minutilla* Vieill. was in fact a real *T. ruficollis* Pall. As a curiosity, it may be added that R. Ridgway (1919, p. 294) in the literature on *Pisobia ruficollis* points to Bean's find and refers to the Stejneger's correction but later, on pp. 296 and 298, mentions Bean's find under *Pisobia minutilla,* presumably having forgotten about the correction.

I found two nests with clutches around Uélen and collected a feathered chick with remnants of down and some adult birds. Nevertheless, the eastern little stint there cannot be regarded as common. On July 21, 1934, crossing the tundra pass between Inchoun village and the Uélen lagoon on foot, I encountered only one eastern little stint. I found one nesting area 15 km southeast of Mitkulen village and another 2 km farther on. At Seishan V.V. Leonovich collected the chicks of two broods. In nearby parts of the Chukchi peninsula interior that I visited, at least along the banks of the Kol'oam- and Utte-Véem rivers, the stint did not nest. In August I encountered lone juveniles on the upper course of the Kol'oam-Véem River. I later came across flocks in the estuary of this river and the immediate surroundings. On July 16, 1913, W.S. Brooks collected a downy chick with a male at Cape Serdtse-Kamen'. The members of the *Vega* expedition came across this shore bird only twice: one male was obtained on June 20, 1879, at Dzhenretlen, and a second on June 21.

In the interior of the western half of the Chukchi peninsula, on the Amguema, eastern little stints according to my observations were quite common in 1956, though numerically far fewer than the dunlins. They remained very much hidden, but in mid-July when the chicks appeared they sometimes became even numerous. From June 6 through 15, 1970, A.A. Kishchinskii regularly found them on the grassy coastal tundra around the Ukouge lagoon, singly as well as in groups of three to five birds. But later they disappeared and did not nest there at all. According to my observations, in 1938, from August 3 through 6, flocks of eastern little stint remained in the immediate vicinity of Cape Schmidt and Ryrkaipiya village. Due to the inadequacy of ornithological field work in the western part of the Chukchi peninsula, the reason for the rarity of the eastern little stint there is not yet known. However, according to my observations it is absent from Wrangel Island.

Some instances are known of the nidification of the eastern little stint at Cape Prince of Wales, Alaska. They are listed in I.N. Gabrielson and F.C. Lincoln's review (1959).

Habitat—The nesting areas of the eastern little stint under the conditions of the Chukchi peninsula are confined to high ground; they are not found on the flat, low tundra. Near Uélen I found a nest on the nearest knoll right under the rock debris at the peak, on the bank of a tiny brook flowing through large grassy mounds but dried up even in midsummer. Near Mitkulen I found chicks which were already running far from the nest. In that area there were fairly high mounds or even small knolls with fanciful outliers on the peaks. I came across cases of adults leaving the chicks at the foot of tiny knolls on rubble tundra with tiny pools and islets of low-sedge.

In the neighborhood of the 91st km on the Amguema, according to my observations, in the summer of 1956 the eastern little stint nested in elevated, relatively dry places: near and at the foot of hills, in the valleys, on high mounds; but also in fairly low, flat places where the grassy or hummocky tundra adjoined the patchy, rubble tundra or was interspersed with it. In one case they colonized the highway alongside the vacant plot of a derelict house.

I.O. Olenev found a nest at Providence Bay, not far from the debris, on an isolated rock 18 to 20 m above sea level. A second nest was much higher, right on the snow line.

A.P. Kuzyakin found a nest at Providence Bay on a gentle wet, grassy slope below the peak of a low knoll. Rock exposure protruded above and beneath. A second nest was located in a wet, grassy meadow in the settlement. The meadow was surrounded on three sides by buildings and open to the bay shore on the fourth side. It was crossed by a telegraph line and a waterlogged, unusable road. A third nest was also found in the wet meadow. The terrain surrounding Providence Bay is so hilly that the eastern little stint could find convenient nesting sites almost everywhere. The nest found 5 km from the settlement at Lawrence Bay was placed on the gentle, grassy slope of a knoll.

Near the Amguema the eastern little stint right from its arrival was confined to the thawed grassy sections of hummocky tundra. On June 10 and 11, 1956, yellowish-brown patches of thawed tundra stood out prominent against a white snowy background; they covered about 30 per cent of the total area. Dunlins, some dotterels, and many Lapland longspurs could be seen there along with eastern little stints. On June 16 a single male, evidently busy in the nesting territory, settled on the surrounding ice when I approached.

I encountered juvenile birds not yet fully feathered at Mitkulen and Uélen at the foot of knolls. Taking to their wings, they evidently gathered by the coast. On August 15, 1934, P.T. Butenko collected a young bird on the banks of the Kol'oam-Véem River on a large spit of gravel and rubble. After a week flocks were to be seen feeding together with other sandpipers in the estuary, on the large silty areas of water which grew shallower with every passing day. At Notapenmen, I noticed young birds on the seacoast and in the lagoons.

For foraging the eastern little stint would fly long distances from the nesting place. On the Amguema, right from its arrival, it foraged by the thawed pools, in marshy places and in the flood plains. On June 26 I found a male on a riverine spit, which was quite unusual for the nesting period. On June 28 I scared an eastern little stint on a wet marsh where there were phalaropes. On July 8 this sandpiper was feeding on the mud below the knolls and later gathered on the banks of a brook.

Arrival—On the tundra near Uél'kal', L.O. Belopol'skii shot a migrating eastern little stint on May 28, 1931. This early date as compared with the other dates given below appears unusual. In 1961, at Uél'kal', V.É. Yakobi collected the first eastern little stint on June 5. According to I.O. Olenev, in 1932 these tiny sandpipers arrived in Providence Bay only in mid-June. In spring, 1938, P.T. Butenko collected the first eastern little stint at Plover on June 6. In the neighborhood of Uélen, according to my observations, there was no spring flight in 1934. On June 10 I encountered a tiny pair and two lone birds arriving, heading straight for their nesting sites. The impression created was that the birds rested on arrival. I have a similar impression from my observations in the neighborhood of Égvikinot and the Amguema. On June 9, 1956, evidently recently arrived eastern little stints were encountered in pairs and singly. Some began calling while others flew leisurely from place to place over small distances.

Nidification—In the second half of June, on the Amguema, I hoped to hear the calling at its peak. But I became convinced that the calling in this stint is far less audible than in others. A calling male would fly low over the ground, 1.5 to 3 m from it, fluttering the wings and gently gliding to earth. On June 28, a calling male, having settled, stared at me for a long time while I froze. Abruptly the stint started up and climbed high into the sky. After a fairly long interval it unexpectedly reappeared near me. Sometimes I heard its characteristic sound "uav" or "uev". Other males flew low over the ground, slowly flapping their wings like a bat that has just taken off.

On June 18, I noticed a male persistently dogging a female. The male alighted and caressed the female with his beak. A.P. Kuzyakin heard vigorous calling at Providence Bay in the first half of June, 1957.

I was able to follow fairly thoroughly the size variations in gonads. The males arriving early had only slightly enlarged testes (Table 41). They gradually enlarged to reach the maximum size by mid-June. They then began to shrink and reverted to normal size by mid-July. The subcutaneous adipose formations, however, varied very widely in the arriving birds. They disappeared altogether during the peak period of sexual activity. They began to develop again thereafter. Of all the specimens listed, I noticed brood patches only in the Mitkulen male.

In June and July females a fine-grained ovary structure was seen. The follicles increased only at the actual period of laying and shrank rapidly thereafter. In females collected from the nest on June 18, 1934, the diameters of the biggest follicles were 5 and 4 mm and brood patches were absent. In another female already with brood patches shot on the same day, i.e. a bird which had incubated, the ovary structure was still fine-grained.

In three of the females having large brood patches collected by P.T. Butenko on July 6, 1938, a fine-grained ovary structure was noticed but the gonads remained big at 6, 7 and 8 mm in length. Most of the females were characterized by appreciable subcutaneous adipose formations. In two of the birds collected on July 18 they were reduced to films and thin layers.

On June 11, 1913, W.S. Brooks found two clutches at Providence Bay, one with

Table 41. Changes in testis size (mm) of the eastern little stint in different years from end of May to mid-July

Locality and date	Left	Right	Locality and date	Left	Right
Markovo, May 28, 1932	3×4	3×3	Uélen, June 14, 1934	4×7	3×5
	5×6	4×5		5×9	3×6
Providence Bay, June 6, 1938	3×6	3×5	Uélen, June 15, 1934	5×10	4×8
	3×7	3×6	Uélen, June 18, 1934	5×7	4×6
Uélen, June 10, 1934	5×7	4×5	Mitkulen, July 12, 1934	2×3	slightly less
	4×8	4×6			
	5×8	4×6	Gek's land, July 18, 1933	2×3	1×1

three and the other with four unincubated eggs. In one nest the male was incubating and in the other the female. Being frightened, both birds took to their wings. The nests were in the form of pits on small mounds on the tundra. They were lined with dry willow leaves. In 1932, I.O. Olenev found four eggs in a nest on a thin lining at Providence Bay; chicks hatched out before his very eyes. After six days he found a second nest high up on the snowline with four slightly incubated eggs.

On June 17, 1934, I found two nests near Uélen. They were located on the same knoll not far apart. When I drew near one of them, the frightened bird, a male eastern little stint, began to fly away. The other bird, evidently a female, jumped off and betrayed the nest. Spreading her wings, the female ran and hid. At the second nest, the tiny bird leaped from under my feet and sat down 10 to 15 paces ahead. Later it disappeared in the grass. No sound whatever came from the eastern little stints at either nest.

Next day, when I approached the first nest, the bird came to within 8 or 10 paces, then fled, partly running, partly flying. Afraid that it would damage the nest, I shot it. The birds from the other nest were not to be seen. I returned to the first nest, gathered it and went back to the second. This time I scared the female in it, which ran away and flew off, finally into the distance. Soon I saw that a male was chasing the female with a cry resembling the distant cry of a long-tailed jaeger. Later the tiny pair landed on a mound near the nest. I shot the male as the female landed within 1 m of it. As before, the female began running, then flew off, but I located her and bagged her.

The nests found were in the form of dishlike shallow pits on dense grassy tundra. The lining at the bottom was fairly thick. It consisted of dry leaves of rust-colored willow. The reddish-brown color of the eggs merged remarkably with the leaves around the nest.

In the first nest the eggs were slightly incubated with the blood vessels visible. The eggs in the second nest were quite fresh.

On June 30, 1965, around the 91st km, I went on an excursion into the foothills and noticed from the peak of a high knoll an eastern little stint wandering among high mounds on the hummocky tundra below. Initially I could hear the call notes "vud'-vud'-vud'-vud'". Later the stint climbed onto the mound and began to make itself more comfortable. I set off toward it and put the bird up from its nest from 50 paces away. There were three eggs in the dishlike pit on a mound with a lining of old yellowish-brown leaves of creeping willow (Fig. 57). Gauging the clutch to be incomplete, I decided to wait, but found it empty when I came back on July 2.

Observations at the nest made by A.P. Kuzyakin in some respects coincided with mine down to the minutest detail but differed somewhat in other respects. In the nest found on June 10, 1957, at Providence Bay, the male parried like a wounded bird, but when the observer left the sandpiper sat on the nest for 15 minutes. The nest had three eggs which had increased to four by the next day. Kuzyakin shot the incubating male; the female was not seen at all. The nest was a deep pit well concealed from all sides by dry grass and lined with annual willow leaves. The lining was altogether dry but the earthen sides and bottom of the pit were moist. Some of the leaves laid on edge served as a lining between eggs. The bright brown color of the leaves resembled the color of the blotches at the blunt end of the eggs and completely masked them.

In the second nest, the deep pit was also lined with willow leaves but most of them were of a dark brown color. The reddish eggs showed up against this brown background. There were only half as many leaves in the lining. On June 13 there were three eggs in the nest. The female sat firmly on them and permitted a close approach. She laid a fourth egg the following day.

A third nest was also well covered from all sides by dry grass and was lined with willow leaves. On June 15 there were three eggs in it and the stint sat firmly on them.

A fourth nest was found on July 12, 1957, at Lawrence Bay. Its design was similar to the preceding ones. The female allowed a very close approach, at once betraying the location of the nest. The eggs were highly incubated and it was only two or three days before the chicks emerged.

Differences in egg size and color are not without interest for purposes of taxonomic assessment of the eastern little stint and little stint. The eggs of the former are perceptibly bigger, commensurate with their much larger build.

The weights of the eastern little stint eggs gathered by A.P. Kuzyakin at Providence Bay from the first nest were 7.87, 7.88, 7.90 and 8.07 g and from the second nest 7.85, 8.02, 8.07 and 8.12 g. The average for the two nests was 7.97 g. The weights of the highly incubated eggs in the fourth nest were 6.95, 6.97, 7.29 and 7.39 g, the average being 7.02 g.

The weights of half-incubated eggs of a little stint from Novaya Zemlya were

Table 42. Dimensions of eggs of eastern little stint and little stint, cm

Locality and date	Length	Width	Locality and date	Length	Width
Pisobia ruficollis ruficollis			*Pisobia ruficollis minuta*[1]		
Uélen, June 18, 1934	3.13	2.21	Archangelsk, 1865	2.89	2.00
	3.10	2.22			
	3.07	2.25	West coast of	2.91	2.12
	2.93	2.21	Taimir Strait,	2.86	2.08
			July 9, 1901	2.85	2.09
Uélen, June 18, 1934	3.14	2.12			
	3.11	2.10	Taimir River,	2.92	2.02
	3.10	2.16	July 13, 1843		
	3.01	2.14			
			Khatangsk village,	2.92	2.08
Providence Bay,	3.07	2.30	1905	2.78	2.08
June 14, 1957	3.08	2.24		2.93	2.12
	3.14	2.28		2.85	2.09
	3.15	2.25			
			Lena estuary,	2.80	2.00
Cape Prince of Wales	3.15	2.28	June 19, 1902	3.04	1.93
(Ford 1934)	3.36	2.23			
	3.18	2.25	Lena delta,	2.82	2.04
	3.10	2.28	July 6, 1883[2]	2.81	2.09
				2.82	2.03
Cape Prince of Wales,	3.01	2.26			
June 15, 1939	2.97	2.28	Lena delta,	2.83	2.05
(Hanna 1940a)	2.97	2.26	July 8, 1883	2.92	2.07
	2.93	2.26			

[1]Based on the specimens in the collection of the Institute of Zoology, Academy of Sciences of the USSR.

[2]S.A. Buturlin (1908b, p. 99) incorrectly assumed it to be the clutch of an eastern little stint.

4.90, 5.80, 6.00 and 6.30 g, the average being 5.75 g.

The eggs of the eastern little stint that I gathered had a very pale rusty ground covered with tiny specks: they looked as though they had been sprayed with burnt sienna. In one clutch the specks were very small but the color of all of the eggs was generally of the same type. After 12 years I noticed that the shell color had turned somewhat pale, having lost the brick red shade and acquired a more yellowish coloration. Using R. Ridgway's color nomenclature (1912) I identified the ground color of the eggs in an Uélen clutch as light pinkish-cinnamon and the color of the blotches as russet. In another, filled with more color, the background was pinkish-buff while the color of the blotches varied from russet to argus brown. In some the color was a light, drab brown. Three eggs which I saw around the Amguema were of a much paler color: a yellowish-ocherous ground speckled with pale cinnamon. They were even paler than the eggs depicted in the plate with N.A. Gladkow's article (1957, plate IIIa).

A.P. Kuzyakin differentiated two types of coloration in the clutches that he gathered. In some eggs the main ground was brownish-ocherous. It was dispersed in innumerable longitudinal (long axis of egg) reddish-brown patches densely covering the ground and merging at the blunt end of the egg. In the light-colored variety the general ground was yellowish-ocherous. The fine brown patches were distributed more sparsely and did not merge at the blunt end of the egg. The third clutch was not gathered by Kuzyakin. This was regrettable since, according to him, the eggs were similar in color to the eggs of the little stint, the semipalmated sandpiper and Baird's sandpiper. According to a description by W.C. Hanna (1940a), the eggs in his Alaskan clutch resembled at first sight the eggs of Baird's or semipalmated sandpipers but were smaller than the former and larger than the latter (Table 42). The main ground color was tilleul buff while the blotches were bay and drab brown; there were tiny blotches of black or slate black color at the blunt end of two of the eggs. E.R. Ford (1934) wrote that the eggs that he brought back from Cape Prince of Wales were exactly like the eggs of *Pisobia mauri* but larger and not so densely speckled; they therefore appeared to be much lighter in color.

In mid-July, when the chicks emerged, the life of the eastern little stint changed radically. During incubation they were hardly to be seen, whereas now they were seen here and there and were not so rare. On the appearance of a man the chicks, forewarned by the adults, would hide while the adults exhibited restlessness much more intensely than at any time. Their behavior varied widely from bird to bird.

On July 14, 1956, around the Amguema, on top of a mound, an eastern little stint flew toward me with the cry "ukha'-ukha'" or "ukhá'li". Later I heard other calls: "vud'-vuvuvu..." or "vut'-vivivi...". Now and again the bird would sit on a mound or other elevation or on low bushes. Unexpectedly, it took off and disappeared high over the lake. After some time it reappeared unexpectedly by my side. While I was rummaging in the grass in search of chicks the stint pretended to be totally carefree. It ruffled up its feathers on the breast, walked a little, then pecked at something. When the stint approached, I was able to pinpoint the place where my presence gave rise to more restlessness. Leaving my rucksack on the ground, I continued a prolonged search around it. Suddenly, the eastern little stint sat down in the grass and stayed for half a minute. I rushed over and found the hidden chicks. I found another one close by. The old bird began flying closer and closer. Probably the chicks had been chirping, faintly because of the cold, but I had heard no sound whatever. The parent bird landed twice more and I caught the last two chicks. Their movement was very weak. Evidently they were stiff with cold; in the box where they were kept they hardly fed and died the following day, though kept in a heated room.

On July 19, on the same tundra, I witnessed another type of behavior. The eastern little stint flew away with a cry: "ukhák-ukhák" or "ukhál'-ukhál'"[1] and began calling. It flew back and forth 1.5 to 2 m or slightly more above the ground, sometimes fluttering its wings rapidly, sometimes gliding, and ultimately alighted. After running a few meters through the grass the stint would climb some elevation, sometimes even a tiny bush. For a long time it would look around, preen its wing and breast feathers and cry "vut'-vut'" or "vit'-vit'"; sometimes sitting, it gave out the call "uév" or "uáv". Remembering where the bird had first started up, where it had repeatedly landed, and where it slowed down in flight over a particular place, I could guess where the chicks were. Sometimes the eastern little stint flew over the chicks, raising its wings high up or flopping from one side to the other, which betrayed intense agitation.

In one case, four eastern little stints flew around me; but sometimes there were only two and most often one. In the latter event, it would be a female. They came within 30 to 40 paces but sometimes not closer than 60. I did not encounter once in the Chukchi peninsula eastern little stints as confident as the little stints on Taimir.

According to I.O. Olenev, at Providence Bay in 1932, eastern little stint chicks were seen on July 2 and 3. V.V. Leonovich collected two or three-day-old chicks in Seishan on July 30 and those of another brood on July 2, 1970. On July 16, 1913, W.S. Brooks collected a downy chick along with a male at Cape Serdtse-Kamen'. The chick had no flight feathers but back and shoulder feathers. In July, 1934, southeast of Mitkulen, I found an eastern little stint with chicks. On July 12 I came across a sandpiper which flew to and fro, sometimes going far off. Later it came close and sat on some mound. It uttered a monosyllabic chirp and behaved altogether differently from an eastern little stint that I had seen near Uélen by a nest with eggs. On July 18 I encountered a pair of adult eastern little stints. They flew uttering the call "tvi-dvi-dvi", which very much resembled the notes of other sandpipers. Sometimes they flew very close. In the chicks I found, the back, wings and belly were covered with feathers while the rest of body was still in down. Remnants of down remained on the nape of a chick that I caught on August 6, 1932, in the neighborhood of Notapenmen village. The chicks I collected from August 10 through 20 had distinctly discernible though very tiny gonads. Subcutaneous fat had begun to be deposited in these specimens either just at the pterylae or in a continuous layer. The remnants of down remained longest around the base of the beak and generally on the head. At that time some stray yearlings were still to be seen. J.E. Thayer (1909) was given a pair of eastern little stints with two chicks collected on July 10, 1908, at Nom.

[1]In some birds this note could be transcribed as "kkhak-kkhak" or even "kkhe-kkhe".

Migration—On July 5, 1956, on a dump at 91st km, I saw a flock of five eastern little stints. They were probably lone birds gathered there to feed. I did not notice any signs of flocking later.

Copley Amory, Jr. collected a male and a female at Émma Bay on August 4, 1914. I noticed old eastern stints at Cape Schmidt from August 3 through 6, 1938. They were the last of the adult birds seen in the fall of that year. The juveniles remained there longer, having been left to fend for themselves.

In the fall of 1933 I began to explore the tundra near Uélen. It was August 27 and the eastern little stints were already flying away. On August 28 I happened to find a lone delayed chick in the estuary of the Vtoraya rivulet (Téeyun-Véem). Though it was flying, down remained around the base of the beak, on the neck and nape. In the fall of 1934 I saw the last of the flocks of young eastern little stints on August 23 and 24. They remained in the company of migrating dotterels, dunlins and pectoral sandpipers, and stayed at the shoals in their company.

According to the observations of O.I. Belogurov in Uél'kal', the eastern little stint did not generally remain until August 28, 1961.

Food—The following items were found in the dissected stomachs: 1) Émma Bay, August 11, 1932, juv. Bits of the heads of three *Curculionidae*, heads and wings of four hymenopterans, jaws of nine caterpillars and coarse sand. 2) Lawrence Bay, August 19, 1932, juv. Head of a *Carabidae*, head and breast of a hymenopteran, heads of two insect larvae and 60 tiny stones. 3) Uélen, June 10, 1934. Tiny bits of three *Carabidae*, tiny spiders and pebbles. 4) Uélen, June 10, 1934. Fine bits of the chitin of 15 *Carabidae* and tiny stones. 5) Uélen, June 10, 1934. Fine bits of the chitin of 12 *Carabidae*, three tiny seeds and pebbles. 6) Uélen, June 14 through 18, 1934. Fine bits of the chitin of a *Carabidae*, about 50 tiny insects larvae and tiny stones. 7) Uélen, June 14 through 18, 1934. Small bits of beetles, 10 to 20 insect larvae and many tiny stones. 8) Uélen, June 14 through 18, 1934. One *Carabidae*, 10 to 20 tiny insect larvae and pebbles. 9) Uélen, June 14 through 18, 1934. Bits of heads of five *Carabidae* and a bit of the head of a hymenopteran. 10) Mitkulen, July 12, 1934. Tiny bits of the chitins of five *Carabidae*, insect larvae and pebbles.

Weight—Two June males weighed 29.2 and 23.9 g. The first specimen had appreciable adipose formations but the second was emaciated. A plump June female weighed 28.9 g.

Systematics—I dealt in detail with the taxonomic affinity of the eastern little stint as a species in my *Fauna of the Anadyr Region* (Portenko, 1939b, vol. I, pp. 192 and 193). Now I am inclined to regard it as only a subspecies. This change of mind is explained on the one hand by my recent fuller acquaintance with the eastern little stint and little stint in the field and in the collections. On the other hand, I have changed some of my views about the general arrangement of species and subspecies as a result of nearly half a century of experience in reviewing most of the species inhabiting Soviet territory.

Being well acquainted with this group of shorebirds, I could not agree to combining them into a single genus *Calidris*. I differentiate a few groups. In particular, the following small-sized shorebirds form a special group: *Pisobia ruficollis ruficollis* (Pall.), *P. r. minuta* (Leisl.), *P. mauri* (Cab.), *P. pusilla* (L.), *P. minutilla minutilla* (Vieill.), *P. m. subminuta* (Midd.) and *Eurynorhynchus pygmeus* (L.).

In this group, the eastern little stint is next to the little stint. There are similarities and differences in many diverse characteristics: in the size and proportions of the body; in the color of adults and juveniles; in the voice, behavior, and life style; and in the size and color of chicks and eggs.

Let us not go into the question who placed the eastern little stint as a species or a subspecies, and why. Recently a special article by N.A. Gladkow (1957) was devoted to the specific status of the eastern little stint. It especially emphasized the fact of nidification of the eastern little stint and the little stint in the same place, in the neighborhood of Tiksi, differences in behavior, especially in calling, and differences in the color of the chicks and, especially, of the eggs. Some objections may be raised.

Tiksi evidently represents the confluence of the ranges of the main populations of the two subspecies. Individual records of the eastern little stint west to the Yenisei do not contradict the view that the little stint is a western form while the eastern little stint is an eastern one. The two stints, as Gladkow points out, do not nest side by side but at a distance of at least 200 m. The distributional boundaries of the subspecies do not always run parallel.

Observations on behavior by N.A. Gladkow do not wholly agree with mine. I have therefore taken observations down to the minutest detail from my diaries, which were written before reading Gladkow's article. I am sure more recent observations will entail correction both of Gladkow's account and of mine. I noticed that sandpipers behave differently when pairing and breeding, when building the nest, when laying, when incubating, when the chicks are hatching, and when they are growing up. Their activity varies in relation to the weather, especially cloudiness and strong, cold winds, etc.

I have seen the little stint in Belushaya Gulf, on Novaya Zemlya and on northwestern Taimir. On Novaya Zemlya, this stint was wary but on Taimir I could extend my hand to within 20 cm of it. The degree of wariness of the bird cannot serve as species-typical behavior. I did not witness the calling of eastern little stints flying up and down.

The color of the eggs may evidently vary as between the two sandpipers. I have with me the sketch of an orange-yellow variety of the egg of the little stint. A.P. Kuzyakin found a clutch of the eastern little stint at Providence Bay that resembled in color the eggs of the little stint and the semipalmated and Baird's sandpipers.

As for the color of downy chicks, it may be seen from the color plate with N.A. Gladkow's article that the difference is confined to the intensity of the shade, while the main pattern is identical. I was able to establish the same phenomenon in bird skins that I carefully prepared myself.

None of the differences noticed in this species exceeds the range observed in the subspecies of various other birds. The changes are quantitative, and not qualitative, and should not be evaluated from a formal point of view.

Specimens— 1) Mechigmensk Gulf, August 9, 1843, ○, 1° anno, Voznesenskii; 2) Senyavin Strait, July 24, 1900, ○, sen., Akif'ev; 3) Émma Bay, August 1, 1914, ♂, 1° anno, Starokadomskii; 4) Uél'kal' village, May 28, 1931, ○, Belopol'skii; 5) Providence Bay, June 8, 1932, ♂, Olenev; 6) Émma Bay, July, 1932, ♀, Olenev; 7) Krest Bay, August 6, 1932, ○, 1° anno, Portenko; 8) Émma Bay, August 11,

1932, ♀, 1° anno, Portenko; 9) Lawrence Bay, August 19, 1932, ♀, 1° anno, Portenko; 10) Uélen, August 29, ♂, 1° anno, Portenko; 11 to 13) same place, June 10, 1934, ♂♂, Portenko; 14 and 15) same place, June 14, 1934, ♂♂, Portenko; 16) same place, June 15, 1934, ♂, Portenko; 17 to 19) same place, June 18, 1934, ♂♀♀, Portenko; 20) Mitkulen village, July 12, 1934, ♂, Portenko; 21) same place, July 18, 1934, ○, 1° anno, Portenko; 22) middle reaches of the Kol'oam-Véem River, August 15, 1934, ♂, 1° anno, Portenko; 23 to 25) Providence Bay, Plover, June 6, 1938, ♂♂♀, Butenko; 26 to 28) Providence Bay, July 6, 1938, ♀♀, Butenko; and 29 to 32) Amguema River, 91st km, July 14, 1956, pull., Portenko.

Biological material—1 and 2) Two clutches of four eggs each, Uélen, June 18, 1934.

70. **Pisobia ruficollis minuta** (Leisl.)—**Little Stint**

Distribution and status—Species flies very rarely to the Chukchi peninsula coast.

On June 13, 1934, near Uélen I collected a female. I shot a male there next day. Other records are not known for the Chukchi peninsula, still less for Wrangel Island.

Habitat—In both cases the stints were encountered on silty shoals and in the straits connecting large and small lagoons.

Seasonal phenomena—The fact that a male and a female were shot on two days successively, though separately, would suggest that the birds belonged to the same pair. The diameters of the biggest follicles in the ovary were respectively 10, 4, 2 mm and less. The testis sizes in the males were also enlarged (3×6 and 2×5 mm) but subcutaneous adipose formations were found only in the female. Had the birds that I collected belonged to the same pair and lived together for a long time their plumpness could hardly have diverged so much.

Food—In the stomach of the male were found tiny bits of the chitin of one or two *Carabidae*, 150 to 200 tiny insect larvae and some tiny stones.

Systematics—I have already discussed the taxonomic relations between the little stint and the eastern little stint under the latter head.

In nature, I did not find these stints side by side but at Uélen I noticed the little stint on June 14, 1934, and an eastern little stint the following day. Consequently I am able to judge them from fresh impressions and from a physical comparison of the birds.

Compared to the eastern little stint, the little stint is built more slender, the body is smaller and it stands higher on the legs. Further, its legs are thinner and the toes longer and not a pure black but a dark olive brown. The beak is longer and thinner and the wings shorter. There is no rusty coloration of the throat. In breeding plumage the breast is ocherous pink with diffuse brown patches. On the upper parts the breeding plumage grows longer than in the eastern little stint. In some little stints these appear even among the upper wing coverts. In juveniles the breast is pinkish-ocherous and the ear coverts rusty-ocherous. The feathers along the sides of the breast covering the wing bend are more rusty-ocherous than in the eastern little stint and have brownish patches. The crown and the upper back are also more rusty-ocherous. With their broad edges the upper wing coverts form a rusty yellow field. The inner secondaries have a broad fringe with sharp edges. Evidently the eggs of the little stint differ from those of the eastern little stint not only in their small size but also in the much lighter, yellowish and not rust-red color.

I saw a little stint and a semipalmated sandpiper literally side by side. The former differed in its greater height, short beak, and measured gait, not to speak of color. It waded far out into the shallow waters but did not attempt to swim far, while the semipalmated sandpiper made free use of its swimming talents.

The little stint nests in the dry sections of clean tundra from northern Norway to the Lena and the Novosibirsk Islands. It is not found in Franz Josef Land, the northern island of Novaya Zemlya or North Land, and is distributed unevenly in our area.

Specimen— 1) Uélen, June 13, 1934, ♀, Portenko and 2) same place, June 14, 1934, ♂, Portenko.

71. **Pisobia minutilla subminuta** (Midd.)—**American Stint**

A lone instance of nesting recorded for the north coast of the Chukchi peninsula.

In the last few days of July (probably July 28), 1909, J. Koren (1910) found a brood of this stint with a flying chick in the neighborhood of Vankarém. Unfortunately the record is somewhat doubtful since Koren at that time did not have much experience in the identification of Siberian birds and could have erred.

72. **Pisobia mauri** (Cab.)—**Semipalmated Sandpiper**

Distribution and status—Nests in small numbers on the marine tundra from Cape Kriguigun to the Ukouge lagoon in the Chukchi peninsula. Not found on Wrangel Island.

E.W. Nelson (1883, p. 88) is the first to refer to this American sandpiper in the context of Russian fauna. In his earlier work he called it *Ereunetes pusillus*. According to him, along the entire coast of Alaska from the Alaskan peninsula to Cape Barrow, as also on the northeastern Asiatic coast and Lawrence Island, in the Bering Sea, this small sandpiper was a common bird nesting wherever the coastal strip was low and dotted with lakelets. It was probably more common among the shorebirds in this region and its rapid trill was heard from all sides all day long in the breeding season. In his much later work Nelson (1887, p. 114) writes under the head *Ereunetes occidentalis* Lawr. that he saw this bird on Lawrence Island south of Bering Strait and at some places along the northeastern coast of Siberia. Such generalizations do not pinpoint the actual place of occurrence and it is my belief that in this instance, as in some others, E.W. Nelson rather carelessly generalized information gathered only on the Alaskan coast for both sides of the Bering Strait.

On St. Lawrence Island, apart from E.W. Nelson's old reference above, we have the latest report by F.H. Fay and T.J. Cade (1959). They saw this species in small numbers every summer near Gambell, Boxer Bay and the Kuzata lagoon, but nests were not found. They reported the following observations: adult bird, June 26, 1950, ♀ July 14, 1953, and ♂ juv., August 9, 1953. In 1960, E.G.F. Sauer and E.K.

Urban (1964) encountered arriving flocks in the neighborhood of Boxer Bay; they found four nests with clutches and later saw chicks and wandering broods. An adult female was collected on June 28, 1960.

A.P. Kuzyakin (1959) made some interesting observations in 1957. According to him the semipalmated sandpiper was distributed along the marine tundras from Cape Kriguigun to Uélen widely and fairly uniformly with up to two or three pairs per sq km. The minimum distance between the nests did not exceed 0.5 km. In all, five adults, downy chicks and five nests with clutches were collected; the locations were one in a lagoon at Uélen, three on the western ledge of the Dezhnev knolls and one on the southern shore of Lawrence Bay. A.M. Sudilovskaya (1965, p. 206) erroneously places the last specimen gathered on July 5, 1957, in a different species: *Ereunetes* pusillus L. According to V.V. Leonovich's field observations in June, 1970, the semipalmated sandpiper was an extremely common shorebird in the neighborhood of Lawrence Bay. Suffice it to say that seven nests and a brood were encountered there. Around Énurmino this sandpiper was found more rarely. I feel that in 1970 there must have been a small invasion by this species, not noticed by former observers. It is difficult to say whether this population will grow in the near future.

On July 14, 1913, W.S. Brooks (1915) collected a male on the western side of Cape Dezhnev and on July 16 two males at Cape Serdtse-Kamen'. In 1934, on June 13 and 14, I noticed some pairs with calling males on a lagoon south of Uélen and by the Pervaya brook. I collected four specimens. In August I came across juvenile birds along the Kol'oam-Véem River: on August 9, I encountered one near the estuary; on August 12 a brood of three birds in the middle reaches of the river; and on August 24, one in the mouth of the rivulet east of the Kol'oam-Véem River.

Finally, in 1970, A.A. Kishchinskii found the semipalmated sandpiper common in the breeding grounds on the hummocky tundra near the Ukouge lagoon. Broods were collected and observations on nidification were made.

Habitat—The semipalmated sandpipers gathering to nest by the Pervaya rivulet selected the tundra at the foot of the Dezhnev knolls, just at the beginning of the slope, only a few meters above sea level. The grassy cover there was not continuous and the tundra could be called patchy with large but low peaty mounds. The sandpipers landed on them during their courtship ceremonies. They also fed on the silty, muddy shoals a few meters away in the lagoons, and especially in the mouth of the Pervaya rivulet. In the fall the young birds were confined to such muddy places as, for example, the sticky shoals in the mouth of a small dried-up rivulet, and a sandy islet among the lagoons exposed at low tide. They were also encountered on the pebbled bank of the Kol'oam River.

According to A.P. Kuzyakin the semipalmated sandpiper inhabited relatively flat sections of wet, low-sedge tundra and gentle slopes. On the rubble slopes they were encountered more rarely (less than one pair per sq km). They fed sometimes on the pebble shoals of lagoons by the sea. According to V.V. Leonovich the semipalmated sandpiper was confined to dry tundra with flat mossy mounds. E.G.F. Sauer regarded this sandpiper as an inhabitant of wet tundra. He found two nests on sedge-grassy tundra, one on a wet meadow and another on a dry flat elevation.

Arrival—In early June, 1934, I spent some time at Uélen and carefully recorded the bird arrivals, but I sighted the semipalmated sandpiper only on the 13th. It was a lone bird which remained in shallow water by a shoal, bathed and swam a little, like a phalarope.

Nidification—At the same time I found three more semipalmated sandpipers on the tundra close by. They were in a very agitated state. Two males were chasing the same female by turns. They were flying low over the ground, generally like other sandpipers, uttering an endless hysterical trill. The trill was so rapid that the calls merged to form a kind of humming or ringing, which may be transcribed by the syllables "i-u, i-u". Another day I found a tiny pair on a mound and later collected a lone bird. The testis sizes in three dissected males were 6 × 8 and 5 × 6, 6 × 8 and 4 × 6 and 5 × 7 and 3 × 5 mm. There was no adipose formation at all in one. Another had it in patches and the third was emaciated.

According to E.G.F. Sauer's observations, the semipalmated sandpipers remained in pairs from June 7 through 10, 1960, on wet tundra on St. Lawrence Island, selecting their nesting sites. When disturbed they uttered the trill "iiit-iiit-iiit-irititi. . .".

The nests found by A.P. Kuzyakin were dishlike pits 7 × 8 cm across and 3.5 to 5 cm deep with a thick bottom lining consisting of brown and gray old leaves of the polar willow. In one nest there were 820 tiny leaves and several hundred in others, but there were fewer than 100 in the last of them. A thin layer of this bedding covered the walls up to the rim of the nest.

Most of the full, unincubated clutches, according to A.P. Kuzyakin, were seen in mid-June. On June 20, 1957, a clutch that had just been completed was gathered at Lawrence Bay. The nests generally contained four eggs each but there were only three in one. The female collected did not have any more large follicles in the ovary.

The eggs of the semipalmated sandpiper are similar in color to the eggs of the little stint and the light-colored eggs of the eastern little stint. Large and small brown patches are scattered on a yellowish or olive-ocherous ground. In addition some eggs have dark gray patches. At the blunt end of the egg the patches are dense. In size the eggs are similar or slightly smaller than the eggs of the eastern little stint: 21.5–22.3 × 30.3–32.0 mm, the average of eight being 21.9 × 30.9 mm. The weight of three fresh eggs was 6.85 to 7.49, the average being 7.2 g, and of 12 highly incubated eggs 5.94 to 7.12, the average being 6.55 g.

The nests found by V.V. Leonovich were 7.6 to 9 cm across and 3.5 to 4.6 cm deep. They were lined with dry willow leaves. The sandpipers would leave the nest and retreat 10 to 20 m. After waiting a little they would give out a restless trill and then approach leisurely and without being noticed. Only in one case did a bird flutter from under his feet, but its clutch had an egg which was already pecked. In the broods the sandpipers were very vociferous. Both the adult birds would be very concerned about the chicks. In color, the eggs were less noticeable and the clutch would be hidden by overhanging grass. The egg sizes in a clutch gathered on June 15, 1970, from Lawrence Bay were: 2.03 × 3.25, 2.11 × 3.24, 2.13 × 3.18 and 2.07 × 3.18 cm. Their weights were: 6.52, 5.97, 6.53 and 6.57 g. They were highly incubated. The eggs of another clutch found there on June 16 measured: 2.10 × 3.05, 2.02 × 3.00, 2.14 × 2.92 and 2.16 × 2.91 cm. The weights were 6.40, 6.32, 6.44

and 6.41 g and the eggs were slightly incubated. The sizes of eggs from one more clutch found there on June 19, 1970, were: 2.21 × 3.02, 2.20 × 3.00 and 2.19 and 3.00 cm. The weights were 6.94, 7.19 and 6.68 g and the eggs were poorly incubated. With the exception of the two slightly incubated clutches the embryos in the rest were so developed that care had to be taken to prevent damaging them. As early as June 14 one egg was pecked. On June 18 a brood of four two-day-old downy chicks was seen. On June 20 a nest was found with an egg and three downy chicks.

A downy chick a few hours old which was not yet feeding weighed 4.5 g and measured 66 mm in length. I am grateful to A.P. Kuzyakin for its skin: a description is given below.

The first thing that struck his attention was the shape of bill which in the terminal half was more intensely enlarged than in the chicks of little stints and eastern little stints of the same age, while in the adult semipalmated sandpiper the beak was characteristically elongated and very slightly broadened at the end.

In the color of down, the semipalmated sandpiper has nearly the same color combination as the little stint, eastern little stint and spoonbill sandpiper, the pattern also being similar. The yellowish rusty color of down in chicks of the eastern little stint and spoonbill sandpiper is replaced in the little stint and semipalmated sandpiper by a more rusty shade (more yellow in the former and darker in the latter).

In the downy semipalmated sandpiper chick the forehead, fillet and sides of the head are whitish: the fiberous ends of the downy fluff are brownish yellow. A black band extends along the forehead and there are two others from the eyes to the beak. On the crown there is a large rusty patch surrounded by a broad zone along the sides and to the rear consisting of isabelline spots on top of the fluff. In the middle of the crown there are two longitudinal isabelline patches with a black diffuse zone between. On the nape there is a prominent bunch of long fluff of a grayish-yellow color with whitish spots. Extending over the foreshoulders and back, the tail and the thighs there is a large black ring. The black fluff on it has isabelline spots on top which form very dense speckles, much smaller than in the eastern little stint, little stint and spoonbill sandpiper. The underside of the body is white with a yellowish-brown bloom on the breast.

The distinctive color characteristics of the semipalmated sandpiper chick do not diverge more than those of other chicks within the group I have formed: eastern little stint, little stint and spoonbill sandpiper.

According to a description by A.P. Kuzyakin, the semipalmated sandpiper behaves differently at different times at its nest. As long as the clutch is not complete it does not stay around it at all. Once incubation begins, if a man approaches the sandpiper silently deserts the nest and does not return for a long time. Toward the end of incubation the male or female sits tight without visible change; on being frightened, they chirp in anxiety and quickly return. When near its chicks the semipalmated sandpiper is particularly vociferous and noticeable. At that time it is found in small numbers in places where it was not to be seen before.

The nests found from June 12 through 30, 1960, by E.G.F. Sauer were built in the grass. In one case the nest was covered by the grass and the bird had made a tiny access tunnel in it. The sandpiper continued to incubate when it was being photographed. In other cases, the birds remained outside of the nest but close by, parrying intruders from the ground and on the wing. On June 27 flocks of these sandpipers comprising up to six birds were seen. On July 11 a week-old chick was noticed on the shore of a lake. A brood of the same age was found on the 13th in the valley of the Boxer River. Toward the end of July the broods joined into a flock and wandered over the wet tundra.

The young females shot in August had filmy ovaries. The subcutaneous fat had just begun to be deposited, initially in the pterylae (in the specimen of August 9). Later the entire body was covered in a film (in the specimen of August 24).

Habits—The semipalmated sandpiper does not stay aloof from other birds. I found it in the fall, for example, in a large flock of dunlins, eastern little stints and pectoral sandpipers.

Food—The stomachs of specimens collected revealed mostly the remains of insects.

1) Uélen, June 13, 1934. Twelve tiny *Carabidae* and two pebbles. 2) Same place, June 13, 1934. Tiny bits of the chitin of a *Carabidae*, about 100 insect larvae (dipterans), two seeds and three pebbles. 3) Same place, June 14, 1934. Tiny bits of the chitin of two beetles (*Carabidae*), about 100 tiny insect larvae (dipterans) and some pebbles.

Systematics—In describing the eastern little stint I have already pointed to the genetic similarity of the semipalmated sandpiper with the little stint and the spoonbill sandpiper. Together they represent a genetically related and integrated group of geographically vicarious species. It is enough to lay the skins of young birds in a row to be visually convinced of the great resemblance in plumage embracing the eastern little stint, the little stint, the semipalmated sandpiper, the spoonbill sandpiper and the American stint. The down of the chicks is also very similar.

Having studied the osteology of sandpipers, P.R. Lowe (1915, p. 616) could not name one character of the skeleton (mainly the skull) that could serve as a basis for separating the genus.

Reassessing afresh all the known features of the skeleton, the outer characters of adult birds, their life style, behavior, voice and other qualities, and taking into account the similarity of the chicks, I classify the semipalmated sandpipers as an American stint. Assigning a special genus *Ereunetes* based mainly on the growth of webs (Fig. 59) between the toes[1] is not convincing. The web at the base of the toes in the American ringed plover *Charadrius hiaticula semipalmatus* serves only as a characteristic of the subspecies.

The question whether the semipalmated sandpipers represent two species or subspecies cannot be resolved for want of adequate material (chicks and eggs) and field observations. S.A. Buturlin (1934, vol. I, p. 90) even questions their separation as a subspecies but here he is not correct. The following distinctive features have been noticed time and again by observers in the Chukchi peninsula:

1) **Pisobia mauri** (Cab.)—In dimensions somewhat bigger than the eastern little stint; has a relatively long, thin bill. In nature, I was able to differentiate the semi-

[1]On this basis I have used the name "semipalmated" applied by M.A. Menzbier (1904 to 1909) for the American ringed plover and the Australian goose.

Fig. 59. Semipalmated sandpiper *Pisobia mauri* (Cab.).

palmated sandpiper in a flock of sandpipers of different sizes; the former is much smaller than the dunlin and somewhat bigger than the eastern little stint, even with respect to bill length. I therefore asked my assistant, P.T. Butenko, to look for a little stint with a long bill. The semipalmated sandpiper also differs somewhat in its voice. The female is bigger than the male and has a very long bill. In the breeding plumage the upper parts are ocherous-gray with black patches. On the head there is a small cap of a yellowish-rust color with broad, black streaks, and rusty patches on the shoulder feathers. The underside of the body is white with arrow-like streaks and blackish streaks on the upper breast and along the sides. Twenty specimens were studied. Their distribution is very limited. The nesting zone is the coast of northwestern Alaska from Cape Barrow to the estuary of the Kuskokwim River, Nunivak and St. Lawrence islands and, finally, the northeastern part of the Chukchi peninsula.

2) **Pisobia pusilla** (L.)—Somewhat smaller in body size than the preceding species but not smaller in wing length (Table 43). The beak is noticeably shorter and slightly thicker. In color the bright yellowish-rust shade is almost gone. The small cap appears only along the rear from the eyes to the nape and is fringed with traces of a yellowish shade. The rust color is altogether absent from the back. In the breeding plumage it is replaced on the shoulders in some feathers by small patches of a much lighter ocherous-yellow shade. The black patches on the upper side of the body including the crown are noticeably bigger. The breast is less speckled: the streaks are narrower and shorter. In young birds too, the rust shade is less evident. Eight specimens were studied. Their distribution runs from the Yukon delta along the northwestern shore of the Bering Sea and beyond from arctic Alaska in the east to northern Labrador.

Specimens— 1 to 3) Uélen, June 13, 1934, ♂♂, ○ Portenko; 4) same place, June 14, 1934, ♂, Portenko; 5) estuary of the Kol'oam-Véem River, August 9, 1934, ♀, 1° anno, Portenko; and 6) same place, August 24, 1934, ♀, 1° anno, Portenko.

Pisobia pusilla (L.)—**North American Semipalmated Sandpiper**

In A.C. Bent's review (1927, p. 252) Plover Bay (Providence Bay) is mentioned in the list of sites of the breeding range of *Ereunetes pusillus* (L.). I do not know on

Table 43. Wing and bill length of semipalmated sandpiper, cm

Species	Adult males				Adult females				Male yearlings				Female yearlings			
	Max.	Min.	Mean	No. of samples	Max.	Min.	Mean	No. of samples	Max.	Min.	Mean	No. of samples	Max	Min.	Mean	No. of samples
Length of wings along cord																
P. mauri (Cab.)	9.33	9.00	9.16	8	9.95	9.38	9.65	7	9.19	9.19	9.19	1	9.87	9.52	9.66	4
P. pusilla (L.)	9.87	9.32	9.52	4	10.00	9.56	9.78	2	9.23	9.23	9.23	1	9.22	9.22	9.22	1
Bill length from feathers																
P. mauri (Cab.)	2.32	2.14	2.22	8	2.79	2.43	2.62	7	2.35	2.35	2.35	1	2.74	2.51	2.58	4
P. pusilla (L.)	2.05	1.72	1.85	3	2.11	2.00	2.06	2	1.78	1.78	1.78	1	1.96	1.96	1.96	1

PLATE VII

Downy fledgelings of sandpipers: *top row*—little stint, eastern little stint, and spoonbill sandpiper; *bottom row*—bright-colored variety of pectoral sandpiper, Temminck's stint, and dark-colored variety of pectoral sandpiper. Pic. by V.S. Rozhdestvenskaya.

what basis this reference was made. Since only *Pisobia mauri* has been found so far in the Chukchi peninsula I am of the view that Bent's reference is erroneous. E.W. Nelson (1883), cited above, mentions St. Lawrence Island in the list of places where this sandpiper was a common summer denizen and in a much later work (Nelson, 1887) states without reservation that he saw it on St. Lawrence Island. But since then no one has reported this species there.

73. **Eurynorhynchus pygmeus** (L.)—**Spoonbill Sandpiper**

Local name—Chukchian: Uljpatschjak in the records of the *Vega* expedition.

Distribution and status—Nests along the shores of the Chukchi peninsula, west up to the Ukouge lagoon, but sporadically, being common at places. Absent from Wrangel Island.

On the south coast of the Chukchi peninsula the spoonbill sandpiper was found at Krest Bay and Providence Bay. According to the observations of V.É. Yakobi this sandpiper was quite numerous in 1961 in the neighborhood of Uél'kal' and in numbers was only fewer than the dunlins among sandpipers. On June 23 a large flock, probably of lone birds, was found feeding. At Providence Bay the spoonbill sandpiper was found by many workers. J. Dixon (1918, pp. 388 to 391) confidently demonstrates that the specimen in summer dress collected by Capt. Moore in 1849 originated from Providence Bay although the locality was shown on the label as Bering Strait. On August 13, 1880, a young specimen was brought to Dr. T.H. Bean (1883, p. 165) from Plover Bay. On June 26, 1881, E.W. Nelson (1883) collected an adult female at the same place. He repeatedly searched the locality but did not see any more of this rare bird there. In June, 1913, J. Dixon (1918) and W.S. Brooks (1915) did not see the spoonbill sandpiper for a long time but then they did not distinguish this species from the smaller eastern little stint, which is very similar. Evidently they encountered a pair of spoonbill sandpipers near the eastern shore of Émma Bay on June 6. But they only found these sandpipers for certain on June 20 on an extensive marsh to the west of Providence Bay. On June 27 J. Dixon found a nest with two eggs but not more than three or four pairs lived there. It is surprising that before me no Russian collector found the spoonbill sandpiper, P.T. Butenko in particular. He spent a year at Providence Bay. I had taught him how to identify spoonbill sandpipers and he had collected them many times before in other places. Finally, on July 12, 1938, returning with Butenko from an excursion to the western part of Providence Bay, to the north of Cape Stoletiya, I found a pair of spoonbill sandpipers and collected the male, evidently not far from the marsh where Dixon found a nesting site. The sandpipers were calling and nested there for certain.

On August 19, 1932, P.T. Butenko collected a lone juvenile female at Lawrence Bay. I made a trip on the same day to the same place but did not find one spoonbill sandpiper. I did not find this species in the neighborhood of Uélen. Only once, during spring flight, did I see a sandpiper on a spit which by its behavior resembled the spoonbill. But it was very wary and I could not get a good look at it even with the binoculars. It is rather interesting that A.P. Kuzyakin did not find it even once in spite of a special search in Providence Bay and Lawrence Bay and around Uélen.

At Cape Serdtse-Kamen' the spoonbill sandpiper was found as at Providence Bay. In 1909, J. Koren (Thayer, 1911, p. 153) collected some specimens at that cape. The following year, 1910, on July 15, Capt. F.E. Kleinschmidt found the first ever nest with four eggs and collected nine downy chicks. At that time it was a valuable record and a sensation in the world of ornithology. In N.P. Sokel'nikov's papers, which I have seen, there is a reference to L.L. Lane, an American, who in the summer of 1911 saw and collected some spoonbill sandpipers, also at Cape Serdtse-Kamen'. A.C. Bent (1927, vol. I, p. 240) referred to two clutches of three and two eggs, collected by Lane at Cape Serdtse-Kamen' in June, 1912. Soon afterward, in 1913, W.S. Brooks and J. Dixon saw seven or eight pairs of spoonbill sandpipers there beside two little marshes at the entrance to a wide lagoon. They collected a brood with three downy chicks on July 17. Finally, in 1934, I was given a specimen from Cape Serdtse-Kamen' collected on July 4. In 1970, V.V. Leonovich undertook special searches but found only two nests and collected a chick in the neighborhood of Énurmino.

In 1879 the spoonbill sandpiper was encountered by members of the *Vega* expedition near Kolyuchin Bay in such large numbers that they found their way to the officers' table on many occasions, according to A.E. Nordenskjold (1881, p. 48). This earned them severe reproaches on the return of the expedition. From June 19 through 28, more than 20 specimens were gathered for purposes of collection alone and 19 were brought home: three as bird skins, eight in alcohol, five salted and then preserved in alcohol, two in the form of skeletons and the beak of a bird preserved in alcohol. Since the species disappeared without trace from the neighborhood of the winter anchorage of the *Vega* after June 28, I.A. Palmén (1887) assumed that the spoonbill sandpiper was encountered in flight by the expedition. But I am convinced that a small colony of spoobill sandpipers sojourning near the winter halt of the *Vega* was exploited by collectors and hunters for eating purposes while the rest of the birds migrated to a more peaceful locality close by.

On July 24, 1909, J. Koren (1910) encountered a brood on the meadow tundra on the western side of the entrance to Kolyuchin Bay. Finally, the spoonbill sandpiper was found at Vankarém. E.W. Nelson reported finding it sometimes at the cape of that name in the first few days of August, 1881. Later, on July 27 and 28, 1909, J. Koren collected some adult males and found a yearling at the same cape, but fog kept him from bagging it. In 1970 A.A. Kishchinskii found spoonbill sandpipers in the nesting area near Vankarém and by the Ukouge lagoon and collected downy chicks. This is the western limit of spoonbill sandpiper records on the northern coast of the Chukchi peninsula.

L.L. Lane told N.P. Sokol'nikov that in the summer of 1911 he saw many spoonbill sandpipers on Wrangel Island but I did not find them there at all.

Outside the Chukchi peninsula the spoonbill sandpiper colonizes the shores of Anadyr Strait and the east coast of Koryatz Zemlya at least up to Tilichikov, where I found (1957) it in the nesting area in 1957. For Alaska, only one reliable case is known of the flight of a flock: on August 15, 1914, 10 miles from Wainwright (Gabrielson and Lincoln, 1959).

Along the coast from Vankarém to Tilichikov the spoonbill sandpiper is distributed very sporadically. In some areas it is quite frequent and is seen regularly in the old nesting sites. If the problem is to collect it at all costs one should go to Cape Serdtse-Kamen' or Stoletiya or, most confidently, to the flat part of the shores of Anadyr Strait.

Habitat—F.E. Kleinschmidt found a nest at Cape Serdtse-Kamen' on the gentle slope of the tundras dotted with freshwater lakelets. Based on observations at Providence Bay, J. Dixon came to the conclusion that the spoonbill sandpiper preferred the grassy banks of freshwater reservoirs. Lone birds often fed along the edges of tundra lakelets lined with algae. They also liked lagoons with sandy banks where rivulets entered the bay. According to observations at Cape Serdtse-Kamen', a freshwater lake with velvety green algae along a sandy bank was a preferred feeding place. E.W. Nelson encountered a lone female at nesting time by a tiny lakelet surrounded by a gravel zone on Plover spit. The nesting section that I detected near Cape Stoletiya was at the base of a knoll adjoining the mouth of a rivulet. In the lower part rubble zones washed by spring streams alternated with marsh on a dry tundra with rock debris. There were no lakelets in the vicinity. A general view of the locality is to be seen in the background of a photograph accompanying J. Dixon's article (1918, plate V, Fig. 2). Finally, P.T. Butenko encountered a migrating juvenile at Lawrence Bay on the flat shore of a small lake. There were many such on the large spit from the southern side of the entrance to the bay. The general nature of the locality there resembled the spits that I studied in the Anadyr region: Gek's land, Zhilov spit and others. According to A.A. Kishchinskii, broods remained at Vankarém and Ukouge on relatively dry, hummocky tundra. V.É. Yakobi saw many spoonbill sandpipers near Uél'kal' feeding on the shores of large lakes and estuaries adjoining small mounds and slopes of hummocky tundra.

Arrival—Evidently the spoonbill sandpiper arrives late in June. In 1879 it was noticed for the first time at the winter station of the *Vega* (Palmén, 1887) only on June 19. That day E.K. Brusevits shot four specimens by Dzhenretlen and P. Johansen shot two. On June 20 F.A. Bostrem caught two males there. On the 21st this species, as also the dunlins, was the most common of sandpipers and some specimens were shot by Pitlekai. On June 22 A. Howhard shot one by Dzhenretlen, on the 23rd A.A.L. Palander shot two and on the 24th Brusevits shot six more. As late as June 27 O. Nordquist noticed at Dzhenretlen that this species was the most common of sandpipers along with phalaropes. On June 28 Bostrem shot a male but later the spoonbill sandpipers disappeared without any trace. In 1913 at Providence Bay, W.S. Brooks and J. Dixon encountered the spoonbill sandpiper for certain only on June 20, ignoring an encounter on June 6 with a pair of sandpipers which were initially taken for eastern little stints. Later those equipped to identify spoonbills were inclined to regard them as spoonbills. J. Dixon nevertheless suggested that the arrival took place at the end of the first week in June.

Nidification—In the spoonbill sandpipers under observation the breeding period had set in on June 6, 1913. The male called vigorously in flight while the female quietly fed among the mounds. For a long time J. Dixon could not locate any nests. The male would fly out singing to meet him from a long way off. The sound recalled a ventriloquist but was similar to the chirp of a cicada in frequency. At an altitude the song of the spoonbill was heard from different directions at different times. Mostly it could be seen flying rapidly at a height of 200 to 300 ft above the ground.

The courtship display alternated between very prolonged sojourns in the air and rapid swoops. The hovering involved rapid fluttering of the wings accompanied by a pleasant, rhythmic, often repetitive humming trill "tsii-i-i, tsii-i-i, tsii-i-i". When a man approached the bird would drop some 10 ft along a short curve and steady again at that point, whirring its wings and all the while steadily giving out its musical trill. After four or five repetitions of this, the sandpiper would descend along a long curve, hardly grazing the ground where the female sat on the nest. Then, flapping its wings, it would rise again almost in a straight line, nearly disappearing from view. From this vantage point the calling would resume as before. After four or five cycles, with the bird approaching the man from different directions, it would drop to the ground, lifting the wings high to form a V-angle before landing, and give out the trill "tsii-i-i", more rapidly and at a lower pitch. On landing, the song stopped and the bird would jog over the moss. At times hiding from view, the spoonbill sandpiper would ultimately disappear altogether. Only scanning with binoculars would reveal it standing or sitting immobile not more than 50 ft from the observer. This vanishing trick is characteristic of other sandpipers too.

The sketch with the article by J. Dixon depicting the aerial acrobatics described above has been copied in the textbooks but it is very schematic. According to W.S. Brooks, J. Dixon's companion, the spoonbill sandpiper and eastern little stint call identically. According to his account the males of both species would rise to a height of 40 to 50 ft (not 200 to 300 ft, as stated by Dixon) and after several brief descents would hover using rapid wing movements, finally descend to earth slowly with a pleasant chirping. The difference between the two species was that the spoonbill sandpiper evidently rose to a great height before beginning to sing in the air.

On July 12, 1938, I arrived in the locality where J. Dixon had recorded his observations, or quite close to it, but it was very late, not June but July, and by then the behavior of the birds had changed. Nevertheless, my observations mostly conformed to Dixon's account. A lone spoonbill sandpiper sitting on a stone flew toward me. A second one landed close by after some time. They remained motionless until I was concealed from them. Then they took off together and gradually gained height, finally calling and fluttering the wings like calling larks (Fig. 60). After some time both of the birds descended to the ground along an incline far from me. I found the male sitting on a rock. On dissection, large testes (3×5 and 3×3 mm) were detected, pointing to recent sexual activity.

On June 7, 1961, V.É. Yakobi encountered a calling spoonbill sandpiper near Uél'kal'. The sandpiper was airborne, whirring the wings for 20 to 30 seconds, flitting here and there, and again hovering. It gave out a very melodious trill.

On June 22, 1913, J. Dixon saw a male at Providence Bay building a nest some 40 ft from him. The bird scratched the ground with its claws and pecked out stalks of old grass and moss with its beak until a pit was formed. Later it sat in the depression and began spinning around, pressing the moss to the sides of the nest. A pit about 3.5 inches in diameter and 1 inch in depth was formed. Old leaves of procumbent polar willow were used to line the nest. It was located where the grass grew densest. In both instances J. Dixon located the nest from the male's take-off. Since it was at a distance of 40 to 50 paces, he had to wait under cover. In one instance, after waiting for 12 minutes, Dixon saw the male return to the nest. He later

Fig. 60. Spoonbill sandpiper *Eurynorhynchus pygmeus* (L.). Drawing by V.S. Rozhdestvenskaya from photographs and sketches by L.A. Portenko.

found two eggs. They are shown in the photograph with his article.

As pointed out above, the credit belongs to F.E. Kleinschmidt for finding the spoonbill sandpiper egg for the first time, although F.D. Fleske (1928, pp. 248 and 249) assigns this honor to the *Vega* expedition. He suggests that the clutch of three eggs found near the winter anchorage of the *Vega* on July 3, 1879, which W. Meves was inclined to regard as of *Limicola falcinellus* (Pontopp.) and I.A. Palmén as of *Heteropygia acuminata* (Horsf.), was of the spoonbill sandpiper. As a matter of fact, a comparison of egg sizes in this clutch with those found by Kleinschmidt would indeed show a similarity.

The egg dimensions of the unknown sandpiper, according to Meves, were 23 × 32, 22.8 × 33, and 23.3 × 31.5 mm. The eggs of the spoonbill sandpiper gathered by Kleinschmidt measured 24 × 31, 23 × 31.2, 22.7 × 31, and 23 × 33.1 mm.

Meves' color description largely corresponds to Thayer's color illustration but the absolutely oval form reported by Meves quite undermines the similarity. I finally concluded that it was the clutch of a Baird's sandpiper.

According to F.E. Kleinschmidt's account the nest he found was a round pit in moss densely lined with dry willow leaves. The egg dimensions were 0.92 × 1.20, 0.90 × 1.22, 0.88 × 1.20, and 0.90 × 1.30 in. Judging from the color picture with Thayer's article (1911), the main ground color was a light brownish-yellow with both small and very large brown patches.

The color of the eggs gathered by L.L. Lane, according to the description by A.C. Bent (1927, p. 240), varied from dark to deep olive buff. The color of the patches and speckles was bister with marks of a drab shade. The spots were dark in one of the clutches: clove brown, even blackish-brown. The dimensions of 11 eggs averaged 21.8 × 30.4 mm; the largest sizes may be judged from the following values: 22.8 × 33, 23.3 × 30.5; 20.8 × 28.7, and 20.3 × 29.3 mm. According to J. Dixon the eggs of the spoonbill sandpiper that he found did not differ noticeably in form, design or color from those of the eastern little stint but appeared somewhat bigger by themselves. The eggs found by F.E. Kleinschmidt on July 15, 1910, were so highly incubated that chicks were just about to emerge.

The nests found by V.V. Leonovich on June 25, 1970, were in a section with very low vegetation (moss, sedge and procumbent willow). One of them took the form of a pit 8.5 cm across and 4 cm deep. The incubating female settled at a distance of 20 to 30 m and soon began to approach with short runs. The four eggs lying on a bed of pygmy willow leaves had probably been incubated for not more than five to seven days. Their dimensions were 2.37 × 3.30, 2.32 × 3.20, 2.40 × 3.19, and 2.30 × 3.02 cm, and their respective weights 8.60, 8.12, 8.10, and 7.84 g. They were similar in color to the eggs of Temminck's stint but differed in their very warm shade. The brown patches were lighter in color. The male called, as usually happens with restless sandpipers. In the second nest, there were three eggs, more incubated, probably for 8 to 10 days. The nest was 9.5 cm across and 3.5 cm deep. The egg dimensions were 2.30 × 3.25, 2.35 × 3.21, and 2.24 × 3.10 cm, their respective weights 8.06, 8.07, and 7.52 g. The behavior of the birds was the same as at the first nest. On July 5, 1970, Leonovich found a one-day chick which was being warmed by an adult bird. The other member of the pair (probably the male) flew in only once.

F.E. Kleinschmidt found tiny downy chicks at Cape Serdtse-Kamen' on July 15, 1910. J. Dixon found some on July 17, 1913. In the latter instance Dixon made very detailed and interesting observations. Crossing spongy green turf by a freshwater lakelet, his attention was drawn to a spoonbill sandpiper which spread its wing as though it was wounded. Soon a second bird, evidently a female, appeared. From the behavior of these two birds it could be assumed that the chicks were close by. Dixon searched the grass thoroughly but unsuccessfully though the grass was not more than a couple of inches high. He then sat in wait 20 paces away behind a grassy mound. The spoonbill sandpiper circled above with anxious calls. A pair of eastern little stints and Temminck's stints soon joined the spoonbill sandpipers; it turned out later that all of them had chicks on the opposite bank of the lagoon. Later, both the spoonbill sandpipers flew away beyond the lagoon and disappeared. But the male quickly returned and landed on the bank of the lakelet as though it had never left. It remained frozen for almost a minute and later ran through the grass straight to the place where it had taken off originally. It stood there for a minute and, satisfied with the outlook, took a few steps, bent down, and gave out a soft low note "plii-plii-plii". When this call was repeated, a tiny chick suddenly shot up right in front of the parent bird as though materializing from underground. Running with unsteady, tiny steps, it stumbled straight toward the parent bird, which continued to call and encourage it.

When Dixon unexpectedly appeared the adult bird immediately gave out a warning cry and the chick sat motionless, laying its neck along the ground. Though the spot was known it took some time to locate it, so well did its color merge with that of the mound of reddish moss behind. Since the second chick could not be found in spite of a thorough search, Dixon again sat in wait. This time the female came, but not close, and did not call the chick. The male returned much later than on the previous occasion. On returning, it waited two or three minutes before giving out the low call note.

As before, the second downy chick quickly got up as though signaled and ran to the parent. On the third occasion the male did not return. At first J. Dixon could not understand why all the chicks did not get up together at the call of the male. Later he noticed that the male in each case came within 2 ft of the hiding chick and gave the call, lowering its head, i.e. turning to a particular chick. The chick's call was a low, hoarse, chirp hardly audible to the human ear and, according to Dixon, very similar to that of the chick of the American ringed plover. Observations showed that the adult birds did not attempt to feed the chicks, which evidently found food for themselves. However, the old birds warmed the chicks, in addition to the warmth they generated in running. In this instance the brood had survived a fairly violent snowstorm the day before.

F.E. Kleinschmidt draws attention to the fact that, as in phalaropes, the male provides all the care by the nest. However, he is not right when he says that the role of the female is limited to laying eggs. He himself shot a female in the immediate vicinity of a nest at a time when the spoonbill sandpipers were with eggs about to hatch and downy chicks.

According to the observations of J. Dixon the male spoonbill sandpiper would engage in construction of the nest, repeatedly flying from the nest which had two eggs in it. In the third case it accompanied the downy chicks. In all my observations at Providence Bay as well as in the Anadyr region, I found males and females by the nests or with the broods. The former were incomparably more active and behaved like the protectors not only of the chicks but also of the females.

On July 24, 1909, J. Koren found the spoonbill sandpiper on the western shore of Kolyuchin Bay, evidently with a brood. The adult bird was concealed in the grass in such a way that he caught sight of it only for an instant running between the rocks and the moss on the dark ground. After waiting for about two hours, for the most part lying on the wet soil, Koren got so cold that he had to give up. Arriving at Vankarém on July 27, he found spoonbill sandpipers again during the next two days and also found a young one which could fly almost 50 paces. According to J. Koren, when with a brood, the parent spoonbill sandpiper behaved exactly like a ringed plover or other small sandpiper.

Being very courageous and intent on deceiving the enemy by any means, it feigns injury. Its cry is heard like a trill, resembling that of other small sandpipers. Its call to the chicks could be transcribed as a faint "pli-pli-pli-pli-pli-pli-", repeated with pauses of about five seconds.

The juvenile female collected by P.T. Butenko at Lawrence Bay on August 19, 1932, had a filmy ovary and subcutaneous adipose films. It was fully grown and the beak had already acquired the angular form as in adults.

Migration—According to the observations of O.I. Belogurov, at Uél'kal' the spoonbill sandpipers were no longer seen from August 16 in the fall of 1961.

Habits—E.W. Nelson (1883, p. 87) did not notice anything special in the habits of spoonbill sandpipers. The bird he encountered was feeding in shallow water and allowed a close approach. On July 17, 1913, J. Dixon watched for half an hour from a hide 50 ft away while two spoonbill sandpipers fed at a freshwater lakelet with a fringe of green algae along the sandy bank. The birds used their beaks like other sandpipers to gather insects or the larvae in the algae. In one case the spoonbill sandpiper lingered for a moment and the corners of the mandibles began moving rapidly as though it wanted to extract something forcibly from the slime. In this process the beak was almost at a right angle to the surface of the water. The bird never used it as a scoop along the surface. In a word, there was not a single instance where it took advantage of the special design of the beak. Based on my own observations, I, too, came to the conclusion that the spoonbill sandpiper in this respect does not differ much from other tiny sandpipers. The form of beak with a flat enlargement at the end could be an advantage when catching insects on the ground or near the surface. The large surface of nerve branches makes for better detection of larvae in muddy soil.

V.É. Yakobi noticed spoonbill sandpipers on the estuary bank at low tide. Running a little in the shallow water, they would rapidly extract food consisting of tiny larvae from the semifluid silt. Eastern little stints foraged along with them.

In external appearance and behavior these sandpipers are difficult to differentiate: the beak of the spoonbill sandpipers is not readily seen from a distance. These birds submerged the beak in the water somewhat more deeply and flicked it from right to left, which is not the case with other sandpipers.

Food—The stomachs of young specimens from Lawrence Bay showed amorphous animal remains of a reddish color and coarse sand. The stomach of a male from Providence Bay was full of the ground remains of tiny insects. According to I.A. Palmén, the stomach of a specimen collected in Dzhenretlen on June 28, 1879, held the larvae of *Coleoptera,* a bit of elytrum and the phalange and other bones of a lemming. Like other tiny sandpipers, the spoonbill sandpiper survives to a large extent on insects. Lemming bones, among other things, were also found in the stomach of a Baird's sandpiper. Evidently the sandpipers picked them up to meet their calcium needs.

Economic importance—Nothing can be said about this because of the small size and limited numbers of this bird. As mentioned above, spoonbill sandpipers were served up at the *Vega* officers' table.

Systematics—The spoonbill sandpiper represents a sharply isolated species. It does not form subspecies and is thus confined to a very limited breeding area. I could not find appreciable variations in the color or size (see Table, Portenko, 1957, p. 464). The male in summer dress is somewhat brighter than the famale and usually, but not always, the rust color on the neck and breast is more intense and distributed more uniformly. The color of adult spoonbill sandpipers in summer dress is unusually similar to the corresponding color of the eastern little stint in very many details and differs in relatively few of them. In the eastern little stint a large number of rusty feathers of the breeding dress grow on the upper part of the body. The black striations are narrower and the patches slightly smaller; on the underside, the striations on the breast do not run very far forward onto the rusty field and onto the anterior portion of the belly, as in spoonbill sandpipers. In the female eastern little stint, the rust color on the neck is much less developed than in the males. This difference is not noticed in the spoonbill sandpipers. Nevertheless the similarity between the flying spoonbill and the eastern stint is not very striking. The plumage of young spoonbill sandpipers is exceptionally similar in color, being almost identical with the corresponding color of juvenile eastern little stints, and very close to that of juvenile little stints and semipalmated sandpipers, which together form a somewhat common type.

The color of the downy spoonbill sandpiper chicks is also very similar to that of the sandpipers listed above. The pattern is identical, the differences being only in the finer details. In my specimen of a downy spoonbill sandpiper chick the neck is yellow, not white, and the striations on the crown are broader and longer than in the eastern little stint and little stint.

I did not see the eggs of a spoonbill sandpiper. Judging from the color illustrations with J.E. Thayer's article (1911) they are similar to some eggs of little stints that I have seen. According to J. Dixon the eggs of the spoonbill sandpiper did not differ noticeably in design or color from those of the eastern little stint.

I have often observed the sandpipers of the genus *Pisobia* and *Eurynorhynchus* in nature, and in particular seen and heard them calling, followed their behavior, and so on. I have recorded their genetic associations quite clearly. Their ancestors were probably only a subspecies of the same species. Later their ranges narrowed and the species began to be isolated under varying geographic conditions. These ranges have now enlarged and frequently overlap, but traces of erstwhile geographic distribution can be still deciphered.

The beak of the spoonbill sandpiper, except for the spoonshaped portion, represents in form a phenomenon not encountered anywhere else in this class of birds. This character alone justifies the isolation of the genus *Eurynorhynchus.* As a matter of fact, the spoonbill sandpiper will probably have to be included in the genus *Pisobia* like the little stint.

Specimens— 1) Lawrence Bay, August 19, 1932, ♀, 1° anno, Portenko; 2) Cape Serdtse-Kamen', July 4, 1934, ♀, Portenko; and 3) Providence Bay, July 12, 1938, ♂, Portenko.

74. **Limonites temminckii** (Leisl.)—**Temminck's Stint**

Distribution and status—Nests in the Chukchi peninsula, not so rare but not numerous either. Absent from Wrangel Island.

V.É. Yakobi encountered this stint in small numbers in the marine zone near Uél'kal' right from their arrival and in the nesting area. Farther along the south coast, because of the hilly terrain Temminck's stint has not been seen by any one so far. It is also absent from St. Lawrence Island. O. Nordquist (Palmén, 1887) thought that he saw this stint on July 21, 1879, near Nunyamo village by Lawrence Bay. In 1957 A.P. Kuzyakin found two or three nesting pairs near the settlement on the bay. On July 21, on the shore of a lake, he found three Temminck's stints. In the neighborhood of Uélen I did not find any. But I found some in the nesting area in the delta and on the middle reaches of the Utte-Véem River, i.e. far inland. In the first case I observed and collected a female incubating in the nest and in the second saw three calling sandpipers simultaneously. On July 17 and 18, 1913, W.S. Brooks (1915) collected some adult birds and downy chicks at Cape Serdtse-Kamen'. In 1970, V.V. Leonovich found six clutches in the neighborhood of Énurmino along the laidas* far from the houses. The members of the *Vega* expedition sometimes collected Temminck's stints by Kolyuchin Bay in 1879. E.K. Brusevits, in particular, shot a specimen on June 14 around the ship at Pitlekai and on the following day at Dzhenretlen. Concurrently, O. Nordquist saw lone specimens and pairs of this stint on the shore at Pitlekai. On June 22 E. Almquist collected a specimen at Dzhenretlen and saw mating birds.

In 1956, I found at least two nesting pairs of Temminck's stints in the flood plains of the Amguema and in the neighborhood of the 91st km. According to A.A. Kishchinskii's observations on the marine tundra from Vankarém to the Amguema estuary in the summer of 1970, this sandpiper was not numerous in the nesting area. In July, 1912, J. Koren (Thayer and Bangs, 1914) collected specimens at Chaun Bay and on Aiok Island. According to the observations of V.D. Lebedev and V.R. Filin (1959) it was a common bird on Aiok Island and in the Karchyk peninsula in 1958. On June 13 a male was collected by the nest and on August 11 a young bird. A clutch was found on Aiok Island and numerous flocks noticed before migration in the Karchyk peninsula.

In the lowlands and the Kolyma delta, Temminck's stints were very common, even plentiful. According to S.A. Buturlin (1960b) it was found at every step in the willow plantations. In June, 1912, J. Koren collected specimens on the lower Kolyma and on an island in the Kolyma delta. Three clutches were found in the delta on June 22, 1917 (Schaanning, 1954).

Habitat—The nest that I found in the Utte-Véem River delta was located on a small flat islet. The calling stints remained on a spit in mid-river. On the Amguema Temminck's stints in one case sat on an islet and in another nested far from the flood plains but near a rivulet. V.É. Yakobi noticed them near Uél'kal' on sandy-silty shoals.

Based on all of my observations on Temminck's stints, I have come to the conclusion that they generally prefer for the nesting area, the flood plain of a river or the immediate proximity or at least low tundra where the tiny lakelets have silty banks overgrown with grass. According to J. Koren, all of the nests he found were located near river banks. However, according to the observations of A.A. Kishchinskii, in the marine zone from Vankarém to the Amguema, the habitat of Temminck's stint was not strictly confined to the river banks. It nested on rubble sections overgrown with *Elymus* and *Astragalus* and on dry hummocky slopes near a lagoon. In the Amguema delta it was very common on the sandy islands and on the Ékug-Véem River entering the Ukouge lagoon. It was found on the sand dunes and spits overgrown with willow and herbage. Farther inland Temminck's stints colonized dry, well-drained areas in the flood plains of rivers. During spring flight O. Nordquist saw Temminck's stints on the exposed sandy mounds around Pitlekai. V.D. Lebedev and V.R. Filin noticed the colonization of flocks on the silty shoals near the estuary of the Kozmina River in the western part of the Karchyk peninsula.

Arrival—In the neighborhood of Uél'kal', V.É. Yakobi collected the first two

*Treeless part of a forest and tundra landscape; low seacoast plain dissected by tortuous rills —General Editor.

Temminck's stints on June 5, 1961. On the Amguema, near the 87th km, I saw this stint on June 13, 1956. The bird was sleepy or tired. There was no doubt that it had just completed its flight. Time and again I saw different species arriving in that condition, especially on Wrangel Island, where their flight course terminated. The observations of the members of the *Vega* expedition in 1879 showed that Temminck's stints arrived late on the northern coast of the eastern part of the Chukchi peninsula, in mid-June. The first of the birds was collected only on June 14. J. Koren noticed the first birds on May 31, 1912, on the lower Kolyma.

Calling—On June 14, 1956, i.e. a day after its arrival, Temminck's stint was already flying, uttering the note "krrué". At midday it was somewhat windy but sunny and warm, the sling thermometer showing +13°C. The tiny sandpiper became increasingly active. In the warmth of the sun it sometimes hovered in the air for a few minutes, whirring its wings so fast that they could not be seen. The almost incessant trill consisted of thin, warbling sounds in the high, chirpy notes made by pipits. The song of Temminck's stint represents an interesting phenomenon in the life of the North and surpasses the songs of other species of sandpipers in the strength of temperament exhibited by the bird. The tiny sandpiper would hover at different heights of 5 to 50 m, later descending and hovering above rivulets and thawed patches where the female sat. If the female flew to another place, the male would continue to call above the female. Sometimes the male would settle on tiny bushes, which I had not seen other true tundra sandpipers do.

Near Uél'kal' V.É. Yakobi noticed the song of Temminck's stint on June 9, 1961. Once, on June 12, he saw a stint sitting on an elevation and singing melodiously, as when calling in summer. According to the description by Yakobi, the breeding flight of Temminck's stint resembled the calling of the spoonbill sandpiper in the whirring of the wings in the air and in the melody of the trill.

Nidification—On June 16, 1956, according to my observations, Temminck's stints behaved very animatedly on the Amguema: they rushed about incessantly, even fluttering at night like bats; their chirpy voice could be heard from a distance.

On June 22, I found a nest with four eggs. It was in the form of a small pit on patchy tundra surrounded by sparse vegetation in the neighborhood of marshes and brooks of thawed water. It contained four eggs of a color characteristic of this species, i.e. brownish-green with cinnamon brown patches. The tiny incubating bird got down two paces from me. It later began to run away chirping, disheveling the feathers on the back, shoulders and tail; finally it hid in the grass by a tiny pool within 10 paces. By the time I could fit the telephoto lens on my camera the bird had overcome its initial nervousness. It flew farther off and went elsewhere. In mobility and rapidity of movement Temminck's stints noticeably surpassed all other tiny sandpipers.

On the morning of June 24 I did not find it in the nest but in the evening it crawled from the nest just 1.5 m away from me. Later, twittering, it began to run zigzag, pressed to the ground and spreading the tail. I moved away gradually 10, 20, 30 paces, but the tiny sandpiper was hidden behind the grassy shrubs, twittering faintly. It was not found in the nest again in day time on July 2.

On July 5, I put up a Temminck's stint two paces away from me (Fig. 61). On that occasion it began post-bathing operations, cleaning itself for a long time. Then it began to forage for food. Until then, only one sandpiper had been seen by the nest. That day, a second one, evidently a male, was also seen. The male alighted not far away and sat on a turfy mound. I searched for the nest, at first assuming that the second bird was a female. At the same time the first bird began flying close to me. It ran rapidly, parried and fussed in such a way that it became quite difficult to photograph it. In the end it began to fly away 100 m or more. I took an egg from the nest, which contained a developed chick.

On July 7, 8 and 9, when I approached the nest, the tiny bird remained 30 to 40 paces away from me. I noticed that the other species of sandpipers also stayed away from the nest for a long time in the day. Evidently the eggs lying directly under the sun's rays did not cool off quickly because of their dark color. It is hardly likely that the embryos in them possessed some property of autogenous development since the chicks on emerging from the eggs froze very quickly.

On July 11, when I approached a nest, the Temminck's stint flew out at me. Later it began to fly low over the nest, landed nearby, chirped, twittered, scraped the ground with the tail, fluttered, etc. There was only one egg in the nest but judging from the behavior of the birds chicks had emerged from the other eggs. I began searching for them but in vain. The second member of the pair also appeared; it also exhibited restlessness but flew off. Finally the first bird landed near the nest, ran to it, and came back in one or two minutes. This it repeated two or three times. Since the bird now permitted an approach within two or three paces I went up to the nest with the camera and to my utter amazement saw two tiny chicks lying side by side (Fig. 62). Evidently they had returned to the nest under their own power guided by the calling parent. During the searches around the nest, I no doubt should have seen them but must have missed them quite evidently because of their merging surface color. As soon as I gathered the chicks, the adult sandpiper sat on the remaining lone egg.

The chicks froze rapidly in captivity though they were kept in a well-heated room. Their movements slowed down, their chirping became faint, they lay on the side or on the back, and remained still. Next day the chicks died.

On July 5, 1934, I found a nest in the delta of the Utte-Véem River; it contained four eggs with developing embryos. In spite of the anxiety caused, the female all the time sat on the eggs though she was chased away several times. She remained away a few steps from the men and when they approached the nest, ran around them, chirped, and parried. The male was nowhere around the nest. Up above the river, on July 7, the author encountered three Temminck's stints, calling in anxiety. The female collected did not have adipose formations under the skin and her ovary already had a fine-grained structure. There were two large brood patches on the belly. When I again approached the estuary of Utte-Véem River on July 11, the stint flew towards me on the bank. It was probably the male from the nest from which I took the clutch on July 5 together with the female.

On June 23, 1961, V.É. Yakobi collected a female near Uél'kal' in the oviduct of which there was an egg ready for laying and on June 21, 1957, A.P. Kuzyakin found a nest with a full clutch of four unincubated eggs in the outskirts of the settlement in Lawrence Bay. As far as he could judge from observations around Anadyr and Apuk settlements, Temminck's stint is not a stranger to the neighborhood of villages. The nest found by Kuzyakin was located in dense grass near a road laid by a tractor. Leaves of low sedge hung over the nest. The nest was 7.5 cm across, its depth being 3 cm. The weights of the eggs were: 6.05, 6.30, 6.30 and 6.30 g, their average being 6.31 g. A.P. Kuzyakin drew attention to the fact that they were on an average 1 g heavier than the eggs of the two fresh clutches gathered by him on Koida river entering Mezensk Gulf. On July 16, 1957, he traced three downy chicks. One of them weighed 4.6 g.

Of the clutches found by V.V. Leonovich from June 25 to July 6, 1970, the eggs were still fresh in a clutch of June 27 while they were extremely incubated in another found on June 26. They were weakly incubated in the rest of them.

J. Koren in 1912, found fresh eggs on June 19 on the lower Kolyma; they were very highly incubated on June 27 and recently emerged chicks were found on July 8. In all cases, both of the parent birds were by the nest and flying young were noticed in Chaun Bay on July 30. In 1916, on the Kolyma, he collected three-day old chicks on July 14, and in 1917 found clutches incubated for two, nine and 12 days on one and the same day, i.e. June 22.

W.S. Brooks collected downy chicks at Cape Serdtse-Kamen' on July 17 and 18, 1913. J. Dixon (1918, p. 400) who accompanied him in the excursions noticed the adult birds of the brood. They left their chicks and flew here and there through the lagoon, adding to the alarm raised by the spoonbill and eastern little stints on the approach of men.

Migration—V.D. Lebedev and V.R. Filin noticed innumerable flocks gathered before migration August 8 through 13, 1958, on Karchyk peninsula.

Food—The stomach of a specimen caught on July 5, 1934, showed the heads of 2 *Carabidae*, heads and shards of 4 *Staphylinidae*, a whole unknown beetle, and 12 hymenopterans. The bird collected on July 7 showed in the stomach the heads and shards of 2 *Carabidae*, head and belly of a *Staphylinidae*, 5 to 10 *Tenthredinidae* (one of them nearly whole), heads of bugs, up to 100 midges, caterpillars, and pebbles.

Systematics—In color, especially of juveniles and chicks, voice, color of eggs, and some features of behavior, especially near the nest, Temminck's stint differs very much from the little stint and all of the groups of sandpiper species genetically related to it. The author has, therefore, isolated Temminck's stint into a special genus.

Specimens— 1) Estuary of Utte-Véem river, July 5, 1934, ♀, Portenko; 2) midcourse of Utte-Véem river, July 7, 1934, ♀, Portenko; and 3 and 4) Amguema river, 91st km, July 11, 1956, pull., Portenko.

Biological material— 1) Clutch of 4 eggs, estuary of Utte-Véem River, July 5, 1934, Portenko; and 2) egg, midcourse of Amguema River, 91st km, July 5, 1956, Portenko.

75. **Actodromas bairdii** Coues—**Baird's Sandpiper**

Local name—In Eskimo language: Surumák on Bol'shoi Diomede Island and ē-lŭkh'-ĭng-ā-ŭk on St. Lawrence island.

Distribution and status—Nests in the marine zone in the eastern part of Chukchi peninsula; nests in the west up to Kolyuchi and Meechken islands but in small numbers and sporadically. Found in the nesting site on Wrangel Island.

L.O. Belopol'skii (1934) collected an adult male on June 7, 1931, on Meechken Island. It was a recently arrived sandpiper and could however have nested only in the vicinity of mountains.

Some finds have been reported at Providence Bay. On June 11, 1913, W.S. Brooks (1915) obtained a male at the apex of the bay. On May 30, 1938, P.T. Butenko shot a female near Cape Stoletiya. On July 18, 1948, V.N. Lyubin collected a juvenile on Érdman Island with remnants of down on the head. On July 11, 1957, A.P. Kuzyakin encountered a Baird's sandpiper in the delta of a rivulet entering the lake between the bay and the sea. On June 15 he found three clutches on a slope between the lake and the knolls. There this sandpiper nested roughly at the rate of one pair in 2 sq km and was even more common than the longspur. A fourth nest was found in the lowland by the brook near the settlement.

E.W. Nelson (1883, p. 88), without citing any evidence, expresses confidence that this sandpiper is encountered in the nesting period on St. Lawrence Island. According to F.H. Fay and T.J. Cade (1959) Baird's sandpiper probably nested on the island but in very small numbers. It is quite accidental that lone birds and pairs were noticed in June and July on the shores of lakes. But in July flocks of up to six birds often joined very large flocks of semipalmated sandpipers. Such flocks were seen near Gambell and along the south coast. Three adult males were collected on August 8, 1953, on the north shore of Lake Trautman. In 1960 E.G.F. Sauer (Sauer and Urban, 1964) found a nest with a clutch in the valley of the Boxer River.

According to E.W. Nelson (1883) there is a young specimen from Arakamchachen Island in the collection of the Smithsonian Institution. This reference has been copied by several authors; it can only be conjectured that the specimen was brought back by the Capt. J. Rodgers expedition in August, 1855.

A specimen of Baird's sandpiper was collected by V.N. Lyubin on July 30, 1948, at Lawrence Bay. It was also found there (on Bennet Island) in 1957 by A.P. Kuzyakin. During my five-day stay on Bol'shoi Diomede Island I encountered Baird's sandpiper at two places on June 22, 1934. Judging from the behavior of the birds and from the date of the finds, they nested there. I succeeded in establishing the nidification of the Baird's sandpiper on the Dezhnev knolls, too. On August 13, 1932, I encountered this species and collected two young ones north of Dezhnev settlement, on the Tret'ya rivulet. Further north near the source of the Vtoraya rivulet, on June 10, 1934, I found a lone bird. I found a pair, with the male calling, near Uélen between the first and second Dezhnev knolls (reckoning from Uélen). In 1948, V.N. Labutin collected four specimens in the vicinity of Uélen on August 9.

On August 11, 1934, by the nest of a peregrine falcon on a cliff on the bank of the Kol'oam River in the middle reaches, I found the wing of a Baird's sandpiper among other remains of the falcon's meals. A.C. Bent (1927, p. 199) pointed out, among others, that Cape Serdtse-Kamen' was a probable point of nidification of Baird's sandpiper in northeastern Siberia. V.V. Leonovich found it between Seishan and Énurmino. On July 1, 1970, he twice found individual birds with chicks. On July 2 they were sighted three times. The *Vega* expedition (Palmén, 1887) did not report this sandpiper but a clutch of three eggs found on July 3, 1879, at Pitlekai was received as a gift and I am inclined to regard this clutch as of a Baird's sandpiper. W. Meves, who processed the biological collections of the expedition, described the eggs and reckoned that they were similar to some eggs of a broad-billed sandpiper. I.A. Palmén thought that they were of a sharp-tailed sandpiper. F.D. Pleske (1928, pp. 248 and 249) attributes them to spoonbill sandpipers. Finally, J. Koren (1910) found a nest of the Baird's sandpiper on June 3, 1909, on Kolyuchi Island.

On July 29, 1939, I found a chick with remnants of down on the head and undeveloped flight feathers; it was therefore a local chick, hatched on Wrangel Island, at the foot of Atternon hills.

Habitat—According to my observations, Baird's sandpipers nest in the upper reaches of hill brooks. Near Uélen I found their nesting area on the knoll second from Uélen going south. I climbed to the highest peak and found sandpipers slightly below the area covered by Iceland moss. The nesting sites were located on the grassy-mossy tundra slopes along the banks of thawed rivulets. On Bol'shoi Diomede Island, I found Baird's sandpipers by a thawed rivulet flowing through the grass and gradually petering out. During the thawing of the snow, this brook no doubt contained more water and flowed farther. On its bed there grew rich grass, splashing green in broad strips amid the rock debris. The sandpipers walked along the grass in the upper zone. Still higher, there were mossy clearings with a very beautiful, variegated cover of green, yellow, brown and white patches. Lichen predominated much higher. In both cases Baird's sandpipers nested directly below an Alpine belt, if such it can be called, on these miniature heights of the Uélen knolls and Diomede Island. On Wrangel Island, I found a young bird in the green valley of one of the rivulets flowing from the eastern forehills of Atternon. For all of my three finds the nature of the locality occupied by the nests was one and the same. In the southern part of Kolyuchi Island J. Koren found a nest on a high, rocky plateau.

The nests that A.P. Kuzyakin found at Providence Bay were placed on a very gentle slope between the knolls and lakes up to 1 km in width. Its surface, still wet in June, was scattered with stones not projecting above the mossy-grassy cover. On one side of the slope was a swiftly-flowing hill brook. Apart from Baird's sandpiper, stray pairs of longspurs, curlew-sandpipers, a pair of blue-headed wagtails and ringed plovers nested there. Pied wagtails, two male buntings and a Mongolian plover were also encountered there. The fourth nest located by A.P. Kuzyakin was built on a wet, grassy lowland near a rivulet but the locality was a scrap iron dump devoid of natural features.

According to V.V. Leonovich, between Seishan and Énurmino this sandpiper lived on the rubble slopes overgrown with lichen. Broods descended to the water holes.

L.O. Belopol'skii collected a Baird's sandpiper in spring flight on the pebbled spit on Meechken Island. On August 13, 1932, I encountered independent young birds in the lower reaches of the Tret'ya rivulet, north of Dezhnev settlement, flowing from the Dezhnev knolls, and even in the lower reaches, where it retained all the characters of a hill brook. The tiny sandpipers remained on the rubble bank and hid between the little rocks.

Arrival—Baird's sandpiper arrives in the last few days of May and early June. The specimen collected by L.O. Belopol'skii on June 7, 1931, was certainly a recent arrival since it was confined to a flat spit. At Providence Bay P.T. Butenko collected a female on May 30, 1938. On a spit at Uélen, on May 31, 1934, I saw a flying sandpiper which to me looked like a Baird's sandpiper.

Nidification—Near the sources of the Vtoraya rivulet on the second Dezhnev knoll, I encountered Baird's sandpipers in the nesting areas on June 10, 1934. A lone bird was evidently resting. From among the pairs encountered later the male was calling. It was sometimes giving out a drawling "ti-i" resembling the voice of a plover. At other times it was an interminable trill: "trrrr' " which is characteristic of most sandpipers. The birds permitted a close approach, this being characteristic of some Alpine inhabitants. On June 22 of the same year, 1934, on Bol'shoi Diomede Island, I encountered Baird's sandpipers in an environment which was entirely characteristic of them. It was the second hour of the night when it was so cold that the pool and the wet grass were covered by a thin crust of ice. The sandpipers walked slowly on the grass and permitted a close approach. One of them was blown aside by a powerful gust of wind from the side.

The males that I collected on June 10 had stray patches of subcutaneous adipose formations. The testis dimensions in one of them were 5 × 8 and 4 × 7 mm. I measured only the right testis of another bird, which was 5 × 9 mm. The female collected on May 30 was distinguished by appreciable adipose formations and a coarse-grained ovary surface. The female that I collected on June 10 did not differ in plumpness from the males shot on the same day. The enlarged follicles measured 7, 5, 4 mm, or even less across. Only thin subcutaneous adipose formations were seen in the female collected on June 22. The diameter of the biggest follicle was hardly 2 mm. The large brood patches on the sides of the belly provided proof of incubation. The eggs found by J. Koren on Kolyuchi Island on July 3, 1909, had been incubated according to him for roughly five days.

On June 11, 1957, A.P. Kuzyakin found a clutch of four unincubated eggs at Providence Bay. Of the three nests that he found on June 15, the eggs in two were in the early stages of incubation while they were half done in another.

All of the four nests were located in areas overgrown with low-sedge, moss, lichen and stray shrubs of procumbent willow. One was found near a rivulet while the rest were far from water. Two of the three nests located on a slope were at a distance of 0.5 km from each other while the third one was more than a kilometer away from them.

The nests were in the form of dishlike pits, 8 to 9 cm across and 3.5 to 4 cm deep. Their bottoms were lined with bits of dry grass and lichen. There were many old brown willow leaves in the bedding of one of them.

Males were shot near two nests and A.P. Kuzyakin thought that they were incubating. When a man approached a nest on June 15, 1957, all the sandpipers noticed jumped down from it but did not fly out. Then they ran away with anxious chirps, dropped to the ground, and feigned injury. If the observer stood aside, the bird returned to the nest and sat in it after some time (15 to 40 minutes). In one case a third bird probably from a neighboring nest joined the restless pair.

It also quivered, from time to time giving the call "piuiuuyt' ", and flew as

PLATE VIII

Spoonbill sandpiper *Eurynorhynchus pygmeus* (L.).
Pic. by V.S. Rozhdestvenskaya.

though calling. The female sat motionless on the rock for about an hour; she sometimes turned her head from side to side but did not preen or look for food as other sandpipers have done in such cases. Exactly an hour later the female suddenly became alarmed, ran for some 10 m to another rock and then stood motionless again. The weather was cold, about +4 to 5° C; a cold, humid wind was blowing. The male at that time was sitting on the nest.

In one of the clutches, the eggs measured 24.4 × 35.1, 24.5 × 35.0, 24.6 × 35.6 and 24.8 × 35.2 mm. The weight of 12 nearly unincubated eggs varied in the range 9.40 to 10.70 g, the average being 10.08 g. The weight of the incubated eggs was slightly less: on an average, 10.05 g. The color of the eggs was a light ocherous yellow with tiny and moderate-sized brown patches, bunching somewhat at the blunt end. Apart from them there were a few deep lilac-gray patches. In color the eggs were similar to the eggs of the semipalmated sandpiper but bigger. In size they approached the eggs of the dunlin but devoid of olive shades.

The eggs of a mysterious clutch from Pitlekai referred to above, according to the description by W. Meves, had an exactly oval form without the least pinching at one end. Their sizes were 23 × 32, 22.8 × 33, and 23.3 × 31.5 mm. The main ground is yellowish-gray-white; the patches are reddish-gray; the tiny speckles are rust or liver brown and merge at the blunt end to hide the ground.

There were three eggs in a nest found on St. Lawrence Island by E.G.F. Sauer (Sauer and Urban, 1964, photograph on p. 50) on June 20, 1960. The nest was on a low knoll north of the river. It was on a grassy mound on wet tundra. Much of the nest material consisted of dry brown willow leaves which in color blended harmoniously with the color of the eggs. On visiting the nest on June 30, there were already four eggs in it. Only an addled egg remained on July 18. On July 12, at another place, a sandpiper was seen feigning injury.

The chick that I collected on Wrangel Island on July 29, 1939, could barely fly a short distance. Fluttering out from under my feet, it uttered a peep. The voice of Baird's sandpiper can be heard only rarely outside the nesting period. The large flight feathers had not grown to more than 2 cm and its wing length was 10.5 cm. The anterior part of the head and nape were covered with down. In the juveniles I collected on August 13, 1932, the wing span measured 11.9 and 12.4 cm. They were females with well-developed ovaries. In one case the fine-grained structure could be seen. All the juveniles were devoid of subcutaneous adipose formations.

It is interesting that new black feathers with broad rusty-ocherous fringes were growing in the central and lower parts of the back of the females collected on July 29, 1934 from Diomede Island.

Migration—There is no doubt that the adults migrated very early and in any case earlier than the juveniles. On August 13, 1932, on the Tret'ya rivulet, I found only juveniles.

Food—In the stomachs of specimens collected on June 10, 1934, at Uélen, the following contents were found: 1) Heads and whole specimens of eight *Carabidae* and 16 hymenopterans, six larvae of flies and three tiny spiders; 2) tiny bits of five to eight *Carabidae*, one *Staphylinidae*, dipteran larva, some shoots of moss and leaves and also tiny pebbles; 3) heads of five *Carabidae*, heads and abdomen of four *Staphylinidae*, 10 dipteran larvae, teeth and bits of a bone of a lemming or field vole and tiny stones. Remains of bones were found in the stomach of a female and this no doubt was to be explained by the fact that the bird had already laid her eggs or was about to do so. On June 28, 1934, the heads and other remains of eight *Carabidae*, heads, bellies and other remains of 45 *Staphylinidae* and tiny stones were found in the stomach of incubating females from Bol'shoi Diomede Island. Finally, the stomach of a chick collected on Wrangel Island on June 29, 1939, revealed the remains of tiny beetles and coarse sand.

Weight—The female from Providence Bay collected on May 30, 1938, weighed 38.0 g.

Systematics—Actodromas fuscicollis (Vieill.) is the nearest genetic relative of Baird's sandpiper; in the historical past the former was probably only a subspecies of the latter.

Specimens— 1) Meechken Island, June 7, 1931, ○, Belopol'skii; 2 and 3) Tret'ya rivulet between Dezhnev and Uélen, August 13, 1932, ♀♀, 1° anno, Portenko; 4 to 6) neighborhood of Uélen, June 10, 1934, ♂♂♀, Portenko; 7) Bol'shoi Diomede Island, June 22, 1934, ♀, Portenko; 8) Providence Bay, Cape Stoletiya, May 30, 1938, ♀, Butenko; and 9) neighborhood of Atternon hills, Wrangel, July 29, 1939, juv., Portenko.

76. **Heteropygia melanotos** (Vieill.)—**Pectoral Sandpiper**

Local name—In Eskimo: Durek on St. Lawrence Island; also applied to dotterel, dowitcher and tattler.

Distribution and status—Nests in the Chukchi peninsula but not everywhere and not in the same numbers; altogether absent from the nesting area on the high south coast but found on St. Lawrence Island. Common in the nesting area in the interior of the peninsula and along the north coast but not everywhere; not numerous in any particular place. Does not nest on Bol'shoi Diomede and Kolyuchi islands. Common even in the fall in flights, being numerous along the north coast. Found in the nesting area and encountered in flights on Wrangel Island, being quite common in fall flight.

Neither P.T. Butenko and I nor L.O. Belopol'skii (1934) encountered pectoral sandpipers at the entrance to Krest Bay, but on June 8, 1956, I saw a migrating flock on the tundra east of Égvekinot.

Based on observations made in 1865 and 1866 V.G. Dall (Dall and Bannister, 1869, p. 292) writes that this species was not rare at Plover Bay. Later, none of the ornithologists visiting Providence Bay, including myself, saw the pectoral sandpiper there. Only in 1938 did Butenko manage to gather some specimens in the spring flight. He shot a juvenile during the fall flight at Cape Chaplin.

At the same time, some records were reported on St. Lawrence Island that point to the pectoral sandpiper nesting there. According to I.A. Palmén (1887, p. 322), it is quite likely (synes det sannolikt) that four of the unfeathered chicks acquired by the *Vega* expedition on August 2, 1879, in Chibukak belonged to this species. Though Palmén gives a detailed description of the downy chicks there is some element of doubt because of one's lack of confidence in his remarks cited above. Harriman's expedition (Friedmann, 1932a) obtained a female on St. Lawrence Island on June 13,

1899, and A.M. Bailey (1926) noticed pectoral sandpipers on July 29, 1921. In both cases the dates related to the nesting period. Nevertheless, it should be pointed out that E.W. Nelson (1883) did not notice pectoral sandpipers on St. Lawrence Island. O.J. Murie (1936) collected only a lone specimen, a male, on September 25, 1929. According to the latest data of F.H. Fay and T.J. Cade (1959) the population of pectoral sandpipers there undergoes wide fluctuations from year to year. They were noticed in small numbers in 1950 and 1957. An adult male was obtained at Boxer Bay on July 27, 1950. In 1956 some flocks consisting of 15 to 30 birds were often noticed in May near Gambell and on the Mogoveiik River. A pair was secured on that river on May 26. Some pairs, probably nested, were noticed on the western and southern coasts in early June and at the end of July. On June 10, 1960, E.G.F. Sauer (Sauer and Urban, 1964) noticed two pectoral sandpipers in the neighborhood of Boxer Bay together with a pair of semipalmated sandpipers and a dotterel. On July 28 he scared two birds which took off with anxious cries.

On the east coast of the Chukchi peninsula the pectoral sandpiper was obtained several times at Lawrence Bay. On August 19, 1932, I shot a juvenile male there. V.N. Lyubin brought back seven specimens shot on July 29 and August 4, 1948. Finally, on July 9 or 10, 1957, A.P. Kuzyakin collected a pectoral sandpiper in the neighborhood of the settlement.

On July 14 and 15, 1970, V.V. Leonovich heard its call at Lawrence Bay.

On Bol'shoi Diomede Island this sandpiper was absent because of the topographic conditions. On the flat tundra between Dezhnev settlement and Uélen pectoral sandpipers, according to my observations, were common. On August 13, 1932, I came across pairs and one of them returned to the nesting section on being vigorously chased. The female revealed brood patches. Hence the pectoral sandpipers nested there. In the 1934 spring flight, around Uélen, I saw only a few pairs but the pectoral sandpipers were innumerable in the fall flights in 1932, 1933 and 1934. On September 8, 1939, I disembarked from the ship for half an hour and was just on my way to the settlement when I came across a juvenile pectoral sandpiper.

In the nearby hinterland of the peninsula these sandpipers were also quite common. On the Kol'oam River, in August, 1934, I saw wandering flocks and lone birds. In July of the same year, along the lower course of the Utte-Véem River, I encountered nesting pectoral sandpipers for certain but in relatively small numbers. On its lower reaches, on July 6, I sighted a few specimens. Later, in the course of my slow progress up the river, I encountered on July 7 a male still in the nesting section. On my way back on July 10 I saw pectoral sandpipers in two places on the lower course of the river and an agitated male on July 12 near the southwestern corner of the Inchoun lagoon.

W.S. Brooks (1915) collected three specimens on July 17, 1913, i.e. positively in the nesting period, at Cape Serdtse-Kamen'. It is not without interest that in 1879 the *Vega* expedition did not get a single pectoral sandpiper in the neighborhood of Kolyuchin Bay. This is all the more surprising since, on the one hand, the expedition secured a pectoral sandpiper (male) on August 19–20, 1878, at Cape Chelyuskin and, on the other, collected many different types of sandpipers in Pitlekai. At Kolyuchin Bay a juvenile female pectoral sandpiper was collected on August 10, 1914, by Copley Amory, Jr. (Riley, 1918). According to J. Koren (1910) this sandpiper no doubt nested on Kolyuchi Island, but according to my thinking, it could not have nested there because of the very nature of the terrain.

In the interior of the peninsula, on the Amguema River near the 91st km, I found the pectoral sandpiper common in the nesting area. There I observed four nests and gathered a clutch and some downy chicks.

According to an eyewitness account by E.W. Nelson (1883, p. 86; 1887, p. 108), at the end of July, 1881, he found the pectoral sandpiper common and numerous in the grassy plains on the north coast of the Chukchi peninsula where the *Corwin* moored, and hence not west of Cape Schmidt. E.W. Nelson assumed that they were the nesting places of the pectoral sandpiper. In summer, 1970, A.A. Kishchinskii found this species common in the nesting area on the tundra from Vankarém to the Amguema estuary (Fig. 63). In early August, 1938, I encountered broods which had begun wandering on Cape Schmidt to the east of Cape Veber. J. Koren (Thayer and Bangs, 1914) found this species nesting all along the arctic coast of the Chukchi peninsula; flying juvenile birds were especially noticed on July 30, 1912, at Chaun Bay. According to an account by V.D. Lebedev and V.R. Filin (1959), the pectoral sandpiper was a common nesting bird in 1958 on the western shore of Chaun Bay, in the Karchyk peninsula and on Aiok Island. They noticed innumerable calling males and small flocks before migration in August.

On the lower reaches of the Kolyma S.A. Buturlin says he came across pectoral sandpipers (1906b, p. 6) at every step. J. Koren received a clutch on June 17, 1912, on the lower Kolyma and found new-hatched chicks on July 5 near the estuary of the Medvezh'ya River. Later four downy chicks from the Kolyma delta were added to his collection (Schaanning, 1954). E.P. Spangenberg (1960) found a clutch on June 15, 1959, on the lower reaches of the river.

In the course of five years of residence on Wrangel Island A.I. Mineev (Portenko, 1937b) collected only one pectoral sandpiper; a female on August 25, 1932, near Rodgers Bay. In the supplements to *Complete Identification of the Birds of the USSR* (Buturlin and Dement'ev, 1941, vol. V, p. 22) G.P. Dement'ev erroneously places this find as a sharp-tailed sandpiper. I encountered pectoral sandpipers often and in large numbers on Wrangel Island. In the 1938 fall flight I found them in large numbers in Tundra Akademii. On August 14, on the tundra south of Bruch spit, up to 30 birds could be counted in some flocks. Pectoral sandpipers were also common near the estuary of the Krasnyi Flag River. There they were found in flocks as well as singly. A.N. Druzhinin (Bannikov, 1941) gave a male shot on August 15 to the Moscow Zoological Museum.

In the spring of 1939, on the southern side of the island, I encountered four pectoral sandpipers, only once, on June 7, at 180° longitude. Later I came across pectoral sandpipers many times in the course of the summer. On July 15 I saw pairs and flocks of different sizes on the tundra by Somnitel'naya Bay. They were perhaps lone birds. On July 22, I encountered pectoral sandpipers near the estuary of the Nasha River and from July 24 through August 7 at the foot of the Atternon knolls. On August 7, I collected an old female with a young bird. On July 27 I encountered a lone pectoral sandpiper on my way to Cape Hawaii. In a dense fog the sandpiper moved away slowly from me; evidently it was a nesting bird.

In 1934, F.B. Chernyavskii also found nesting pectoral sandpipers on Wrangel

Island. Their population, according to him, was noticeably smaller than that of turnstones, plovers and robin sandpipers. He heard the voice of the calling spring male only once. He found a nest with a clutch in the northwestern part of the island, in the watershed of the Tundrovaya and Medvezh'ya rivers.

According to a report of R.L. Newcomb (1888; also Nelson, 1883, p. 86), on August 18, 1880, a pair of pectoral sandpipers landed on board the *Jeannette* when it was stuck in the ice northwest of Wrangel Island at roughly 76° north. Such flights evidently were not a rarity because the collection of the Institute of Zoology, Academy of Sciences of the USSR, contains a specimen which alighted on the deck of the icebreaker *Litka* on August 8, 1929, when the ship was 71°05′ north and 175°01′ east. It was a juvenile female.

Habitat—In the breeding as in the migratory period, the residence of pectoral sandpipers is closely associated with extensive grassy areas of tundra or meadow types. But these must be wet and quite marshy, or at least just wet in the immediate vicinity of lakelets or streams. Pectoral sandpipers avoid hilly relief and love flat plains. On the lower reaches of the Utte-Véem River the nesting places were found in the lower meadows on the banks of rivers where there were many lakelets and old stagnant pools. In such meadows, I encountered pectoral sandpipers together with Lapland longspurs and common snipes. Further up the river pectoral sandpipers crossed my path in the marshy meadows and on wet, grassy tundra. According to my 1956 observations, on the tundra adjoining the Amguema pectoral sandpipers nested in the grassy marshes with waterholes and peaty mounds or hummocks. They mostly preferred a fairly wet, hummocky tundra. They are not found at all on flat areas that are grassy, sodden and without mounds; nor were they found on dry elevated tundra.

On Wrangel Island they were found in summer at the grassy waterholes on a flat plateau by Somnitel'naya Bay, and very rarely on the banks of lakelets. At the foot of the Atternon knolls I found them on flat, wet, hummocky tundra. But near Cape Hawaii I came across a lone pectoral sandpiper on the patchy tundra characteristic of the arctic wasteland scenery in the northern part of the island. F.B. Chernyavskii found a nest in the flat mossy-herbage tundra in the northwestern part of the island.

In spring flight, near Uélen and on Wrangel, I encountered pectoral sandpipers on the grassy tundra; they chose the wet, hummocky section. In fall flight, they were particularly common between Dezhnev settlement and Uélen. There were extensive stretches of grassy tundra that were quite marshy or lay next to such areas and the pectoral sandpipers selected the grassiest, wettest sections. They spread right up to the Dezhnev knolls and were encountered in the marshy sections on the lower slopes right at the foot, usually along the edges of tiny meadows or brooks where there was succulent green grass. I also saw the birds flying into the settlement, headed for the luxuriant grass growing on soil well fertilized with domestic wastes. Even during the intense movement of flocks these sandpipers preferred to stay on the grassy banks of rivulets though they could sometimes be found feeding on the sandy islets in the rivers or in the slimy zones in estuaries. I had occasion to make such observations on the Kol'oam-Véem River. In northern Wrangel Island, in the fall of 1938, I came across migrating pectoral sandpipers on the marshy ground. As an exception, I saw them in the fall on pebbled spits, for example on the upper course of the Kol'oam-Véem River and also on Wrangel Island north of the Krasnyi Flag estuary together with gray phalaropes.

Arrival—In the spring of 1938, at Providence Bay by Cape Stoletiya, P.T. Butenko collected some of the first pectoral sandpipers to arrive on May 30 and the last of them on June 6. He did not see them at all in the course of the summer. The migration lasted just a week. In 1934, near Uélen, I noticed the first sandpipers on June 4. I sighted two females and a male; they were sitting so close together that I bagged all of them with one shot. On June 7 I saw two or three pairs. Right from their arrival they evidently settled only on the tundra. They did not at once begin calling, just sat silently, usually very close together. In the spring of 1956 I put up a flock of pectoral sandpipers east of Égvekinot on June 8. They sat in the snowy meadows. Finally, in the spring of 1939 on Wrangel Island, I saw the first pectoral sandpipers on June 7. I found two pairs on a long-distance flight, i.e. they had not yet settled down. F.B. Chernyavskii heard the voice of a calling male in the first few days of June, 1964.

Condition of gonads and subcutaneous fat—Right from their arrival the pectoral sandpipers revealed greatly enlarged testes. My Anadyr series collected from May 27 through June 3, 1932, measured as follows: 7 × 15 and 5 × 14, 7 × 15 and 7 × 11, 11 × 14 and 8 × 10, 7 × 14 and 7 × 12, 6 × 14 and 6 × 11, 11 × 13 and 8 × 12, 8 × 13 and 5 × 12, 11 × 12 and 8 × 10, 7 × 12 and 8 × 12, 6 × 12 and 4 × 10, 7 × 11 and 6 × 9, 9 × 10 and 7 × 8, 7 × 10 and 7 × 9, and 8 × 9 and 5 × 7 mm. The testes of males collected at Providence Bay on May 30, 1938, were of similar dimensions: 5 × 12 and 4 × 10, and 4 × 12 and 4 × 11 mm. The size in an Uélen male obtained on June 4, 1934, was 8 × 12 and 6 × 9 mm. The testes were noticeably smaller in the summer males. In the specimen from Utte-Véem collected on June 6, 1934, they measured 5 × 8 and 4 × 6 mm and in the males from Somnitel'naya Bay collected on July 15, 1939, they were 4 × 7 and 3 × 5 and 3 × 5 and 2 × 4 mm.

It should be pointed out that the testis dimensions in the young males in the first fall were sometimes relatively greater than in other sandpipers at that time of the year. In a series of young males collected in the Chukchi peninsula and on Wrangel Island in the period from August 13 through September 9, the following measurements were recorded: 4 × 6 and 3 × 5, 2 × 4 and 2 × 3, 2 × 4 and 2 × 3, 2 × 3 and 2 × 2, 1 × 3 and—, 1 × 2 and 1 × 2, 1 × 2 and 1 × 1, 1 × 1, and 1 × 1 and 1 × 1 and 1 × 1 mm.

In the females collected at Providence Bay on May 30 and June 6, 1938, a coarse-grained ovary structure was noticed. At the same time, the follicles were a maximum of 4 to 5 mm across in arriving birds collected in Anadyr on May 28 and 29, 1932, and at Uélen on June 4, 1934. In the females collected at Uélen on June 7 the biggest follicle was 6 mm long. A specimen from the lower reaches of the Utte-Véem River collected on July 6, 1934, with large brood patches had follicles reduced to 2 mm. An adult female obtained in the neighborhood of Dezhnev settlement on August 13, 1932, still preserved large brood patches but the ovary had degraded to a fine-grained structure. The adult female collected at Rodgers Bay on August 7, 1939, had brood patches. The ovary length reached 10 mm, the diameter of the biggest follicle being 0.5 mm. A filmy ovary could be seen in young females in the first fall. In a specimen from Uélen collected on August 23, 1933, the length of the ovary was 7 mm.

The condition of subcutaneous adipose formations was not closely dependent on the activity of gonads. In most cases the birds obtained could be called fairly plump. Arriving pectoral sandpipers numbered very few fat birds but only three of a total of 30 birds were totally devoid of subcutaneous adipose formations.

On the lower reaches of the Utte-Véem River, I collected a male and a female evidently belonging to different pairs on July 6, 1934: the male appeared emaciated but the female was plump in spite of the fact that she had brood patches. Another female with brood patches shot at Dezhnev settlement on August 13, 1932, lacked adipose formations. The young fall pectoral sandpipers were mostly fat. Toward the end of the fall they became even fatter. The Uélen specimen collected on September 9, 1933, was unusually plump. All the pectoral sandpipers that I collected on Wrangel Island, even in the summer, for example two males shot near Somnitel'-naya Bay on July 15, 1939, were characterized by appreciable subcutaneous adipose formations. In a young bird from the estuary of the Krasnyi Flag River collected on August 17, 1938, the subcutaneous fat covered the whole body.

Voice—In 1956, I was able to study in great detail the nesting habits of the pectoral sandpiper at the 91st km on the Amguema. By June 15 the males had already occupied their nesting territories. On the hummocky tundra near the settlement, only 30 paces in front of me, I noticed a male sitting on a mound alongside an eastern little stint. It was quietly preening the feathers of the shoulders and back and ruffling the feathers in the lower part of the breast. As a result a dewlap (the term used for cattle) was formed. Noticing me, the sandpiper took off, flew past me for some 10 paces with a special gurgling sound and, circling around, alighted at a distance. It stretched out its neck so that the dewlap took on the form of half a lentil. In flight the pouch appeared spherical. The pectoral sandpiper had thus arrived in its nesting territory and was ready for calling.

For three days from June 13, i.e. up to the 16th, the weather was sunny and warm. The temperature went up to +16° C but dropped in the evening (at the top of a knoll it was only +4° C). That day I encountered some calling males. They permitted a close approach to within 10 or 20 paces, even when they were put up a second time. The singing began around evening. In the bright afterglow the males flew low, 1.5 to 2 m or slightly more above the ground.

I had occasion to scrutinize a pectoral sandpiper which flew near me. Its dewlap was dangling, looking something like a tiny filled sack. Drawing the head back onto the shoulders, the calling bird extended the base of the neck downward and the thickened skin together with the elongated feathers formed a thick fold. The elongated, blown-up form was created that prompted earlier observers to refer to it as an inflated crop. The calling pectoral sandpiper flew a little way at low speed. As it landed, with the last syllable, "ut", the "crop" momentarily returned to normal size and form. The bird stretched out its neck and the hanging fold slammed behind.

The calling flight of the pectoral sandpiper is accompanied by special dull, muffled sounds which I can transcribe as "ut-ut-ut-ut...". These sounds resembled the call of a hoopoe but consisted not of three but of many syllables, following each other interminably in the same tempo and without stress on individual syllables. It produced the somewhat uncanny impression I have had sometimes in the North Urals when a deaf cuckoo calls. It could be heard for 100 to 150 m though audibility depended on the environment and on the sharpness of the observer's ears.

The pectoral sandpipers can generate these sounds even sitting on the ground but faintly. I several times saw males sitting on the ground without making any noise, the dewlap suspended. But I did not see birds flying with a blown crop and not making the buzzing sound. On landing and reverting to silence the male holds the body horizontally, often stretching the neck upward. Like the female, it quite often swoops directly into the water up to the belly and begins pecking at something or other.

The intense calling of pectoral sandpipers did not continue for long in Anadyr, the average being about a week. On June 20 I encountered two males on the shore of a lake. I saw only the female on June 24 after carefully tracing the nesting site.

Nidification—On June 24, 1956, I came across three females separately. They were not timid and permitted approach within the range of a good shot. They uttered alarm calls. I transcribed this call as "dzhzh-dzhzh-dzhzh, tstrr, tsrr, trrzh". The alphabetical transcription cannot be very exact, and the sounds in fact varied under different conditions. Sometimes, I heard the call as "kut'-kut'-kut'-kut' " or as "kvet'-kvet'-kvet'-kvet' ", similar to the call of a dunlin or an eastern little stint.

I sat for about an hour on a peaty mound and observed a single bird. It stopped for long and looked at me. Then it began to feed or give the impression of looking for food, but only briefly: finally it again rested on the mound where it preened for a long time. I noticed this mode of behavior in other sandpipers too. Most often they touched the breast feathers with the beak. On losing patience, the female pectoral sandpiper would walk away for 15 m, return to the original spot and suddenly with a cry approach me to within 8 or 10 paces. I photographed her but could not find her nest.

The dates of egg laying on the Amguema were late compared with those at Chaun Bay and on the lower Kolyma. V.D. Lebedev and V.R. Filin collected a female with an egg in the oviduct on June 10, 1858. On June 15, 1959, E.P. Spangenberg found an already incubated clutch on the lower Kolyma from which chicks were due in about seven days.

On June 29, 1956, a female flew at me with an alarm call and began to run along the hummocks. On the grassy marsh with hummocks, I noticed a section where this restlessness became more intense. There was a sharp, bitter wind. I reckoned that the female should soon be sitting on the eggs to warm them up and started a patient hunt. It was rather a tough experience for the bird and for me, too. I was dressed in a warm jacket but standing in the wind (it was wet everywhere and there was nowhere to sit) I soon began to shiver. Even inside my pockets my hands grew stiff with cold. Half an hour passed. Unexpectedly, the bird hid in the grass. I turned in that direction as the female withdrew 20 paces from me and exposed the nest. Then she fluttered her wings along the ground and chirped, ruffling the feathers on the back in exactly the same way as the female Temminck's stint in such a situation. According to my observations the behavior of American knots and big sandpipers is also exactly the same at the nest; this behavior was even more pronounced in the case of the ringed plover and turnstone. But the eastern little stint, little stint, curlew-sandpiper and dunlin behaved quite differently.

The nest of the pectoral sandpiper was located on a dry place by the edge of a flat peat mound. It was in the form of a pit among thin grass which could hardly hide the clutch. The bottom of the pit was lined with a fairly thick layer of thin, dry blades of grasses with an admixture of some 20 tiny leaves of *Betula exilis* Sukacz., stray shoots of *Vaccinium vitis-idaea* L. var. *microphyllum* Herd., some bits of *Cetraria cucullata* (Bell.) Ach. and a few tiny feathers of the bird itself.

The clutch consisted of four eggs of dark and variegated colors which made them very hard to see.

While I was setting up identification signs with bits of peat around the nest the female came near, flapped her wings as though they were broken, calmed down, again parried, and so on.

On June 30 I visited this nest but the bird was not sitting in it (Fig. 65). When I was placing some marks the female ran to within 8 or 10 paces of me and behaved as before. From the clutch I took one egg in which the small embryo could be seen. On July 1 the female was again not to be seen in the nest but she soon appeared and ran quite close, chirping and crawling as usual. When I was walking away she flew for some time behind me for a distance of 100 to 150 paces. This time there was another female in the vicinity but she did not reveal any anxiety. On July 5 the owner of the nest met me near it but behaved calmly, being evidently accustomed to my visits (Fig. 64). I took the second egg; the chick in it was not quite developed. It was covered with down. On July 7 I did not see the female at all but the eggs remaining in the nest were warm.

On July 8 I could not at first find the female but soon she came and watched the proceedings at the nest with indifference. For one more week the weather was mostly warm with a day temperature of +11 to 15.5°C. At times the mosquitoes, generally rare in that area, were troublesome. Most of the birds did not stay in the nests and the pectoral sandpipers were no exception. The development of embryos in the eggs took a long time because of insufficient warmth: the birds incubated with appreciable intervals in between. The warm, gentle, moist weather prompted their absence.

On July 11 the female flew toward me, ran very close, preened and parried. There were now two chicks in the nest. On July 16 I visited this nesting area for the last time and saw two females. One of them exhibited slight restlessness. This probably was the mother of the chicks, trying to reconcile to the fate of her five-day-old offspring. The second female was only a co-partner but showed some restlessness on my appearance.

On July 5 I found a second nest under fairly similar conditions. While I was engaged in searching for the nest of a dunlin a very confident female pectoral sandpiper came quite close to me with the cry: "tstrr" or "trrzh". She leisurely ran a short distance and parried, finally hiding in the grass 50 paces away from me. Here the nest with clutch was located. Another female came on hearing the alarm, alighted and left again.

Since the nest was located on wet soil the bird had to lay a very thick lining, more than 3 cm. The lower layer consisted of dry leaves of *Betula exilis* Sukacz.

and *Salix fuscescens* Anderss. with a small admixture of shoots of *Vaccinium uliginosusm* L. On top were laid dry blades of grass, sometimes whole plants pulled out by the roots, and fresh shoots. The top layer consisted of dry leaves of a reddish rust color.

On July 10 I detected a third nest, also when tracking a dunlin. A female pectoral sandpiper suddenly approached and landed with the same call "tsrr-tsrr", preened and attentively followed me; finally she settled and spread her wings. It was a distraction display, since I could not find anything in that place. After 10 minutes she again landed and dropped a wing. She was sitting on a nest built on top of a mound. There were four downy chicks and an empty shell in it. They were freshly hatched and one was still wet. I took two of the chicks for my collection. The other two were not to be seen in the nest next day and the female was 30 paces away from the empty nest but returned later. Evidently the chicks were hiding in the grass. On July 12 even the female had gone.

I found a fourth nest on July 11. The female got off 15 paces from me and began running with a twitter and fluttering of wings. Having thoroughly searched the dry area, which was not more than 20 sq m, I withdrew some 100 paces and waited. Within 5 minutes the female got off the nest and exposed it. It was located 250 to 300 paces from the third nest on a section of bushy tundra in the neighborhood of grassy marshes. It was a circular pit on top of a low-sedge mound. It was lined at the bottom with a uniform mixture of fine, dry blades of grass and leaves of *Betula exilis* Sukacz. They were mixed with bits of tiny branches of *Vaccinium vitis-idaea* L. var. *microphyllum* Herd., bits of lichen *Cetraria cucullata* (Bell.) Ach. and *Dufourea arctica* Hook, moss *Sphagnum fuscum* (Schimp.) Klingrr. and even lumps of peat. The nest contained three eggs and a wet chick which had just emerged (Fig. 66). On the morning of July 12 I found all four chicks. The female clambered off them and ran close, fluttered, hissed, twittered, chirped, and so on.

On June 30, 1964, F.B. Chernyavskii found a nest with quite a fresh clutch on Wrangel Island. The nest lining, as in the nests that I found, consisted of dry blades of grass and lichen. The female fluttered 3 or 4 m from the nest ahead of the intruder, then flew away. But 2 minutes later she returned and ran around silently. Chernyavskii thought that it was a second clutch since he had heard the calling as early as the first few days of June. There had been a snowstorm on the island on June 20 and 21, when most of the clutches of sandpipers perished.

From July 10 through 12, 1956, on the tundra along the Amguema, there was a mass emergence of chicks of different species of sandpipers. Only then could it be clearly seen how abundantly the pectoral sandpiper had colonized there. They did not settle in dense colonies but were well dispersed. Nevertheless, pectoral sandpipers were absent from a neighborhood a few kilometers from their colony with an altogether similar environment. Three pectoral sandpipers, a dunlin, a red-throated pipit, blue-headed wagtails, finches and longspurs nested in a section of hummocky tundra that I inspected. It was a community of birds brought together by common requirements for living.

The eggs in the first nest that I found differed from the others in their very light cold coloration—a faint greenish shade. The main ground was isabelline. The patches were pale violet-gray and sepia. The patches scattered at random in the narrower part of the egg were 0.5 to 3 mm long. At the blunt end the patches thickened into a kind of halo and measured up to 6 or 7 mm. Since the eggs lay in the nest with the blunt end upward the dark, variegated color of the clutch merged with the background of the surrounding. The egg sizes were: 26.4 × 36.7 and 25.8 × 35.7 mm.

In the rest of the nests the eggs were a very warm yellow shade. The main ground was a light, dull ocherous-gray. The grayish-violet patches were darker while the brownish ones were lighter; they measured 7 to 15 mm in length and merged at the blunt end. The sizes of the eggs in the second nest were 27.5 × 40.1, 28.1 × 39.9, 27.3 × 39.6, and 27.6 × 38.8 mm. The eggs in the third nest were somewhat lighter in color, approaching those of the first nest. In the fourth nest the eggs were most yellow in color and more densely covered with patches.

When comparing the eggs of the pectoral sandpiper I collected with the sketch in Plate XI of *Ibis* (1907), the former appeared to be darker and of a much colder shade.

The pectoral sandpiper chicks that I brought home were more active than those of the eastern little stint and Temminck's stint but most of them died on the second day. I warmed a frozen chick by holding it in my warm hands and breathing on it but it died in the night: the warmth provided by the heated room was inadequate.

The one-day chicks that I collected are depicted in the colored plate with my article on the curlew-sandpiper (Portenko, 1959). The existence of two color forms was noticed in the specimens gathered from three broods: 1) more whitish and 2) an intense brownish-yellow bloom. The general coloration on the upper parts was blackish-brown with markings in isabelline or dirty cream. The underparts are dirty white with a tea yellow bloom on the breast. Three constituent components could be differentiated in the markings: patterns on the head, neck and back.

There is a pentagonal patch along the center of the crown; the patch is yellowish-brown in the center and almost black along the edges. From the sides it touches the broad cream bands while in the center there is a *Λ*-shaped isabelline spot or stripe formed by the light-colored tip of the fluff. The front of the crown patch ends in a black trident projecting onto the yellowish forehead. The central prong of the trident is longer than the lateral ones. The sides of the head are cream or yellowish with blackish-brown stripes.

On the upper side of the neck there is a tiny stiff collar formed of dense, long fluff of a dirty cream color with a central brown patch on the nape and a brown translucent ripple.

The shoulders and back are blackish-brown with isabelline loops in a dotted design. This design is obliterated when preparing the skin. In a live chick there are four patches with an irregular oval shape in the pattern; there are also patches on the shoulders and thighs. When the chick is pressed the tea brown color is less noticeable; when it is spread out the down becomes thin and the tea brown shade appears very light.

I made a comparison of the colors of downy chicks of different species of sandpipers based on the patterns described above. The color of the chick of a light-colored form is exactly like that of dunlin chicks. Dunlin chicks of the same age can be distinguished for certain only by the much shorter middle toe.

The beak of downy pectoral sandpiper chicks is of a dark horn color and the legs are an uneven flesh gray, being darker at the joints. The lower surface of the toes is lighter and more yellowish in color.

From July 6 through 12, 1934, during my journey up the Utte-Véem River, pectoral sandpipers were often encountered. They became restless at my appearance, flew low around me (in the nesting period pectoral sandpipers generally do not fly very high) and sometimes landed very close. On July 6 a female with brood patches was collected. On July 11, going around the shores of lakes, I came across a very agitated pair. On July 12 I was hunting cranes when I came across the nesting territory of a pectoral sandpiper. It exhibited the same alarm whether I or the crane came close; the crane, however, did not pay any attention to the sandpiper. The restlessness of the pectoral sandpiper with respect to the crane was, however, not without cause, since it is known that cranes do not spare tiny vertebrates and probably think nothing of swallowing a downy pectoral sandpiper chick. In one or two cases, I heard the brief drone of a pectoral sandpiper sitting in the grass. In 1932, near Dezhnev settlement, I found local broods even on August 13, though fall movements had already begun by then. In one case a pectoral sandpiper, on being chased, kept returning to the same peat mound, revealing attachment to its nesting territory. I came across pairs of adult birds as also broods of juveniles. Lone young birds often appeared from the grass within a few paces of me. Quite often the voice of pectoral sandpipers was heard along with that of dunlins nesting side by side.

On Wrangel Island, on August 7, 1939, I collected an adult female having brood patches together with young ones already flying. On the tundra near Somnitel'naya Bay, on July 15 of the same year, I came across pectoral sandpipers in pairs as well as in flocks of a few birds, and even flying flocks. The sandpipers were not particularly wary. They did not reveal even once the alarm which was characteristic of them when any danger threatened the nest.

Migration—Local movements of juvenile birds representing the commencement of gradual migration begin in August. In the fall of 1932 on the tundra between Dezhnev settlement and Uélen, I happened upon wandering flocks on August 13. I saw pectoral sandpipers flying along the seacoast on August 15 and 16 and noticed fairly large flocks on two occasions. In the fall of 1933, on the same tundra, I set out on an excursion on August 27 and put up young pectoral sandpipers from the grass singly, and two, three, four or sometimes more birds together.

Evidently they represented disbanded broods. On September 9 they were encountered in smaller numbers than in the last few days of August and soon migrated. The following fall, in 1934, I noticed wandering pectoral sandpipers near Uélen after August 5 and on the Kol'oam-Véem River from August 9 through 24. In the estuary of that river, they remained in a mixed flock together with dunlins, eastern little stints and dotterels. Flying flocks were encounterd quite often although not daily. On August 9 and 10 small flocks were sometimes flying; on the 11th the flocks were wandering and occasionally flying. On the 12th a lone bird was noticed. A few were flying on the 13th but the birds were not seen at all from August 14 through 17. On the 18th I saw three pectoral sandpipers flying at a height of at least 250 m; on the 19th and 20th they were not noticed. They were seen on the 21st and one was secured: they were not sighted on the 22nd but a lone bird was obtained on the 23rd and flocks were seen. On the 24th pectoral sandpipers were seen in a mixed flock of sandpipers. After that I made no more excursions.

In the fall of 1938, on the north coast of Wrangel Island, I noticed flocks and lone pectoral sandpipers from August 14 through 20. In 1939, I noticed flocks of pectoral sandpipers on the south coast of Wrangel even in mid-July. Evidently they deserted the island very early. I put up a small flock on July 24, heard the voice of a pectoral sandpiper on the 26th, encountered a lone bird on the 27th, and scared a whole flock on August 7. I also collected an adult female with a young bird. In spite of the fact that I stayed on Wrangel Island until August 28 I did not come across pectoral sandpipers after the 7th. Evidently they left the island in the first two or three weeks of August and did not remain up to September as on the Chukchi coast. On September 8, 1939, I disembarked on the coast at Uélen and encountered a lone juvenile.

V.D. Lebedev and V.R. Filin noticed small flocks gathered before migration in the western part of the Karchyk peninsula on the shoals in the Kozmina River from August 8 through 13, 1958. Pectoral sandpipers fed together with Temminck's stints and ruffs.

Habits—Some common features can be seen in the behavior of pectoral sandpipers and common snipes. The young birds love to hide in the grass. Sometimes, I would see before me a sandpiper which suddenly appeared from the grass and was very confident but later ran away, again hiding in the grass.

In other cases, when they cannot endure the approach of a man, pectoral sandpipers take off like common snipes, remain flying about in the air for a long time and finally swoop to earth. On seeing them I noticed that on landing the sandpipers would run away into the grass to quite a distance and take off again far from the point where they landed. They ran very fast through the grass. Some would rise nearby, fly a short distance and land again; they would fold their wings leisurely, holding them high for some moments. On August 18, 1934, near Lake Kool'ong, I noticed three pectoral sandpipers high over the meadow; they rushed about irresolutely in rapid flight but did not land as migratory common snipes do. Some birds were surprisingly confident. On the Kol'oam-Véem River, my party pitched the tent on a small, sandy islet. A flock of pectoral sandpipers flew toward us and landed literally two paces away. They took off again the moment somebody moved. On Wrangel Island the birds I came across were mostly wary.

Food—Some dissected stomachs turned out to be empty. Others revealed the following contents:

1) Uélen, June 4, 1934. Four *Carabidae* and an unknown beetle, two dipteran larvae, seven larvae and three pupae of unknown insects, three seeds and tiny stones. 2) Same time, 10 *Carabidae*, two *Carabidae* larvae, two caterpillars, two fly larvae, the pupa of an unknown insect and some tiny stones. 3) Same time. Heads and other remains of 13 *Carabidae*, bits of two or three caterpillars, eight dipteran larvae, beetle larva, two seeds and tiny stones. 4) Uélen, June 7, 1932. Shards of *Carabidae*, bits of two or three insect larvae, 18 seeds of four species of plants and tiny stones. 5) Utte-Véem River lowland, July 6, 1934. Bits of shards of two to four tiny *Carabidae*, some 100 invertebrates (horny, round, flat discs with a concentric

structure), five tiny seeds and small stones. 6) Same time. Heads and other remains of 16 *Carabidae*, aquatic beetle (*Dytiscidae* or *Hydrophilidae*), heads of four tiny beetles, heads of two hymenopterans, head of a bug, bits of the legs of *Tipulidae* and dozens of their black eggs. 7) Wrangel Island, August 14, 1938. Much digested remains of caterpillars. 8) Wrangel Island, August 17, 1938. Fourteen caterpillars, three tiny beetles, and 0.5 g sand. 9) Same time. Six tiny beetles, 38 caterpillars and 0.25 g sand. 10) Same time. About 20 caterpillars and 1 g quartz sand particles 0.5 to 4.0 mm in diameter. 11) Wrangel Island, July 15, 1939. Finely ground remains of tiny insects and 0.5 g quartz sand. 12) Same time. Remains of tiny insects, 0.5 g beetle larvae, ground-up plant remains and 0.5 g coarse sand. 13) Wrangel Island, August 7, 1939. Beetles of type *Poecilus* (tribe *Platysmatini*), head of a hymenopteran, two insect larvae, five tiny branches of moss *Polytrichum juniperinum* Willd. and nine tiny stones. 14) Same place. Three tiny beetles, much digested remains of two beetles and 0.1 g sand.

The *weights* of males collected at Providence Bay on May 30, 1938, were 88 and 81 g. The weights of females collected there on May 30 and June 6 were appreciably less: 64.5, 58.9, 55.8 and 53.0 g.

Systematics—The pectoral sandpiper does not form geographic races or subspecies. Together with the related species *Heterophygia acuminata* (Horsf.) it belongs to a special genus quite distinct from other sandpipers. The ruff is the nearest genetic relative of both of these species and this assumption has been adopted time and again in ornithological literature. Even I.A. Palmén drew attention to the similarity in the color of the downy chicks of the pectoral sandpiper and the ruff. S.A. Buturlin (1905a, pp. 171 and 172) drew the analogy between the enlargement of the pectoral sandpiper's crop and the growth of a feather collar in the ruff. Several ornithologists later described the similarities of these sandpipers. Most recently, F.A. Pitelka (1959, p. 234) pointed out the genetic similarity of the pectoral sandpiper and the ruff.

In fact there is much similarity in various respects, especially in the behavior of females by the nest, in the color of the chicks and juveniles, and so on. The size difference between the male and the female in the two species is manifest more distinctly than in any other sandpiper. Speaking of a genetic similarity, the pectoral sandpiper is perhaps closer to the ruff than any other species of sandpiper, including the sharp-tailed sandpiper.

Specimens— 1 and 2) Dezhnev settlement, August 13, 1932, ♂, 1° anno, ♀, Portenko; 3) Lawrence Bay, August 19, 1932, ♂, 1° anno, Portenko; 4) Rodgers Bay, August 25, 1932, ♀, 1° anno, Mineev; 5 and 6) Uélen, August 28, 1933, ♂ ♀, 1° anno, Portenko; 7 and 8) same place, September 9, 1933, ♂ ♀, 1° anno, Portenko; 9 to 11) same place, June 4, 1934, ♂ ♀♀, Portenko; 12) same place, June 7, 1934, ♀, Portenko; 13 and 14) Utte-Véem lowland, July 6, 1934, ♂ ♀, Portenko; 15) lower course of the Kol'oam-Véem River, August 23, 1934, ♂, 1° anno, Portenko; 16 to 19) estuary of the Kol'oam-Véem River, August 24, 1934, ♂♂ ♀♀, 1° anno, Portenko; 20 to 24) Providence Bay, Cape Stoletiya, May 30, 1938, ♂♂ ♀♀♀, Butenko; 25) Plover Bay, June 6, 1938, ♀, Butenko; 26 to 29) north coast of Wrangel Island by Bruch spit, August 14, 1938, ♂♂♂ ♀, 1° anno, Portenko; 30 to 32) estuary of the Krasnyi Flag River, August 17, 1938, ♂♂, 1° anno, Portenko; 33) Cape Chaplin, August 18, 1938,

♂, 1°, Butenko; 34 and 35) Somnitel'naya Bay, July 15, 1939, ♂♂, Portenko; 36 and 37) Rodgers Bay, August 7, 1939, ♀, sen. and ♀, 1° anno, Portenko; 38 and 39) Amguema River, 91st km, July 10, 1956, pull., Portenko; 40 and 41) same place, July 11, 1956, pull., Portenko; and 42 to 45) same place, July 12, 1956, pull., Portenko.

Biological material— 1) Two eggs of a clutch, middle reaches of the Amguema River (91st km), June 30 and July 5, 1956, Portenko; 2) clutch of four eggs, same place, July 5, 1956, Portenko; 3) egg, same place, July 10, 1956, Portenko; and 4) nest with an egg, same place, July 11, 1956, Portenko.

77. **Heteropygia acuminata** (Horsf.)—**Sharp-tailed Sandpiper**

Distribution and status—Found in the fall on the north coast of the Chukchi Peninsula but rare, at least in the eastern part. Nidification not established.

Though the sharp-tailed sandpiper has not been recorded at all on the southern and eastern coast of the Chukchi peninsula it should be present there as it was found on the northern coast and was collected in the neighborhood of Anadyr village.

On St. Lawrence Island O.J. Murie (1936) gathered three males and two females at Kukuliak village on September 24, 1935, and three more specimens on August 27, 29 and 31 of the same year.

In the fall of 1933 I encountered these sandpipers on the tundra near Uélen, but in small numbers, and collected only two young females. In the fall of 1934 I came across a lone specimen on the upper course of the Kol'oam River. The *Vega* expedition did not find sharp-tailed sandpipers at Kolyuchin Bay and the three eggs that I.A. Palmén (1887) regarded as possibly of the sharp-tailed sandpiper I am inclined to identify as the clutch of a Baird's sandpiper. On August, 1, 1881, E.W. Nelson (1883) found this species plentiful in the neighborhood of Vankarém on the plain directly adjoining the seacoast. In a later compilation (1887) he repeats that he found those birds very common but near Cape Schmidt (North Cape). Ignoring the ambiguity of location, one can rely on Nelson's identification: he differentiated the sharp-tailed from the pectoral sandpiper quite well and illustrated his work with sketches of both. Because of various circumstances, especially behavior, Nelson believed that the locality he visited should be regarded as the nesting zone of sharp-tailed sandpipers. There is nothing improbable in this assumption. On June 1, 1970, A.A. Kishchinskii found a dead specimen on the spit by Cape Schmidt. The sharp-tailed sandpiper was found in the nesting area on the lower reaches of the Kolyma. On May 3, 1905, S.A. Buturlin (1906b) noticed not only intense calling there but even a gathering of these sandpipers, though they later vanished until August 26. On July 9 and 14, 1915, Copley Amory, Jr. (Riley, 1918) caught two females in the Kolyma delta. J. Koren (Schaanning, 1954) collected a male on May 30, 1918, on the lower Kolyma. E.P. Spangenberg (1960) possibly found the sharp-tailed sandpiper in the nesting area on the lower Kolyma, although his data are somewhat confused. Judging from the fact that he drew attention to a clayey fluid covering the skin on the crops of birds of both species during preparation and that he was inclined to place the pectoral and sharp-tailed sandpiper in the same species, he cannot have identified them correctly. K.A. Vorob'ev (1963) finally found nests of the sharp-tailed sandpiper, particularly a nest with a clutch on the

Kon'kovaya River 150 km northwest of Pokhodsk.

The sharp-tailed sandpiper has not been found on Wrangel Island and G.P. Dement'ev's note (Buturlin and Dement'ev, 1941, p. 22) that a female was collected by A.M. Mineev at Rodgers Bay on August 25, 1932, should be regarded as a reference to the pectoral sandpiper.

Habitat—Near Uélen, I encountered sharp-tailed sandpipers on the same wet, grassy sections of the tundra in the vicinity of lagoons which the pectoral sandpipers favored.

On the upper course of the Kol'oam-Véem River I noticed a stray specimen in a flock of juvenile marine sandpipers wandering along pebbled spits. West of Vankarém E.W. Nelson noticed innumerable sharp-tailed sandpipers on the wet, grassy plain where the soil was covered with reindeer tracks. These sandpipers foraged among these tracks.

Autumn flight—According to my observations, in the fall of 1933 and of 1934 the sharp-tailed sandpiper was seen later than the pectoral sandpiper in fall wanderings. Both my specimens were collected around Uélen on September 9, 1933. They had filmy ovaries and were devoid of subcutaneous fat. On the Kol'oam River the bird was noticed on August 21, 1934.

Habits—E.W. Nelson and I both noticed sharp-tailed sandpipers among pectoral sandpipers. Once I encountered this sandpiper in a flock of juvenile marine sandpipers which also included dunlins. According to Nelson, sharp-tailed sandpipers were very confident, permitted a close approach or circled around men.

Food—The stomach of one of the specimens revealed bone fragments of a tiny vertebrate, parts of the head and shards of two *Carabidae*, the head of a hymenopteran, and bits of the legs of several hundred very small insects.

Specimens— 1 and 2) Uélen, September 9, 1933, ♀♀, 1° anno, Portenko.

78. **Philomachus pugnax** (L.)—**Ruff**

Distribution and status—The eastern boundary of the nesting zone touches Chaun and Krest bays but farther east only rare instances of flight up to Wrangel and St. Lawrence islands are established.

In 1961, V.É. Yakobi collected two females, evidently by a nest in the neighborhood of Uél'kal'. The ruff has not been recorded at all farther along the south coast or on the east coast of Chukchi peninsula. Tayan, who lived most of his life in Providence Bay, did not once see it.

According to H. Friedmann (1934b), in June, 1933, a flying female was obtained at Gambell in northwestern St. Lawrence Island. On June 7, 12, and 14, 1933, O.J. Murie (1936) obtained three males from eskimos there, possibly of the same flock flying on the island.

A.A. Savich's collections (Artobolevskii, 1927) contained the skin of a ruff from Cape Schmidt or, probably, from the Kolyma estuary. As É.V. Schmidt told me, the ruff was encountered once in the spring in the estuary of the Chaun River. V.D. Lebedev and V.R. Filin found it fairly common on Aiok Island, where males and females were collected on the southwestern and southern coasts of the island from June 10 through 16, and on the west coast of the Karchyk peninsula from August 5 through 13, 1958.

According to É.V. Schmidt, in the fall ruffs were encountered around Sukharnoe village in the northern Kolyma delta when wide streams were flowing south along the Kolyma at the edge of the forest. In 1905, S.A. Buturlin (1906b) found this species unusually numerous in the Kolyma lowlands.

According to Tayan, in 1937 he noticed a ruff at Rodgers Bay, Wrangel Island. It was a male with yellow breast feathers. Tayan gave me a pencil sketch of the bird.

Habitat—The nesting section near Uél'kal' was on a slope not far from a brook among hummocky grassy tundra.

Seasonal phenomena—V.D. Lebedev and V.R. Filin saw the display of males on Aiok Island on June 16, 1958. On June 17, 1961, V.É. Yakobi shot a female near Uél'kal'. The biggest follicle measured 7 × 15 mm. He collected another female on June 30. She was flying in circles over the place where the nest was evidently located.

79. **Tryngites subruficollis** (Vieill.)—**Buff-breasted Sandpiper**

Only one record for the north coast of the Chukchi peninsula, not confirmed by any one since. Most recently, a case of nidification on Wrangel Island established.

In early August, 1881, E.W. Nelson (1883 and 1887) found[1] buff-breasted sandpipers quite common in the neighborhood of Cape Vankarém. He (Nelson, 1887, p. 120) believes these birds had their nesting places there. Some visual identifications of birds made by Nelson turned out to be erroneous and the present reference does not appear to be totally reliable because of the exceptional rarity of these birds.

According to a report by V.E. Flint (1967), on July 27, 1965, a female buff-breasted sandpiper was collected on Wrangel Island at Somnitel'naya Bay. The locale of the find, 9 or 10 km west of Zvezdnyi settlement and 100 to 150 m from the shore, was dry rocky tundra where rubble sections alternated with patchy lichen *Thamnolia*, moss and procumbent willow. On the approach of a man the birds flew around restlessly, landed and again took off. The female collected showed a brood patch and recent scars were found on three follicles. On August 19, 1965, V.A. Leonov succeeded in collecting a flying chick near Cape Predatel'skaya, i.e. 5 km west, perhaps of the same brood.

V.A. Leonov kindly sent me the specimen he collected. It bears the label "O subad., Wrangel Island, Mamontovaya River, August 11, 1965, V. Leonov".

As V.E. Flint noticed, the buff-breasted sandpiper is easy to identify at sight from the bright yellow-orange color of the legs which, however, disappears within a few hours of killing the bird.

80. **Phalaropus fulicarius** (L.)—**Gray Phalarope**

Local name—Chukchian: Pekitschedlin according to the records of the *Vega* expedition, pékych'yn according to Velizhanin. In Eskimo: Ssuhmyhak at Provi-

[1]In a description of the buff-breasted sandpiper E.V. Kozlova (1962, p. 177) reports that Nelson collected it. As a matter of fact, he only observed it.

dence Bay and sō-ghō-mŭ'-ghŭk on St. Lawrence Island. Known as the phalarope or red phalarope and palmated duckbilled plover among residents of Kolyma, according to Argentov.

Distribution and status—Being mostly a marine bird, nests along the coast of the Chukchi peninsula, in appreciably larger numbers on the north and east coasts than on the south coast; on the latter, rare at places. In flights and wanderings, common and numerous, collecting in large flocks in the fall. Rare or uncommon in the interior of the Chukchi peninsula in the breeding grounds and in flights.

The seasonal movements are complex. Single birds are encountered in the summer in groups and flocks not only in the maritime zone but on the coast itself. The nested females wander in flocks along the coast moving around the peninsula from the east and halting at some places on the south coast until the fall. Following them, the young birds and the adult males move in the same direction and gradually thin out by massive migrations.

On Wrangel Island it nests in small numbers but becomes numerous in fall wanderings and flight.

Distribution in the breeding grounds—In the neighborhood of Uél'kal', according to the observations of V.É. Yakobi, the gray phalarope is encountered somewhat more rarely than the northern phalarope. On August 6, 1932, I collected nonflying chicks near Notapenmen village. Neither I nor P.T. Butenko, who spent a whole year at Providence Bay, nor any other ornithologist has found this species in the breeding grounds. A.P. Kuzyakin recorded the gray phalarope at Providence Bay as a rare species at less than one pair per sq km, but did not locate any nests.

According to E.M. Nelson (1883) gray phalaropes were found nesting on St. Lawrence Island in the summer of 1881. According to A.M. Bailey (1925), on July 1, 1921, his assistant R.W. Hendee found a nest there. W.S. Brooks (1915) collected breeding specimens, presumably because this species was found to be common from June 24 through 27, 1913, east of Cape Chibukak on the south side of the island and at the southeastern tip. As reported by H. Friedmann (1932a), on July 24, 1930, a male in breeding plumage was collected. According to F.H. Fay and T.J. Cade (1959) some pairs were noticed every year on small elevations at Boxer Bay and these sandpipers were common near the Kuzata River. On June 27 and 30, 1950, specimens in breeding plumage were obtained and downy chicks noticed every day at the end of July at Boxer Bay. On June 23, 1954, near Kavuk village, a nest was found with three eggs. E.G.F. Sauer and E.K. Urban (1964) found some pairs by Lake Malyi near Boxer Bay in the latter half of July, 1960. On July 2 a nest was found with three eggs 5 km north of the Mogoveiik River.

W.S. Brooks referred to a record at Cape Chaplin, unfortunately without any date. Evidently the adult male obtained by P.V. Ushakov on July 31, 1929, at Lawrence Bay may be regarded as a nesting bird. A.P. Kuzyakin in 1957 found the gray phalarope as a rare species (less than one pair per sq km) all along the southern shore of Lawrence Bay, by Akkani, Yandagai and Poutyn. He found it common near Lawrence settlement, where he collected downy chicks from two broods on July 16, 1957. In June, 1970, V.V. Leonovich saw flocks on the lakes; in my view the flocks may have been of females that had completed breeding.

Gray phalaropes did not nest on the Diomede Island because of the topographic conditions. E.W. Nelson, who aboard the *Corwin* spent the summer of 1881 cruising the coast waters from Wrangel to Herald islands to the south up to Providence Bay and St. Lawrence Island, came to the conclusion that this species nested mainly along the north coast of the Chukchi peninsula. W.S. Brooks saw some gray phalaropes on July 14, 1913, at East Cape, i.e. probably near Uélen. On August 13, 1932, in the neighborhood of Dezhnev settlement, I encountered a small number, possibly of still local broods. In the summer of 1934 I found some post-breeding pairs on the tundra not far from Uélen. According to the observations of A.P. Kuzyakin, in 1957, this phalarope was rare near Uélen although he found three nests with clutches on the lowland south of the lagoon.

In the eastern interior of the peninsula I found a male only once, on July 11, 1934, in the lowlands of the Utte-Véem River, the nesting section. On July 17, 1913, W.S. Brooks encountered this sandpiper by Cape Serdtse-Kamen'. In June, 1970, V.S. Leonovich noticed lone birds on the lakes at Énurmino.

Near Kolyuchin Bay the members of the *Vega* expedition (Palmén, 1887) gathered reliable data on the nidification of this bird. On his journey to Cape Dzhenretlen on June 27, 1879, O. Nordquist encountered gray phalaropes as the most common representatives of sandpipers. A similar observation was made on July 1 on a journey to Tjapka. On July 10, on a lagoon at Pitlekai, Nordquist noticed a phalarope which probably had its nest in the neighborhood. On July 12 a nest was found with a clutch and a male was shot nearby. In mid-July, 1909, J. Koren (1910) found gray phalaropes innumerable from the west side of the entrance to Kolyuchin Bay. A.A. Kishchinskii found many birds, and in addition several clutches, in the summer of 1970 on the marine tundra from Vankarém to the Amguema estuary (Fig. 58).

On July 8, 1956, in the interior of the country on the Amguema by the 91st km, I found males in their nesting territories only in one place.

As V.Ya. Isaev told me, gray phalaropes nested near Cape Schmidt all over the coastal tundra and were abundant. J. Koren (Thayer and Bangs, 1914) noticed flying juvenile phalaropes on July 30, 1912, at Chaun Bay and on July 20/21 collected what was evidently a breeding specimen in Malyi Chaun Strait (once known as "Sabadeev"). V.D. Lebedev and V.R. Filin (1959) found this species very numerous in the nesting area on Aiok Island. They noticed individual pairs on the tundra and innumerable downy chicks; a nest with a clutch was found.

According to the observations of S.A. Buturlin (1906b), in the Kolyma lowlands the gray phalarope nested on the open tundra and was numerous in the delta. Copley Amory, Jr. (Riley, 1918) collected two males in the Kolyma delta on July 7, 1915. J. Koren (Schaanning, 1954) collected the downy chicks of two broods on July 2 and 3, 1917.

Based on an oral report by G.A. Ushakov, A.G. Bannikov (1941) writes that the gray phalarope was common in the nesting area on Wrangel Island. My observations would not allow me to call it common. In the first half of June, 1939, I found two or three isolated pairs on the south coast; on July 15 I found two lone males in their nesting territories at Somnitel'naya Bay, judging from the nature of the habitat. In one case, the phalarope flew over the marsh with a chirp. According to the observations of S.M. Uspenskii and his colleagues (Uspenskii, Bëme and

Velizhanin, 1963) it was not a common breeding species on Wrangel Island.

Direction and intensity of spring flight—The spring flight course is over the sea, which at that time is filled with hummocky ice with leads exposed here and there. The gray phalaropes fly west along the north as well as the south coast of the Chukchi peninsula.

On St. Lawrence Island E.G.F. Sauer and E.K. Urban often noticed small flocks until June 15, 1960, on the shores of Boxer Bay. On June 14 gray phalaropes were very numerous on the flat coast west of Kangi, where flocks of more than 40 birds were found. According to F.H. Fay and T.J. Cade, every year large flocks of gray phalaropes flew over the sea ice near Gambell on St. Lawrence Island. At Providence Bay I.A. Olenev noticed a very early flight in 1932. P.T. Butenko recorded a much delayed flight in 1938. Evidently the flight could not be seen from the closed bay. On Meechken Island, according to the observations of L.O. Belopol'skii, gray phalaropes were seen in small flocks in the spring of 1931.

According to K.W. Kenyon and J.W. Brooks (1960) a few migratory gray phalaropes halted at Malyi Diomede Island. In the spring of 1934 I tracked the spring arrival and flight around Uélen. Gray phalaropes flew in from the sea and landed on the neighboring tundra; I was visually convinced that it was from the direction of the sea, i.e. from the North. While the local phalaropes settled the migrating birds continued to move in flocks over the sea. In the spring of 1879 their arrival was noticed by members of the *Vega* expedition in Kolyuchin Bay.

In the interior of the Chukchi peninsula gray phalaropes in flight are rare. On June 13, 1956, on the Amguema, before the breakup when large gullies had formed in the ice, I saw a flock comprising 15 northern and only four gray phalaropes.

V.D. Lebedev and V.R. Filin noticed flocks of 30 birds each on Aiok Island in early June, 1960. A.I. Argentov (1861a) cited the "red" phalarope as an arriving and migratory bird for the entire Trans-Lena region. J. Koren noticed the arrival of gray phalaropes on the lower Kolyma.

There is no spring flight of gray phalaropes on Wrangel Island. G.A. Ushakov collected June specimens in 1929. But V.F. Vlasova and A.I. Mineev, in the course of a five-year stay on the island from 1929 through 1934, did not notice this sandpiper at all in the spring flight. This in spite of the fact that at that time of year it stands out with its bright rust color. In the spring of 1939 I carefully observed the arrival of birds on Wrangel. Only a few pairs of gray phalaropes were seen.

Locations of residence and wanderings of lone birds—It is generally known that many sandpipers do not breed in the second year of life. On the other hand flocks of phalaropes were noticed when other birds of the same species were already busy at the nest. Evidently the lone birds followed the breeding sandpipers. It should be possible to confirm this by studying the gonads of specimens.

On Malyi Diomede Island on June 10 and 14, K.W. Kenyon noticed 10 to 15 gray phalaropes vigorously searching for food on the edge of the ice. The first female in breeding plumage had been noticed as early as May 29.

On July 11, 1921, A.M. Bailey saw thousands of gray phalaropes at Uélen. The flocks looked like clouds. They were so dense that individual birds could not be distinguished at some distance. Thousands of them fed along the shore. When they flew across the spit it was a continuous stream reminiscent of sand sucked up by a tornado. In a much later work he (Bailey, 1943, p. 99) quite correctly remarks that a surprising flock of phalaropes noticed on that day consisted of non-breeding birds. He had never seen anything like it on the Alaskan coast. The phalaropes were in such a state of molting and the stubs in the plumage were so many that the specimens killed did not provide a single bird suitable for preparation. In 1934, around Uélen, I accurately recorded the appearance of the first wandering flock on June 17. Later, on July 4, I noticed large flocks east of Mitkulen on a special feeding ground. Finally, on July 28, on the front at Uélen, I saw a huge assembly of gray phalaropes. Even from a distance it could be seen that the flocks comprised exclusively adult birds; when the flock took off the observer saw them as brown patches as the birds turned in unison and showed their backs. When they turned their bellies toward the observer a variegated mixture of red and white patches appeared. F.L. Jaques (1930) noticed innumerable gray phalaropes on July 30, 1928, north of Bering Strait and later over the Arctic Ocean, especially around the ice. In his diary they are reported as numerous through September 1. Only on September 2 did their numbers begin to decline. Writing at the end of the 18th century, Th. Pennant (1785, vol. II, p. 495, under "phalarope red") states that this species was found by seafarers between Asia and America.

In 1879 the members of the *Vega* expedition for the first time noticed the arrival of gray phalaropes in the neighborhood of Pitlekai; they began gathering increasing numbers of specimens after June 16, and shot very many on June 22 and 23. Probably it was a wave of lone birds. On June 21 two specimens were obtained from Kolyuchi Island where these birds could not nest anywhere because of the topographic conditions.

According to an eyewitness account by the naturalist aboard the *Jeannette*, R.L. Newcomb (1888, pp. 183 and 289), phalaropes were secured in 1880 in considerable numbers while the ship drifted northwest of Wrangel from mid-June through mid-July.

There is reason to believe that nonbreeding lone gray phalaropes remain in flocks on the coast and on the ice in Bering Strait and in the Chukchi Sea at least in the first half of summer. Flocks sometimes consist of a colossal number of birds.

Habitation of females after breeding—For understandable reasons, the females leaving individual nesting sites scattered over large territories do not form such huge flocks as wintered single birds. Some males, at least lone birds whose clutches have been damaged, join the females.

I regard it as probable that the reference in P.S. Pallas (1811, vol. 2, p. 205) to *Phalaropus rufus* noticed in the Arctic Ocean near the Kolyma estuary pertains to post-breeding birds. Copley Amory, Jr., collected molting adults: three females and two unidentified specimens on August 16, 1915, in the estuary of the Baranikha River. Only the gray phalaropes noticed by W.S. Brooks on July 19, 1913, around the ice in the sea 80 miles south of Wrangel Island can be regarded as nonbreeding.

Copley Amory, Jr., collected an adult female on August 12, 1914, near Cape Vankarém. The members of the *Vega* expedition accurately recorded that the females that had completed their clutches gathered in flocks around the winter halt of the ship. On July 19, 1879, such flocks were encountered around the ship swimming away from the wintering areas along the coast to the east. It is possible that some phalaropes noticed by W.S. Brooks on July 17, 1913, at Cape Serdtse-Kamen' and on July 14 near Cape Dezhnev also belonged to the group of birds that had concluded nesting.

A.M. Bailey had with him information that the phalaropes were usually innumerable in the first week of July at Lawrence Bay.

At Providence Bay É.E. Arngol'd collected two adult females on July 20, 1913, and at Émma Bay an adult male on August 7. From August 2 through 7, 1913, L.M. Starokadomskii collected three adult males and a female at Émma Bay. They were identified personally by V.L. Bianki but later destroyed because of bad storage. Also in Providence Bay, on a spit in Plover Bay, I encountered some adult birds on August 26, 1932. Though even juvenile phalaropes were seen on that day the adults held themselves aloof. Together, Starokadomskii's and my own records establish two simultaneous waves of movement: the decreasing tempo of the migration of post-breeding adult birds and the commencement of the wanderings of juveniles. Finally, in June, 1931, L.O. Belopol'skii (1934) noticed a large number of post-breeding gray phalaropes on Meechken Island, especially at a cape on the west coast where up to 1,000 birds sometimes gathered. At one time Belopol'skii (1933) thought somewhat erroneously that the gray phalaropes nested there in colonies together with terns.

Direction and intensity of autumn flight—Having migrated, the gray phalaropes advance en masse, quite often in very large flocks, and over a prolonged period. They follow the seacoast or fly over the sea ice when they come close inshore. In flight the gray phalarope avoids inland water reservoirs and becomes a coastal bird.

In 1878 the members of the *Vega* expedition encountered gray phalaropes as a very widely distributed species along the entire north coast of Siberia, especially in fall flight. From September 2 through 4 a small number of them were noticed near the Medvezhii islands.

A.I. Argentov (1861b, p. 8) writes that in the fall flight period he saw birds on the lower Kolyma that were not found there at all in the spring or summer. These included a large plover having webbed feet and a broadened bill. His other remark (ibid. p. 7) that in early September (old calendar) of 1850 he noticed a multitude of tiny birds known there as gray phalaropes (*Phalaropus cinereus*) flying from the Arctic Ocean to Bol'shoi Baranov Kamen' should also be regarded as referring to gray phalaropes. On reaching the coast these birds moved southeast. Probably Copley Amory, Jr. collected a flying male on August 11, 1915 (since it was already mostly in winter dress), by Bol'shoi Baranov Cape.

On August 29, 1911, É.E. Arngol'd collected a juvenile female aboard the *Vaigach* when the ship was 11 miles west of Cape Schmidt and 10 miles out to sea. J. Koren collected gray phalaropes on the wing on September 5, 1911, in Ryrkaipiya and on the Ténkérgyn River somewhat to the east on August 29. On August 7 and 8, 1938, I noticed a multitude of sandpipers of this species on the surf line along the coast east of Cape Schmidt. A.N. Druzhinin, who was with me, collected some specimens. On September 8 and 9, 1878, these phalaropes were noticed in large numbers around 69°25′ north on the Chukchi coast south of Wrangel Island. On

September 18, O. Nordquist saw a lone bird somewhat to the east. There is a reference in G.V. De Long's diary (1883, pp. 438 and 445) to a flock of phalaropes being sighted flying south on August 30, 1880, when the *Jeannette* was in the ice at 73°46′ north and 176°48′15″ west. Based on this observation, De Long concluded that there must be an open expanse of water to the north. The diary records that on September 2 small flocks were noticed, in general consisting of up to 100 birds which flew northeast-southwest. Next day the ship moved to 73°52′ north and 176°51′ west. On the same lines R.L. Newcomb writes (1888, pp. 279 and 290) that gray phalaropes were noticed in the first half of September, 1880, northwest of Wrangel Island. They only halted occasionally, in general advancing in small flocks of six to eight birds each northeast-southwest. In 1879 they were noticed on September 4 off Herald Island, also in small flocks of 6, 10 or 12 birds. E.W. Nelson again noticed the gray phalaropes on the ice when the *Corwin* was cruising the coasts of Wrangel and Herald islands in the summer of 1881. On September 17, 1911, É.E. Arngol'd collected juveniles which, judging from the season, were certainly migrating birds, at the southwestern tip of Wrangel Island near Cape Foma (70°51′ north and longitude 180°, the spit in the lagoon).

At the end of summer, 1922, an adult male in a state of molting was collected on Wrangel by A. Crawford (Snyder, 1926). According to the observations of D.I. Mineev and V.E. Vlasova from 1929 through 1934, gray phalaropes were seen in fall flight on Wrangel Island in a small number of flocks. Sometimes the shore was dotted with them and the flocks contained 50 to 100 birds. In the fall of 1938 I encountered them in large numbers on the north side of the island but in the fall of 1939, spending all my time on the south side of the island, I did not see phalaropes once right up to my departure on August 28. According to the observations of A.G. Velizhanin (Uspenskii, Bëme and Velizhanin, 1963) there was a flock of 500 to 600 birds in the Davidov lagoon on August 16, 1960.

L.M. Starokadomskii collected three juvenile males on August 19, 1914 at Kolyuchin Bay. Near Cape Serdtse-Kamen' a migrating specimen was collected on August 23, 1911, by J. Koren. F.S. Hersey (1916) shot some specimens of August 28, 1914. Around Uélen I made fall observations for three years and found that the gray phalaropes in flight were invariably abundant. On August 14, 1932, there were many at places on the shore near Dezhnev settlement. On August 15, I encountered them on my way to Uélen and on the 16th among the ice right up to Uélen. On August 9, 1948, a specimen was obtained at Uélen by V.N. Lyubin. The accession register of the Zoological Museum of the Academy of Sciences of the USSR lists under No. 448 of 1912 a male collected by É.E. Arngol'd on August 24, 1911, on the north coast around 66°31′ north and 169°38′ west, but I could not locate this specimen.

According to Th. Pennant (1785, p. 494, under phalarope gray), phalaropes in light-colored plumage were found on the ice between Asia and America.

From Lawrence Bay, I.N. Akif'ev brought back a specimen collected on August 1, 1900. On August 19, 1932, I found a small number of phalaropes on the southern shore of the bay where, along with the dunlins, they outnumbered all other species of sandpipers. On September 10, 1939, during a brief landing in Lawrence Bay, I noticed a flock flying just above the water. According to W. Stimpson (Cassin,

1863, p. 322; also Heine, 1859, vol. III, p. 169), in the second half of August, 1855, during a violent eastern storm, a large flock of phalaropes arrived in search of refuge by the sheltered shore of Senyavin Strait. T.H. Bean (1883, p. 165) saw huge flocks of gray phalaropes near Cape Chaplin on August 15, 1880, and collected two of them. On August 24, 1932, I saw these sandpipers swimming there by the surf in small numbers. The following year, 1933, I passed Providence Bay and Cape Chaplin in fine, calm weather on August 12. Mostly young phalaropes were swimming in large numbers in the placid coastal waters. It was a very typical picture of the life of seabirds. On August 18, 1938, P.T. Butenko collected a molting male at Cape Chaplin.

We do not know how massive the flights are on St. Lawrence Island but H.B. Collins (Friedmann, 1932a) collected two molting males on October 1 and 7, 1930, at Gambell.

According to the information gathered by W.H. Dall (Dall and Bannister, 1869) gray phalaropes were encountered in large flocks in July and August of 1865 and 1866 at Plover Bay. I.O. Olenev encountered gray phalaropes in fall flight at Providence Bay. Neither P.T. Butenko nor I found noteworthy flights there, the reason being the isolation of the bay.

On August 6, 1932, I found the gray phalaropes innumerable in the neighborhood of Notapenmen. V.É. Yakobi noticed flocks on August 21, 1961, by the estuary at Uél'kal'.

Habitat—The characteristic nesting places of this species are sections of grassy tundra in the neighborhood of small lakelets. The lakelets, sometimes only a few square meters in area, where a duck has no room to turn around, are the water which the phalaropes, one of the smallest of water fowl, generally favor. Around Uélen I saw how a tiny pair of even two females with a single male had taken up positions on a lakelet measuring a square sagene (2.13 m). During movement the gray phalaropes constantly flew from one such lakelet to another. On July 11, 1934, I found a typical nesting site in the estuary of the Utte-Véem River. There were tiny lakelets with aquatic vegetation on a plateau of dry, drained tundra. They were surrounded by a border of bright green velvety grass. The male was flying from one lakelet to another but the chicks were evidently hiding in the grass. As noticed by other observers, the chicks are not seen on the water until they begin flying. They are very light and hence cannot dive. They are very easily vulnerable to the attack of jaegers in the open water but they can easily hide at any moment in the grass. On August 6, 1932, near Notapenmen, I collected a nonflying chick on the grassy tundra with lakelets, wet, not dry. It ran across the tundra while the flying juveniles were already swimming in the lakelets. On July 8, 1956, I found a nesting area on the tundra by the Amguema. The male gray phalaropes remained among the aquatic vegetation in the most extensive water-flooded marsh. Around it there were common snipes and pectoral sandpipers.

According to A.P. Kuzyakin the gray phalarope is found in the Chukchi peninsula in the breeding season everywhere on the wet, depressed tundra overgrown with low-sedge. Around Uél'kal', according to the observations of V.É. Yakobi, this phalarope most often remained among the aquatic vegetation and rarely emerged onto the open water. V.D. Lebedev and V.R. Filin found innumerably downy chicks on the southwest coast of Aiok Island on the banks of small lakes. According to the observations of S.M. Uspenskii and his associates, males with broods remained on the marshy shores of lakes in Tundra Akademii.

In the immediate vicinity of lagoons or the sea gray phalaropes leave the nesting places to feed by the surf line, in the straits, in the estuaries and wherever else they can find much food. Once, on August 26, 1932, when the phalaropes were in flocks on the sea, I encountered some adult sandpipers on a spit with lakelets at Plover Bay. It was very close to the sea.

Outside the nesting period the gray phalarope becomes a true sea bird and the very rare records of this species inland should be regarded as occasional halts.

In the spring, on arriving on the coast of the Chukchi peninsula or Wrangel Island, the gray phalaropes tend to stay around the lagoons where openings in the ice appear earlier than on the sea front. In the spring of 1939, on Wrangel Island, I collected the first arriving pair on a lakelet of meltwater formed on the snow cover of a spit. In 1879, near the winter halt of the *Vega*, the first flock of four birds was noticed on a lead. K.W. Kenyon saw this phalarope off Malyi Diomede Island feeding in meltwater on shore ice. On the Amguema, I saw flying phalaropes over the thawed parts of the river, which had not yet completely opened.

Females after nesting and, later, females weaning away the broods, remained in flocks on the sea, quite often far from shore, especially among the ice floes.

The *Vega* expedition encountered a small number of gray phalaropes near the Medvezhii Islands among the fast ice. On July 17, 1879, large flocks were noticed near Pitlekai in coastal pools not far from openings 500 to 600 ft in width.

Gray phalaropes often settled on the open water between the shore and the ice. On August 16, 1932, I arrived at Uélen when the ice had come right inshore and the phalaropes were living on the ice together with alcids and Sabine's gulls. In this icy environment there was a dense fog on September 12 and 13, 1933. The phalaropes moved about the leads and the spit exhibiting the restlessness that I had noticed in eiders and other seabirds in foggy weather.

On the night of August 7/8, 1938, I had to go along the coast east of Cape Schmidt along a broad stretch of open water. It was quite a bright night and the sandpipers were dozing on the water restlessly. Their twittering could be heard from afar. Some lay with the head tucked in the wing while others were spinning around in search of food without arousing their neighbors. With the sunrise the sandpipers began to crawl out onto the shore to warm up. On the morning of August 8 it was so warm that I bathed in the sea.

The gray phalaropes fed regularly by the surf line even when the sea was a little rough. In that case they remained in the more placid zone between the surf and the gently undulating shore run-off. When this zone is very narrow or at times seen and vanishing at others, the phalaropes take off constantly and settle again, doing this so often that one is surprised at their inexhaustible energy. They are not afraid of being rocked by the gentle waves and look like floating corks as they sit high in the water. When calm is restored at sea, most phalaropes cover huge areas along the coast, this being an altogether typical sight. These birds love the quiet and in such periods frequent the shore, but they go far out into the bays or retreat to the lagoons and other protected places when the sea is rough.

Arrival—The gray phalarope arrives in the last few days of May or in early June. According to the observations of L.O. Belopol'skii, in 1931 the first small flocks of phalaropes were seen on Meechken Island on June 1. According to I.O. Olenev, in 1932 they were noticed at Providence Bay as early as mid-May, when the ice still covered at least half of the bay. However, in the spring of 1938, P.T. Butenko collected an arriving female at Plover Bay only on June 6. According to F.H. Fay and T.J. Cade, large flocks of these phalaropes were seen every year between May 20 and 30 on the ice off St. Lawrence Island. According to the observations of E.G.F. Sauer, in 1960 large flocks were encountered up to June 15 at Boxer Bay.

According to K.W. Kenyon and J.W. Brooks, innumerable flocks were seen off Malyi Diomede Island by the edge of the ice at the end of May and in June. On May 29, 1958, a lone female was noticed in a meltwater pool. On June 6 two birds flew among the ice eight miles north of the island. From June 10 through 14 flocks of 10 to 15 phalaropes were feeding around the coast. According to my observations, the first pair and flock were noticed at Uélen in the spring of 1934 on May 31. The sandpipers arrived from the sea, crossed the spit and turned toward the thawed lagoon banks. On June 1 a flock flew in from the sea heading for the tundra passing high above. On June 3 flocks were passing over the sea quite often. On June 4 they were over the tundra or sat in the neighborhood of dunlins and dotterels; the flight had ended.

In the spring of 1879, near the winter halt of the *Vega*, O. Nordquist noticed the first phalaropes on May 31: four birds landed in an opening, splashed, preened and soon flew away with a cry, a whistling, outpouring trill resembling the voice of a tower swift. Later a female was obtained on June 3, and apparently another female on June 16. Thereafter the gray phalaropes were collected almost daily. On June 20 some specimens were shot, still more of them on the 21st and large numbers on the 22nd and 23rd. The arrival had ended by mid-June.

In 1955, I noticed gray phalaropes only on June 13 on the Amguema. On Aiok Island in 1956, according to the observations of V.D. Lebedev and V.R. Filin, in the first few days of June flocks of up to 30 birds were sighted though pairs had already been encountered on the tundra. Evidently the arrival and flight proceeded simultaneously. J. Koren noticed the arrival on the lower Kolyma on June 1, 1912.

According to the observations of G.A. Ushakov (Bannikov, 1941), gray phalaropes arrived on May 28 on Wrangel Island in 1928 and were confined at first to flocks of 100 or more birds each. In the spring of 1939 on Wrangel Island I saw and collected a pair for the first time on June 4 and 5 near my camp on the Mamontovaya River; a lone bird was seen on June 9 and many were sighted on the 12th. In the last few days gray phalaropes were taken by hunters at Rodgers Bay.

Nidification—Gray phalaropes arrived in individual pairs or flocks consisting of pairs. In 1934, in the neighborhood of Uélen, tiny pairs were noticed on small pools even on June 4. It was at once plain that the female was bigger than the male. In other species of birds, when the males were in abundance I have quite often seen two males to a female in the nesting areas. On the contrary, I found two females living with a single male in the case of gray phalaropes. Moreover, I came across lone females or two of them together, which is not seen in other birds at the commencement of the breeding period. On June 7 gray phalaropes were seen flying over the tundra chirping and constantly settling on water reservoirs of different sizes. In this respect their behavior was somewhat similar to the animated spring behavior of teals. Their chirp could be represented by the syllable "pik" and resembled the voice of magpies or creepers (*Ochotona*). Being in overwhelming numbers, the females did not exhibit any aggressiveness toward the males and did not take upon themselves a more active role. I saw how the male persistently fawned upon and ultimately lay on the female. From June 13 through 15 I encountered tiny pairs at the feeding places but they later disappeared from the immediate vicinity of Uélen, evidently on dispersing to the nesting areas.

Males that have just arrived possess enlarged testes, as may be seen from the following measurements in birds gathered from Markovo and Uélen, and in three specimens from Wrangel Island: 6 × 13 and 5 × 12, 7 × 10 and 6 × 9, 6 × 14 and 6 × 9, 9 × 13 and 6 × 10, and 6 × 11 and 5 × 9 mm. For the most part I noticed significant adipose formations but the Markovo specimen was emaciated. In July, the testes reverted to the normal size (2 × 4 and 2 × 3 mm), which remained constant right up to the time of migration. Only in the male collected at Cape Chaplin on August 18, 1938, with molting unusually delayed, were the testes 2 × 3 and 2 × 2 mm in size. It was emaciated, where the other August specimens had filmy adipose formations.

The arriving females collected around Markovo on the Anadyr revealed absence of adipose formations. In one of them the ovary had a fine-grained structure but two others showed large follicles up to 3 and 5 mm in diameter. A female that I shot on Wrangel on June 4, 1939, had an ovary 12 mm in length with a maximum follicle size of 3 mm. The subcutaneous fat was in patches, as in the female collected on June 26. The arriving females collected by the *Vega* expedition, like almost all the specimens collected, were plump. The females obtained on June 3 had an internal and surface fat layer on the belly to a thickness of up to 12 mm. It was about 5 mm in a specimen collected on June 16. The females that I collected in the estuary of the Turmanskaya River on June 10, 1931, had a fine-grained ovary structure. In the *Fauna of the Anadyr Region*, I wrote (1939b, vol. I, p. 165) that they were lone birds not breeding in their second year. Later I realized my mistake; in fact, they were nested females which were beginning to flock.

On June 29, 1957, A.P. Kuzyakin found three nests south of Uélen in mossy, grassy tundra at least 30 to 50 m from the lake. They were pits 8.5 to 9.5 cm across and 3.5 to 4 cm deep, lined with dry, soft low-sedge. In one of them, apart from grass, there were many dry leaves of procumbent willow. Each contained four incubated eggs. One clutch was highly incubated; the eggs weighed 6.88, 6.95, 7.08 and 7.37 g. In two of the less incubated clutches the weights were 1) 6.50, 6.57, 6.62 and 6.69 g and 2) 7.55, 7.95, 8.00, and 8.25 g.

The female collected by V.D. Lebedev and V.R. Filin on Aiok Island on May 3, 1958, contained an egg in shell in the oviduct. A nest with four eggs was found on June 13.

On July 12, 1879, around Pitlekai Bostrem found a nest and shot a male near it. Four eggs lay in a depression in the ground without any lining. One of them measured 23 × 31.5 mm and weighed 0.38 g. On St. Lawrence Island R.W. Hendee found a nest without two eggs on July 1, 1921. F.H. Fay found a nest with three eggs on July 23, 1954. It was in a sedge-moss part of the lake.

On July 8, 1956, on a marsh near the Amguema, an agitated male flew around me chirping, then settled at a distance. I could not find its nest. Another male also behaved very warily and settled in the shrubs on the water. I encountered two more gray phalaropes. On July 19, 1960, S.M. Uspenskii found two lone phalaropes in Tundra Akademii on Wrangel Island. They behaved as though they were by their broods.

On July 13, 1879, near Kolyuchin Bay, 11 birds were shot from a large flock. All turned out to be females. The biggest follicles in their ovaries did not exceed 1.5 to 2 mm in diameter. There is no doubt that they were nested females already formed into flocks. Similar flocks were also noticed on the 17th.

On July 16, 1957, A.P. Kuzyakin collected three downy chicks from two broods at Lawrence Bay. On July 7, 1958, V.D. Lebedev and V.R. Filin noticed innumerable downy chicks on Aiok Island. On July 2 and 3, 1917, J. Koren (Schaanning, 1954) collected downy chicks from two broods in the Kolyma delta. According to T.J. Cade, at the end of July, 1950, downy chicks were seen every day at Boxer Bay on St. Lawrence Island.

When a man approaches the chicks the males fly to meet him with a chirp and flit restlessly from lake to lake. It is difficult to determine how long they remain attached to the chicks. In the fall wanderings adult molting males were regularly encountered among a multitude of young birds but the former were in incomparably smaller numbers. On the other hand, for example, I found a nonflying chick on August 6, 1932, near Notapenmen. It was altogether alone in the total absence of the adult bird. The whole of its head was still in down, its wing length with undeveloped flight feathers being 8.2 cm.

On the same day I also noticed flying broods dispersed along the tundra lakelets. A much large number, literally a multitude of young birds, swam offshore. Among them I noticed only three adults. One of them was swimming with young ones, probably its offspring; two of the other males, however, remained altogether alone.

According to the observations of J. Koren, at Chaun Bay young gray phalaropes took to their wings on July 30, 1912. According to V.D. Lebedev and V.R. Filin, flocks of phalaropes remained in the sea off Aiok Island from mid-July. On Wrangel Island, around Somnitel'naya Bay, A.G. Velizhanin found the first flying young birds on July 25, 1960. On August 6, 1932, I found gray phalaropes numerous in the neighborhood of Notapenmen village on the eastern shore of Krest Bay. Innumerable juvenile birds swam by the surf line. A much smaller number remained on the edges of tundra lakelets. Though I obtained chicks that were not yet flying on the tundra that day I did not think that all the innumerable young birds I saw were of local broods. There is no doubt that the wandering had begun while the gathering was explained by the local abundance of food.

Molting—On July 15, 1939, at Somnitel'naya Bay, I noticed only an adult male beginning to molt. On September 12 and 13, 1934, at Uélen, males were almost totally molted. At different times between the above dates I saw old males in a more or less similar condition of molting. It proceeds quite slowly in the majority of birds but varies widely in some. On August 6, 1932, near Notapenmen, I noticed two males which had already acquired almost complete winter dress; on the other hand, on August 26, 1932, at Providence Bay I saw birds with feathers dappled red and white among several adult phalaropes which were almost totally molted. The specimen collected by P.T. Butenko on August 18, 1938, at Cape Chaplin in very worn-out plumage is of interest; it still had not commenced molting.

In a very similar way molting in the young proceeds quite differently in different birds. I have before me two young females from Uélen shot on September 26, 1933. One of them has grown new winter plumage almost to the same extent as the feathers of juvenile dress still worn by the other bird. Even among very late specimens, I did not find the juvenile plumage totally replaced by the winter dress. The young birds collected in the first half of August did not have subcutaneous fat. Later plump specimens were encountered, more often in the later periods of observations, but there were some among them with negligible formations even at the end of September.

Migration—Gray phalaropes migrate late, in the last few days of September and in October. V.D. Lebedev and V.R. Filin noticed flocks of phalaropes on the day of their departure from Aiok Island on August 31, 1958, and at Cape Pevek on September 8, but this was certainly not the end. In 1946, A.P. Andriyashev noticed lone birds pecking for food in the water by the shore at Pevek on September 28.

On Wrangel Island, according to the observations of V.F. Vlasova and A.I. Mineev, flocks of migratory phalaropes were seen in large numbers at the end of August and in September. N.M. Vakulenko noticed lone birds even on October 9, 1934. According to my observations in the fall of 1938, gray phalaropes were encountered in large numbers on the north coast of the island, sometimes above Tundra Akademii. On Bruch spit, I noticed them in a huge mass on August 14 but in relatively small numbers on August 27. Later they were found near the estuary of the Krasnyi Flag River. On September 12, I encountered four juveniles at Rodgers Bay. On the 15th small flocks were still to be seen on the coast but they migrated altogether in the days immediately following. On October 5 Tayan encountered a lone phalarope on his way from Tundra Akademii into the hills. The bird had settled on the snow but flew away on the approach of the party. It did not create the impression of being sick but was probably confused by the disappearance of open water, and was resting on the snow. In 1960 A.G. Velizhanin saw the last of gray phalaropes on the south side of the island on September 26. According to my observations in the fall of 1933, around Uélen, phalaropes were encountered on the shore at the end of August. On September 12 and 13, which were foggy, flocks moved animatedly about the spit and in openings in the ice. But later, during September, they were seen in small numbers, mostly by the banks of the lagoon. On October 1 there was an intense migration of different species of birds and phalaropes were noticed in large flocks. But I saw them for the last time on October 3 in very small numbers, only some pairs and single birds. The shore was piled with ice and ice banks were seen on the lagoon, and the phalaropes disappeared. In the fall of 1934, when there was a south wind and it was calm on the front at Uélen, migrating phalaropes gathered en masse together with gulls.

According to E.G.F. Sauer, in 1960 tiny flocks of gray phalaropes were seen as early as August 17 and 18 on the sandy shores of Boxer Bay.

In 1912 L.M. Starokadomskii and É.E. Arngol'd collected six juvenile sandpipers of this species at Émma Bay on September 24.

Some gray phalaropes remained as an exception up to the first few days of November. But they did not winter and did not appear in the open sea off the south Chukchian coasts during the winter.

In 1937 P.T. Butenko arrived at Providence Bay on October 29 and on November 6 stumbled on a delayed flock of five gray phalaropes.

Food—On August 6, 1932, near Notapenmen, I saw juvenile birds feeding on the tiny lakelets so common on flat spits by lagoons. Catching something in the water, they would turn around like tops. It looked as though the birds were possessed of some fury on being hit on the cerebellum. This unusual feature of turning the head around evidently earned them very little food as the specimens obtained turned out to be very emaciated.

On June 13, 1956, I noticed phalaropes on the Amguema, both gray and northern, feeding in the exposed leads in the rapids. From time to time the birds would peck in the water. As the current was strong and kept carrying the birds away they sometimes took off and settled a few dozen meters further upstream, where the entire procedure was repeated endlessly.

On August 13, 1932, not far from Dezhnev settlement, I wounded a long-tailed jaeger which was feasting on a gray phalarope chick, torn to bits. In the stomach contents of the chick were found bits of the heads of two *Carabidae*, the body and wings of butterflies, the heads of insect larvae and bits of bones of an unknown vertebrate.

On October 1, 1933, near Uélen, I noticed flocks gathering in the tiny bays of small lagoons in the form of a chain of water reservoirs draining into a large lagoon. The dissection of four stomachs revealed that the phalaropes lived on tiny crustaceans. Apart from these deformed remnants and tiny stones nothing could be found in their stomachs.

In the stomach of a male collected at Uélen on June 4, 1934, a lower insect, the chelicera of a tiny spider and 27 gemmae or buds were found. In males shot on Wrangel Island on June 12, 1939, the stomachs contained: 1) 16 caterpillars and 1 g coarse sand, and 2) tiny insects, a ground-up mass of plant shoots and 0.12 g sand; the female collected on June 26, 1939, contained a ground-up mixture of plant remains and tiny insects, as also coarse sand.

In the stomachs of specimens that had just arrived, collected in Pitlekai on June 3 and 16, 1879, only sand and organic particles were found. In those collected from June 2 through July 13 were found fragments of *Harpalidae* beetles in imaginal as well as in larval stages. In some flies or the pupa of some insect and grains of sand were found.

The gray phalarope evidently lives on insects and crustaceans and hence can survive on the tundra as well as at sea. According to E.W. Nelson whalers inferred the presence of Greenland whales from the assembly of phalaropes in the sea and called them bowhead birds.

Enemies—The gray phalaropes are constantly persecuted by jaegers and glaucous gulls. An instance was cited above of a long-tailed jaeger catching a young phalarope. On June 17, 1934, I noticed how an adult phalarope escaped from a chasing glaucous gull and long-tailed jaeger by hiding under the overhanging edge of an ice floe.

Economic importance—Because of its small size the gray phalarope does not attract the attention of the hunter. But in the fall, when large numbers of young birds are on the surf line foraging, Chukchian youths do not miss the chance to practice on them with their eplicathets. The phalaropes bagged are generally thrown to the dogs.

In August, 1855, Capt. J. Rodgers' expedition bagged dozens of phalaropes for the table. These sandpipers were so tasty that the day they were sighted was marked on the calendar of the expedition as *Schnepfen Sonntag*. Phalaropes were also used for the table by the *Jeannette* expedition in 1880.

Systematics of the subspecies—Appreciable individual variability, especially in two-year-olds, is observed in the color of gray phalaropes. This is more particularly so in the width of the fringes on the upper feathers of the body and in the intensity of coloration, which is sometimes almost creamish and sometimes light ocherous. In a good series available in the collection of the Institute of Zoology, Academy of Sciences of the USSR, I could not find any differences that could be regarded as characteristics of a subspecies. I therefore refrain from recognizing the subspecies *Ph. f. jourdaini* Iredale.

Specimens— 1) Lawrence Bay, August 1, 1900, ○, Akif'ev; 2) Cape Schmidt, 11 miles west and 10 miles from the coast, August 29, 1911, ○, 1° anno, Arngol'd; 3 and 4) southwestern tip of Wrangel Island, September 17, 1911, ○○, 1° anno, Arngol'd; 5) Émma Bay, July 20, 1912, ♀, Starokadomskii; 6) Providence Bay, September 24, 1912, ♂, 1° anno, Arngol'd; 7 to 9) Émma Bay, September 24, 1912, ♂♂, 1° anno, Starokadomskii; 10) Providence Bay, July 20, 1913, ♀, Arngol'd; 11) Émma Bay, August 7, 1913, ♂, Arngol'd; 12 and 13) Kolyuchin Bay, August 19, 1914, ○○, 1° anno, Starokadomskii; 14 and 15) Wrangel Island, June 15, 1929, ♂○, G.A. Ushakov; 16) Lawrence Bay, July 31, 1929, ♂, P.V. Ushakov; 17) southeastern Wrangel Island, August 19, 1931, ○, 1° anno, Vlasova; 18) sea beyond Rodgers Bay, August 24, 1931, ○, 1° anno, Zvantsev; 19) sea beyond Providence Bay, May 2 (?), 1932, ♀, Olenev; 20 to 23) Krest Bay, August 6, 1932, ♂♂, ♀, 1° anno and juv., Portenko; 24) Dezhnev settlement, August 13, 1932, ♀, 1° anno, Portenko; 25 to 27) Uélen, September 23, 1933, ♀♀○, 1° anno, Portenko; 28 and 29) same place, September 26, 1933, ♀♀, 1° anno, Portenko; 30 to 34) same place, October 1, 1933, ♂♂♀♀, 1° anno, Portenko; 35) same place, June 4, 1934, ♂, Portenko; 36) same place, August 9, 1934, ○, Portenko; 37) Providence Bay, Plover, June 6, 1938, ♀, Butenko; 38 to 41) Cape Schmidt, August 8, 1938, ○○, Druzhinin; 42) Cape Chaplin, August 18, 1938, ♂, Butenko; 43) Wrangel Island, Akatylanva (180° longitude), June 4, 1939, ♀, Portenko; 44) same place, June 5, 1939, ♂, Portenko; 45 and 46) same place, June 12, 1939, ♂♂, Portenko; and 47) Rodgers Bay, June 26, 1939, ♀, Portenko.

81. Phalaropus lobatus (L.)—Northern Phalarope

Distribution and status—Common in the breeding grounds in the western part of the Chukchi peninsula; less so in the eastern part. Encountered only in the migratory season and in small numbers on the north coast east of Chaun Bay and in the hilly sections of the south coast. Altogether absent from Wrangel Island.

E.M. Meller brought back a female he collected on June 8, 1939, by Pereval'naya Station northwest of Krest Bay. On September 2, 1932, I saw northern phalaropes on the southwestern shore of Krest Bay in the neighborhood of Uél'kal' village, evidently just before their migration, and on August 6 on the southeastern shore, near Notapenmen village. In 1961, V.É. Yakobi found this species common in the nesting area around Uél'kal'.

At Providence Bay, J. Dixon (Brooks, 1915) collected an evidently nested female on June 22, 1913. In 1932, I noticed young birds there in flocks on August 26 and in small numbers on August 28. In 1938, P.T. Butenko collected only early migrating specimens on Plover spit and near Cape Stoletiya.

The northern phalarope nests and is common on St. Lawrence Island. W.S. Brooks found this species very common on June 27, 1913, on the southeastern tip of the island. According to H. Friedmann (1932a), on June 26, 1913, a clutch was gathered there. According to the observations of T.J. Cade (Fay and Cade, 1959) the northern phalarope was somewhat less common than the gray phalarope in 1959 on the western tip of the island. Pairs were noticed; around 10 nesting males were found near Boxer Bay and even downy chicks were later seen. Females were collected there and around Gambell. In the following years the population of northern phalarope was only one-half that of gray phalaropes. In 1953 the commencement of migration was studied and a female was obtained on June 4. Some pairs and broods of downy chicks were noticed on June 23, 1954, near Kavuk. In June, 1960, E.G.F. Sauer and E.K. Urban (1964) encountered some pairs settled on the flooded shores of Lake Maloe near Boxer Bay.

On August 19, 1932, I came across northern phalaropes in small numbers at Lawrence Bay. On July 30, 1948, a specimen was obtained there by V.N. Lyubin. A.P. Kuzyakin found downy chicks on July 16, 1957, near the settlement at that bay and an adult bird around Poutyn. According to him, on the southern shore of Lawrence Bay only stray pairs were noticed. He did not see this sandpiper at all at Providence Bay or around Uélen.

On August 13 and 14, 1932, I sighted northern phalaropes in very small numbers among masses of gray phalarope near Dezhnev settlement. In the neighborhood of Uélen, I encountered this species only twice: a juvenile on August 22, 1933, and a pair in flight on May 31, 1934. This covered the fall and spring flights, respectively. On my excursions in the eastern part of the Chukchi peninsula I encountered the northern phalarope on the lower reaches of the Utte-Véem River. There I came across a male which was restless at the nesting area and later many, probably, nested females or lone birds. The *Vega* expedition (Palmén, 1887) saw this sandpiper in one case and under strange circumstances: on June 23, 1879, A.E. Nordenskjöld found a freshly killed female in a heap of refuse near the ship.

According to the observations of A.A. Kishchinskii this sandpiper nested in the coastal zone of the tundra from Vankarém to the Amguema but everywhere in small numbers equal to 5 percent of the number of gray phalaropes. At the eastern end of the Ukouge lagoon a clutch was found. Downy chicks were collected later. On the Ékug-Véem River entering the lagoon pairs were seen somewhat more frequently on June 27 and 28, 1970. Northern phalaropes were even more common in the Amguema delta, where clutches were found.

I encountered northern phalaropes in the nesting site along the Amguema, found four nests and collected a clutch as also downy chicks. This sandpiper was common there but not abundant. A flock of 15 birds was sighted in spring flight.

In 1912 J. Koren (Thayer and Bangs, 1914) encountered northern phalaropes at Chaun Bay and obtained a male in Malyi Chaun Strait on July 20.

According to the observations of V.D. Lebedev and V.R. Filin the northern phalarope was common on Aiok Island but less numerous than the gray phalarope. On the southwest coast of the island broods were found. Copley Amory, Jr. (Riley, 1918) collected a specimen on the Baranikha River on August 16, 1915. During the second half of June, 1965, F.B. Chernyavskii encountered a pair and broods in the valley of the Yarak-Véem River in the eastern part of the north Anyui range. A.I. Argentov (1861a) cited both the species of phalaropes for the Trans-Lena region including the gray phalarope *Phalaris cinereus*. Both species are placed partly in the subgroup of migratory birds. It is possible that what Argentov writes in his article Severnaya Zemlya (Northern Land) (1861b, p. 7) pertains to the northern phalarope: on the lower Kolyma, the birds of that species were seen only in the spring; they could be seen in the summer from time to time along the coast. On the lower Kolyma, according to S.A. Buturlin (1906b), the northern phalarope nested everywhere in large numbers and in the delta the two species of phalarope were equally abundant. J. Koren (Schaanning, 1954) gathered a clutch on the Kolyma on June 22, 1912, and downy chicks on July 16, 1916. Copley Amory found a clutch in the Kolyma estuary on July 16, 1915.

According to E.W. Nelson (1883, p. 91) the northern phalarope was found on the north coast of Siberia in moderate numbers in places where the gray phalarope was most abundant. The two species joined to form common flocks and were found in the sea as far north as the *Corwin* penetrated in the summer of 1881. But the northern phalaropes became steadily fewer as the ship advanced.

In another article E.W. Nelson (1887, p. 100) writes that he saw them quite commonly near Herald and Wrangel islands in July and August, 1881. The northern phalarope was not found on Wrangel by later visitors, including myself.

Habitat—On flying into the tundra after wintering at sea the northern phalaropes become inhabitants of tiny lakes and their banks and wet marshes fairly inundated with water. They spend much of the time in the water. Apart from the time spent in the nest it is not often that the phalarope is seen on land.

When the tundra is not yet free from the snow cover the arriving phalaropes settle on any suitable body of water. On June 10, 1956, in the flood plain of the Amguema, I came across lone phalaropes in meltwater pools. On June 13, 1956, I saw a flock feeding at a lead in a section of the river with a strong current. In another place, a single pair was swimming on a tiny lake formed by meltwater among large aquatic bushes. As soon as the tundra became free of snow, the northern phalaropes began to be seen on tiny lakelets whose banks had thawed to some extent, sometimes on the low-lying areas at water level and sometimes on the banks with hummocks or aquatic vegetation of varying depths. They would also sit in the open water and on the grass still growing along the bank. Once, on the evening of June 24, 1956, I noticed two pairs on a lead in a large lake where the ice had just begun opening up.

On July 10, 1934, near the estuary of the Utte-Véem River, I encountered a flock on tiny lakelets overgrown with bushes. Snags and dead branches stuck out of the water. Only tiny birds could swim among them.

Since the downy chicks do not swim, the adult males guarding them sit more often in the grass than at any other time. It is often very wet. Flying broods were confined to the lakelets. They gradually assembled on the larger water reservoirs, in the lagoons and finally on the seashore.

But even during the fall flight the northern phalarope could be seen on tiny lakes. In the neighborhood of Uélen, on the terrace of the closest knoll, I came across young sandpipers in a pool by a little mountain spring. I saw flocks of juvenile northern phalaropes in the lakelets on a spit by Plover Bay, Providence Bay, though other birds of the species were swimming by the shore in defiance of big breakers. On the surf line, I noticed them together with gray phalaropes by Dezhnev settlement and at the entrance to Krest Bay. They remained far out in the bay near Uél'kal' on September 2, 1932.

Arrival—In the spring of 1938, judging from the specimens obtained by P.T. Butenko, the arrival proceeded at Providence Bay from May 27 through 30. According to F.H. Fay and T.J. Cade, near Gambell, on St. Lawrence Island, the first phalaropes of this species were noticed on June 4, 1953, and on May 17, 1954. In the spring of 1934, I noticed a pair at Uélen on May 31. On the north coast, from Vankarém to the Amguema, A.A. Kishchinskii recorded their arrival only from June 10 through 13, 1970. J. Koren found them on the lower Kolyma on May 30, 1912.

Nidification—Two males collected near Cape Stoletiya on May 30, 1938, possessed enlarged testes: 6×12 and 6×11, and 5×11 and 4×10 mm. They were plump specimens. The male obtained on the Utte-Véem River on July 10, 1934, had shrunken gonads: 2×5 and 2×4 mm. The subcutaneous adipose formation was reduced to a filmy state. An Anadyr male from Tumanskaya collected on July 10, 1931, had even smaller testes: 2×3 and 2×3 mm. It was a plump bird. The series of migratory females from Markova comprised only plump birds. In three of them collected on May 29 and June 2 the biggest follicle in the ovary measured 4 mm. In one collected on May 29 it was 3 mm. But the female shot at Plover on May 27, 1938, was characterized by the absence of adipose formations; in an ovary 11 mm in length the largest follicle did not exceed 3 mm.

According to a report by A.A. Kishchinskii, on June 27, 1970, a clutch was found on the eastern bank of the Ukouge lagoon. Downy chicks were collected there on July 11. On June 28, on the Ékug-Véem River, a female with yolk in the oviduct was shot. It may have been the last egg. On an islet in the lake in the Amguema delta a nest was found with a clutch of four eggs right on the water on July 4.

According to V.D. Lebedev and V.R. Filin, on Aiok Island the northern phalaropes begin nidification in the first few days of June. According to my 1956 observations on the Amguema nest building did not occur before the middle of that month. On June 13 I noticed a single pair in courtship. The tiny birds were swimming animatedly among bushes inundated with water and their soft twitter could be heard. It was difficult to recognize who was courting whom: whether the male was running after the female or vice versa; the birds were courting each other so tenderly. Finally the male, rising slightly out of the water, caught the female and mounted her. Mating took place in the water. The male wanted to repeat it but the female was indifferent. After some time the activity of the male weakened noticeably. I sighted another pair on June 18. The birds were sitting side by side in shallow water and twittering quietly. It was a moving sight of harmony and friendship in stark contrast to the prolonged if not eternal separation that lay in store. Being disturbed by my presence, the phalaropes swam away but continued to float side by side.

On June 22, 1956, I took my camera and crept stealthily toward the phalaropes dispersed among the network of lakelets. I began to study the behavior of a pair (Figs. 67 and 68). The male was very active and even swam toward me but the female remained very quiet and was wary. After my long wait the female emerged onto the bank and hid in the grass by a hummock. The male persistently searched her out, attempted to mount her and bothered her in many ways. When the pair entered the water the male again attempted to mount the female but the latter escaped, became even more sluggish, and appeared ill. By then I had investigated the mound and found a nest on it with two eggs. I lay in wait and the female returned to the nest and sat on it. I had to leave and check the nests of other birds but, when I returned, the phalaropes were no longer there. There were now three eggs in the nest.

The nest was well covered by overhanging, interlaced blades of grass. It was in the form of a depression lined with dry willow leaves. The eggs were brownish-yellow with small brown speckles. Like the other eggs I found later, they were pear-shaped and very similar to the eggs of quails.

On June 24 I visited the nest again. The phalarope ran 50 paces and flew off like lighting. There were four eggs in the completed clutch. On June 28 I found the male incubating in the nest. On my appearance it got down into the water, assumed a dignified mien and splashed around. Later, during subsequent tours of the nests on June 30 and July 2, 5 and 7, I did not find the male in the nest. On July 5 I removed an egg. It had an embryo with developed extremities. On July 10 the male was again absent from the nest but when I was moving off it appeared with an anxious chirp and settled in the lakelet. On July 14 the eggs in the nest were cool. I took them for my collection on the 16th and found chicks inside with traces of down. The nesting material comprised the following plants which were identified by V.N. Vasil'ev: first and foremost sedge *Carex* followed by the leaves of *Acomastylis Rossi* (R. Br.) Greene, *Vaccinium vitis-ideae* L. f. *microphylla*, *Vaccinium uliginosum* L., *Salix pulchra* and *Betula exilis*.

On June 28 I found a second nest not far from the first one in a neighboring lakelet. I sat in wait quite close and the agitated male flew into the lakelet many times. On landing it jabbed the water with its beak out of restlessness, later submerged it sometimes to the left and sometimes to the right, and repeated this movement many times. It flew away with surprising agility, behaving like a swallow slipping from side to side. When I moved away and sat at a distance the phalarope sweeped straight onto the nest. It was built on a mound among waterlogged grass 15 to 20 paces from the lakelet (Fig. 69). At first very wary, the male continued to sit with bated breath on the nest until I came within five paces of it, then finally got down when I was two steps away. In the evening when I collected the nest, the male flew a meter away from me, then ran some distance, and began to flutter. The embryos in the eggs were not fully developed. The nest was built of different *Carices* among which were blades of cereal grasses.

On June 30 I was given two eggs with small embryos taken from a full clutch.

On July 1 I found the last of the nests. It was situated on a grassy marsh near the nest of a pectoral sandpiper. The male took off with a cry when I was a few paces away. It parried but soon left altogether. Only in one of the four eggs were blood vessels to be seen: the rest were quite unincubated. The nest material was partly year-old, partly fresh stalks and leaves of sedge, blueberry and willow (also catkins). Among them were found tiny year-old leaves of *Betula exilis* and turf of *Dicranum* moss.

In 1956, on the Amguema, the northern phalaropes had completed laying by the last few days of June. Nevertheless, I found females with males, i.e. pairs, much later, right up to my departure in mid-July. On June 30 I saw a male chasing a female over a large lake. To elude him she settled in the wet grass and the male flew off. I had not seen this active role in females. Apart from much brighter plumage the female possesses one more characteristic quality. When fluttering the wings she is capable of uttering a special chirpy sound. On July 14, when the pair was sitting in a lakelet, I still heard this call which I had noticed earlier.

Before this I had come across many lone females that had certainly completed breeding. They would not leave the breeding area immediately after laying was over. The males incubated, often absenting themselves from the nest for long intervals. As a result, in the last 10 days of June and in the first half of July phalaropes of both sexes could be seen everywhere, moving in different directions, flitting from lake to lake, sitting on the marsh or simply in the wet grass. Their calls could be heard.

The distinct presence of a population of lone birds was not established on the Amguema. On July 10, 1934, near the estuary of the Utte-Véem River, I came across flocks gathered on lakelets whose banks were overgrown with vegetation. They were undoubtedly lone or nested phalaropes or both. On the same day, on the tundra by the river, I encountered a male which got very agitated at my presence and uttered a special twitter. It probably had chicks with it.

On June 15, 1961, V.É. Yakobi collected a female near Uél'kal' with an egg in the oviduct ready for laying. On June 26, 1913, W.S. Brooks got a clutch which was already one-fourth incubated. On St. Lawrence Island Copley Amory, Jr. collected a clutch of four eggs in the estuary of the Kolyma on July 16, 1915. The chicks were ready to emerge.

In 1956, on the Amguema, I found the first emerging chicks only on July 14. Others also noticed them on the days that followed. There was mass hatching not only of phalaropes but also of other sandpipers.

On July 14 I had found a dunlin's nest when a very agitated male phalarope appeared. It went from place to place, crying "chiri-chiri" and sometimes uttering sounds similar to those of common snipes when frightened. The phalarope settled twice in the same place, where I found three chicks (Fig. 70). They lay motionless on thin moss over an unstable grassy marsh concealed in fairly open space. They could hardly hobble and it could be concluded from their weakness that they had only just emerged. In captivity they showed more vitality than downy sandpiper chicks. They did not stiffen due to cold very fast because of their long, dense down.

With the appearance of chicks the northern phalaropes became especially active. Where other species of sandpipers would rise out of alarm the phalaropes were agitated all the time.

On the Kolyma J. Koren collected recently emerged chicks on July 16, 1916. According to his observations, at Chaun Bay young phalaropes were already airborne on July 30, 1913. According to V.D. Lebedev and V.R. Filin, on Aiok Island broods were noticed at the beginning of July in 1958. At Lawrence Bay A.P. Kuzyakin collected downy chicks weighing around 5 g on July 16, 1957. On the western tip of St. Lawrence Island T.J. Cade saw downy chicks at the end of July, 1950. Near Kavuk, a brood of three downy chicks was noticed on June 23, 1954. I find this date unbelievably early.

Migration—Occurred much earlier than in gray phalaropes. The last dates of my observations were: September 2, 1932, at Krest Bay and August 22, 1933, at Uélen. In 1958, V.D. Lebedev and V.R. Filin encountered the northern phalarope on Aiok Island up to August 31.

Food—In the stomach of a male shot on the Utte-Véem River on July 10, 1934, were found the heads of nine hymenopterans, tiny spiders and the legs of several dozen tiny insects. E.M. Meller found beetles in the stomach of a specimen collected at Pereval'naya on June 8, 1939.

Weight—P.T. Butenko weighed the specimens he had collected at Providence Bay on May 27 and 30, 1938. The males weighed 39.5 and 33 g and the females registered 37.8 g.

Economic importance—The northern phalarope is too small to be of any use as game. Nevertheless, hunters shoot it as an easy moving target with no justification. I found shot and wounded phalaropes in the flood lands of the Amguema.

Systematics of the subspecies—I did not find any subspecies differences in northern phalaropes.

Specimens— 1) Dezhnev settlement, August 13, 1932, ♀, 1° anno, Portenko; 2) Utte-Véem River, July 10, 1934, ♂, Portenko; 3) Providence Bay, Plover, May 27, 1938, ♀, Butenko; 4 and 5) Cape Stoletiya, May 30, 1938, ♂♂, Butenko; 6) Pereval'naya, June 8, 1939, ♀, Meller; and 7 to 9) 91st km by Amguema, July 14, 1956, pull., Portenko.

Biological material— 1) Two eggs from a clutch, middle reaches of the Amguema River, 91st km, June 30, 1956, Portenko; 2) nest with a clutch of four eggs, same place, June 28, 1956, Portenko; 3) nest with a clutch of four eggs, same place, July 1, 1956, Portenko; and 4) nest with a clutch of four eggs, same place, July 5 and 16, 1956, Portenko.

Supplementary notes to color plates III, VI and VII

The sketches are based on the following specimens of bird skins and eggs.

Plate III

1—One-year-old male, without date, Leno-Khatangsk expedition, A.A. Romanov; 2—Two-year-old male, Uélen, June 12, 1934, Portenko; 3—Two-year-old male, Uélen, October 15, 1933, Portenko; 4—Three-year-old male, Uélen, end of June, 1934, Portenko; 5—old male (older than three years), Matochkin Shar, August 24, 1927, Gorbunov; and 6—male older than three years, Omolaya River, June 6, 1935, Balabin.

Plate VI

1 and 3—*Pisobia minutilla subminuta* (Midd.), Bering Island, June 20, 1930, H. Johansen; 2—*P. m. subminuta*, flood land of Magadanka River, June 11, 1944, A.P. Vas'kovskii; 4—*P. ruficollis minuta* (Leisl.), Mamontovaya River, north Taimir, July 22, 1949, Portenko; 5—*P. r. ruficollis* (Pall.), Uélen, June 5, 1934, Portenko; 6—*Limonites temminckii* (Leisl.), Amguema River, 91st km, July 5, 1956, Portenko; 7—*P. r. minuta*, west coast of north Taimir, July 9, 1901, Val'ter; 8—*P. r. ruficollis*, Uélen, June 5, 1934, Portenko; 9—*P. r. ruficollis*, Uélen, June 18, 1934, Portenko; 10—*L. temminckii*, fort, upper course of Anadyr, July 4, 1932, Portenko; and 11, 12 and 13—*Heteropygia melanotos* (Vieill.) (from the same clutch), Amguema River, 91st km, July 5, 1956, Portenko.

Plate VII

1—*Pisobia ruficollis minuta* (Leisl.), ♂?, Mamontovaya River, north Taimir, July 30, 1949, Portenko; 2—*P. r. ruficollis* (Pall.), Amguema River, 91st km, July 14, 1956, Portenko; 3—*Eurynorhynchus pygmeus* (L.), Gek's Land, Anadyr Bay, July 18, 1933, Portenko; 4—*Heteropygia melanotos* (Vieill.), Amguema River, 91st km, July 12, 1956, Portenko; 5—*Limonites temminckii* (Leisl.), ♂, Apuka, Koryatz upland, July 9, 1959, Portenko; and 6—*Heteropygia melanotos*, Amguema River, 91st km, July 11, 1956, Portenko.